BIO-MEDICAL EXCURSIONS

Paul Weiss

BIO-MEDICAL EXCURSIONS:

A Biologist's Probings into Medicine

PAUL A. WEISS

HAFNER PUBLISHING COMPANY
NEW YORK
1971

Published by

HAFNER PUBLISHING COMPANY, INC.
866 Third Avenue
New York, N.Y. 10022

Library of Congress Catalog Card Number: 74-100393

Printed in the U.S.A.

CONTENTS

IV. THE LIVING-NERVE CELL AND THE NERVOUS SYSTEM

V. NERVE REGENERATION AND NERVE REPAIR

Page and plate numbers of the original papers have been retained

FOREWORD

In spending more than half a century in research in the life sciences, I had full opportunity to become aware of its evolutionary trends. In essence, they all seem to be but some special aspects of a single evolutionary phenomenon—the emergence of the body of knowledge from what in organic evolution corresponded to the single-celled protozoan state to a multicelled metazoan. Research as source of the growth of knowledge passed through the same transition. Its signs and consequences are familiar: staggering increases in volume: mounting differentiation of tasks with specialization and fragmentation in its wake: a corresponding rise of interdependence and group coordination: and some attendant gain in efficiency—all signs of the changes in spirit, motives and methods that transformed research from the avocation of individual craftsmen in their solitary workshops of yesteryear to the massive group enterprise of a modern industry.

As I have pointed out in a recent assessment of the intellectual and social "cost-benefit ratio" of this development in progress (see the article appended to this Foreword), there are some risks in letting it roll on blindly by the sheer force of its momentum. General warnings against some of those risks are not uncommon—warnings against "excessive fragmentation," "overspecialization," "redundancy"; of course, what is really meant by "excessive," is any amount that gets beyond the mark at which the natural evolutionary benefits from growth are set off by serious losses—loss of cohesion, of perspective, of consistency, of orientation, of relevance, of proportions, and above all, of comprehensibility. In some degree, this has already come to pass. However, the diagnostic pertinence of the general realisation of the mounting price we stand to pay for the accelerating rate and momentum of scientific production is not matched by a commensurate measure of preventive antidotes. Faced with a real trend toward progressive disintegration of the fabric of knowledge, as a result of its becoming so immensely splintered, the obvious countermeasure to forestall total disruption is, of course, *"reintegration."*

This word is likewise not uncommon in our day. How conscious of its need thoughtful people and responsible groups have become, is illustrated by the rising call for *"inter*disciplinary" and *"inter*national" enterprises—

journals, meetings, courses, etc.—in a spirit of scientific ecumenism. This is all to the good as far as it goes. Yet it is still far too narrow, on two counts. In the first place, it overlooks the truism that the less far one lets segregation proceed the less restorative reintegration will be needed; and this is a matter to be corrected by systematic educational and research policies, rather than to be left to episodic *ad hoc* arrangements. Second and even more shortsighted is the implied limitation of integrative effort to the bridging of gulfs between disciplines or nations, that is, across reasonably well delineated intellectual, methodological or historical boundaries. What remains unattended, is the harmonization of the no less severe divergencies, dissonances and inconsistencies among the views, conclusions and statements of people or groups that cannot be identified with discrete categories but are ranged along a continuous graded scale of shades from one extreme to another. Not being fenced in by categorical borders, they are unnoticed and bypassed by the various "*inter*categorical" attempts at integration.

Compare, for instance, the subtle, almost imperceptible, yet ceaseless, changes with the course of time regarding objectives, attitudes, methods of measurement and assay, practices in the evaluation and validation of evidence, and so forth, with the inflexible persistence of the static and rigid frame of terms, principles and concepts, in which we keep on dealing with that evolving knowledge, and you will appreciate the stresses and strains bound to arise from the discrepancy between a growing content and an unyielding container. Many conclusions and conceptions based on data and arguments which at one time seemed validly established are still embedded in our thinking and our textbooks even though their premises have changed so much as to render them wholly inconclusive, and hence, obsolete. Why? Because they keep on sailing under the same old names. Conversely, many new contentions and propositions could hardly stand the test of credibility if they were confronted with the solid proof to the contrary, firmly established in a distant past. Why does such crucial evidence remain obscure? Because its name symbol has either been forgotten or expunged from the abridged record of contemporary media of information. In short, unbroken lines of developmental changes are apt to go unnoticed by those most closely and continuously involved in them, and it usually is left to the historians later to trace them and package them artificially into separate epochs, stages and phases.

A similar artifact is the customary categorical distinction between "basic" and "applied" research. No more realistic is the conceptual separation between "theory" and "practice"; no empirical procedure is wholly devoid of elements of theory in its foundations and expectations, nor is theory that is concocted in a vacuum of facts more than vacuous divination. All such distinctions are a matter of degrees of interest and focus and varying proportions in the mixtures of methodologies applied, but certainly are not properties of the subjects under study. As nature knows no pigeonholes, so knowledge, and the research leading up to it, constitute unbroken continua. That is to say, no borders, fence posts, or other signs of discontinuity are met along the roads from the most fundamental principles of physics to the most sophisticated devices of technology; from plant physiology and genetic theory to the practice of agriculture and the fight against crop diseases; and—to come to the point—from the most elementary discoveries in the cellular and developmental biology of animals to the prevention and cure of human disease. Pigeonholing is plainly a managerial device for the convenience, expedience and efficiency in handling practical affairs; in the infinitely graded diversity of the real world, however, there is no counterpart for the labels that designate the various pigeonholes. Nevertheless, the structure of our academic and social systems still tends to perpetuate such definitional distinctions instead of blurring them.

My reason for singling out here the "basic-applied" antithesis for criticism is that it constitutes a demonstrable obstacle to optimum progress in bio-medical research. In saying this, I fall prey to the errors I have tried to emphasize; for even the hyphenated term "bio-medical," given much currency of late, while well intentioned in the sense of an "integrative" move, is still rather indicative of the perseverance of the residues of an old schism. Of course, curious and purposeful investigators and practitioners alike ignore straightjackets to their thoughts and searchings imposed by extraneous formalisms. They shuttle freely between the "basic" and "applied" directions of the research continuum. Indeed, enlightened official policy tries to encourage this free-wheeling in disregard of traditional "no trespassing" signs. And yet, if one takes a broad overview of the current research scene in the biomedical arena, one recognizes that the distribution of dominant interests and efforts is still strictly *bimodal,* centering on "bio-" and on "medical," respectively.

My own research attitude happened to have been ianus-faced and thus I found myself quite often isolated on the arid land between the two fertile domains. And from that vantage point of an assessment of needs for the future, I have come to the conclusion that both medical and biological science, but foremost the former, would stand to gain immeasurably if more thought and effort were spent on filling up the trough between the two research peaks with true knowledge and understanding of biological mechanisms, a veritable reunion—"reintegration"—in fact, as against a mere spanning of the intervening space with verbal gossamer.

To instill realism into such a broad program, requires examples taken from reality. To serve this cause, I offer in this booklet specific miniature samples of ways which in my own experience have proved successful in approaching the overall objective of closer biomedical integration—practical antidotes to creeping fragmentation. The first two chapters deal with personal and educational premises. The next two are a tutorial on the linkage between insight into cellular and developmental dynamics and the approach to practical medical problems. The last chapter elaborates even more directly a specific instance—the demonstration of how insight gained from experimental studies on the cellular mechanisms of nerve regeneration has led compellingly to improved practical procedures in the repair of peripheral nerve lesions.

All articles in this book have been published previously. The facts that they have been widely scattered through the literature, and that many are difficult of access or out-of-print, would not of themselves have justified their republication. What has induced me to present them in assembled form is only the expectation that cumulatively, forming a new whole through their joint bearing on the focal cause of keeping knowledge unsplintered and in their logical concatenation, they might reach the critical mass of effectiveness that they could not possibly attain singly and severally. I am rededicating them to my colleagues in biomedical research and teaching, in medical practice, and above all, to the students, who hopefully will both help to strengthen the biological roots and links to medicine and share in the resulting achievements and rewards.

I wish to express my deep gratitude to all my staff members, collaborators, students, technicians and laboratory helpers, who have, over the years, made it possible for me to translate ideas into tangible products; to all the institutions, foundations and agencies who have generously contributed to the support of my work; and to the Publisher and his staff, for the excellent exhibit in which the products are now displayed.

I. BIOGRAPHICAL

Research in Retrospect

IT WOULD BE fallacy and folly to presume that the young will adopt the ways and precepts of the past. All they can and should do, is to adapt them appropriately to the present and the future, which are theirs. In that sense, to let them share the record of one's scientific life, with all its vagaries, elations, failures and rewards, for their judicious choice of what to emulate and what to shun, becomes a mandate for their seniors. In his spirited book *From Dream to Discovery,* Hans Selye has nobly served this mission. In joining distinguished colleagues in a tribute to him on his sixtieth birthday by presenting the following "autobiographic" extroversion of my own scientific life line extending over well-nigh half a century, I find the only mitigating circumstance for doing so in the thought that it may offer further illustrative examples to validate points made in his book; and above all the key point with which Selye concludes the Introduction: "Scientists are probably the most individualistic bunch of people in the world. All of us are and should be essentially different; there would be no purpose in trying to fit us into a common mold."

Emerging from three years' service as officer in World War I, I entered the University to study engineering and biology. The motivation to do so dates back to the inspiration received from my teachers in secondary school (gymnasium), who had encouraged laboratory research and humanistic studies in equal measure. The combination of engineering and life sciences proved to have hybrid vigor, both in conceptual and technical regards. Right in my doctor's thesis (1922) on *Animal Behavior as System Reaction,* I departed from antiquated mechanistic doctrine to introduce to the study of organisms the more flexible "system" approach, which since has come to be a standard tool in both the physical and behavioral sciences. Concurrent experi-

237

mental studies on organ regeneration led me then to a logical counterpart of system theory—a pragmatic "field" concept of development, contrasting sharply with the vitalistic "field" theory of Gurwitsch. Intent on exploring the actual formative factors that give a regenerating amphibian limb its shape, I tried and succeeded for the first time to graft fully developed limbs from one animal to another with complete restoration of function.

This turned out to be one of those lucky strikes which by sheer accident yield unexpected information of far greater import than what had been looked for. The pattern of regeneration of the limbs, which had been the initial issue, was soon eclipsed by the discovery of the totally unorthodox, but absolutely rigorous, regularity in the mode of their functional activity, as follows. Each muscle of an extra limb grafted near a native limb contracted always and without exception exactly together with his *namesake* muscle in the neighboring normal limb, regardless of whether or not the resultant movement of the graft was of any use to the animal. Regardless of how wasteful or even obstructive these duplicate movements were, they remained the same for life. Thus was discovered a principle of "resonance," or "matching specificities," of central-peripheral correspondences, which revealed how individual nervous systems can manage to come through the developmental process with the same stereotyped repertory of inherited coordinated performances despite the enormous individual variability of their embryonic histories, and wholly without the benefit of practice.

Even while pursuing this new track, I carried on the analytical studies on morphogenesis. Recognizing that organ formation was basically a cooperative product of cells and the matrix ("ground substance") in which they are embedded, I went to the tissue culture laboratory of Albert Fischer in Berlin to try to impose form of formless cultured cell masses through their matrix. By subjecting the colloidal blood plasma medium of fibroblast cultures to mechanical stress, I could indeed orient cell movements and tissue growth at will. After establishing the main effect, the identification of its mechanism was a relatively straightforward task. It revealed two components—the mechanical

(4)

alignment of filamentous molecules into submicroscopic guide tracks for cell migration, and a proclivity of cells for following such tracks. The lessons learned in these experiments have later proved crucial for the understanding of the mechanics of wound healing in general and especially for the design of improved methods of peripheral nerve repair.

In 1930, after 3 years of work in various European laboratories for the acquisition of wider technical experience, I decided to accept an earlier invitation by Ross Harrison, the great experimental embryologist, to move to his Yale University laboratory. Harrison had invented the method of tissue culture specifically for the study of nerve growth. I immediately proceeded to test whether his own earlier results on enforced cell orientation would also hold for nerve fibers, as he had intimated. They did. In consequence, a general rule of "contact guidance" for protoplasmic movement could be established, soon to be supplemented by the demonstration of "selective contact affinities" between given nerve fibers and their specific pathways.

The focus of my work thus was back on nerve. I found that even completely isolated nerve centers, for instance, thoroughly deranged nerve cell pools transplanted into no-man's-land of tissue, exhibited intrinsic rhythmic automatism. This further substantiated the intrinsic autonomy of the activity of the central nervous system, which I had derived earlier from the results with transplanted limbs, and even more directly, from a series of experiments in which normal coordinated motor activity was shown to develop and persist in limbs totally lacking sensory control, either withheld from the start or secondarily removed in later life. Nevertheless, one still encounters propositions that tend to concede to the central nervous system no more autonomy than to a telephone exchange or railroad station, in which incoming messages or trains (of impulses) are merely properly recombined and rerouted.

Even though it would have been most challenging to exploit the opportunities opened by this work on isolated nerve cell pools, the outbreak of World War II forced their discontinuance. The moral obligation of making one's experience available for the mitigation of human suffering became an over-riding commitment. I therefore readily placed my experience in the service of the task which I felt best prepared to serve—a search for improved methods of surgical nerve repair. My basic knowledge gathered earlier on the guidance of cell and nerve growth in culture lent itself at once to such an application. So, with the energetic collaboration of my staff, I designed and elaborated a technique of sutureless splicing of severed nerves by arterial (later, Tantalum) cuffs, which besides surgical effectiveness (and a merit citation by the U. S. Government), also yielded the following two developments of much broader significance.

The urgent need for a steady supply of arteries for splicing had led me and my associate, A. C. Taylor, to test the feasibility of using frozen-dried and stored pieces for that purpose. Having proved practicable for blood vessels, the method was then refined and extended to include frozen-dried, vacuum-storable, nerve stumps, as well as corneas, for grafting in general. Thus originated the first "tissue bank" for surgical use.

A second outgrowth of the nerve splicing technique was the discovery of "neuroplasmic flow"—an unsuspectedly intensive internal growth activity going on permanently in what had been supposed to be the "resting" nerve cell and nerve fiber. This again came about quite accidentally. Some of the arterial cuffs used were so tight as to constrict the enclosed stretch of nerve. Such locally constricted nerves were noted to develop chronic swellings at the cell-near proximal entrance to the narrows, coupled with commensurate shrinkage at the distal side. While part of the swelling could be traced (in one of the earliest biological applications of the high-powered isotopes from the Chicago Atomic Pile) to the throttling of a continuous fast centrifugal stream of interstitial fluid *between* the fibers of peripheral nerve trunks, the major force of the effect proved to be due to the existence of a perpetual, but slower, flow of the content *within* each individual nerve fiber away from its central cell of origin. The widenings up-stream from bottlenecks are simply the results of damming. From continued research on the phenomenon, combining techniques of microsurgery, explanta-

(6)

tion, radioautography, electron microscopy, cytochemistry and cinemicrography, we could ascertain that the nerve cell body is engaged in continuous reproduction of its macromolecular mass, foremost protein, which then is passed on to a conveyor-like mechanism of the nerve fiber channel for shipment to sites of internal consumption and repair, as well as for export of some products to extra-nervous tissue. My double training in biology and engineering has undoubtedly predisposed me to recognize and interpret correctly this "neuroplasmic flow" and its role in the adaptive functioning of the nervous system.

With the end of World War II, collateral work on more general cell-biological problems was resumed, establishing in greater detail the mechanisms of movement, orientation, shape, and lodging of cells, individually, in artificial groupings, and in the normal organism. These studies demonstrated the high differential specificity, distinctive for cells of different tissue types, which had already been intimated by surgical experience with wound healing. It was most tellingly revealed in the "homing" in their precisely matching tissue sites of cells of a given type that had been injected into the blood stream for indiscriminate dissemination throughout the (embryonic) body. These experiments (with Andres) then led to a long series of studies (largely by Moscona in my laboratory) on the type-specific sorting out of mixed cell populations in tissue culture, and further, the cinemicrographic analysis by Taylor and myself of the manner in which cells establish contact, recognize each other and react in accordance with their respective likeness or unlikeness. This series culminated in our demonstration that random-mixed and random-reassembled suspensions of cells from differentiated organs, if placed on the vascular bed of a nurse embryo for nourishment, can reconstitute themselves into complete and typical miniature replicas of the donor organs.

With the advent of the electron microscope, I carried the studies of morphogenesis down into the submicroscopic range. Wartime acquaintance through my friend, Francis O. Schmitt, with his classical studies on collagen, led me to investigate the geometrically highly regular collagen fabric in the membrane underlying larval skin and the mode of the restoration of its characteristic pattern after wounding (with Ferris). The data pointed to the existence of a principle of "macrocrystalline lattices" in the collagen matrix, thus linking up, on the macro-molecular scale, with my much earlier conclusions about the ordering role of ground substances in morphogenesis.

In general, as can be readily seen, I have tried to keep balance between analytical experimentation and theoretical inter-pretation. My theoretical formulations, for instance, of system behavior, of the field concept, of macrocrystallinity, of the molecular basis of cell specificity and cell differentiation, of growth control (including a rigorous mathematical treatment with Kavanau), of neuronal resonance, and so forth, have all grown out from first-hand observations and experiments and have, in turn, engendered the design of further research. Not only did I discount the imaginary categorical boundary line between experimentation and conceptualization, but I found the con-ventional sharp distinction between "basic" and "applied" re-search equally inapplicable to my way of thinking. Although most of my work would presumably be classified as "basic," I also take equal satisfaction from having earned a patent for a strictly "practical" metallurgic process: on how to confer resilience to Tantalum foil.

Besides my laboratory, teaching and literary activities in academic posts in Europe, Yale, Chicago, the Rockefeller In-stitute and Texas (and Visiting Professorships at 10 major Universities), I have given much of my attention and efforts to such broader problems as the role of science in education; the historical and philosophical foundations of science; the relations between science and art; the place of science in society; the husbanding of natural resources; and science in the inter-national scene. My faculty of rendering service to those more general relations of science to human affairs (at variance with a "Two-culture" concept) has been greatly enhanced by my experience in several administrative functions, such as my service as member of the Science Advisory Committee of the President of the United States; as Chairman of the Division of

Biology and Agriculture of the National Research Council; as member of the Council of the National Academy of Sciences; as special consultant to the U. S. State Department; as Chairman of U. S. delegations to the International Council of Scientific Unions and the International Union of Biological Sciences; as Chief Science Adviser to the Brussels World's Fair; and as designer and Dean of a new Graduate School of Biomedical Sciences of the University of Texas.

I am listing these activities for the simple reason that one might suspect them to be a serious encroachment on research, the basic precept for which can be summarized in the three key words: *continuity, selectivity,* and *consistency.* Let me point out, therefore, that such extraneous duties are not at all incompatible with literary and educational pursuits. What they force one to do is to make the choice among research problems competing for time and energy with a heightened sense of relevance, selectivity, and parsimony. Since my experience has convinced me that this is all to the good, I obviously cannot subscribe to the plaint of research workers that time devoted to teaching or other service functions is time misspent; for tightness of time is apt to foster concentration on essentiality, creativity and efficiency, even as it curtails redundancy and sheer profusiveness—altogether gains for both the worker and science as a whole. In my view, blanket exemption from participation in educational pursuits in academic life should be turned from a privilege into a stigma denoting some personal defect.

In further illustration of my thesis that effectiveness in one's scientific life is not confined by boundaries of disciplines of subject matter or technique, and as a plea to the imaginative and resourceful young investigators for not letting their sense of perspective succumb to atrophy from overindulgence in technical specialization, let me point to a last personal lesson. Although I have had no medical training, my research and teaching have had, in many instances, some bearing on problems of medical education and practice. As a result, I have been called upon repeatedly to serve in the role of adviser to medical schools and major hospitals (besides earning the rare award of two honorary degrees of Doctor of Medicine and of Doctor of Medicine and Surgery, as well as honorary lectureships and awards in the medical sciences). In singling out these distinctions accorded to a hybrid engineer-biologist by the medical profession, while leaving unmentioned rewards received that are more readily identifiable with my disciplinary training, I wish to stress a precept for the budding scientist: Achievement is marked not so much by what one has learned, but by how one is using that which one has learned, with eyes and mind wide-open to the immense range of *terra incognita* in the life sciences and the untapped resources and opportunities for its elucidation and penetration by observation, experiment and theory.

Reprinted from AMERICAN SCIENTIST, Vol. 58, No. 2, Mar.-Apr. 1970, pp. 156-163
Copyright© 1970 by The Society of the Sigma Xi

Paul A. Weiss

Whither Life Science?

*What are the great unanswered questions that
serve as beacons for biological research?*

Faced with such questions as those above, one gets a
sense of entering from the wings onto the stage of
history, realizing that one's diagnosis may in itself bias
the course of future events. One thus assumes a much
heavier load of responsibility than if he were simply to
predict the outcome of an experiment. After all,
assessments like the one I am about to make, if carried out conscientiously and judiciously, can in the
long run serve in much the same way that regular
medical checkups of individuals contribute to the
overall improvement of public health. Therefore,
comparing my task with that of a medical examiner—
in view of the still infantile stage of the life sciences,
specifically that of pediatrician—I must include in my
concern with future healthy growth any diagnostic
signs of abnormalities, such as, for instance, symptoms of incipient gigantism or obesity.

This is a task to be tended to in the spirit of a critical
clinician, not of a doting parent. Thus, I shall offer no
apologies for being critical. In sober critical examination, then, what is the state of vigor of contemporary

*Paul A. Weiss is Professor Emeritus at the Rockefeller University,
where he was head of the Laboratory of Developmental Biology before
his retirement. Educated in Europe, both in engineering and the life
sciences, he came to this country in 1931, as recipient of a Sterling
Fellowship from Yale University, where for the next two years he was
associated with the late Professor Ross Granville Harrison in the Osborn
Zoological Laboratory. After a brilliant career at the University of
Chicago, punctuated by visiting appointments in a number of leading
universities, he joined the Rockefeller University in 1954. He has served
on the President's Science Advisory Board and as Chairman of the Division of Biology and Agriculture of the National Research Council.
In his research, Professor Weiss has delved deeply into the problems of
development, cell biology, and the growth and functioning of the nervous
system. As a university teacher, he has raised a generation of graduate
students. He has also participated in various policy-forming and administrative functions in the organizational network of science. It is from
this range of experience that he writes: no one would appear to be better
qualified to deal with the subject of this essay.
Saturday Review originally published this article in condensed form,
entitled "Living Nature and the Knowledge Gap," in the November 29,
1969, issue as part of its series "The Great Unanswered Questions,"
copyright 1969 Saturday Review, Inc.*

biology, measured on the dual scale of the aspirations
of its own practitioners and the expectations of a
public hoping for miracles by and for the supreme living being, man?

I shall not parade as soothsayer, bringing glad tidings
of scientific "breakthroughs," in which some of our
media of public information tend to indulge in answer
to the public cry for the thrill of novelty. To those who
have a flair for statistics, I propose the following instructive pastime. Go to a library and scan back copies
of newspapers that have reported science items for the
last twenty-five years (there was no such spate of
science news before World War II as since). Note
down the grand and grandiose predictions of how a
given observation or insight would soon provide the
cure of this disease or the solution of that mystery, or
furnish new means for man to manipulate his destiny,
and so forth. Then try to track the fate of those items
through subsequent periods, and discover for yourself
how quickly most of this erstwhile burning "news"
gets cold, eclipsed, doomed to oblivion.

Glitter and glamor are not the true marks of the
steady march of science, and the hot spur-of-the-
moment fascination with novelty does not last. In the
first excitement, a new discovery is viewed only
against the background of past ignorance, over which
it stands out as a step of major magnitude. But having
regained perspective, one often recognizes it as still
infinitesimally small in terms of what remains to be
discovered and understood. In fact, any scientific feat
first presented in overmagnified dimensions is soon
cut down to size and proper proportions by the skep-
ticism and criticism of the scientific community. True,
solid, and enduring scientific knowledge advances in a
steady, consistent carrier wave, the trend and rate of
which cannot be diagnosed from the temporary ripples of "spectaculars" any more than daily fluctuations of the stock market can be taken as indicators of
long-term trends in economics.

Is there a goal?

Let us look both backward and forward from this instant in time, called "present," at which the certainty of knowledge of the past changes abruptly into the indefiniteness of a future that is uncertain; just how uncertain varies with the designation of a *goal*. By defining a future course, a goal restrains the uncertainty inherent in blind rambling. Ostensibly, the question above takes it for granted that biology has such a goal or goals toward which research effort is being steered. But is this premise valid? Even if validated, are the goals we can discern identical with the august and cardinal "unanswered questions" of our query, in the sense of stable, long-range beacons, or are they just auxiliary stakes set out for temporary tactical guidance at close range? In other words, does research in biology take bearings, as in navigation, from fixed stars, or does it follow the erratic lures of capricious will-o'-the-wisps?

Is research goal-directed? What the observer of the current scene can see is only that it is vigorously on the move and moving forward along given lines. This progression is called "progress." However, the mere fact that research has direction in no way implies that it is purposefully orienting itself toward a defined far-off goal. The sheer record of progression does not reveal whether its track has been consciously, conscientiously, and considerately chosen with sights trained at some distant guiding light, or whether it has simply continued blindly in its rut, driven by the inertial momentum of past impetus. Of course, it would seem gratuitous to deal with such a question in terms of an abstract generality. After all, research is carried out by real people, who vary enormously in their individual aspirations, motivations, interests, and circumstances. So, one might answer, the pioneer still follows his star, while the dullard or drudge prefers the beaten track.

On the other hand, a comparative survey of trends during the half century of my own research experience has convinced me that the proportions and relative weights of these two extremes of the total spectrum of researchers have become so markedly reversed of late that the pertinence of the old doctrine of absolute freedom of research can no longer be accepted unreservedly. In fact, the original meaning of that "doctrine" has been perverted; for what it proclaimed was not freedom of "movement" but freedom of "choice." To merit that freedom, one must have the wish, the will, and the faculty to choose one's goal with deliberation. These virtues are not as prominent in research today as they were at the time of my apprenticeship. Examples of research production that, on the face of it, is aimless, grinding out senseless or redundant data, are mounting.

Therefore the answer to the question posed at the head of this section remains, at best, ambiguous. Some research is still decidedly goal-directed; some other research shows direction but no goal; and there is also some that even lacks direction. Moreover, what used to be clear macrogoals for orientation have gradually crumbled into innumerable disconnected microtasks; and many of the original major targets for research have become splintered, blurred, obscured, or totally lost from view. Consequently, the corresponding great focal questions whose resolution was the original concrete goal of research have not only remained unanswered but have faded to indistinctness.

True, some "great questions" are still familiar through the currency of their names; but like the names on tombstones, those are just symbolic mementos no longer denoting the essence of their defunct carriers. The problem of "organism" and "organization" is a good example; I shall turn to it below for special consideration. Other questions have simply assumed another verbal guise—perhaps more adequately phrased, though not necessarily nearer to solution; such a one is the origin of life. Still others, such as the mind-body dualism, have been relegated to the attic of philosophy as being beyond the ken of science. Yet, on the whole, if anyone wants to find the "great problems" of biology explicitly treated in current literature, he must turn to encyclopedias or the writings of historians, "generalists," or publicists—and writers of science fiction—rather than to the literature reporting or summarizing bench research.

In passing, it should be added that the recent influx of mathematicians (other than biometricians) into theoretical biology has started to establish a promising link, albeit by shortcut, between the generalists, who see the problems, and the researchers, who have the facts, through the effort to apply rigorous mathematical discipline to the formulation of the "great problems" of biology. Unfortunately, these problems are often conceived of in terms so general, unrealistic, and grossly oversimplified that in the final account, "any resemblance to beings living or dead is purely coincidental." Even so, merely to have raised the sights to the broad unsolved questions is to be hailed as providing an antidote to the trend to myopia in bench research.

Let me return then to that trend of movement by past momentum instead of by the vision of distant goals.

Some crucial questions come at once to mind. Is it inexorable? If it is, will the advancement of knowledge gain or suffer? If it is not, can its reversal be expedited, and how? The history of its origin and growth might yield some answers. To trace it, I turn from diagnosis to anamnesis.

How goals have changed

Half a century ago, when I began my explorations in biology, the field was sparsely populated, like pioneering country, with everybody who entered thrown essentially on his own devices. Textbooks were few, comprehensive, original, and unique, almost every one of them bearing the signature of a master; but obviously there were wide gaps between the areas they covered. Yet they had one important feature in common: they tried, some more than others, to balance overindulgence in their particular specialty by pointing up the place and context of that specialty within the continuum of the living world. In this way we became aware of both the fundamental interconnectedness of all aspects of life and the appalling dearth of concrete knowledge about the interconnections, provisionally labeled by symbolic terms.

The vistas of these wide-open spaces to be explored aroused an exhilarating pioneering drive in the curious student, who then had a relatively free rein for exercising imagination and resourcefulness to the full. He could choose his research problem for its novelty and promise and pursue it into the uncharted land of the unknown. Techniques being few and rather elementary, he could design his own adaptations to the tasks at hand. Above all, he was apprentice of a master, who exposed him to the broad perspective of the land of knowledge with its vast blanks of ignorance even as he imbued him with the discipline of minute accuracy in workmanship. Mobility of shuttling between the deep shafts of specialization and the free surface above ground in order to retain perspective and bearings thus became second nature.

Even then, of course, favored topics emerged which attracted a disproportionate share of the work force. But this did not lead to progressive clustering; it was counteracted by the suction from the wide expanse of vacua of knowledge, which, either clearly recognized or dimly sensed, attracted entrants with a spirit of adventure, unmindful of the risk of failure. What fanned that spirit was the sense of immediacy of the frontiers of the unknown and the uncomprehended, offering limitless challenges and opportunities for individual accomplishment. Thus *individuals*, with little to guide them other than questions and ideas—

goals visible or visualized, or sometimes just visionary —could blaze their own pioneering trails through the virgin land. The more men that manned the front, the more new paths were opened, even as some of the older ones were widened by followers. And so the power of the pioneering urge preserved a sound balance between the creation of new settlements and the enlargement of earlier ones, between new explorations and the consolidation of past acquisitions of knowledge.

Biological science was still essentially a preserve for the individual, the solitary worker, pursuing freely and unhurriedly a self-set goal selected from the broad perspective of the problems of the living world open to him. No captive of prefabricated instrumental gadgets, he worked with modest means; inadequacies were not a source of complaint but incentive for improvisation and invention. Perfection in craftsmanship and scholarship were not allowed to be encroached upon by time schedules, deadlines, and pressures for publication. In sum, research in biology was mostly left to the brains and hands of individuals in physical and social settings comparable to the workshops of the days of the guilds.

This is the science that was. Its products are still with us—but its ways have changed. Modern science has grown, by the snowballing of its own success, from an assembly of little workshops into an enterprise of the size, methods, and attitudes of a gigantic industry, with all the benefits and drawbacks such a development implies. One of the drawbacks is that a mass of single-tracked workers tends by its sheer momentum to amplify any trend once that trend has started rolling. A fashionable course thus becomes grooved ever more deeply, draining interest, attention, encouragement, and talent away from solitary prospecting ventures. As a result of these social dynamics, the research scenery is gradually becoming converted, metaphorically speaking, from a lush mountain meadow evenly irrigated by a profusion of anastomosing rivulets into a landscape of deep canyons with raging rivers, separated by wastelands of arid mesas. Breadth is given up in favor of depth, and universality and versatility are traded for the thrust of concentrated effort. We are so fascinated by the achievements of the latter trend that we are apt to forget the price it exacts by drying up the precious sources of discovery, innovation, and, above all, of the *understanding* of nature.

The physical branches of science seem to be mature enough to afford turning a major portion of their energies over to what in industry is called "development"—the postpioneering phase of improvement and exploitation of propitious research results. Biology, however, is still by far too ignorant to follow that course. It is not ready to be turned into a mass production enterprise; to do so would consolidate prematurely the scanty patchwork of basic principles that are truly known. In fact, the various current promotional attempts to propel or lure biology into manufacturing drives give, by their very innocence, evidence of the immature state of our branch of science; they prove that the awareness of how remote we still are from a profound understanding of living nature has grown dim in the glare of spectacular massive advances in certain limited sectors, such as "molecular genetics."

There are sectors in which brilliant progress is still being made on the old pattern by self-directed individuals, for instance, in the physiology of vision; but time has changed this approach from standard rule to rare exception. Besides, vast areas are left totally deserted and in obscurity. Who is to say what crucial clues to the understanding of life they hold which may be missed because of our compulsive submission to the spell of a few favorite topics? Will the established favorites of today keep being swelled by masses of epigones, acclaiming the familiar, and disdainful of the odd, adventurous, and risky? Will more and more workers busy themselves with fewer and fewer tasks, and tasks shrink to the posing of questions that fit the answers we already have? Is this trend inexorable or can it be countered? I shall now try to answer.

Old goals in new light

Growth of a body has three main aspects: (1) increase in mass; (2) mounting complexity; (3) change in proportions. Danger signs of erratic growth that bear watching, therefore, are mass increase to tumorous dimensions; loss of integration with growing intricacy; and distortion of harmonious proportions to the point of freakishness. Let me review briefly in terms of these three criteria the growth of contemporary prepuberal biology from its earlier phase of infancy.

Measured on a numerical scale—i.e. the increased piling up of items of information—growth has been steady and impressive. The increase in what we know now in certain branches of the life sciences that we did not know half a century ago, or knew only very vaguely, is truly imposing—in retrospect, that is, in terms of increments over the past. Whole areas of science now heavily populated, and even overpopulated, had then neither identity nor name, let alone university departments, societies, and journals for their specialties.

Those were the days of the emergence of genetics, of ecology, of biochemistry as an offshoot of physiology. Virology did not exist, for viruses were just on the horizon. Endocrinology, pharmacology, biophysics had not yet split off from their mother sciences. Only twenty years ago the term "molecular biology," now in the daily vernacular, had not yet been coined. This differentiation of new problem-oriented or subject-oriented disciplines was further variegated by the formation of auxiliary technique-centered specialties, like electron microscopy, ultracentrifugation, tissue culture, cinemicrography, radiology, etc., each with its own problems, rules, skills, and slang. Moreover, specialties have kept right on splintering further into subspecialties and subsubspecialties, each attracting into its service increasing numbers of acolyte researchers by both its aspect of novelty and the relentless operation of Parkinson's Law.

In this manner the life sciences have grown vigorously, both in size and in diversity, exuberantly forging on without compunctions about the resulting diaspora. Some of these massive concentrated attacks on specified problems have borne rich fruit. Deservedly spotlighted, they stand out in the public mind as monolithic achievements; for instance, the deciphering of the genetic code, the synthesis of proteins and enzymes (not of "cells" or "life," as has sometimes been glibly hinted), the electrochemical explanation of nerve excitation, or the analysis of the mechanisms by which muscles contract, cells divide, and food and blood charge tissues with life-supporting energy.

But let me point out two qualifications to that success story. In the first place, none of those pinnacles was reached by blind mass assault; each trek was spearheaded by a few pioneers of exactly the kind of mind, vision, and ways of practice that I have cited above as hallmarks of the researcher of the preindustrial phase of our science. Second, most of their "breakthroughs" can be traced to residues of the catholicity of thinking of that earlier age, for they were generated largely by the interdisciplinary cross-fertilization of ideas of different parental origins to yield offspring with hybrid vigor, comparable to the superiority of hybrid corn. Molecular biology, for instance, arose from the confluence of genetics, bacteriology, biochemistry, cytology, and biophysics. This example holds a deep lesson. There is ample documentation in genetics for the innovative and invigorative value of compatible crossbreeding, in sharp contrast to the degenerative and sterilizing effects of inbreeding. The transfer of this simile to cultural evolution, of which science is an integral part, points up the risk biology incurs by

(14)

overindulgence in monomaniac proliferation of ever more splinter lines, followed by smug self-isolation in those branches. As I have said, macrogoals degenerate then into microgoals and submicrogoals, ending in choiceless single dead-end tracks with no aim other than self-perpetuation.

If this were to come to pass, the growth of biology would have failed to satisfy the third criterion on my list of diagnostic signs of healthy growth: the *harmony of proportions* to be maintained by *integrative interactions* throughout the growing system would have been allowed to vanish. Biology, even in its early life, has never been truly unified. In matters of subject, interest, methodology, concepts, principles, terms, units, and standards, it has never attained the degree of unification displayed by the physical sciences. All the more is it crucial and urgent to counteract the trend to further atomization and disintegration. There is still time, but for how long?

Really nothing more drastic is called for than to bring back into full view as research targets the faded age-old, unresolved "great questions," stripped of the obscurant verbiage which has enveloped them. Peel out their essential naked kernels of clearly and objectively circumscribed phenomena and properties. Let imaginative researchers draw a bead on them and find out whether the unveiled problems yield to explanations in terms of what we know (they probably will not) or whether we must expand the frame of our concepts in order to encompass and accommodate them. There are many curious and resourceful students in my acquaintance alone who are bored and dismayed by their enforced engagement on rote mopping-up operations in the quest for knowledge in sectors where the front has already become stagnant. I have no doubt that they and many like them would welcome the challenge if only the goal were presented to them concretely and realistically, and the feasibility of an approach to it plausibly demonstrated. My faith in this segment of the new generation—not necessarily large in numbers, but imbued with the vision, courage, steadfastness, and versatility of pioneer explorers—prompts my prediction that, on the whole, the downward tide of research trends from quality to quantity will be stemmed and reversed.

Our task, then, is to illuminate the old goals with the strong light of modern scientific scrutiny, and by throwing into sharp relief the solid core of our present knowledge, without embellishment, accentuate again the immensity of our remaining ignorance. The great voids and flaws in the tenuous fabric of our knowledge, now covered up by illusive verbal wrappings,

which insinuate knowledge where there is none, must be exposed openly and set forth explicitly as targets for research and the conceptual integration that promises to make the map of knowledge not only more complete but more consistently coherent.

That word "must," I am afraid, will raise immediately in many minds the specter of "planned research." Let me lay that ghost to rest at once. In the first place, much of the current research effort is, unavoidably, if not planned, at least steered by two forces outside the research enterprise—the policies that control the wherewithal for research (funds, manpower, facilities, publications, etc.), and the public attitudes, somewhat fickle, which influence those policies. Yet those extraneous directive influences become effective solely to the extent to which they affect the self-determination of the independent researcher (I am not speaking here of his auxiliary forces of technicians with or without doctor's degrees). The real force that gives shape to his amorphous desire to add to knowledge is his *education*. Education can make or break him. It can give him scope for self-direction and creativity or it can mold him into a mere cog in a mass production machine. Society needs the latter kind, well trained practitioners, in increasing numbers; but we are here concerned primarily with those aiming at the advancement, rather than the application, of knowledge. If research is not properly goal-oriented, then education has failed to point out the goals and the ways to approach them. If goals have been too narrowly, too vaguely, or too forbiddingly presented, or, what is worse, concealed, the blame must again be laid at the doorstep of education. And above all, if the incipient investigator is enticed to keep on riding currents of fashion, instead of being challenged to chart his own course toward self-chosen destinations, it is his education that has been at fault. So what is needed is certainly not planned research but sounder plans for *education for research*. Many treks toward neglected research destinations might then start moving again.

To instill concreteness into this plea based on my diagnosis, I shall cite two examples of the basic "unanswered questions" in the life sciences which in my view have not been brought significantly nearer to solution in this half century: the problems of *organization* and of *specificity*. These stereotypes of colloquial language, which designate two of the most fundamental attributes of living systems, are highly ambiguous; yet one finds them throughout biological literature indiscriminately intermingled with the rigorously defined symbols of the so-called "exact" sciences, in a precarious misalliance between the body of science and phantoms. Phantoms make no fit targets for research. Can they not be made to materialize?

Great goals: organization

To say that organization is what distinguishes an organism from a sheer pile of matter sounds like a platitude. And yet in this distinction lies what poets call "the mystery of life." Popular science, more optimistic, would speak of "the secret" of life, on the presumption that a secret is more likely to be cracked than is a mystery. Descriptively, the difference between a pile of matter and an organism is, of course, quite plain: an ordinary pile of matter, scrambled, remains a pile of matter, whereas a living organism whose parts are scrambled is dead—reduced to just another pile of matter. If the comminution of any organism were reversible, restoring its life, the phenomenon of organism might emerge from mere description to scientific understanding. But it is not reversible. True, organs of multicellular organisms can be dissociated into their component cells, many of which remain viable and can be reared in isolation ("tissue culture") for countless generations of single-celled progeny. But this only proves that the living cell itself is an organism superior to a mere assembly of its constituent materials—superior by virtue of its "organization." The higher organism of which it formed a part is simply of a higher order in a hierarchical cadre of organizational levels.

The step from higher to lower levels of organization is not irreversible. In fact, we have observed cell masses, isolated from well differentiated livers or kidneys or skin of advanced chick embryos and then scrambled into haphazard heaps, reconstitute themselves into typically organized miniature livers or kidneys or skin with feathers, respectively. Yet observation is not tantamount to explanation and understanding, and scientifically the "mystery" has remained. At any rate, the experience cannot be duplicated as one descends further downward from the cell; fragments of a fractionated cell have never been shown to be capable of putting themselves together again to compose a living cell: their "organized" state has been lost irretrievably by the disruption of the system of which they had formed the elements. Logically, the epithet "life" therefore cannot be granted to subcellular units. Viruses, for instance, which sometimes have been called "alive," are not, because they cannot "live" and reproduce except inside and through the agency of a living cell. The confusion here is semantic: tin soldiers do not "reproduce"; they are reproduced, by devices and procedures contrived by a living organism—man with his brain.

Leaving aside semantic sophistry of definition, we can apply to "organization" the remark Lord Bryce made with regard to political systems: "Though we cannot define either oligarchy or democracy, we can usually know either the one or the other when we see it": we can tell the "organized" state from an "unorganized" one. But this is about where the science of life has left it. For instance, "normal tissue growth is 'organized,' cancer is not." What does this mean in concrete terms? We do not know. We read about chemical "organizers" telling tissues what to become and do; does this submit that a pile of molecules can instill an order not their own into an equally naive respondent? Now, with the recent upsurge of molecular genetics, what used to be unknown under the catchall term of "organization" has been transliterated to "information," which thereby is made to be synonymous with "lack of information."

This semantic change started from the classical demonstration of the ordered linear array of genes in chromosomes which was resolved into a correspondingly unique seriation of chemical constituents arranged along enormously long filamentous molecules of a nucleic acid (DNA), comparable to the letters spelling out a message on a tape. Parts of this are then "read" by other molecules, which, in turn, translate the seriation (the "message") into a corresponding sequence of amino acids, which are the building blocks for the assemblage of proteins. So far, so good: one form of order is converted into another, one-to-one. But then what? How do we get from a bag of proteins to the organized shape and functions of a living cell, let alone to the integrated, viable masterpiece of a human organism? The standard answer one is apt to get is: "Genetic information does it." This is the point where scientific language becomes utterly unscientific. Machines and houses are built *from* blueprints ("information" charts) but not *of* blueprints. The information must be translated into reality through the brains of human beings. Brain function being a paradigm of "organization" (= "information"), we find ourselves thus caught in a tautological trap.

The truth is that the entrenched analytical and reductionist brand of scientists, who are committed to the prejudicial verdict that exclusive study of the *smallest* elements of any natural system is the royal road to knowledge about nature, have, in their concentration on ever smaller fractions of the universe, lost irretrievably the view and cognizance of the rules of order that prevail at the higher levels of cooperative *group operation* of those units. And when they are put to it to explain how, in objective terms, the phoenix can rise from the ashes, they either prove to be "organization-blind," or else bring up those terminological stopgaps which, as I said before, are blindfolds to hide ignorance.

Let me highlight the problem by just one striking example. I have pointed to the "organized" character of brain function. What does that mean? It means the operation of a *principle of order* that stabilizes and preserves the total *pattern* of the group activity of a huge mass of semiautonomous elements (in this case, brain cells), notwithstanding a tremendous range of individual variation and flux of and among the elements themselves. Our brain contains more than ten billion nerve cells, each of which averages about ten thousand connections with others; each cell, in turn, contains at a minimum ten thousand complex macromolecules, not only in constant agitation but being renewed about ten thousand times in a lifespan. Thus, looking at it from the worm's-eye view of the macromolecule, brain action must deal in a lifetime with at least 10^{22} (10,000,000,000,000,000,000,000) macromolecular constellations in various degrees of instability and impermanence. A fact that the individual molecule, of course, cannot know but which our integral brain cannot help but ponder is that throughout all that churning and changing of a population of molecules, which is ten thousand billion times as large as the human population on earth, we retain intact our sense of individual unity and identity, our habits and our memories.

Just what sort of principle will be revealed, or will have to be postulated, in order to account for that relative stability of a pattern as a whole despite the infinitely greater autonomous variability of its elements—*order in the gross with freedom in the small*—is as obscure for the case of brain action as it is for the co-ordinated activities of cell life or for the integrated wholeness of the development of an individual from an egg. It is one of the great unsolved questions of biology, temporarily bottled up under the label "organization." Other names have been coined for it (Gerard's "org," Koestler's "holon"), and I have couched it in terms of "field" theory. These were attempts to specify the problem, not to solve it. They differ from the axiomatic "soul" of the theologian or the "entelechy" and "élan vital" of the vitalist only by their intent, which is to go beyond the simple acknowledgment of the principle and to arrive at formulations and propositions of properties that can be rigorously verified by controlled tests and can thereby acquire some predictive value. It is doubtful that the current conceptual frame in biology is wide enough for this task. The influx of physicists into biology might help to widen that intellectual bottle-neck and bring this fundamental problem down from the attic into the workshop. But the first thing to do is for education to make budding researchers face the problem soberly instead of looking the other way when they meet it.

Great goals: specificity

If "organization" refers to a collective property of groups of elements whose interrelations bind them dynamically into a unit of higher order, then *specificity* is one of the chief biological devices for the establishment and maintenance of such bonds. The dictionary defines "specific" as "having a special determining quality." In the living world, such qualities are used universally as means of communication, recognition, affinity relations, selectivity, the basic principle being *matched* specificities—a sort of resonance between two systems attuned to each other by corresponding properties. Man has adopted this principle from nature for many of his technical devices, from the elementary structural interdigitation between key and lock to the ingenious use of wave-length correspondence between sender and receiver in broadcasting. And when I submit that most of what is known about specific interactions in living systems is still interpreted essentially by referring back to one or the other of those man-made inventions as models, this will explain why I bring up this problem here as an example of major unanswered questions. Luckily, in contrast to "organization," at least some of the instances in which the principle is used are currently recognized as major goals of research.

The following brief sampling may give an idea of the diversity of circumstances in which living nature has made use of the principle of specificity. Starting from our personal experience: there is the selective recognition of optic wave lengths within the narrow band of only one octave by our visual system (colorvision); the tonal identification of sound waves by our ear; the identification of chemical compounds by our senses of smell and taste; the capacity of cells of the alimentary canal for selecting what to absorb and what to reject among ingested foodstuffs; the even more exclusive screening out, by each type of cell in the various organs, of its specific requirements from the passing blood and lymph stream; the faculty of cells of different tissues to recognize each other's types and to form associations like to like, which, for example, helps to restore order in the healing of complex wounds; the selectivity that enables nerves growing out from given nerve centers to make functional connections only with predestined types of peripheral tissues to be innervated; the faculty of a hormone to act exclusively or preferentially on specific target

(17)

tissues, even though the agent is indiscriminately diffused throughout the whole body; the differential effect which different stimulating or depressing drugs exert on different nerve centers; and so on. The eggs of higher forms accept insemination by sperm of their own species, while rejecting foreign sperm. A parasite recognizes its host and finds the proper route for invasion guided by matching chemical cues of the host. Similarly, in embryonic development many cell types execute guided migrations along ostensibly "marked" pathways before arriving at their destinations; there they become lodged, presumably bonded to their surroundings by mutual affinity.

This list, which could be greatly extended, contains a rich collection of well documented phenomena, which evidently have some fundamental principle of operation in common. But save for a very few of the listed items, we know practically nothing definite about that underlying common principle. To single out just one example, many hormones have been isolated, purified, crystallized, chemically identified, and even reproduced synthetically, but how a given one manages, on its own part, to identify and latch on to a particular matching type of cell among the myriads of cells it bathes is still nearly as obscure as ever.

A bright ray of hope, however, has appeared on the horizon, coming from the field most intimately concerned with the problems of specificity because of its direct bearing on human health—the field of immunology, the self-defense of higher organisms against harmful invaders of alien and incompatible chemical constitution, whether microbes or organic compounds. A special segment of the population of white blood cells of a body which has been penetrated by the foreign chemicals (antigens) can turn out proteins (antibodies) molded to match some features of the antigen molecule; antibody and antigen thereby become related, in a vague analogy, like two adjoining pieces of a jigsaw puzzle, and as the former combines with the latter by virtue of reciprocal fitting, it captures or in some other way renders the invader innocuous. This is the process for which Paul Ehrlich was the first to suggest the metaphoric key-lock simile. But recent work in many lands has brought the understanding of the actual molecular processes involved down from that symbolic level to realistic hypotheses linking up with the advances in molecular genetics. If strengthened and widened by further research, this might become the advance post from which the further search for a common clue to the universal principle of matching specificities could be conducted.

Epilogue

The practical examples of the preceding sections intimate why the outlook in biology seems not all gloomy. I believe, though, that progress could be faster, steadier, and on a broader front if the research forces could distribute themselves more evenly and widely over the vast field remaining to be explored. There is need to rekindle target- or goal-consciousness and to make deliberate choice of goals with a deep sense of relevance, as counterpoise to the downdrift of mass movement along lines of least effort that leaves piles of trivial and redundant data in its wake. Much as I admire the progress in the life sciences in this century if measured as a relative increment over the past, it must appear diminutive to anyone who is aware of the enormous distance yet to be traveled— and traveled the hard way—to reach a true, comprehensive, and consistent understanding of the phenomena of life.

This assessment of the current state of the science of life will seem to some to be too sweeping, to others too restrained. Phrased in the plural form—life sciences— it would indeed have to be qualified, as some branches are far ahead of others in their development. At any rate, with due allowance for the margin between optimistic and pessimistic interpretation, my assessment clearly disavows the contention that we are in the midst of a knowledge explosion. The semblance of one has come from using the wrong yardstick. No doubt, there has been a data explosion, liberally equatable with an information explosion, though not all of the collected data are truly informative. Furthermore, since a data-oriented research enterprise is prodded by its sponsors, supporters, administrators, and auditors, who provide and control its wherewithal, to publish serial installments of work progress as tangible evidence of productivity, if not necessarily creativity, we are also faced with a publication explosion. But knowledge explosion? Not by criteria of measurement on a scale of relevance. Major steps in our approximation to the missing answers to the great unsolved questions in biology seem not to have come significantly oftener in the second half of the past hundred years than in the first; some were more massive, perhaps, but the pediatrician is wary of the distinction between growth and obesity.

(For a more detailed critical discussion of the factual and conceptual state of life science, the reader is referred to a book by the author in press: Life, Order, and Understanding: Three Variations on a Common Theme. *Supplement to The Graduate Journal, The University of Texas, Austin, Texas, 1970.)*

Reprinted from Harvey Lectures, Series 58.
Copyright 1963 by Academic Press

REMARKS MADE BY PRESIDENT PAUL WEISS PRE-CEDING THE HARVEY LECTURE DELIVERED BY DR. CARL W. GOTTSCHALK

Three mainsprings feed the stream of scientific progress: new concepts, new objects and phenomena, and new techniques. The preceding lecture showed lucidly how much our knowledge of the excretory function has profited from the widening of the range of animal forms that were explored. This lecture follows in logical sequence in that it illuminates the spurt of progress in the same field brought about by a new *method* cleverly exploited: the delicate probing into the microplumbing system of the kidney. Barely three centuries ago, the man whose name these lectures bear disclosed the workings of the macroplumbing system of blood circulation. If one considers that the lumen of a kidney tubule is no more than about one-fifty-thousandth of the cross section of one of the larger blood vessels, one marvels at the daring and skill involved in trying for the first time to puncture such a minute space to obtain microsamples of its fluid contents. The feat, as many of you know, was splendidly accomplished in the laboratory of Newton Richards—as he assures me, by his younger colleague, Wearn. Of course, techniques rate only by what one makes of them, and Richards certainly has made the most of his. It is a matter of deep regret that owing to a recent illness Dr. Richards could not accept our invitation to be with us tonight as witness of a display of some more recent fruits of his achievement. He did, however, send me a letter retracing the origin and early development of the idea, which I should like to read to you.

"I regret very much that I shall be unable to hear Carl Gottschalk's Harvey Lecture on the 20th and his description of the splendid work he is doing. Since my name is mentioned in the notice, it may not be out of place if I tell you of some of the events which took place more than forty years ago which are related to what Dr. Gottschalk is doing.

Warfield Longcope was president of the Harvey Society during the year 1919–1920. He invited me to give one of the lectures of

95

the following season. I accepted, having done some perfusion experiments on the rabbit kidney in collaboration with Cecil Drinker and Oscar Platt, which led to the belief that the efferent arteriole was a contractile structure and could take part in the regulation of glomerular capillary pressure. I thought that a description of those experiments might serve as the nucleus of a Harvey Lecture.

During the months preceding the proposed date of the lecture, I read August Krogh's work on the capillaries of the frog's tongue and the thought occurred, if Krogh could see the minute vessels in the tongue, perhaps if I tried, I could see the small vessels in the frog's kidney. Carl Schmidt and I tried and found that blood vessels of that kidney could quite easily be visualized, and some of our work supported the view that the efferent vessel contracts when subjected to minute concentrations of adrenalin.

I gave the lecture in January 1921 and included in it a description of the behaviour of the frog's glomerular capillaries.

In April of that year I saw Robert Chambers puncture erythrocytes and imagined that I might, with one of his pipettes, apply a little adrenalin to an exposed efferent vessel. In September of that year, Joseph T. Wearn came to work in my laboratory. After he had learned how to expose a living frog's kidney for direct microscopic study and had come to realize its possibilities, I suggested that we make some capillary pipettes and try to apply adrenalin to an efferent vessel and see what happened. He countered with the suggestion, why not puncture a glomerular capsule with the pipette, get some glomerular fluid and find out what was in it. He went to work, succeeded, and this experiment gave the first direct proof of reabsorption of glucose and Cl from the tubule and pointed to the identity of glomerular fluid with protein-free plasma. Then followed a long series of quantitative studies of plasma, glomerular and tubular urine of amphibia, culminating in the work of Walker, Bott, Oliver, and McDowell (1939–1941) which gave similar quantitative information concerning the composition of fluid taken from different levels of the mammalian nephron. The war necessitated stoppage of the work and neither Walker nor I could take it up again.

The work was exceedingly difficult because of the crudity of the apparatus, all of which we had to make ourselves. Many days in 1921–1922 elapsed before Wearn succeeded in withdrawing uncontaminated glomerular urine from a frog.

Wearn, Mudge, and I visited Dr. Gottschalk in 1959 (I think), and each of us, using the sophisticated apparatus he had assembled, was able to puncture with relative ease and precision a mammalian tubule which he had made ready for us."

II. BIO-MEDICAL EDUCATION

Reprinted From the Journal of the American Medical Association
July 20, 1964, Vol. 189, pp. 209-216
Copyright 1964, by American Medical Association

Interface Between Basic Medical Sciences and Their University Roots

Paul A. Weiss

AN INTERFACE, when viewed at close range, loses its absolute sharpness, especially in molecular terms. There is transition from one phase to the other, although it is quite steep. To think in terms of absolute discontinuity is no more than a convenient device of the mind which always tries to dissect the continuum of the Universe into parcels and squeeze the pieces into separate, tidy, verbal compartments. We do the same thing whenever we organize human affairs: We break continua up and stuff the fragments into mental pigeonholes. The educational process is just such a continuum. Therefore, the interfaces we are talking about are, in reality, artificial partitions between compartments set up artificially for practical administrative reasons.

It is important to keep this fact in mind because precollege, premedical, preclinical, clinical, postgraduate, etc, education are not disjointed pieces, but are—or at least, should be—a steady and continuous progression, like all development, from the more general to the more specific. Viewing education then as something like a tree, it is clear that if you expect good fruit from it, you must tend the roots. It is impossible, therefore, for me to deal otherwise with the problem of the foundations on which a good medical education should rest than in the context of the total educational spectrum, with higher education obviously as our main focus.

While taking this broader view, it is to be kept in mind that what is to be presented is from my own personal slant of limited perspective, dispelling any notion that it is a generally accepted or acceptable thesis. In fact, if there were any wide concensus, one would have to regard it with distrust. The educational system is in need of greater diversity and differentiation, not of greater uniformity and standardization. There is already too much of that pervading our national culture and

education ought to counteract it, rather than insidiously act as a prop for it. If my thoughts and contentions turn out to be more provocative than palatable, they will quite properly give rise to critical and constructive discussion and hence will have served a purpose.

Now, in looking at the roots of education in the sciences that lead up to medical theory and practice, it has become ever more evident to me that the period of patching up past mistakes by piecemeal improvements—the way we have been improving what in essence are still model-T automobiles by constantly adding trifling gadgets and making minute changes here and there to strike consumer fancies—has come to an end; and that nothing short of a complete review and drastic redesigning of the whole system of higher education is going to do the trick for the future. Therefore, I will indulge in some star gazing, although from a rather realistic and practical point of view, on how this remodeling should be conceived and why premedical and medical education stands to benefit from it.

When I advocate a thorough review, revision, and remodeling of our whole academic structure, I certainly do not imply that this should or could be done by starting all over again from scratch by constructing some synthetic paper scheme of educational policy. This would be as preposterous as it would be futile. On the contrary, unless we adopt the wisdom of the time-proven device of evolutionary success, which lies in retaining conservatively what is reasonably serviceable and simply adapting it to new needs and conditions without disrupting its cohesive structure, we would end up worse off than by doing nothing at all. Yet, I do propose that the required adaptations of the educational system be of major scope, consisting of more than just trifling frills and patches.

Before considering the broader aspects of educational philosophy, to which the needs of medical education must be related, I should like first to get some concrete tactical problems out of the way,

Dr. Weiss is a professor and member of the Rockefeller Institute.
Read, in conjunction with a film presentation, before the Annual Congress on Medical Education, Chicago, Feb 9, 1964.

because being narrower they are easier to solve. They involve some sort of understanding of what the irreducible prerequisites really are for any kind of medical education, traditional or prospective.

We need not labor the role of the study of biology as a basis for medicine, for it is almost universally taken for granted. It is to be made clear at the outset, however, that this does not reduce medicine to just another branch of the biological sciences. Medicine is rather a hybrid of two equal parental lines, only one of which lies in the science of objective measurement and logical deduction, while the other stems from the subtle, but subjective, powers of evaluation and judgment of the human mind to be tapped whenever the doctor faces the individual patient, the single case in its uniqueness. Science does not deal with unique events; it only encompasses them. It deals with the general rules, usually statistical, common to large numbers of cases—the average behavior of categories. Physics does not deal with a particular electron or a given atom, nor does meteorology deal with a specific cloud in its uniqueness. No two cells will ever behave exactly alike and no two disease courses duplicate each other down to the last detail. Predictive science takes an interest in individual cases only for what they may hold in supporting old or directing new generalizations and theories. It then discards them as non-recurring items. Scientific prediction can be positive about what cannot happen and what might happen, but it can only approximate reality in anticipating just precisely what will happen in the individual event. This is where the physician cannot afford to be a scientist. His interest must sharpen as it focuses on the single, unique, and nonrecurring specimen, the human individual whom he aims to help.

There are thus two strains running through medicine, one of impersonal scientific method, which furnishes the rules and tools for guiding judgment, and another of personal responsibility for judicious decisions to deal with each specific and unique case and situation at hand. The trend over this past century for the scientific line to grow in vigor and in volume should be no cause for alarm, since the two lines are not competitive, but strictly complementary. In the expanding universe of human welfare, there must be room for both happily to expand in unison.

As science, with its method, tests, and critical checks, provides personal judgment with ever safer guides and narrower margins for error, it expands legitimately into what the ministers of the healing art of old might have claimed to be their exclusive domain. But as it does so, it also frees time and energy for the cultivation of those human values and powers of application for which science has furnished no proper substitute. Let us not overlook the fact that the human body contains some of the subtlest precision devices of discrimination and evaluation. Our eye can detect a few quanta of light, our nose a few aromatic molecules. True, we can design technical apparatus of equal sensitivity to register the elementary stimuli involved, but for the perception and evaluation of the kaleidoscopic variety of patterns and combinations in which they meaningfully appear in nature, there is no substitute for that discerning power of the human mind which we call judgment. The time and effort that science saves us could, therefore, be profitably spent on sharpening by practice those peculiarly human faculties.

In this sense, one current countertrend bears watching. A tendency seems to be growing in our society to equate effort with drudgery and in trying rightfully to abolish the latter, to disdain the former likewise. Well, the training of the faculties I have spoken of does call for effort, conscious effort and, indeed, concentrated effort. In an age of abdication to effort-saving machines, we therefore also risk the danger of abandoning the effort-requiring drive to develop those uniquely subjective human powers to their fullest potential. Of course, if that comes to pass, if we let those subtle, personal faculties of observation, sensing, and rating atrophy from sheer disuse, then, as you must give withered muscles the support of braces, so the sciences will have to come to the rescue of withered, unperceptive minds with the poor substitute of automatic rules in order to prevent at least the worst malfeasance and the fatal error.

Perhaps we are inescapably heading that way. When there are not enough teachers of native talent to go around to fill the needs of an expanding educational system, then society, depending more now on the lesser lights, has to protect itself against incompetence by giving them some hard and fast mechanical rules of procedure. Likewise, if an expanding program of medical care should be unable to fill its quota from those with native talent and calling for the profession, the rest will have to be supplied by science with some firm guide ropes to make sure that even those with blurred vision will not fall off the safe trail and drag their charges with them. Science will never dehumanize medicine. But conceivably it might one day be called to the rescue of a dehumanized medicine.

I made these introductory remarks to convince you that I am not one who would grant a monopoly to the scientific approach to medicine. Having made this clear, let me then proceed to deal with those tactical prerequisites to medicine which lie definitely within the domain of science; to begin with, let us consider biology.

Most of our traditional units of instruction in the life sciences used to be based either on forms or stages of life, such as bacteriology, botany, zoology, embryology, etc, or on methods of approach, such as anatomy (for morphological dissection), biometrics (for measurement) or biochemistry (for chemical dissection). With the growing realization of the general validity of certain basic principles common to all forms of life, a more natural organization of biology according to inherent principles is gradually superseding the old pattern. Thus investigators and teachers have begun to draw promiscuously on bacteria, plants, animals, and man for knowledge and illustration of the principles of cell structure, metabolism, growth, heredity, excitation, adaptation, ecology, and evolution. Many of the greatest advances of biology have come in places where different specialties have combined forces in a conjoint study. Genetics, for instance, owes its spectacular development in this century to the correlation of facts from such diverse fields as cytology, animal and plant breeding, biochemistry, immunology, statistics, and taxonomy. As a result, the old alignment is giving way to a new, more natural, and more consistent order. The important thing in the present context is that in this new order the biology of man should be included as an integral part. Genetics courses should encompass human heredity, development be taught with reference to congenital malformations, wound healing, and tumors, and animal behavior, with an eye to social psychology.

Now, in the on-going revision of curricula in the basic sciences, college biology has proceeded essentially on its own except for a certain catering to what was thought to be prerequisites for professional outlets into agricultural, medical, or veterinary fields. A lot of this has been spurious because of unrealistic notions of the purported outlets. It is in this area that medical interests might raise their voice by spelling out the kinds of medically relevant examples and references which, other things being equal, could be used in the instructional program in biology. This would have the added advantage of appeal to the self-interest and motivation of students by showing them what the subject matter means and why they should be interested in it, not in an abstract sense, but because of its concrete bearing on their more immediate objectives. In the face of this realistic generation, this is by no means a minor consideration in the educational picture.

Turning to the nonbiological basic disciplines, mathematics should be taught not only for its substance, but as a screening test for the ability to think logically, which is a basic implement for everyone intending to go into any profession. If one cannot make the grade in mathematics, he probably is not fit for logical operations in general.

Regarding the teaching of physics to students who intend to go into medicine, I do have some reservations. The current tendency in college physics is to go more into the teaching of the modern developments of thermodynamics, nuclear physics, and atomic structure and less into the classical lines of mechanics, optics, acoustics, and electricity. This is bound to leave the student sitting high and dry when he comes to the application of the less sophisticated areas of physics to immediate problems of medical research, theory, and practice. For instance, it gives him no sure foundation for the understanding of patterns of stresses and strains in bone structure in orthopedics or of the hydrodynamics of non-Newtonian blood flow or even of those elements of optics necessary to operate a microscope with competence. Some restoration of balance would seem desirable, but evidently this suggestion comes from one not fully competent to judge the opposing pressures to which the practicing teachers of college physics are exposed.

As regards chemistry, it seems to an outsider that contrary to physics the needs of medical education are reasonably well covered. In fact, the imbalance between the backgrounds in physics and chemistry carries over into the later disproportion in both interest and research between biophysics and biochemistry. However, the recent upsurge of biophysics is likely to redress this inequality with a telling effect on programs of instruction.

So much about the subject matter of science instruction. More to be stressed, however, is our obligation to give the student a feeling of the scientific attitude. He must be pointed to the method of scientific thinking and the objective approach to the solution of problems as a habit to be cultivated. Scientific offerings to the student, therefore, should contain in the place of some inconsequential supplemental facts, which he can obtain from reading the literature, a larger share of indoctrination with the critical spirit of science, as contrasted, for instance, with public attitudes underlying political action.

It is no less important, of course, to lead him to appreciation, not just tolerance, of the humanistic side of life, with which he will have to come to terms not only in the spiritual sense of culture, but quite practically in his personal and social relations.

Only from lack of acquaintance with, or understanding of, the true spirit of science could one maintain that such humanistic contributions to education are the official preserve of the humanities. Not only does science blend intimately with philosophy, literature, and art, cognizant of their deep human motives, but it also, by its own code, has a clearer conception of how far its competence extends, or rather where it ends—a boundary not equally well recognized and respected in the humanities. For this, if for no other reason, cultured science teaching seems to deserve a more central place in an enlightened program of general, rather than just preprofessional, education.

Then why is there so little prominence given to this crucial civilizing role of science in education? Presumably, because too few in the academic population have been exposed to the broad cultural content of science, which is a reflection not on science itself, but on the narrow and faulty manner in which it is customarily being taught and popularized. As a result, the image of science in education is often a caricature, dominated by the training of specialists. Why is it so difficult to make the entire academic community absorb the truism that science is not just a handy tool but an integral part of our civilization, inseparably interwoven with the total fabric of our culture and rightfully deserving a commensurate place in the replica of the cultural pattern in education?

Why? While I cannot admit the existence of such a sharp antithesis of *Two Cultures*—one scientific and the other humanistic—as has been promulgated by C. P. Snow, I do realize that party lines are beginning to be drawn along that artificial distinction. "Liberal education" versus "scientific training" is turning from a slogan into a battle-cry. Would both sides only learn more about each other, the misconceptions and perverted meanings, which underly the noise, would readily subside. Without a scientific core liberal education remains hollow; conversely, scientific training removed from its cultural context is sterile.

The contributions of a liberal education to the making of a good scientist have been stressed so often and so convincingly that it would seem superfluous to labor the issue once again. One aspect of this, however, calls for comment. It raises the old question of the optimum ratio between the irreducible common denominator of a general education for all professionals and the essential prerequisites for greatest professional effectiveness in one's chosen occupation. But it also raises the new question, arising with the voluminous growth of science, whether that optimum is necessarily to be alike for everyone regardless of his particular future station relative to science. Is it the same for those who are destined by unusual aptitude, vision, aspirations, dedication, and courage to approximate the ideal of all-around scientists, capable of promoting knowledge by steps of telling magnitude, as it is for the ever-growing proportion of those who neither desire, nor would be qualified for, such an august station, but are content in executing competently their tasks of limited scope as partners in that campaign for human betterment and service which goes under the collective name of "science"?

Now, evidently, this alternative does not really exist in that exclusive sharpness. We have before us a graded scale rather than sharp categories. Nevertheless, however arbitrarily the dividing line may have to be set, the process of differentiation of tasks in our society has reached the stage where we can no longer dodge the call for corresponding differentiations in the schools preparing for those tasks. The voices advocating earlier specialization among science students are growing louder, but so are the counterclaims for keeping higher education

unified through at least the early years of study. It surely would be disastrous if the branching points were to be left to be determined by power equilibria between vocational empiricists on one side and academic purists on the other.

There are auspicious beginnings of a penetrating general discussion of this issue, but the deliberations seem to suffer from a certain unfounded timidity. It is as if there were no choice except to emasculate either liberal education or professional propaedeutics, whereas what is called for is not a decision in favor of one against the other, but rather a combination of both in balanced proportions. The same applies to decisions about the training of teachers, technicians, administrators, etc.

The problems involved cannot be solved by extremists, neither the ultraconservatives holding out in rockbound positions of status-quo philosophy nor the ultraprogressives giving in to the extraneous momentums of political and economic pressures. Unquestionably, the growing differentiation of the scientific process has created the need and demand for a corresponding educational differentiation that would cleave the specialized branches of the academic tree further down off their common stem. However, if this were allowed to go too far, the whole trunk would lose cohesion and fall apart. This risk can only be averted by judicious exploration and agreement among all parties concerned as to how far it is both necessary and safe to go. And since this limit will appear different to the men living in the trunk and those living in the branches, science cannot claim to enter the negotiations with a single unified voice.

The pressures for an earlier separation of the branches of professional training from the trunk line of general education are, of course, a direct reflection of the progressive fragmentation of science into evermore specialized branches. This trend has become such a familiar subject for both complaints and justifications that we can take it for granted here without further documentation. I personally believe that if this proliferation of branch lines were presented as a necessary evil, rather than as a proud achievement, and if it were not actively promoted by rewards to human vanity, such as the openings which it creates for officerships in new splinter societies, splinter journals, and eventually university departments, it could still be held in check. But, at any rate, the trend is with us and must be faced.

The challenge can only be met by better differentiation of what for whom? Differentiation, rather than standardization, must become the key objective of the modern university. Higher education must learn to reconcile insistence on a broad general education as a means of salvaging that rare and precious resource of the future, the truly creative individual, with the increasing clamor for the training of more practitioners and technical specialists soon and fast. Both objectives are compatible, provided they are applied discriminately to the respective types of candidates. Some students look for a broad background of knowledge, others just for training in the "tricks of the trade."

The main pressure for early specialization seems to come from the crowd of individuals who are heading for a limited occupational field in which to earn a living and want to get there as directly and as quickly as possible. Since this applies to large numbers of prospective physicians, chemists, veterinarians, teachers, engineers, etc, one can rightfully question whether it is justifiable to shortchange the more highly motivated and qualified minority of true and superior budding scientists by forcing them to share the same pablum with the average, who do not care for a richer diet.

My own position is that much as I advocate differential treatment for different groups according to their respective aspirations and aptitudes, I still think that it would be ruinous to surrender to the growing demands for almost pure professional or vocational training at the expense of breadth and flexibility, comparable to the raising of sterile workers in an ant colony. At the same time the demands will persist and we cannot afford to look the other way when we are pressed for answers.

My own answer, which I cannot possibly expound here in detail, transcends the biological and scientific concerns of the university. It rests on my conviction that the single college, the single university, the single professional school, as an independent individuality, has ceased to serve its function as an integrated and harmonious organism, and that the only possible next step is one that evolution has discovered long ago, namely, a combination of the various specialized units into cooperative groups so that between them they can form again effective, proportionate, and viable organisms. There are certain tendencies already emerging in this country for colleges and universities to enter into regional compacts, which are in essence precursors to this kind of collective model operation. In a systematic perfecting of this concept, I submit, lies the salvation of a system of higher education equal to its obligations and commitments.

The college has a different task from that of a university and both have different tasks than do vocational and professional schools. Moreover, the swelling manpower demands of industry and government have imposed still further ramifications upon a formerly more unified system of higher education. Can such diverse functions be harmonized so that the system as a whole will regain cohesion and sound proportions? No doubt, they can, provided the various entities, now separate, combine forces and resources in conjoint planning for best mutual supplementation. Groups of institutions will have to band together to constitute

themselves as new higher entities—"University Systems." Each such system would then serve the purpose which in the past the single university was, at least ideally, intended to serve.

I forsee that in a future framework of this type, it will be easier than it is at present to satisfy the growing variety of educational needs by a corresponding variety of suitable programs, without having a rigid one-to-one connection between any given program and any one given institution. By definition, the integrated group would contain collectively such a complete set of major offerings that any essential program, however broad or narrow, could be composed from them simply by combining an appropriate selection of items from that comprehensive list into program packages. It would, of course, necessitate a far greater liberalization of student transfer among institutions to suit individual needs (which, incidentally, would be one feature reminiscent of the great universities of bygone centuries), as well as greater equalization of standards at reasonably high levels. It would also place greater burdens of responsibility on both administrations and students, the latter having to give up a good deal of their sense of security, engendered by lock-step indoctrination and togetherness, in favor of a wider range of the insecure, but personality-building, freedom of choice.

Such an ideal university system of the future is both conceivable and practicable. What it would achieve is the restoration of the very principle of continuity, unity, and universality of knowledge, the loss or abandonment of which our universities bemoan. In this scheme universities would not renounce diversity and individual identities, but they would learn to contribute harmoniously to a group performance, less haphazard in its total aspect than heretofore. In short, they would ascend from the state of a loose mosaic to that of a cohesive system of diverse, mutually complementary, and sensitively interacting parts or partners.

I submit that nothing short of such a collective integrated system of plural universities with diverse functions can fulfill the ideal overall function of "The University." Any attempt at making any one existing university over into a miniature version of this total scheme is bound to end up as an exemplary showcase of mediocrity and triviality, for in trying to be comprehensive, it would have to spread itself so thin that it would lack depth and quality. The differentiation of both knowledge and its users has gone too far for any single institution to be able to attain the necessary critical mass for dealing with the total spectrum comprehensively, profoundly, and competently. Yet, united in groups, the various institutions of higher learning can come up to the requirements. They, therefore, should join to form such integrated compounds, as in the evolution of the higher organisms single-celled precursors joined to form many-celled communities, taking advantage of the efficient principle of "division of labor." Instead of being a "community of scholars," I visualize the university of the future as being a community of scholarly institutions.

Now, at present, it is neither. In fact, the ideal university, singular, does not even exist except as an allegorical abstraction. This is not to imply that individual universities may not have definite general goals, as well as the will to pursue them. But one need only strip their histories of the rhetoric adornments to realize how limited their power to stay on self-set courses has been. Great leaders with vision or special interest groups with more limited objectives may design blueprints for the future, but as the latter come to materialization, their development is deflected and distorted so much by outside influences beyond the control of the originators that the original design is largely obliterated. The facts are too familiar to need recounting here. University histories are full of examples of how environmental factors unrelated or even inimical to good educational philosophies and practices have often defeated self-determination; among such factors were political pressures and lures, manpower needs, alumni whims, deficiencies of pre-university education, physical stringencies, economic bribes, excessive intrusion of unacademic managerial technicians and, at times, even a fifth column of contrariness with the faculty.

Faced with such vagaries, some institutions have had the moral and financial strength to hold as firmly as possible to their self-set course, while others, lacking in either clear goals or determination or resources, have kept from drowning only by riding the waves of opportunism. But here they are, these products of history, each one performing some major or minor service, useful despite their utter disparity, from the most highly principled, almost monastic centers for the search and propagation of truth at the one end to nearly mercenary trade schools and diploma mills at the other.

Confronted with this gamut of institutions, the question to contemplate is not whether diversity as such should be renounced in favor of any one academic ideal or not even at what point along the scale the epithet of "university" becomes inapplicable, but rather what degree of institutional diversity is essential to meet the enormous diversity of needs of our differentiated society and to match the wide spectrum of motivations, interests, and aptitudes of individuals to be served.

The latter point is not always taken into account with a realistic attitude. It is fortunate that our society, being in need of mounting numbers of practitioners in medicine, in law, in schools, and in parishes, can count on a large quota of citizens who want to be just competent physicians, lawyers, teachers, and priests without aspiring to the more erudite stations of scientists, jurists, scholars, or theologians. So, the graded scale of colleges and universities truly reflects the graded needs, wants, and aspirations of people. Therefore, next to the replacement of individual self-sufficiency by integrative realignment in collaborative groups, the universities of the future face the added task of identifying more precisely what needs of culture, society, and people they must serve and of subdividing and farming out among themselves their appeals and offerings accordingly. Personal preferences and predispositions for workbench over library, theorizing over gadgeteering, naturalist exploration over experimental analysis, dealing with people over dealing with concepts, and professional and economic advancement over sheer satisfaction in self-improvement, must be honored instead of being stymied in a common mold purporting to serve all of them and matching none.

Unquestionably, a critical reexamination of the degree of correspondence between the current mosaic of university offerings and the pattern of needs would reveal major incongruities between the two. Should corrective action toward better congruence then be undertaken on the small scale of the individual campus? That would hardly lead to the right solution; for supposing there is an overwhelming urge to train, for instance, more doctors, engineers, or business administrators, would not any given university, which in response to the demand was to decide to enlarge the respective schools, then also have to choose between the academically equally undesirable alternatives of either trying to preserve its former proportionate structure by inflating the less marketable branches commensurately or else abandoning the latter to relative eclipse, with all the symptoms of inferiority and competitive self-assertion such a course commonly engenders?

Again, the solution lies in the recourse to the principle of the collective system, in which each member can choose to play, instead of an imagined universal role, a realistic partial one, avoiding thus to let its energies be distracted, diluted, and dissipated by ancillary commitments, historical or prestige-dictated, which no longer fit into its context; while at the same time the proportions of the whole can be preserved by other members selecting partial tasks of compensatory or complementary character.

The proposition I am here expounding is the evolutionary compromise between conservation and progress. Since no single university can encompass any longer the full scope of the ideal "universal university," it should resist the urge "to be all things to all men" and "to go it alone." Instead, each one should concentrate its major energies on those selected sectors of the total field of knowledge which it is supremely qualified to investigate and teach.

For a concerted program of this sort to succeed would, of course, presuppose, besides the reallocation of educational tasks and subject matters, the harmonization of standards of performance, the free movement of students, and the facultative sharing of staff members within the association.

In any future reorganization and reallocation of academic tasks, some serious attention should be also given to the growing need in the life sciences for well-trained technical specialists of professional status, vaguely comparable to the role of engineers in the physical sciences. A large number of students embark on a career in science with a desire to become useful members of the scientific community, but with no particular expectation or aptitude for setting the world afire by feats of startling originality. Compared with the frustrating experience of remaining second-raters in research, they would be happier if their role as first-raters in some limited technical speciality were properly recognized. They are eminently useful, indeed indispensable, in what in military language would be called the logistic support of all the front lines. Just like prospective leaders, they end their formal training with a doctor's degree. Yet, this cannot conceal the fact that a true division of labor between the two groups is gradually emerging. The sooner we shall give official recognition to this fact and create a respectable status for the growing corps of needed technical specialists, the better for them and the rest of our science. There is no reason why high-class technical experts in, let us say, electronmicroscopy, biostatistics, electronic recording, x-ray analysis, histochemistry, anthropometric measurements, assay of nutrients, etc, who have neither a flair nor gift for original investigative work, should feel forced into it to make the grade of respectability just because academic tradition has pronounced research as a virtue in itself. Such expert service personnel with higher degrees should be certified as valuable and full-fledged members of the scientific community with no explicit or implied pressure for research production. That class already exists in hospitals and some other institutions, but it has not yet spread into the academic places where it is badly needed.

This brings me now to the broader problem of research in the college and the university, particularly in its relation to teaching. The role of research in education is variously underrated and overrated. The glorious achievements of research notwithstanding, it is true that there has been recently a certain laxity of aim and effort which has given rise to a good deal of inconsequential, redundant, uncritical, and ill-conceived research encouraged by the availability of "soft money." However, this need not worry us too much so long as we return in our education to propounding a philosophy and moral sense of revelance, which is so easily lost in the narrow, deep, and dark shafts of rote performance in a given specialty. Because of this, and in order that the universities may reassert their moral

right to plead for freedom of research, untrammeled and uncontrolled, it is imperative that they shun any sort of investigative engagement that does not qualify on two counts: that it holds promise to contribute to the advancement of knowledge, and to the building of a person possessing knowledge with the ability to use it. The moto for scientific research in the university should become again one to foster the turn out of scientific personalities, not scientific products.

At the same time, only those who have been through the process can truly understand how far superior an education is that has let the student experience the thrills, as well as the disappointments, of exploration, the elation of success in resourceful effort, and the disciplining power of tests of evidence, which his participation in active research engenders, in contrast to book learning and passive submission to secondhand indoctrination. I thus conclude that every kind of institution in the diversified spectrum I have outlined would stand to gain from having some degree of scientific research conducted on its campus, motivated not chiefly by the need for training specialists, but by the disciplining power of research in developing critical thinking. In industry, the scientific worker, by and large, has to do what he is told. In universities he should do nothing without questioning whether it has some significant meaning.

This immediately introduces the problem of proper ratio between science teaching and research. Of course, the general principle of the indissociability of instruction and research is gradually becoming the rule. Sporadic opposition to it by educational tacticians is as one-sided as is the contrary move by technically preoccupied scientists to let handiwork in laboratory or field crowd out the cultivation and exercise of intellectual endeavor. Once again, the question is one of balance—not a whether or not, but how much for whom and when? In full awareness that the student's time, resources, energies, and absorptive faculties are limited, whatever their range may be, I still submit that a more sizeable share than in the past can be spent on research without encroachment on the effectiveness of teaching.

Elementary research experience should be encouraged as early as the high school level. A trend in this direction has made some striking gains in recent years. As for the colleges and universities, such earlier initiation to research would certainly relieve some of the competitve pressure of research for time that would have to be taken off teaching.

Contrariwise, the teaching load in higher education can certainly stand radical curtailment. This evidently is not the place for a phillipic against the overstuffing of present curricula with offerings from both the ultraconservative and ultraprogressive fringes of the academic scale—petrified wood at one end and excessive fertilizer crop-destroying at the other. But let the teaching practice squeeze the water out of its own substance and revert to concentration on essentials, and let research likewise set an example of relevance-mindedness, and time will cease to be the limiting factor of tending the legitimate needs of both.

I do not believe in any rigid formula that could be applied to the proportion of research in teaching programs, and I do not intend to go into this matter much further at this juncture. In general, the proportion will have to increase gradually from high school through college to graduate or professional school, but otherwise wide latitude must be left on each level for the variety of individual and institutional objectives. There can be no universal answer. It seems essential not only for every prospective teacher to have participated in some research activity but, conversely, for every professional and research man in science to have had some experience in teaching. Having to explain matters to students not only clarifies one's own thinking but, above all, it trains the ability to articulate one's own thoughts and observations. Reciprocally, it also presents an opportunity to develop the student's facility at communication. Complaints are increasing about the ineptitude of students to express themselves articulately. There is no easier remedy than frequent dialogues with an articulate and benevolently critical teacher.

These have been a few symptomatic, although somewhat sketchy, comments on what, in my opinion, is in the cards for the academic patchquilt of today in its groping to transform itself into a more rational pattern adapted to the needs of our evolving social scene, as we can foresee it. The rapid increase in population, the even greater increase in both claims and need for higher education, and the pressure for including ever-wider strata of the population in the benefits of the advances of science and the social services—all these developments have reached a momentum which can no longer be met by pragmatic nostrums. No longer will it do to correct errors of the past, one by one. Developments are getting too precipitous and times are too short for symptomatic remedies. The time has come to take a bold look forward in order that, for once, we may get ahead of the game. With future objectives clearly focused, the tactics by which to get there can be worked out, sometimes by foresight, at other times by trial-and-error. On no account, however, does blind continuance of the tactics of the past measure up to the challenge of the future tasks.

It is for this reason that I do not see how significant advances in pre-professional and professional education could be brought about except in the framework of a comprehensive adaptive reconstruction of the academic system as a whole. I hope to have indicated my reasons for optimism that this evolutionary change can be effected without drastic surgery by reasonably conservative "group therapy," but certainly not by the continued administration of tranquilizers.

York & 67th St, New York 10021 (As of Oct 1, Dean of Graduate School of Biomedical Sciences, University of Texas, Houston).

After this general comment on the academic taproots of biomedical education, the following two articles spotlight, by way of example, a few branches of the tree. Viewed in that light, it seems that there are much wider ramifications with growth potential and opportunities for exploration and application to medical progress than are exploited in the current routine of biomedical teaching and research.

THE PLACE OF PHYSIOLOGY IN THE BIOLOGICAL SCIENCES[1]

PAUL WEISS

In proper perspective, Physiology appears as an organic part of Biology; one of its strongest, vigorously growing, but still dependent for food and guidance on the common stock, to which, in turn, it renders vital contributions. Our problem of defining Physiology thus becomes simply one of delineation: Just what segment of the great continuum of the biological sciences are we to identify with physiology? The answer varies, depending on whether we follow history, theory, or administrative practice. The three versions do not jibe, and this may be the time to bring them into harmony.

Literally, 'physiologia' means 'knowledge of nature'. Historically, it has come to refer to the dynamic functons of the living organism, in contradistinction to static form and structure. This distinction, however, has collapsed in what might be called the 'analytical revolution' of biological thought through which morphology has just passed. We have discovered that form and structure, far from stable, are in themselves but patterns of activities, no different in kind from the ones encountered in physiological functions. Skin color is but the end product of a pigmentation process; a tissue fiber, the result of molecular alignment; a spindle cell, the product of elongation; any inherited 'character', the last link of a long chain of gene-controlled processes, and so forth. In consequence, we now have the hyphenated brands of Developmental 'Physiology', 'Physiological' Genetics, Histo 'physiology', 'Physiological' Gradients, etc. Sciences that used to rate as morphological, thus give notice that they have adopted the analytical techniques and ways of thinking of physiology and that they, too, aim beyond formal description, at the causal analysis of underlying mechanisms. This has happened, or is happening, throughout biology.

But does it presage a merger into a super-physiology of all branches of biology interested in mechanisms of life? There are many signs that such an expansive trend is under way. Unchecked, it would lead to an absurdly watered-down concept of 'physiology'. Unheeded, it would leave physiology behind in an absurdly obsolete position. There are voices advocating such a position. This places us in the midst of a dilemma. Which way are we to move?

Let us first examine the expansive trend. Is it really legitimate for physiology to absorb all that deals with 'mechanisms of life'? Or can we draw a logical demarcation line somewhere closer to the old core? I submit that we can, if we define physiology as the study not of 'mechanisms', as is the tendency, but of 'functions', as of old; the term 'function' to be used in the following explicit sense.

All biological systems can ultimately be resolved into populations of molecules. The activities, transformations, and interactions of these molecular groups with the attendant transfers and conversions of energy are the basic instrumentalities of life. They can be measured objectively in units of grams, centimeters, seconds, and so forth, units that contain no reference whatever to the role of the measured events in the household of a living system. We can have complete knowledge of what goes on on the elementary physico-chemical level, without knowing that all of it has a bearing on the maintenance and viability of the organism, and, in fact, makes no sense otherwise. This is strictly analytical procedure. It reveals processes, causal chains of events, facts without meaning in themselves. Yet, what makes life possible, is the very fact that the component processes do make sense, do have meaning, not in themselves, but in terms of the interests of the higher unit. I propose to reserve the term "functions" for processes that have such a referred meaning for the whole, when we are considering them in that relationship.

We can study the operation of a machine without knowing its function. We can likewise analyze physical and chemical processes in the cell without bothering about their functional significance. But if this is as far as we go—and it may be fully far enough for a particular purpose—we need not call it physiology. Let us call it simply biophysics or biochemistry, as the case may be, and speak of physiology only where there is, in addition, search for functional understanding. I say advisedly 'in addition', for, clearly, biochemical and biophysical analysis form the basic tools of physiology. Yet they furnish only part of the story, and what remains is of enough weight to dispel the apprehension that biochemistry and biophysics might soon partition physiology between themselves. The distinction between 'functions' and mere 'processes' should make it easier to decide what to rate as physiology and what not. A cat falling from a roof is an object of physics as long as we are merely interested in the velocity of its

---

[1] Address delivered at the symposium on "Perspectives in Physiological Education" at the annual meeting of the American Physiological Society in Chicago, May 19, 1947.

fall, or even the acceleration of its endolymph. Physiology enters when we want to know how it always manages to land on its feet. To this extent, physiology marks an attitude rather than a subject matter.

To clarify the relation between physiology and the rest of biology further, we must dwell for a moment on the fact that all biological systems have a dual aspect. They are causal mechanisms as well as products of evolution. Their construction and operation follow universal and immutable laws of physical and chemical causality, just as an automobile is constructed and operated by chains of causally interconnected events, no matter what its style. Of the infinite variety of conceivable forms, however, only a small selection has been actually materialized on this earth. These constitute the existing species and varieties of organisms—or automobiles; and their peculiar patterns are unique and mutable. The causal mechanisms are universally valid and predictable in their operation; the particular configurations in which they are combined to form given types of organisms, however, are historical incidents in a transition of evolutionary styles, and as such, singular, novel and unpredictable. Here is, therefore, a logical borderline. Physiology may want to stay on the side of the repeatable and controllable phenomena and leave the singular and non-repetitive course of historic evolution to others.

This is not to de-emphasize the physiological distinctions with which evolution has endowed the various forms. In fact, we never really study respiration or excretion or reproduction as such. We always start from a respiring, excreting, reproducing cat or snail or lobster, or the like. Only secondarily and by abstraction do we derive our generalized concepts. Even then we return again to the specimen to point out how those general functions are specifically fitted to its way of life. But you note that our results will in no way depend on whether this fitness is a product of creation or evolution, or coincidence, for that matter.

This discussion is also pertinent to the recurrent attempts at dividing Physiology neatly into a 'General', a 'Specific', and a 'Comparative' compartment. Such distinctions are expedient for filing purposes, provided we recognize their artificiality. They may become a menace when abused for the purposes of sectarianism. Let me repeat: No function is ever observed primarily in disembodied or 'general' form. We know it only as manifestation of a concrete and specific system. Comparing a variety of such systems, we note common features as well as distinctions. Focusing closely, we recognize specific details; taking distance, details become blurred and general principles emerge in perspective. For the individual, it is a matter of personal predilection how close to the ground he

wants to stick. For science, which aims, beyond mere recording, at insight, it is vital that there be a strong contingent of individuals who are interested in general conclusions and theories. But let us not forget that in any inductive science, such as Physiology, all workers, even those with the most 'general' aspirations, must start from a specific object. It would thus seem indefensible on academic, and most unfortunate on practical, grounds to set off 'general' Physiology as a separate discipline from the 'special' Physiology on which it must draw for its material. The relation between 'general' and 'special' Physiology is as between the stem and the roots of a tree. They can thrive only jointly. Such harmony, of course, requires adjustments from both ends.

We are witnessing increasing strains between the spirit of General Physiology expanding to ever wider orbits, and the practice of Special Physiology contracting to an every narrower sphere. I have indicated before how to check overexpansion. I am now adding a plea for corrective measures from the other end, to counteract and reverse the excessive contraction on the ground floor of 'Special' Physiology.

Practical considerations force official Physiology into some degree of subservience to professional Medicine. Naturally, man is in the foreground, the nearest mammals are next, and other objects become rather marginal. While acknowledging this development as a practical necessity, we must ask ourselves how far it can go without impairing the progress of Physiology as a whole. In mining, one can go just so far with the intensified exploitation of a narrow strip of land; to persist in mining exhausted low-grade ore, when prospecting in fresh areas might yield pure deposits, does not appeal to the scientific mind. By the same token, it would seem utterly mistaken to overcultivate mammalian physiology to the point where it begins to drain an inordinate amount of attention, manpower, funds, and facilities away from the prospecting activities of a more broadly conceived physiology. Whether this is actually happening or not, you can certainly see signs of apprehension that physiology is drifting into that course.

To realize its hazards, let us just remember, for example, some of the rich returns from past prospecting in invertebrate physiology: the elucidation, in one stroke, of the workings of static sense organs by the ingenious smuggling of magnetic otoliths into the crayfish; the giant nerve fibers of earthworms and squids; the tonic muscles of molluscs; the neurospora assay of biochemical systems; the horseshoe-crab model of pacemaker action; the multiple innervation of muscle in crabs; and a host of others. These were strategic break-throughs in an otherwise plodding campaign against the unknown. Innumerable more such strategic objects are waiting to be spotted and exploited. The physiology of lower forms has scarcely been opened up. Why this lag of Comparative Physiology behind Comparative Anatomy? Presumably for lack of motivation. Comparative Anatomy was sparked by the doctrine of evolution, for which it compiled documents. Comparative Physiology has had no symbol around which to rally. Perhaps, a wider realization and assertion of its far-reaching benefits for the advancement of physiology as a whole might do the needed priming. It would also restore better proportions to physiology.

In conclusion, I believe that what physiology needs is pulling its family members closer together, rather than breaking up into clans. If differentiation and social entropy make for disintegration, then our scientific intelligence ought to provide the constructive energy for reintegration.

Well, can this academic blueprint be translated into practical action? After all, we have to recognize that there are certain constraints which economical, administrative, and educational realities place upon our philosophical desiderata. And when we leave lofty theory and come down to the plane of practical affairs, we realize that we are really no longer dealing with the nature of physiology as a science, and what it is or ought to be, but rather with the established connotations of the term in administrative and professional matters, such as departmental structure, teaching cirricula, editorial policies, society affairs, fellowships, grants, appointments, and the like. Are we prepared to bring these practical connotations and our concept of physiology into harmony? Let us see what this would imply.

It is evident that Physiology, even in the restricted definition I have advocated, covers a much wider field than do most of the traditional physiological agencies—departments, societies, and journals. It would seem advisable, therefore, that these agencies widen their scope so as to ac-

commodate, rather than obstruct, the new expansion. Yet, we should not expect them to be so over-accommodating as to sacrifice their own identity. Therefore a large area will still be left outside. This marginal area will have to be parcelled up among the nearest border sciences—Zoology, Botany, Bacteriology, Pathology, Psychology, and so on. It will be necessary for these sciences to recognize their responsibility for taking charge of the respective segments; they are not always aware of this responsibility now. For instance, the amount of systematic instruction and research in animal physiology, offered in Departments of Zoology, is still disproportionately small. One of the subsequent speakers will have some more to say on this point.

Such omissions are usually not matters of deliberate policy. Often it is just a case of nobody having pointed them out. Physiology and its border sciences will, therefore, have to get together and find out how many deserving fields they have left out between themselves because each thought they were the other's ward. Undoubtedly, the new American Institute of Biological Sciences could render invaluable assistance in the administrative re-zoning of our biological districts, provided there is the will and spirit on all sides to see the job done. Biology, after a period of groping and dispersion, is recovering its perspective and sense of unity. Physiology, one of its strongest branches, cannot but profit from this trend. Let us, therefore, as physiologists, profess our allegiance to our mother science, Biology, but let us also send a determinate call to our fellow biologists to give physiology its proper share in their scheme. Combining our efforts, we can cope with the problems of an expanding Physiology. We cannot if we keep on fragmenting. Let Physiology and the other life sciences each assert its sovereignty within its own legitimate sphere. But let them, at the same time, wake up to the spirit and the obligations of a One-Life Doctrine.

Proceedings 1st National Conference on Cardiovascular Diseases

pp. 174–176, 1950

Contributions of Biology in Cardiovascular Research

PAUL WEISS

The benefits accruing to any branch of medicine from general advances in biology are sufficiently well recognized to need no affirmation in this special context. Therefore, only samples of more direct bearing on cardiovascular problems will be cited.

Biological disciplines in this category, not covered by other assignments, include primarily (1) embryology, (2) genetics, and (3) comparative physiology. (Evidently, other biological branches are marginally involved, as for instance, botany, in raising radioactive digitalis plants for pharmacological tracer studies.)

I. PAST AND POTENTIAL CONTRIBUTIONS

1. *Embryology*, including the experimental study of growth, differentiation, morphogenesis, histogenesis, teratology, regeneration and wound healing. A great deal of information on the causal factors instrumental in the development and morphological adjustments of the cardiovascular system has been brought forward by research in experimental embryology. Specifically, the following phenomena have been investigated as to their causative mechanisms, but are in need of more penetrating analysis: Shape of heart; intrinsic differentiation vs. functional adaptation; inherited vs. functional determinants of size; asymmetry (situs inversus); origin of automatism and pacemaker action; origin of differential drug sensitivity; interdependence between heart and liver differentiation; mechanics of vascular development, including branching, anastomosing, organ-specific patterns, regional density; hypertrophy and atrophy; development and specificity of vascular innervation; orientation and growth rate of capillary sprouts; etc. Contributions to the configuration and chemical differentiation of different parts of the vascular tree by (a) intrinsic factors, (b) inductive influences of the specific tissue environment, (c) hydrodynamic factors, (d) hormones and nutrients, have been established, but not yet explored in detail. Such research not only furnishes a basis for the understanding of developmental variation and abnormalities, but also reveals the range of residual powers of regulation and adjustment left to the organism and the means to activate them for repair.

2. *Genetics*. Fundamental insight into the relation between innate and acquired properties of the cardiovascular system may be expected from a systematic study of crosses among animal breeds with different cardiovascular systems; particularly those differing considerably in body size, activity, blood volume, heart rate, blood pressure, capillary permeability and fragility, etc. Such studies would also be basic to the

understanding of the inheritance of cardiovascular defects (morphological and functional) in man.

3. *Comparative Physiology.* Many of the fundamental properties of hearts can be studied more expeditiously, in larger numbers, and under simpler conditions in lower vertebrates and even invertebrates. Since the former are being treated under "Physiology," it may suffice here to point to the important contributions to the knowledge of cardiovascular functions made by past experimentation on the hearts of insects, crustaceans, tunicates and molluscs. Even the rhythmic pulsations of jelly-fish have proved to be a pertinent model for the understanding of heart function and its anomalies (arrhythmia, block, alternans, etc.). Further singularly favorable objects will undoubtedly be found if an intensified search is made. Also in the field of comparative physiology lie the studies of climatic variations and adaptations in different animal forms (arctic, tropic, alpine, desert, etc.), indicating natural solutions for problems of cardiovascular` adjustment to load and stress. Similar clues as to the survival value of different cardiovascular systems could be gained from observations on the evolutionary trends (toward expansion or extinction) of animal populations which differ with regard to their cardiovascular regulations. These studies would link up directly with related ones in human anthropology.

II. METHODS AND TECHNIQUES

The array of techniques used in the outlined types of research is too wide to be enumerated in brief. It includes standard and special techniques of transplantation, explanation, tissue culture, cytochemistry, biophysics, statistics, genetics, electrophysiology, ecology. It may be mentioned, for example, that developed hearts can easily be transplanted, and remain permanently functional, under a fully transparent dorsal skin fold of certain amphibians, where the results of any physiological, morphological, nutritional or pharmacological experiment can be followed visually for indefinite periods. This is merely cited as one example among many of the highly promising methods available but as yet wholly unexploited.

III. NEEDS

Experimentation in the outlined fields is still in a pioneering state, which means that major advances can still be made with relatively simple means and at comparatively low expense. Many fundamental studies on growth, differentiation, functional adaptation, etc., can be carried out with equal advantage in any number of objects, yet if subsidized from cardiovascular research funds, could be redirected to give preference, other things equal, to the cardiovascular system, with a consequent spurt of knowledge in this field. Any major research center on cardiovascular problems should envisage the inclusion of a biologist on its teams, as investigator or at least as consultant.

Evidently, the welfare of a society in equal need of steady advancement of bio-medical knowledge and of the most efficacious application of that knowledge to human health and disease calls for a certain divergence of emphasis according to whether a given educational program aims at serving principally the budding investigator or the aspiring practitioner. This implies, far from a sharp dichotomy, yet some degree of weighting subject matter and methods in the directions most suitable for the attainment of either one or the other objective. While practitioner-training has a venerable tradition, programs designed for primarily research-oriented careers *are rather a novelty. Having participated in the pioneering efforts toward that particular objective by the Rockefeller Institute for Medical Research in New York (later renamed Rockefeller University), I embodied some of its basic philosophy into my planning for a new Graduate School of Biomedical Sciences in Houston (established in 1963 by action of the 58th Legislature of the State of Texas), which I was called upon to organize as a new unit of the University of Texas. This program is outlined in the following chapter. Despite the fact that, due to local circumstances, its full realization has not—or, at least, not yet—proved feasible in that locality, it has furnished* a blueprint for the educa-tional foundations essential for leadership in biomedical research.

A Graduate School of Biomedical Sciences: New Venture in Higher Education

By Paul A. Weiss
(1964)

The task of a Graduate School of Biomedical Sciences is to offer singularly favorable conditions for attracting and educating students preeminently qualified for a career in biomedical research and teaching, with emphasis on breadth of perspective, creativity, and excellence of performance. Each student must be considered and treated individually as the apprentice of a master, but with full opportunity to develop his own special talents to the best of his inclinations and aptitudes. The following outline indicates the guide posts and guide lines for such an undertaking.

OBJECTIVES

Graduate Education

The aim of the *educational* process is knowledge; more specifically, (1) the acquisition of knowledge, (2) its application, (3) its dissemination, (4) its critical evaluation, and (5) its augmentation. The hierarchy of educational systems deals with these five objectives in a progressive order, with (1) at the most general lowest level and (5) at the summit.

Graduate education converges on the upper end of this scale, beginning in the middle of (2). It leads from rote to judicious application, from the blind acceptance of rules to their critical reexamination and adaptive improvement, and from sheer productivity (of data) to creativity (of novel concepts and methods). It thus calls increasingly upon those powers which are the unique province of the critical and creative human mind.

Unquestionably, modern society needs ever more professionals thoroughly trained to apply and spread the available products of knowledge for the benefit of the people. But it also needs more of that scarce supply of truly creative minds through which knowledge is expanded so that deeper insight into nature may yield products more rationally, efficiently, and amply. It needs, much as in music, not just performers and conductors, but above all, composers—in science, individuals endowed with imagination, skill, resourcefulness, drive and perseverance. These traits, though latent in various degrees in many individuals, fail to develop to their full potential unless they are detected, cultivated, and exercised. And since their pattern varies from individual to individual, each gifted student is a separate special case requiring careful individual attention. His study programs must be tailored to his special needs so as to bring his superior faculties to full expression. To subject him to no more than routine mass training, would doom those faculties to the atrophy of disuse.

Accordingly, one of the prime concerns of a Graduate School of Biomedical Sciences must be to establish research and educational programs of sufficient breadth and versatility to meet the great diversity of potentially creative students by offering each a challenge matching his particular aspirations and powers.

Research

"Education" literally means "to bring out," and not "to pipe in." Since this places learning by experience from active practice above learning from passive memory, the principal teacher in graduate education is research. Research itself, however, has many facets and degrees of relevance: from sheer data compilation to invention and discovery; from wider application of the known to deeper penetration into the unknown. This scale reflects degrees of both visibility and vision—of what there is within view and what one actually sees. While vision is a personal trait, visibility is an external feature. The gifted student, endowed with a wide perimeter of vision, therefore, must not be made to face a program that artificially restricts the visibility of the vast areas of knowledge and ignorance through which he is to chart his course. Yet, many academic programs insist on building just such artificial blinders into their structure, purportedly for the sake of fostering concentration and mastery in given specialities. Instead of being provided with a map of the land of knowledge, with both its travelled lanes and its vast blanks, students are thus funneled into rigid channels, which they can broaden then and groove further, but hardly ever escape to make discoveries through novel explorations. This is a proven way to train practitioners, not to prepare explorers; to produce followers, not to encourage leadership; to satisfy the clamor for quantity, at the expense of excellence. It is a poor way to raise creative minds and to advance the life sciences broadly, harmoniously and fast.

The need for the perpetuation and deepening of existing trends of specialization is not to be disputed. However, unless the resulting fragmentation of the life sciences is offset in equal measure by efforts to preserve an integrated perspective of how the fragments fit into the total picture of the living system, chances for new advances in the life sciences of telling size are significantly reduced. Continued work along established older lines, done competently, but not necessarily from a broad perspective, unquestionably leads to jobs, which need to be filled; fresh work along new lines, or recombined old ones, however, carries the promise of major discovery and important progress. In general, graduate education must provide students with a choice of either course. But there must also be *some* graduate schools that place a special premium on those students who possess the curiosity, talent, and courage of pioneers and who prefer the potentially more rewarding course of intellectual or technical adventure to the comfort of routine activity. Being blessed with superior native endowment implies a moral obligation to develop it fully for service to mankind as well as for personal satisfaction. Some graduate schools must make it their special goal to help individuals thus endowed and motivated fulfill that mission.

In short, a Graduate School of Biomedical Sciences must strive to optimize the conditions for the development of the student who has the attitudes and aptitudes of the pioneer by exposing him to the broad spectrum of the phenomena and problems in the life sciences, with its wide stretches of ignorance waiting for exploration, instead of just blinding him with the bright highlights of fashionable current trends. The life sciences are not yet sufficiently mature to afford leaving their advancement to just the amplified and intensified continuation of existing lines of research. As always, new discoveries can be expected to come from the imaginative recombination of formerly separate lines of investigation, from striking out in new directions, and from the reorientation of older ones. To prepare the student explorer-in-training for such opportunities, he must not be given his direction solely by the inertial momentum of the past, but he must be led to reorienting himself with regard to, and in full view of, the vastness of the unsolved problems that lie ahead. Yet, at the same time, he must also be instructed in the expert use of the tools and procedures on which he must rely in whatever problem he aims to tackle.

The main objective of a Graduate School of Biomedical Sciences must therefore be an education in two dimensions—"T-square" fashion, as it were. It must aim at

(a) well-rounded exposure of the student in breadth to the continua of problem areas that are at present fragmented in numerous separate, and often unconnected, channels of technical specialization—leading to broad integrated perspective (the *horizontal* dimension);

(b) training in depth in one or several skills of potential bearing on a given problem area leading to disciplined workmanship (the *vertical* dimension); and

(c) selection of students who hold promise to profit maximally from the combination of (a) and (b).

(a) is a matter of overall design of programs; (b), a matter of individual instruction; (c), of individualized admission and screening standards of high caliber.

Biomedical Sciences

Research, on which graduate education centers, is traditionally of the variety called "basic" i.e., not purposely and directly aimed at the solution of an immediate practical problem. This distinction is validly rooted in the historical fact that most solutions to practical problems have stemmed from unpredicted and unexpected basic discoveries. It does not validate, however, the purist attitude that it is debasing the pursuit of basic knowledge to keep eventual practical applications in mind and in view. There is already more knowledge amassed in the basic biological sciences than has been properly exploited for adaptation to use in medicine and public health; also, considerable "basic" research effort of purported bearing on medical problems has suffered from inadequate understanding by the "basic" investigator of the true nature of the medical problem; and conversely, the application of "basic" results to clinical practice has suffered from lack of intermediate processing of "basic" knowledge. A Graduate School of Biomedical Sciences located in a medical center offers a favorable setting for bridging this gap by letting the "basic" scientist's orientation profit realistically from the contact with medical problems and, reciprocally, by providing the clinical research enterprise with a high-grade "basic" underpinning; above all, by raising a generation of "basic" investigators thoroughly steeped in the spirit and methodology of this mutual and continuous interaction between the "basic" and "applied" components of biomedicine.

PROGRAM

Outline

The following key precepts should guide the implementation of the objectives outlined in the preceding.

(1) All teaching programs should be organized with major emphasis on continuity, consistency and inner coherence so that the student may learn to relate any particular thread of specialized work or view to the integrated fabric of the life sciences.

(2) More specifically, all students should be offered a "core" program of lectures, demonstrations and exercises, which will give them a critical synopsis of the present state of knowledge in the life sciences; of its historical, technical and conceptual development; of its achievements as well as of its gaps, inconsistencies and incongruities; and of the promising avenues to its future progress—the selection of topics to be made with an eye to their relevance and balanced proportions, without undue bias toward fashions of the day.

(3) The student should be made familiar with essential methods and techniques current in biomedical research; deficiencies in his preparation can be corrected by course attendance in neighboring institutions or by tutorials.

(4) The student must be made to acquire competence in a few technical or methodological specialties and to master at least one.

(5) Doctoral research should be tailored to the individual interests and aptitudes of each student, preferably by encouraging him to combine a variety of approaches in novel ways in the exploration of a given problem. This will foster his chance of breaking in a new line of thought and work peculiarly his own for further development in his subsequent career.

(6) The student should be given opportunity to develop appreciation for the non-scientific aspects of our culture, such as the arts, as well as for the role of science in our civilization and its obligations in serving society.

(7) In general, every possible effort must be made to counteract the growing fragmentation of the life sciences by rearing a new generation of pioneers endowed with a broad perspective for critical self-orientation, but at the same time trained in the disciplined application of their talents to a chosen, preferably self-chosen, path in a given discipline.

The only bias admissible in such a program might be its weighting, *other things being equal,* in the direction of potential benefits to human welfare through the promotion of health and the fight against disease, that is, to medicine in its broadest sense.

Execution

In compliance with the program, outlined in the preceding points, Ph.D. degrees should be given in "Biomedical Science" without explicit reference to subdivisions. "Departmental," or other sharply delineated distinctions should be omitted in the interest of flexibility and versatility. To counter the risk that the abolition of categorical distinctions might lead to an undesirably amorphous scheme, the program should be structured, but around *key problems* presented by living organisms as foci, rather than along traditional disciplinary lines. The student should be made to sense that all phenomena of life are interrelated and interacting and that he must keep his eye on this integrated continuum even as he concentrates his work on no more than a small sector of the whole. Organizational emphasis will thus shift from disciplinary margins, which tend to hem the student in, to focal issues, from which his mind and work can radiate out.

Such central foci may be chosen, for instance, from the following four major problem areas: I. *Molecular and Cellular Biology.*—II. *Developmental Biology.*—III. *Environmental Biology.*—IV. *Regulatory Biology (Vascular, Hormonal and Neural Biology).*— This pattern is broad and flexible enough to accommodate unpredictable future developments in the life sciences, including additions and regroupings, as new needs and opportunities arise.

The "core program" should present to all students well-rounded accounts of both the state of knowledge and the open problems in those four priority areas. A major part at least of their first year of graduate study ought to be allocated to this portion of the program. During this period, time and emphasis should gradually be shifted from lectures and seminars to practical exercises and research propaedeutics. These presentations should be rather strictly programmed as regards logical sequence and proportions and be amply supplemented by modern visual aids, laboratory demonstrations, library assignments, exhibits and discussion sessions. Experiences gained in this "core program" will give a student not only a broad outlook and firm basis from which to formulate his doctoral research, but also the necessary critical perspective under which to pursue his research and evaluate that of others.

Concurrently the student should receive introductions to the various technical and mental disciplines of general applicability to modern biomedical research, including, for instance, methods of biostatistics, enzymology, microbiology, ultra-structural analysis, electrophysiology, cell culture, surface chemistry, radiation genetics, chromatography, microsurgery, etc. Having obtained some general acquaintance with many of these disciplines, the student will then select one or several of them for further methodical specialization under the expert guidance of an appropriate staff member.

Each of the technical skills thus acquired is pertinent to several of the program areas listed above. By applying them in various combinations to the investigation of common problems (e.g., brain function; wound healing, parasitism; etc.), the student's thinking and working will gain that essential second dimension which cross-connects the single-tracked channels of the established disciplines into topically unified programs. Each student will thus be induced to think and operate on a dual scale: to be no less concerned about consistency of subject matter than about clean methodology and technique. While he will be solidly trained in a given specialty, he will also be enabled to orient and rate his specialist endeavors with regard to their broader bearing on the clarification of life processes, normal and abnormal.

In order to succeed, this program requires a faculty of highest professional competence, breadth of knowledge, cooperative team spirit, and enthusiastic dedication to educational ideals. The growth of knowledge has made it practically impossible to assemble a *resident* faculty which in addition to those traits would have command of all the subject matter essential for a balanced presentation of the life sciences. It is essential, therefore, to supplement the resident faculty by a large contingent of *visiting* lecturers, specifically selected to fill in the gaps, on repetitive appointments of from one to several weeks.

From the "core program," the students will branch out into their individual doctoral programs (master's programs being considered optional stepping stones). Prime attention should be given to superseding the lockstep training of the ordinary undergraduate curriculum by offering full opportunity for individual self-development. Originality and independence in the exploration of a problem area will have to score much higher than sheer plodding along well-trodden paths. In the selection of doctoral projects, the heavily trafficked routes of greatest popularity, which are pursued superabundantly in many other institutions, will have to rank second to the more neglected problem areas of high significance and promise. This would call for considerable personal attention to each student by the faculty. Conversely, the student will have to make the most of the available aids in self-development, such as libraries, practice laboratories, and outside lectures.

To grow to leadership and, in turn, to raise leaders, a person must be more than informed; he must be broadly cultured. Therefore, it will be incumbent on such a school to give the student opportunities for furthering his cultural interest by participating in lectures, exhibits, field trips, and literary exercises of broad cultural scope; in this way, he will be made to experience intimately the fertile interaction between science and the humanities. Moreover, wherever practicable, the presentation of scientific subject matter should be interspersed with references to the philosophical and historic foundations of scientific methodology, as well as to the relation of biomedical sciences to human thought and welfare. In addition, there should be seminars and discussion sessions aiming at developing not only the student's sense of factual accuracy and conceptual perspective, but also his facility at articulating and communicating his thoughts clearly and concisely.

EXAMPLES

The following tables of content of the four programs are samples; they are neither comprehensive nor sequentially ordered.

I. MOLECULAR AND CELLULAR BIOLOGY

Submicroscopic organization of the cell
Biosynthesis
Enzymology
Energetics
Metabolic pathways
Biochemical compartments; sites and mechanisms of macromolecular assembly
Intracellular transport mechanisms
Properties of cell surfaces and intracellular membranes

Cell morphology, reproduction and regeneration in bacterial, protozoan and protophyte cells

Chromosomes and cell genetics

Cell and nuclear division

Nucleo-cytoplasmic interactions

Cell shape

Cell movements

Cell interactions

Cell variation, differentiation and modulation

Cell hybridization

Cell growth and nutrition

Dynamics of cell populations

Cell aggregations and tissue formation

Cell secretions, cell products and intercellular systems

Cell degeneration and cell death

Life span and tolerances of cells

Ageing

Drug reactions

Hormone response

Immune reactions

Radiosensitivity

Cell-virus interactions

Tissue mechanics

Cell pathology

Malignancy

Replacement of damaged cells

Specific cytogenesis: skin, muscle, blood and connective tissues

II. DEVELOPMENT BIOLOGY

Chemical and structural organization of egg and sperm

Mechanisms of fertilization

Fertility control

Parthenogenesis

Embryo formation

Segregation of organ rudiments

Interactions ("inductions") among segregated tissues

Morphogenetic movements

Nuclear differentiation

Gene reactions

Cytoplasmic specialization

Somatic cell variation

Tissue architectonics

Mechanics of organ formation, normal and abnormal

Growth rates

Growth controls and trophic interactions
Teratology
Tumors and cancer
Wound healing
Tissue and organ regeneration
Metamorphosis
Tissue and organ transplantation
Immunoembryology and tissue incompatibilities
Development and maturation of functional activity
Functional adaptation
Involution and ageing
Specific organogenesis: cardio-vascular, urogenital, nervous and skeletal systems

III. ENVIRONMENTAL BIOLOGY

Relation of organisms to their environment
Elements of ecology
Soil-plant relations
Biohydrology, bioclimatology and biometeorology
Tropical ecology
Aerobiology
Parasitology
Epidemiology
Natural resources, human nutrition and conservation
Physiology of response to environmental stresses
Susceptibility and resistance to disease
Stress tolerance and adaptation
Biological rhythms
Comparative ethnology and population dynamics
Artificial improvements and impairments of man's environment (sanitation; detoxication; food preservation; air conditioning; recreation; pest control; etc.; versus pollution; smoke; noise; radiation hazards; nutrient deficiencies; industrialization; urbanization; etc.)
Psychological, cultural, technological, social and esthetic variables in man's interrelation with his environment

IV. REGULATORY BIOLOGY

Integrative systems of higher organisms: humoral, endocrine and neural homoeostasis
Specificity and localization of endocrine response
Sympathetic and parasympathetic sectors of the nervous system
The neuron: its structural, microstructural, biochemical, metabolic and electrophysiological properties; its differentiation, growth, degeneration, regeneration, and ageing
Receptors and effectors (sense organs; muscles; glands)
Transmitter mechanisms
Neurons and glia

Intracentral organization of nervous systems
Origin, patterning, coordination, integration and maturation of neural functions
Specificity of neurons, neuronal connections and neuronal responses
Cybernetics of nerve nets
Physiological psychology
Animal behavior
Instincts
Conditioning and learning
Emotion
Plasticity of nerve centers
Genetics of behavioral traits
Neuropharmacology and neuroendocrinology
General neuropathology and nerve repair
Trophic influences of nerves on tissues
Mental development, health, defects, and compensations

V. COMBINED PROGRAMS

Elements of the four itemized key programs can be freely recombined in various selected groupings for special subprograms of which the following two may serve as illustrative examples.

(a) Nutritional studies

This study program would receive pertinent contributions from many basic items of I to IV. To these would have to be added special offerings, such as: physiology of taste, smell, food comminution, resorption, and digestion; food technology; psychology and ethnology of food habits; agricultural genetics; agricultural economics; demography; cultural factors; elements of medical dietetics.

(b) Biomathematical studies

Although mathematical tools are indispensable in almost any scientific study, there are areas in the biomedical sciences requiring the concerted application of more specialized mathematical techniques in order to achieve greater efficiency and reliability in the compilation and evaluation of data and conclusions. Biostatistics, systems analysis, and computer science, for instance, are such emerging specialties. To be of true benefit to biomedical sciences, they must be practiced by persons combining mathematical (and sometimes, engineering) competence and skills with thorough knowledge and understanding of the biological phenomena concerned. For the benefit of such individuals, appropriate items selected from I to IV would have to be supplemented by separate more specialized courses, both factual and methodical.

VI. DISCIPLINES CONCERNED

Experts from disciplines concerned in the four core programs and auxiliary programs will include: biochemists, biomathematicians, climatologists, cytologists, demographers, ecologists (or comparative physiologists), electro-physiologists, embryologists, endocrinologists, experimental pathologists, geneticists, histologists, immunologists, microbiologists, neuroanatomists, organ physiologists, parasitologists, pharmacologists, physical anthropologists (or ethnologists), physico-chemists, psychologists, radiobiologists.

FACILITIES

The concept of unification underlying the outlined program makes it advisable to maximize the sharing of universally useful *technical facilities,* such as, preparation of media, maintenance of animal colonies, cell strains, bacterial type cultures and viral strains; standard bioassays; routine techniques of fractionation, electrophoresis, chromatography, isotopes, radioautography, electron microscopy, cytochemistry, cinemicrography, irradiation, electrophysiology, statistical analysis, etc.; glass blowing, instrument and electronics shop; and illustration services. By placing these services in charge of expert specialists and giving both students and faculty in any of the programs access to them according to demonstrable research and training needs, much duplication and amateurish use of routine facilities and standard instruments can be avoided, while at the same time, those investigators who need separate, even though duplicate, special equipment for their own research will be protected against the indiscriminate incursions upon their time and tools by the routine requests of colleagues and the training needs of students.

Special efforts should be made to supplement lectures, demonstrations, exercises and reading material by *visual aids* in the form of models, slides, and particularly motion pictures. This part of the program might envisage the setting up of (1) a comprehensive registry of visual aids; (2) a slide and film "library" accessible to students and investigators; and (3) a film laboratory for the production of original motion pictures as research and teaching aids.

Given adequate facilities, many of these resources could then be used collaterally in an auxiliary program of *public displays* expounding the ways, means and attainments of biomedical sciences, including their social, esthetic and cultural aspects, in periodic exhibits, popular lectures and educational motion pictures.

SUMMARY

Of all the sciences, those closest to man's self-interest are the *life sciences.* They hold the key to the systematic improvement of his physical and mental health. Steady progress in medicine hinges on their achievements. Being still in their infancy, their prospects for vigorous development in the immediate future are uniquely favorable. The students of today are the developers of tomorrow. The best among them, therefore, must consider it their calling to build for the future—and not just to perpetuate the past. A forward-looking system of higher education must offer them full opportunity to do so, and in an age of expanding education, society can ill afford not to provide them with that opportunity.

Graduate Schools of Biomedical Sciences should dedicate themselves to this very ideal. It will provide the highly motivated, curious, imaginative, disciplined and skillful student with guidance and an environment in which to bring his creative urge to full fruition. This is the meaning of "education for excellence." It involves education both in breadth and in depth: in *breadth,* by widening his horizon so that he may encompass the wide perspective of the unfragmented total range of phenomena and problems in the life sciences, instead of being made to train his sights myopically on a few narrow sectors of temporary prominence; in *depth,* by teaching him thorough competence in special technical disciplines and their application to the solution of important problems. The former object will be served by a *"core program,"* strictly designed for integration and overall balance of proportions, to be offered in a coordinated plan by resident and visiting faculty members; the latter object, by intensive individual guidance of each student in his research, taking into account his aptitudes and predilections.

All of these activities must engage student participation in research and critical research evaluation, and wherever appropriate, be cued to potential bearings on problems of medical concern. Attention must also be given to the enlargement of the student's *cultural* horizon by facilitating contacts with the humanities and social sciences.

Traditional curricular constraints must be held to a minimum. *Research* must be fostered in areas where ignorance is great, not only in those of most conspicuous recent progress. Mature investigators will continue to choose their own research, whether wide or narrow, orthodox or inventive, according to their own judgment and sense or responsibility. Their gifted students, however, should be allowed to diversify, rather than just replicate and amplify, the course of their research preceptors.

Consistent adherence to the outlined policy is bound to bring about a new generation of Ph.D.s steeped in the spirit of striving for excellence through effort and destined to advance the life sciences in a broad front—for their own satisfaction and gain in doing it, for the growth of human knowledge and understanding that comes from it, and for the promotion of human health through medicine that benefits from it.

III. THE LIVING CELL AND THE CELL COMMUNITY

Reprinted from Laboratory Investigation, 8, No. 2. Copyright 1959, by the International Academy of Pathology

The Cell in Development

Paul Weiss

D URING THE LAST 50 YEARS the study of development has undergone drastic reorientation of special significance to pathology. The following changes seem particularly relevant:

1. The developmental process has been recognized to proceed continuously and in essentially the same manner from conception till death. The study of development, therefore, has come to cover the whole life span, including embryonic development, postembryonic development, maturation, and aging, as well as compensatory changes, regeneration, restitution, and repair after damage.

2. Emphasis has shifted from the descriptive seriation of developmental stages to the processes of which those stages are expressions, which means a change from a static to a dynamic outlook.

3. Accordingly, attention has shifted from the morphologic products to the morphogenetic processes. Morphologic, particularly microscopic, expressions of cells, tissues, and organisms are being treated less as absolute phenomena in their own rights than as diagnostic signs of the chains of events through which they have come about. In studying these formative processes of cells and organs, one has become increasingly impressed by the fact that they do not go on in each part independently, as if in isolation ("self-differentiation"), but that the component parts are bound into a network of complicated interdependencies and interrelations, the nature of which is gradually being revealed by analytic experimentation.

4. The views regarding "normality" and "abnormality" have changed sub-

From the Rockefeller Institute, New York.

Original work referred to in this paper has been aided by grants from the American Cancer Society and the National Cancer Institute (National Institutes of Health of the Public Health Service).

stantially. The individual steps in the chains of processes that lead to the developed form are subject to a considerable degree of variability, and their interrelations vary accordingly. Within a certain central range, such variations produce viable products. Being in the majority, they are then labeled "normal." As soon as a process strays beyond that empirically defined range, it is customarily referred to as "abnormal." But no sharp demarcation line sets off this marginal from the central range. In causal view, one is as sound as the other. The pathologic is thus being recognized as merely an extension of the normal range of reactions of the living system in its development.

5. Analytic insight is being substituted for verbal symbols, largely by the application to the study of development of tools and concepts derived from mathematics, physics, and chemistry. They have brought us an enormous amount of information about the elementary constituents of the living system and the nature of their reactions. True, they have not yet been able to supersede the study in its own right of the organized, self-developing, self-sustaining, complex system of the living cell, the tissue, the organ, and the organism. However, progress is being made in resolving some of the abstract symbolism inherent in such terms as "constitution," "organization," "induction," "differentiation," etc., into tangible problems amenable to further experimental attack and clarification.

Throughout these marked changes of attitude and outlook, there is one basic postulate that has proved its value and the validation of which is worth stressing in this hundredth anniversary year of Virchow's *Cellular Pathologie:* It is the thesis that the sole agents through which an organism operates are its individual cells. They do this (1) through their progressive transformations; (2) through their products; and (3) through their manifold interactions.

As for the first point, a cell in its developmental history undergoes progressive transformations by series of changes of its molecular populations, both as to composition and relative proportions, as well as by changes in the relative distribution and localization of the chemical systems which control the metabolic and functional activity of a cell, hence its products.

As for the products, they are of both chemical and physical nature. New chemical compounds of varying complexity up to the giant macromolecular complexes are being fabricated and either retained within the cell or discharged either for use as intercellular matrix or to be circulated, like blood and hormones, and eventually eliminated. Physical products are the alignments of such chemical compounds in fibrillar, lamellar, or corpuscular shapes; the generation of tensions; deformations; electric potentials; and the like.

As for the interactions, they can be subsumed under no single formula. This is natural in view of the enormous diversity of transformations and products just cited. At best, two classes can be recognized, the one in which cells can act on distant cells through freely diffusing agents, and the other in which cells must be in intimate contact in order that specific interaction may occur.

A brief introduction into the problems of "the cell in development," as my assignment reads, can do no more than very sketchily present a few of the better known illustrations of the three features of cellular dynamics just listed. I shall confine myself to examples for (1) the development of cell shape; (2) the development of cell type, or differentiation; (3) the development of supracellular order in organogenesis and the feedback control of growth; and (4) the development of patterns on the submicroscopic level. No static description, however, can approach the vivid impression of the dynamic nature of cells in action that time-lapse motion pictures, such as I presented at the meeting,* convey.

DEVELOPMENT OF CELL SHAPE

The problem of cell shape furnishes an excellent example of the change in attitude that has occurred as a result of modern experimental approaches. It is also of definite concern to pathology, where cell shape is frequently used as a diagnostic tool. Actually, an individual cell taken by itself has no particular shape, or rather we should say that when left to itself it assumes spherical shape; for instance, when suspended in a liquid. Any deviation from that spherical shape is the result of an active or passive deformation of the cell, due either to the production by the cell of some characteristic internal apparatus or skeleton, or else to a response of the cell to some polarizing or otherwise distorting effect of its external environment. In the case of the cells of the mesenchyme system, which we shall use here as example, the latter factors are the more prominent. In tissue culture, such cells assume a wide spectrum of shapes, from the slender bipolar spindle cell of the so-called "fibroblast" to the large, flattened, star-shaped forms resembling the classic macrophage both structurally and in their phagocytic activity. All these shapes can be explained as the reactions of a given cell strain to the varying configurations of the fibrous network of macromolecules—that is, of fibrin in the case of a blood plasma medium—in the vicinity of that cell.[23] This relation between the physical properties of the medium and the resultant morphology of the cells residing in it could even be expressed quantitatively. The normal range of variability of the shapes of cells of a single type encountered in such media therefore reflects essentially the inhomogeneities in the ultrastructure of the medium.

On the other hand, more definitely predictable shapes can be evoked by

* This article is a summary of the introductory address given at the Conference on the Chemical Organization of Cells.

direct external intervention; for instance, stretch. Tension applied to a blood plasma clot orients the chains of fibrin molecules in parallel directions along the lines of stretch, whereupon the cells, bound to apply themselves to these fibrin fibers as guide ropes, assume bipolar shape in the same direction.[17] This has further functional consequences, as spindle shape and unobstructed parallel pathways combine to enhance the advance of cells through the medium.[23] The flattened disk-shaped epitheloid cells with phagocytic properties, produced by the spreading of a cell on an isotropic planar surface, represent essentially the opposite extreme; as the cell border tries, as it were, to extend in all radial directions at the same time, it holds the cell frozen to its position. Elongation of a cell also affects the direction of its growth, for as the mitotic spindle tends to orient itself in the main cell axis, a spindle cell moving along a linear tract will become consecutively subdivided crosswise, resulting in a string, instead of just a pile, of cells. A lot more could be said about the structural adaptations of cells to their physical environment, the results of which we then record as cell shape, but the present example may suffice to make the point clear.

Now the essence of this point has been that any particular expression of a given cell we record is only one sample from the multiple repertory of reactions with which that cell was endowed. Consequently, a true description of any cell should cover all the reactions of which that cell is potentially capable under the greatest possible variety of conditions to which it can be exposed. This repertory is characteristically circumscribed for each cell type and differs from one cell type to another. The changes which a cell of a given type can undergo I have referred to as "modulations."[16] This is merely to distinguish this group of rather plastic and often reversible cell modifications from those more durable ones which result in the more deep-seated differences among the various cell types for which the term "differentiation" should be reserved. We shall proceed now to consider this latter class of developmental processes—"differentiations" in the strict sense.

DEVELOPMENT OF CELL TYPES

Let us start with a comparison of the specific cells—for instance, epithelial ones, as sampled in different organs of the mature body, such as the liver, the kidney, the skin, the thyroid, and the like. We can recognize and identify these cells even away from their normal sites and associations by certain cytologic and histologic criteria. But we realize that such criteria are again but the terminal results of the three developmental components of their developmental histories—cell transformation, cell products, and cell interactions—and that, therefore, the distinctions between these cell types must date way back to an earlier period, before those visible end products that serve as signals for identification have made their appearance under the microscope. In that earlier period, the liver cell was a hepatoblast, already endowed with the properties that would turn it later into a cell that could produce glycogen, but did not yet produce glycogen itself; the neuroblast was a cell endowed to form a nerve cell with all its specializations, without having the diagnostic criteria of a nerve cell, such as neurofibrils or Nissl bodies; the thyroblast already had the faculty to turn into a thyroid cell that later, if and when properly stimulated by a thyrotropic hormone, would produce colloid; the myoblast had already the machinery to produce the contractile apparatus of myosin and actin in their characteristic alignment to myofibrils, but itself did not have that specialized contractile apparatus by which we recognize muscle. In other words, long before there are typical terminal criteria by which the visual observer can distinguish cell types, the strains of cells in the body are no longer alike, but are characteristically specialized in regard to those future performances. This fact has been tested and verified by numerous experimental methods, by transplantation of embryonic tissues to abnormal sites, or by explantation into tissue culture, where cells past a certain stage were found to continue to develop according to their original destinations, even though no manifest differences between them could be discerned by conventional methods of observation at the time of their translocation.[16] They must have been intrinsically different, or else they could not have taken specifically different courses after having been placed into a common environment equally indifferent for all of them.

It thus becomes clear that the term "differentiation" is being used in two entirely different meanings,[18] which obviously also confounds the use of the term "dedifferentiation." On the one hand, "differentiation" refers to the progressive appearance of cell types of distinctive properties from originally more equipotential cell groups, such emerging differences not becoming immediately detectable; and on the other hand, the term refers to the elaboration by a given cell, which may already have become single tracked, of tangible specialized equipment by which we then identify that cell. "Dedifferentiation," conversely, may mean merely the loss of some of these tangible criteria without the loss of the constitutional specificity of the particular cell or cell strain— and this occurs readily under conditions of atrophy, degeneration, or transfer into tissue culture; but it also may mean the loss of type-specific character, which distinguishes one cell strain from another, and the recuperation of faculties it had shared in an earlier developmental period with other strains from which it had later become dichotomously separated. The extent to which such recovery of a once-lost type specificity can actually occur, is an empirical question. Some cell types never go the full way of terminalization with all their cells; and in those cases, dormant faculties can be reactivated, the arrested cells be made to resume their unfinished course and to express themselves in manifestations different from those observed in the same cells during the state of dormancy.[2, 13] But two things seem to be well established. One is that in higher animals, except for the germ cells, all somatic cell lines are specialized to some extent, and therefore in postembryonic stages no truly "undifferentiated" cells exist; and, second, that any such transformations of one cell type into another as have been empirically demonstrated, have been of relatively limited scope, far too narrow and sporadic to challenge the basic fact of the essential irreversibility of the divergent character of different somatic cell types.

This somewhat academic introduction to the problem of differentiation has been necessary in order to place the facts known about normal development and its pathologic aberrations in their proper perspective. It should be clear now that what in pathologic lingo is called an "undifferentiated" cell, refers simply to one which has not yet declared color, as it were, by displaying its particular signal flag, mostly of microscopic delineation, which would reveal to the observer the strain to which it belongs. We know now from numerous experiments that such supposedly "undifferentiated" cells are by no means truly indifferent, but are already definitely specialized and earmarked by their specific physicochemical endowment for particular limited performances. In many cases, we also know that this does not imply that they are necessarily single tracked, but that they may still have open to them two or more alternative ways of reacting, when exposed to a wide spectrum of external conditions, including general or specific stimuli from other cells. As development proceeds—and, as we saw in the beginning, this goes on throughout life—cell strains thus become more and more definitely set in their courses, and concomitantly more and more restricted in their repertory of faculties. Any somatic cell we study has already advanced to some point along that course. A precise statement of just how far it has progressed, as measured by what it still can and what it no longer can do, will henceforth have to replace the fallacious distinction between "undifferentiated" and "differentiated" stages.

It might be expedient to refer to that terminal phase of a cell's history, in which it produces the specific characters by which we recognize its type, as "cytodifferentiation," in contradistinction to the less overt antecedent part of the course. The problems of cytodifferentiation are straightforward and their analysis seems to offer little difficulty in principle. How basal cells of the epidermis gradually rise to the surface and turn into keratin; how neuroblasts form their neurofibrils; how myoblasts form muscle fibers; how osteoblasts produce bone; all these and similar mechanisms are under active investigation, which promises early returns. This is not equally true of that earlier phase of differentiation which has produced the divergent cell strains in the first place. There the difficulties are enormous. For one thing, since the initial differences among the various cell strains are not overt, it requires indirect and frequently circuitous methods to spot them short of waiting to see "into what plant the seed will grow." Secondly, once the later overt differences have been tracked down to earlier, less-manifest differences, the problem of how such differences have arisen still remains. One example each may illustrate how these two difficulties begin to yield to analytic experimentation.

The first pertains to our ability to identify individual cell strains early by nonmorphologic and premorphologic criteria. Since emergent differences among cell strains are related to distinctions in their chemical makeup, and since these must obviously involve differences among molecular species with antigenic properties, such as proteins, immunologic methods sometimes permit us to detect such early differences;[4] but again, of course, only after the differences in question have become fairly well established, rather than at the stage of greatest interest, namely, that of their inception. Even so, this method has great merits. It is based on the ability of an organism to "recognize" a foreign protein and produce a specific antibody to it. The discriminatory powers of the living organism are thus much subtler than are our own. They have proved their assay value in a second, nonimmunologic, detection test of premorphologic differentiation, as follows:

Normal cells of a given type are so designed in their physicochemical constitution that they fit adaptively into the particular niche for which they are destined. Their behavioral and metabolic requirements are matched to those of their ordinary environment. A number of recent investigations have now produced evidence that cells of a given type are actively accepted or rejected by a given cell community, depending on whether or not they are of compatible constitution. The discriminative response to a cell by its neighbor is evidently a surface reaction upon contact.[20] The point of interest in the present context is that this recognition of cell type specificity antedates by a considerable period the more overt criteria hitherto at our disposal. The test consists of isolating embryonic cells from a site of known destination, but prior to the appearance of overt criteria of differentiation, and letting them scatter among the tissues of an organism or among other cell groups in tissue culture to see whether they will be incorporated or rejected according to their matching or nonmatching character. Loose cells abandoned in an organism must, of course, carry a suitable marker by which they can later be identified as to their origin.

The first experiments of this kind were therefore done by using precursor cells of the future pigment cell population of a black breed of chickens and injecting them into the blood stream of a slightly older embryo of an unpigmented race.[21] It actually turned out that a sizable proportion of host embryos so injected developed pigmented spots, the cells of which could be conclusively traced to the injected test cells. Characteristically, such cells were found exclusively at the precise places where pigment cells normally reside, and in no case anywhere else. Evidently these cells had been correctly recognized by their appropriately matching environments in the host embryo long before they ever formed pigment, and had been fished out and incorporated in their proper places. These experiments furnish the prototype for the selective resettlement of radiation-damaged hematopoietic sites by healthy blood stem cells injected into the circulation. Incidentally, it will be noted that in this regard the normal embryonic cell behaves totally differently from the metastasizing cancer cell, which readily lodges at sites foreign to its mother tissue.

As every surgeon knows, and as experiments with the deliberate experimental confrontation of skin with other epithelia have confirmed,[3] this mutual recognition and selective behavior among cells of various types remains active in the mature tissues, so that, for instance, in the healing of wounds involving several types of tissues, those of like character will preferentially merge.

The most remarkable manifestation of this ability of cells to identify one another according to type is seen in tissue culture. Suspensions of free cells can be obtained by trypsin-dissociation of embryonic organ rudiments of known destination. Such cell suspensions, when allowed to reaggregate and cultivated in a plasma clot, have been seen to continue to develop according to the character of the organ from which they were taken. But when suspensions obtained from two different organs were mixed and scrambled and seeded out in culture, the results were not tissues in which the two kinds of cells were amalgamated at random, but rather cleanly separated organs of pure composition of each type lying side by side.[9] Evidently, the cells of either type had succeeded in sorting themselves out like-to-like.

To study the nature of this reaction, we have taken phase-contrast time-lapse motion pictures of encounters in tissue culture between cells of identical and nonidentical types (with A. C. Taylor; a sample film was shown at the meeting). It has become clear from these observations that epithelial cells of all kinds will at first make contact with each other, but then, secondarily, react discriminately, depending on whether the encountered partner belongs to the same or another type.[20] In the former case, they will draw together and remain associated, while in the latter case, they pull apart and bypass each other. These experiments have not only shown that cells have much subtler means of recognizing early stages of divergent differentiation of cell character than we possess as observers, but they also provide a technic which promises more penetrating insight into the mechanisms by which the cells achieve this feat.

In connection with these examples of rather nonexplicit signs of the early divergence of properties among cell strains, which ought to be classed as differentiation, it should be added that while many such characters remain occult and certainly morphologically indistinguishable throughout mature life, actually every selective reaction to a drug or to a hormone is a test of the specifically differentiated character of the responding cell.[18]

Having now acknowledged the existence of so many different cell strains in the mature body, the question of the origin of their divergence becomes pressing. Unfortunately, in most cases all we know is that it does occur, and when; but rarely how, and why. We know that the total repertory of modes of reaction available to any cell of the body is strictly limited by the original inherited endowment of genes present in the fertilized egg, but in view of the present evidence that this genic endowment is replicated rather faithfully in each cell division and passed down without major alterations to practically all cells of the body,[12] the question of how, despite this common endowment, cell strains with inherently different properties can gradually emerge, becomes rather perplexing. On balance, the present concept is about as follows:[26]

The diagram in Fig. 1 shows the organism in schematic representation as a system of concentric shells: the body composed of tissues, which are composed of cells, each of which contains a nucleus enclosed in its cytoplasm; the nucleus in turn containing chromosomes, which house the genes. Now,

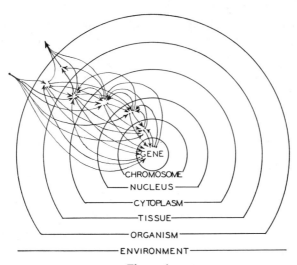

Figure 1

the fertilized egg in its oöplasm is by no means an unorganized isotropic homogeneous system. Molecular populations along different sectors of its surface are quite different, and as the cleaving egg becomes divided into cells, each one inherits directly a different parcel of the egg surface and of the egg content, so that they are not really all identical. Then each such oöplasmic portion interacts with the nucleus enclosed in it and its genes. In this manner, different responses are activated or evoked from the innermost shell in accordance with the initial differences of the more outer shells, and the reaction products are correspondingly diverse. Then as the germ breaks up into more and more cells and the various cell groups shift relative to one another, new types of cellular interactions of progressively increasing complexity are engendered, all of which places the gene complements entrapped in the various cells in cytoplasmic environments which differ substantially from place to place. By guiding the genic responses, these specialized cytoplasms can thus enforce the continued reproduction of their own type, hence, perpetuate their differentiated characters. There is evidence now that even though the genes do not partake in the processes of differentiation, the extragenic part of the nucleus does.[1] This constant playing back and forth between the stable genome at the core and the stepwise and progressively transforming extragenic cell space gives us at least a rational basis for the understanding of how differentiation can occur.[15]

Yet, the actual mechanisms operative in each particular case are still largely obscure. Roughly we can distinguish two major classes of mechanisms:[6] (1) self-organization, and (2) induction. The former applies when in a group of cells having demonstrably identical endowments and potentialities, an inner dichotomy occurs, after which some cells follow one course, and others another course. This intrinsic division can usually be related to some positional or geometric feature of the group,[18] which presumably signifies differences in the physicochemical conditions to which cells in different parts of the group are exposed; for instance, cells nearer the surface being triggered into one type of development, while those in the interior are switched in a second direction. Such "self-organization" within cell masses has even been seen and studied in tissue culture, where random aggregates of isolated and scrambled cells have been observed to combine to form rather well-organized integrated tissue and organ systems.[9, 24]

On the other hand, we speak of "induction" when the course of differentiation in a given cell group is determined not solely by events within that cell group, but is significantly steered by some action from outside, mostly an adjacent cell group. Examples of this type of extraneous switching range all the way from very trivial and unspecific influences to rather specific and selective, key-lock type activations of changes of cell constitution. Many examples are known where embryonic tissues have been thrown into a course different from their original destinations by a variety of well-defined chemical administrations.[6] However, it is still problematic how direct the relation between the inducing agent and the particular type of induced tissue response is. At any rate, it seems assured that the effect is produced not by telling the cell what to do, but by selecting from among several preformed response mechanisms residing in the cell one to the exclusion of some others. Inductive effects of this kind extend way into the postembryonic history, where they are exemplified by the induction of bone formation by grafts of various kinds,[7] even of devitalized tissue, the responding tissues in this case containing cells that evidently had not reached the terminal and irreversible stage of differentiation.

A most instructive model of inductive switching of cells into one or another of two alternative courses is found in tissue-culture experiments with embryonic chick skin, the cells of which can be deliberately switched into either a squamous keratin-producing type or a cuboid mucous-producing type, depending on whether the content of the medium in vitamin A is low or high.[5, 24] Some similar cases have been described in insect metamorphosis, in plants, and in microorganisms, and even the phenomenon of induced enzyme formation in bacteria[8] has been proposed as a possible model for the mechanism of divergent differentiation of cell types. But any sober evaluation reveals that the main clue to our understanding of this process is still missing.

The fact of the acquisition of differential properties by cell strains, however, is directly related to the problem of differential growth.

DEVELOPMENT OF GROWTH CONTROL

Just as members of different species grow at different rates, so the tissues likewise acquire different growth rates in the process of their divergent differentiation.[17] Some tissues keep on reproducing throughout life, like skin and blood and intestine, while others remain stationary, and still others come to rest but can be reactivated by a variety of stimuli to resume reproductive growth. However, when we make these distinctions, we base them on a consideration of the cell population and the way in which the population maintains its equilibrium. As soon as we turn to the individual cell, the distinction disappears; for all living cells are in a state of perpetual growth.[19] The population of their molecules is subject to continuous drain in the process of metabolism and the discharge of products, and must be constantly renewed by synthetic processes. Only when the latter overshoot the metabolic loss, do we immediately recognize and record the net gain as growth.

Such growth can take alternative courses, with the metabolic and energetic machinery of the cell engaged in either one of two mutually exclusive pathways: The one is concerned with the reduplication of the cell, starting with the replication of the genes and chromosomes and leading to mitosis, cell division, and proliferation; this is quantitatively correlated with an increase of the desoxyribonucleic acid systems of the nucleus. The other is concerned with the production of specific products by the cell and is related to the activities of the ribonucleic acid systems, particularly as they bear on protein synthesis, and through the enzyme proteins, on all synthetic processes in the cell. From what we said before about differentiation, it is evident that the schedules and intensities of these various processes depend on the type of specialized chemical machinery a particular cell type has at its disposal as a result of its prior developmental history. Yet, if each one of the local growth processes in a body were to proceed independently, after it has once been instituted, the harmony of relations among such independent parts would soon be lost because of the fortuitous and unpredictable variability of local conditions to which each part would be subjected. It is on this level then that new reintegrating principles must enter into action to hold the total growth pattern within a norm compatible with the orderly functioning of the whole organism. Such integrative mechanisms are many and varied. They include the nervous system, the homeostatic mechanism of the blood, the hormone system, and other regulative and compensatory provisions.

One such system of presumably general validity is a chemical feedback mechanism in which each cell type limits its own growth rate by specific inhibitors designed for its own type and discharged into the common circulation in proportion to its own growth.[25] In this manner a given organ, as it gains mass, is also faced with correspondingly increasing restraints by its own products, until equilibrium (that is, cessation of net gain) is reached. Since this equilibrium applies to the total mass of that particular cell type, regardless of whether it is in one piece or scattered throughout the body, this principle explains why after the reduction of total organ mass, as for instance after the extirpation of one kidney or part of the liver, the remaining parts of the same character automatically and promply start gaining mass until the former mass equilibrium for that cell type has been restored.

The significant point about such findings is that they provide a clue as to how the maintenance of harmony among the cell populations of the body, counting by the many millions, could be accounted for solely in terms of interactions of the individual member cells. To the analytic scientist this is a comforting thought, but whether it will be sufficient actually to resolve all the problems of supracellular organization and coordination with which the living organism presents us, remains to be seen.

DEVELOPMENT OF SUBMICROSCOPIC ORGANIZATION

Support for optimism comes from relatively recent work on the powers of self-organization among complexes of macromolecules outside the body. The best investigated example is that of the collagen fiber. The molecular unit of collagen has been determined to be a three-stranded, twisted rodlet with a length of several hundred Angström units. In the body, they are found assembled in long chains, the chains grouped into bundles of submicroscopic or microscopic dimensions. By acid treatment of tendon or other connective tissue, the fibers can be dissolved into their elementary units. When such solutions are dialyzed against salts in a given range of ionic strength, the units aggregate again end-to-end and flank-to-flank and by such polymerization build up fibers of the same type as are found in the native tissue.[11] These fibers reconstituted in vitro show the same regular internal periodicity along their axis and strict alignment in register among adjacent chains that give collagen in the body its imprint of supramolecular order. There is even some recent evidence that the spacing of the periodic bands along the fiber axis is of such dimensions that it uniquely favors the combination with hydroxy-apatite, the main inorganic component of bone, so that the fiber can serve as backbone for the process of calcification.[10] In the organism, further regularities arise from the interaction of the submicroscopic collagen fibrils among themselves, which it has not yet been possible quite to duplicate in vitro, but which since they occur in the intercellular spaces, at least offer promise of being reproduced someday outside of the body. They are exemplified by the following:

The membrane underlying the epidermis of amphibians and other animals is laminated like plywood, consisting of about 20 layers of ground substance in which collagen fibers are embedded, but with alternating orientations so that the fibers of one layer, all parallel throughout the layer, run at right angles to the fibers of the next layer. The fibers are cylindrical, straight, and of a standard diameter of a few hundred Angströms. The whole fabric thus is one of highly regular supramolecular architecture. Now, in order to study how the body can build such an architecture, holes were poked in this membrane and the mending of those holes was observed.[22] It turned out that the fibroblasts of the connective tissue would deposit at the lesion immature collagen, which would aggregate into a matted feltwork of no particular organization but that, secondarily, from the underside of the skin, a laminating influence would spread over this mass, and either by reorientation or re-crystallization, straighten the fibers into planes with the typical pattern of fiber directions alternating from plane to plane by 90 degrees. In other words, a higher degree of ordering sweeps over an already chemically defined system as a result of actions emanating from a cellular sheet. The phenomenon bears some formal resemblance to orderly crystallization in randomized or amor-phous chemical systems, although if anything like crystallinity is here in-volved, the lattice period would be of the order of several hundred Angströms, instead of only a few, as in ordinary crystals.

CONCLUSIONS

The example just presented links up with our introductory remarks on form. Instead of accepting as a given fact a regular pattern that we observe, we must dig down into its prior history and origin and disclose the processes by which the pattern has come about. And whether we deal with intra-cellular or extracellular patterns, whether on the molecular, macromolecular, cellular, or supracellular level, the problems are mostly quite similar. They revolve essentially on two kinds of properties of the systems to be studied: (1) the properties of the elementary constituents; that is, an inventory of what is present in the system and how it acts; and (2) the orderly distribution and coordination in space and time of the component events on all levels. The study of development, therefore, must concern itself with the exploration of the changes that occur at all levels with regard to both these aspects. And the one rule that has already emerged beyond dispute is that these changes occur never abruptly, never in one single jump, but constantly and progres-sively in numerous small steps; each of which must be viewed as a response of the system as it has been molded and modified by its past ontogenetic history. This is why such distinctions as between a "differentiated" and an "undifferentiated" cell as two different entities are utterly unrealistic and to be discarded along with all those sharp distinctions as between an "em-bryonic" and a "mature" cell; and perhaps even between a "normal" cell and an "abnormal" cell, unless one were to ask more specifically: normal or abnormal with regard to what particular property? For cells can be quite normal with regard to one, and quite abnormal with regard to some other feature, and only the total balance of properties will decide whether or not they are viable.

If I have succeeded in conveying at least some feeling of the fluidity, in contrast to fixity—that is, dynamic behavior, rather than static form—as the key to the understanding of the living cell in its development and function, I may have contributed in a small way to furthering the historical trend of the science of development which I have summarized in the beginning: from the static to the dynamic. But it is one thing to assert such trend and another to follow it in practice. Therefore, I have tried to show that far from being an abstract notion, it has been a constructive aid to experimentation, to more penetrating analysis, and to more profound understanding of the mechanisms of development. Yet, we are just at the beginning, left with most problems still full of large question marks. These question marks are the same for those students of development who focus their interest on the standard processes that are more or less similar for the majority of a population, be it of men or of cells; and for those who concentrate on the less frequent excursions from those standard patterns. That, for practical purposes, the former are classed as developmental biologists, and the latter as pathologists, is rather incidental and should not detract from the realization that they both have to travel a common road and that neither can make steady progress without the other.

REFERENCES

1. ALLFREY, V. G., MIRSKY, A. E., and STERN, H. Chemistry of the cell nucleus. *Advances Enzymol. 16*:411, 1955.
2. BLOOM, W. Cellular differentiation and tissue culture. *Physiol. Rev. 17*:589, 1937.
3. CHIAKULAS, J. J. The role of tissue specificity in the healing of epithelial wounds. *J. Exper. Zool. 121*:383, 1952.
4. EBERT, J. D. Appearance of tissue-specific proteins during development. *Ann. New York Acad. Sc. 55*:67, 1952.
5. FELL, H. B., and MELLANBY, E. Metaplasia produced in cultures of chick ectoderm by high vitamin A. *J. Physiol. 119*:470, 1953.
6. HOLTFRETER, J., and HAMBURGER, V. "Progressive Differentiation: Amphibians." In WILLIER, B. H., WEISS, P., and HAMBURGER, V., *Analysis of Development*. Philadelphia, Saunders, 1955, p. 230.
7. McLEAN, F. C., and URIST, M. R. *Bone. An Introduction to the Physiology of Skeletal Tissue*. Chicago, Univ. Chicago Press, 1955.
8. MONOD, J. Enzymatic adaptation and its bearing on problems of cell physiology, genetics and differentiation. *Growth 2*:223, 1947.
9. MOSCONA, A. Development of heterotypic combinations of dissociated embryonic chick cells. *Proc. Soc. Exper. Biol. & Med. 92*:410, 1956.
10. SCHMITT, F. O., GLIMCHER, M. J., and HODGE, A. J. Macromolecular aggregation states in relation to mineralization: The collagen-hydroxyapatite system as studied in vitro. *Proc. Nat. Acad. Sc. 43*:860, 1957.
11. SCHMITT, F. O., GROSS, J., and HIGHBERGER, J. H. States of aggregation of collagen. *Symp. Soc. Exper. Biol. 9*:148, 1955.
12. STERN, C. "Gene Action." In WILLIER, B. H., WEISS, P., and HAMBURGER, V., *Analysis of Development*. Philadelphia, Saunders, 1955, p. 151.
13. STONE, L. S. Regeneration of the iris and lens from retina pigment cells in adult newt eyes. *J. Exper. Zool. 129*:505, 1955.
14. URSO, P., and CONGDON, C. C. *J. Hematol. 12*:251, 1957.
15. WADDINGTON, C. H. *Principles of Embryology*. London, England, Allen & Unwin, 1956.

16. WEISS, P. *Principles of Development.* New York, Holt, 1939.
17. WEISS, P. "Differential Growth." In PARPART, A. K. (Ed.) *Chemistry and Physiology of Growth.* Princeton, N. J., Princeton, 1949, p. 135.
18. WEISS, P. Some introductory remarks on the cellular basis of differentiation. *J. Embryol. & Exp. Morphol. 1*:181, 1953.
19. WEISS, P. "What is Growth?" In SMITH, R. W., GAEBLER, O. H., and LONG, C. N. H. (Eds.) *Hypophyseal Growth Hormone, Nature and Actions.* New York, McGraw-Hill, 1955, p. 3.
20. WEISS, P. Cell contact. *Internat. Rev. Cytol. 7*:391, 1958.
21. WEISS, P., and ANDRES, G. Experiments on the fate of embryonic cells (chick) disseminated by the vascular route. *J. Exper. Zool. 121*:449, 1952.
22. WEISS, P., and FERRIS, W. The basement lamella of amphibian skin: Its reconstruction after wounding. *J. Biophys. & Biochem. Cytol.* (Suppl.) *2*:275, 1956.
23. WEISS, P., and GARBER, B. Shape and movement of mesenchyme cells as functions of the physical structure of the medium: Contributions to a quantitative morphology. *Proc. Nat. Acad. Sc. 38*:264, 1952.
24. WEISS, P., and JAMES, R. Skin metaplasia in vitro induced by brief exposure to vitamin A. *Exper. Cell Res.* (Suppl.) *3*:381, 1955.
25. WEISS, P., and KAVANAU, L. A model of growth and growth control in mathematical terms. *J. Gen. Physiol. 41*:1, 1957.
26. WILLIER, B. H., WEISS, P., and HAMBURGER, V. *Analysis of Development.* Philadelphia, Saunders, 1955.

This article has been no more than a sort of annotated inventory of the problems which analytic research on development has uncovered. Categorical terms of old, such as "growth," "differentiation," "ageing," "pathological," "mature," and so forth, have turned almost meaningless in their generality and indefiniteness. They can serve neither as aids to understanding nor as objects for research. Progress, therefore, hinges on our ability to discover, identify and specify by critical analysis the factual content of phenomena, processes and mechanisms hidden under those general labels. The following two articles offer examples of this procedure, taking the phenomena of "growth" and "differentiation," respectively, under intellectual and practical dissecting lenses, as it were.

1

What is Growth?*

Paul Weiss

The invitation to give an introductory address to this meeting is a distinct honor; it also carries a mandate to set the phenomenon of growth in proper perspective before discussing "growth" hormone. Unfortunately, "growth" itself has received much less critical attention than have the agents for which it serves as indicator and assay. To put it bluntly, "growth" is a term as vague, ambiguous and fuzzy as everyday language has ever produced. Adopted into scientific language without precise and consistent meaning, it may be passable for crude description, but is ill-fitted to analytical application. Hence, if you ask: "Just what is Growth?", the correct answer is: "A word that covers, like a blanket, a multitude of various things and meanings." To know "growth" for what it really is, rather than what we are wont to call it, we must remove that blanket and uncover the underlying facts it has concealed. This I propose to do in rudimentary sample form as time permits. A close look at the facts will do far more for clarification than would a host of academic definitions and circumlocutions.

Our notions about growth have been shaped more by usage than by incisive study; they form a sort of scientific folklore. As a result, we find that various groups, while they all just plainly speak of "growth," do not all mean and talk about the same thing. Thus growth has come to connote any and all of these: reproduction, increase in dimensions, linear increase, gain in weight, gain in organic mass, cell multiplication, mitosis, cell migration, protein synthesis, and perhaps more. It would seem inconsistent to apply the most exacting standards of precision to our research data and then proceed to mix into their description and interpretation such vague ter-

* Research supported by grants-in-aid from the American Cancer Society upon recommendation of the Committee on Growth of the National Research Council, and from the National Institutes of Health, Public Health Service.

3

minology as this. The mixture can be no more precise than its vaguest ingredient.[1]

Then, what is wrong? Why such diversity of views and versions? The reasons lie in our unfounded expectation that growth is a single, simple, measurable entity. In this conviction, each of us has tended to deal with his own limited aspect of the problem as if it were a representative sample of the total perspective. Yet, far from being a single, simple and unitary phenomenon, growth is conglomerate, complex and intricate, and this is why it defies formulation in simple terms. What usually deceives us is the simplicity of our tools and terms of measurement, which all too easily produce the illusion of similar simplicity of the measured systems.

Just bear in mind how we get to know about growth: by taking measurements at different times, comparing them and noting a net gain—of size or mass or numbers. These serial measurements then define a growth curve, as descriptive of the particular system as, let us say, a fingerprint—and equally empirical. This is the blanket under which a host of disparate events lie hidden; events, moreover, of opposite signs, some adding to, others subtracting from, the measured body. Since they are not all of one kind and their shares are unequal, growth can be recorded, but it cannot be understood, without identifying these tributaries and determining their respective contributions.

Let me phrase this in terms of an analogy. The body is a community of cells; each cell a community of smaller particles; and each particle an assemblage of molecular species. Thus, the proper analogue of biological growth is the growth of a human community; for example, of a city. Here we rate as growth, for instance, any increase in population over a given interval. But a simple tally will not tell us how the increase has come about. It takes census data to give a more detailed accounting. They reveal that additions come from two different sources: reproduction from within, and immigration from without; losses, likewise, from death as well as emigration. The results would be altogether different if instead of just counting noses, we chose to include in our considerations the physical wealth of the community, that is, the net gain in goods and estates produced by the members of the population. To understand its sources would require running inventories of raw materials, production, conversion, consumption, imports, exports, storage and wastage. Moreover, in either reckoning, the data can have meaning only in reference to fixed boundaries which divide what we count as "within" from that which we count as "without."

Now, as we apply this simile to biological growth, the whole indefiniteness of our customary position becomes obvious. First, let us consider the matter on the tissue level. Suppose we note an increase in the number of cells of a given organ. What does this really tell us? As in the human population, some cells have reproduced, others have immigrated, still others have been lost by shedding or disintegration, the proportions and rates of these component events varying from tissue to tissue. The final tally—no more than a crude balance sheet—discloses none of these details. According to Hamburger and Levi-Montalcini,[2] for instance, abnormal enlargements in the early central nervous system, formerly ascribed simply to "hyperplasia," that is, overproduction, are partly due to the fact that fewer cells degenerate, rather than that more are being proliferated, and partly to the fact that the cell group being counted has received additions from an indifferent pool outside the counted area. Another shortcoming of plain cell counts is that they ignore all growth of individual cells (e.g., hypertrophy) not followed by division.

If, then, we turn from cell counts to over-all dimensions or total mass, we are on even weaker ground. In terms of our community analogy, we first have to agree as to what is, and what is not, real property of the system we measure, or what has been acquired and what discarded during the measured period. Food in the alimentary tract is still distinctly out-of-bounds; even if stored for weeks, as in a hamster's pouch. But what of this mass once it has passed into the blood and lymph stream? Though strictly on the inside, it still has not become converted into substance of the body proper. Then, what about the food stuffs stored in modified form, for instance, as glycogen or fat in liver or fat bodies? Their fluctuations up and down are not conventionally considered growth and degrowth. Why? Because we sense that growth connotes some *permanent* addition, and merely temporary physiological variations do not qualify under this title.

Then, what about the wastes not yet eliminated? And the products manufactured by our organs? Take hair or nails or even red cells—terminal products destined to be shed or otherwise eliminated. In counting bodily productions, is it fair to include just those fractions which happen to be present on the measured body when we take our measurements, and leave out all the unknown mass that has been similarly produced in the interim but irretrievably lost? Evidently, we ought to be consistent and either count it all in or all out, neither of which is practicable. We certainly would not collect secretions, such as slime, urine, sweat and sebum, over a measured period and add them to the growth record. Yet, we do customarily include the bulk of cartilage and bone and other connective tissues, which consists of residues of cellular secretions, just like those other ones, but incidentally deposited, instead of extruded, hence accruing to the measured mass. Thus what we measure, is related not so much to the process of production as to the accident of the disposal of the products. If they persist, we count them; if they drop out, we miss them.

The arbitrariness attached to our measurements is about the same, whether we use total mass, dry weight, nitrogen content, volume, length, or what not, as reference system. It is even worse when we turn from the body to its component cells. The cell is bounded by a surface, and we are in the habit of ascribing any increase in the volume thus enclosed to "growth." But water, electrolytes, food stuffs and wastes pass in and out across that boundary without revealing to the observer just when they lose their original small-molecular identity to become merged with the complex specific compounds of the cell, or when they emerge again from decomposition of the latter; we thus cannot determine what fraction of a given increase to allocate to protoplasmic synthesis proper, and what fraction to substances that just reside within the confines of the cell but, strictly speaking, belong to it either not yet or no longer, comparable to food and wastes in the alimentary tract. Then how should we consider the formed cell inclusions which vary according to each type of cell? Obviously, the production of myofibrils, which accumulate within the muscle cell, thus adding to its mass, is not fundamentally different from the production of collagen fibrils, which leave their cell of origin—the fibroblast—hence, do not enlarge it. Conversely, a fat cell inflated by unextruded fat of its own production cannot be compared to a macrophage similarly dilated by fat from stuff it has engorged from the outside. Evidently, the attainment of equal or unequal sizes, as such, can give us little information about the identity or difference of the underlying causes of the enlargement.

It is this habit of confining ourselves deliberately to a single parameter of a highly complex system—for instance, mass—and then measuring all changes on this single scale only, which tempts us, as I said before, to confound the arbitrary simplicity of our method with an inherent simplicity of the object itself. We are fundamentally in error if we prorate the average over-all changes in a complex system evenly over all parts of the system, as if all of them took equal shares in the result. In doing so, we commit an act of "mental homogenization," as it were, obliterating the organized complexity of the heterogenous events which are the very center of our interest.

To this we usually add a second and similarly unfounded simplification whenever we consider growth rates. We measure two comparable parameters—let us say, weight or length—at the beginning and end of a convenient period, divide the difference by the time elapsed, and call the quotient "growth rate." Empirically, this gives useful descriptive data. But before using these for analytical or comparative purposes we should realize that we have again "homogenized"; in this case, the time interval. We have tacitly assumed that during this interval the bracketed change has been steady and continuous. Yet, if the change occurred unevenly, in spurts separated by phases of quiescence, any inference as to the kinetics of the system would be misleading. Two different systems can achieve the same amount of growth increment in precisely the same period by wholly different means: the one by growing faster for shorter spells; the other growing more slowly, but with fewer interruptions or shorter lags.

But this example also contains the clue to overcoming our predicament. You note that the two systems just mentioned would become readily distinguishable if they were sampled at shorter intervals; that is, by letting factual information replace supposition and extrapolation. And this is a lesson which cannot be overstressed. Interpretations and comparisons in matters of growth will remain of little value and validity if they are based on over-all generalizations instead of such detailed and painstaking sorting and recording of the component events as is practically feasible. Tally must give way to detailed census. There are insuperable limitations set to this census by our ignorance of cell life and the inadequate resolving power of our tools; but it would be unpardonable not to carry the analysis at least as far as the objects and techniques would permit.

Therefore, turning to practical correctives, let me indicate how a first breakdown of the problem could be attempted. Growth is the surplus accruing in the balance sheet of a complex account. Our task is to itemize the accounting. Here are some major items. In listing them, I shall artificially separate them as if they were consecutive steps, while in reality, you understand, they proceed more or less concurrently (Fig. 1).

We follow a system through a period of growth from A to G. The system may be a cell, an organ, an individual. Now, in the first place, we must distinguish within each such system between two major fractions—a reproductive and a non-reproductive one; the former capable of giving rise to more of its own kind—more protoplasm in a cell, or more cells in a tissue—the latter merely dead bulk in point of growth—fibers, granules and all sorts of functional equipment in a cell; or fully differentiated, non-proliferating

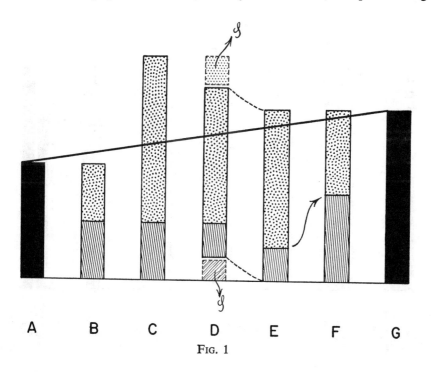

Fig. 1

cells in a tissue. Their proportions vary according to cell type, species, age and activity. In our example, about 50% are assumed to be reproductive, as shown (stippled) in B. During the recorded growth period this mass will increase to the dimensions shown in C. At the same time, however, there will occur some losses from degradation, lysis, shedding, extrusion, emigration, and so forth. These will reduce both fractions by the amounts indicated in D. The resulting state E has larger mass than the initial A. You note, however, that the proportion between the reproductive and non-reproductive fraction comes out markedly altered. In most cases, this is then rectified by the conversion of freshly reproduced protoplasm into sterile differentiated products, as indicated in F. As you can readily see, this conversion, which drains the reproductive potential of the system, is of crucial influence on what we externally discern as "growth rate." In the end, we find our system in the enlarged state G. The point I want to stress with this diagram is that even assuming the simplest case, namely, proportionate growth, the result cannot be interpreted to mean that all parts have taken part in growth, let alone grown at equal rates or taken equal shares in the composite effect. And nothing short of detailed study will tell the real story.

This confronts us with a major task, which we mostly dodge rather than face: dodge by attaching real biological meaning to such purely descriptive terms as "growth stimulation" or "depression"; rather than face by finding out just *why* a given system, subject to certain agents, turns out to be either

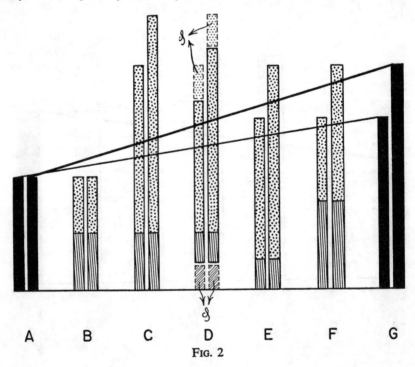

Fig. 2

larger or smaller than a chosen reference standard. For this is all we usually determine; and yet, we imply far more. Just let us take for once a closer look. Let us return to the diagram of Figure 1 and assume that it represents a "normal" reference condition. Suppose we now doctor an identical system with an agent, let us say "growth hormone," that entails an even greater increase during the observed period (Figs. 2, 3, 4). We sum up our observation by stating that growth has been "stimulated," like an invested principle that suddenly yields higher returns because the interest rate has gone up. Yet, greater gain may come not only from faster earning through stepped-up production, but also from reduced consumption, or even from diverting less of the working capital to non-productive uses. These various possible modes of action of our agent are illustrated in the remaining diagrams, in which the left one of each pair of bars always gives the control data from Figure 1, while the right one represents the experimental case.

In Figure 2, we actually let the velocity or intensity of reproduction be increased (from B to C). This alone naturally leads to faster growth; but at the same time it also modifies the distribution of reproductive and sterile mass (compare the two bars in F) which, if uncorrected, would distort the whole growth pattern. So, even this seemingly simple change is not so simple as it seems.

The second alternative is shown in Figure 3. Here we assume that our so-called "stimulating" agent has simply reactivated part of the normally quiescent fraction to become reproductive (in B), thus recruiting a larger

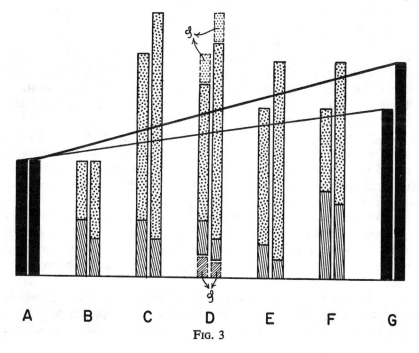

A   B   C   D   E   F   G

FIG. 3

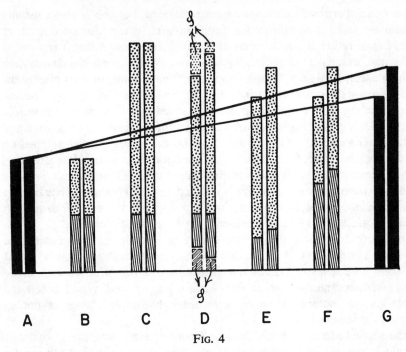

FIG. 4

source for active growth, without however, stepping up the growth rate of the elements at all. The target process here would be the conversion of reproductive mass to specialized products. Reduce or retard this conversion, and you have the picture of "growth stimulation."

Lastly, the same picture would be obtained (Fig. 4) if merely the debit side of the balance sheet of growth is reduced (in D), that is, when there is less than the normal amount of destruction, consumption and dissipation.

There are many further variants of this complex account, but these few here will have served our purpose: to show that the same net increase can be brought about by a variety of unrelated means; hence, that comparing different systems or different agents on the sheer basis of net increases observed may lead, or rather mislead, to quite gratuitous interpretations. Perhaps in such critical illumination, the term "growth" hormone may eventually turn out to have been overly suggestive.

But to leave this critical and somewhat defeatist note, what is there in the way of positive information that could give sharper focus to the growth problem? However fragmentary this information still is, it begins to piece together. The tentative result may be summarized in the following seven theses:

(1) *The general common denominator shared by all organic growth is protoplasmic reproduction,* which involves the replication of those high-molecular systems in each cell that are characteristic of the particular cell

(76)

type and are compounded only inside of cells of that kind. It is important, however, to make a clear distinction between primary protoplasmic reproduction and secondary elaboration of protoplasmic products. All such cell products, including the fibers and ground substances, whose deposits form the bulk of most bodies, are derived from protoplasm secondarily, either by direct transformation or by synthesis with the aid of enzymes which in turn have originated in the process of protoplasm synthesis. The current shorthand habit of equating protoplasmic reproduction with protein synthesis, apart from by-passing the non-proteinaceous constituents of protoplasm, fails to take this fundamental distinction into account. For instance, while such proteins as collagen or melanin cannot themselves give rise to more collagen or melanin under any known conditions, the protoplasms of the fibroblast or melanoblast in their growth evidently multiply the chemical machineries that can synthesize more collagen or melanin. Thus, only a fraction of the cellular protein is actually engaged in protoplasmic reproduction, the rest is sterile; but just what those fractions are, remains to be determined. In the following I shall use the term "growth" in the restricted sense of protoplasmic reproduction.

(2) *Growth in the indicated sense has its sources not uniformly distributed throughout the cell, but is of localized origin, centering on the nuclear territory.* The nuclear source of protoplasmic reproduction has been deduced from cytochemical studies[3] and demonstrated by our own experimental studies on neurons.[4] The nucleated part of the nerve cell body issues continuously a fresh supply of neuroplasm, which, wicklike, moves peripherad in the nerve fiber to replenish basic protoplasmic systems at the rate at which they are breaking down by ordinary wear and tear. Evidently, although any reasonably large fragment of a nerve fiber can carry out complex metabolic functions and syntheses by virtue of its enzyme content, the enzyme systems themselves cannot be reproduced ubiquitously but must be furnished from the nuclear supply center. Although even the mature neuron maintains itself in a state of perpetual growth renewal, not all somatic cells can be assumed to retain this faculty. Those that have lost it are destined to die precociously and they can be replaced only from those reserves that still have it. In the epidermis, for instance, the squamous outer cells are in the former state, the basal cells in the latter. A single neuron could be viewed as comparable to a vertical column of epidermal cells (the perikaryon corresponding to the basal cell), in which cell boundaries had become obliterated.

(3) *The nuclear growth process is intimately related to, perhaps engendered by, the multiplication of chromosomal genes.* As a result, cell growth is closely associated with nuclear growth. Accordingly, haploid nuclei and cells, with only half the normal complement of chromosomes, are of half the normal size, whereas polyploid nuclei and cells, with multiple chromosome sets, acquire correspondingly excessive sizes. Parenthetically,

there is by no means a binding relation between cell size on the one hand, and organ and body size, on the other; while haploid organisms are dwarfs because they are made of dwarf cells in normal number, polyploid organs and animals often remain of normal dimensions, as the giant size of their cells is offset by the use of smaller numbers.[5] Although true cell growth is reflected in nuclear increase, the reverse is not always true, and nuclear enlargement as such is not sufficient evidence of true growth, but may be simply a sign of functional hyperactivity. The two types of increase can sometimes be told apart cytochemically, as true growth is accompanied by augmentation of nuclear DNA, whereas hyperactivity is not.[6] DNA seems to assume ever increasing significance as index of true growth.[7]

(4) *Despite the fact that the genic equipment, according to current thought, is essentially the same in all somatic cells, mode and rate of growth of each cell type are specific for that type;* that is, neuroplasm begets more neuroplasm, myoplasm more myoplasm, thyroplasm more thyroplasm, and so forth. To deal with this matter, which touches on the complex problem of differentiation, is beyond our scope here. We mention it merely because it reveals that genic replication, while seemingly the initiating step in the growth process, is followed by chains of events the nature of which is determined by the specific constitution of the (extragenic) rest of the cell; and in this regard, the different cell types differ crucially. Besides certain basic prerequisites in common to all of them, each type has its private needs; for instance, in tissue culture, one tissue will grow better in one kind of medium, while another tissue thrives better in another kind, usually without our knowing just why. Understandably, the more conspicuous common factors necessary for all growth have received more attention. Those basic to the maintenance of life in all cells, whether growing or non-growing, have no particular relevance to the growth problem as such. But up and above these common prerequisites for life are the special needs of growing, versus non-growing, systems, and the differential needs of different growing systems according to their kinds. These include specific building blocks, factors to insure the proper physical framework for growth, and perhaps separate energy resources and enzyme systems to support growth, in contradistinction to stationary maintenance. Signs are increasing that the growth process is not a mere quantitative shift of the normal steady state between anabolism and katabolism in favor of the former, but a process of different character sustained by auxiliary biochemical systems dormant during states of sheer maintenance. At least, this is a conclusion suggested by metabolic studies on forms in which periods of maintenance and growth are clearly separated, as in some insects.[8]

In view of the qualitative and quantitative differences between the growth requirements of different tissues and organs, we must concede to each one its characteristic chemical kinetics. And this explains the following familiar experience.

(5) *Given optimal conditions, superabundance of all prerequisites and freedom from active inhibitions, each cell strain, tissue and organ grows at its own characteristic rate.* This rate represents the maximum output of which the particular system is capable (at a given temperature). It is a "ceiling" rate and varies according to species, genetic constitution, kind of tissue and organ, state of differentiation, and perhaps age. It manifests itself, for instance, in the fact that transplants between different species or breeds of different growth rates, if successful at all, continue to grow according to their native growth patterns.[9]

Now, under normal conditions in the body, tissues do not grow at ceiling rates. This shows that conditions are not usually optimal for total output; either because of bottlenecks in the supply of some essential elements, which may be a matter of timing or of competition for limited supplies, or because of suboptimal physical conditions, or lastly, because of the presence of factors that actively repress or retard one step or another in the reaction chain. Now, as you note, any of these situations, by holding growth to a level below its potential ceiling, gives the external appearance of an "inhibitory" influence, and is likely to be so labelled. Yet, between them, they have no more in common than the various agents that may cause an automobile to stall. Reversing the argument, any lessening of the effectiveness of any one of them may enable the system to come closer to its optimal growth output, and if so, will give us the impression of stimulation; a more correct term would be "desinhibition." Some recent work of ours strongly supports this view.[10] In the epidermis of starved amphibians, cell growth followed by mitosis can be evoked in two different ways: (a) throughout the skin by sudden feeding; or (b) in a localized spot by fragments of certain organs inserted under the skin. The magnitude of the unit response is the same for (a) or (b) alone and for (a) and (b) combined. This demonstrates the existence of a "ceiling." On the other hand, when the same agents are applied at any stage at which growth is submaximal, a new peak of growth activity appears which again has the height of the "ceiling." This evidently proves that these agents have acted not by boosting the growth process by a given amount, as would be the connotation of "stimulation," but by releasing the system from certain depressive effects that had previously been in operation.

Obviously, factors restraining growth by holding any of its contributory steps to a suboptimal level belong to a great variety of categories and need have nothing in common except their eventual effect on the growth result. Similarly then, the agents which offset these restraining factors, thereby reversing the net effect on growth, are likewise manifold and varied. One might thus question whether the search for over-all "growth stimulators" is at all realistic and promising.

To judge from virus reproduction, the multiplication of basic protoplasmic units presumably takes up no more than a very minor fraction of the time needed for a given growth interval, let us say, the interphase between two somatic mitoses, where according to the DNA index the crucial events seem to be crowded toward the end.[11] The rest of the time is evidently used for processes preparing this crucial step, as well as for the subsequent elaboration of differentiated products. Since these vary from one cell type to another, any observable shortening of interphase—appearing as "growth stimulation"—is due more probably to the speeding up of some of the prefatory or consecutive steps, rather than of the crucial act, of genic reproduction.

(6) *Growth and cell division are often, but not necessarily, coupled.* Present evidence indicates that in this correlation cell growth is the primary event, with mitosis then supervening facultatively. In such cases, and with due caution, mitosis may be used as index of preceding growth. Even then, comparisons are difficult for in all cases in which only a fraction of the cell population takes part in proliferation, a rise of the mitotic index need not signify either a shortening of interphase or a protraction of the mitotic act, but simply the mitotic involvement of a larger portion of the population. Again, speaking of "growth stimulation" would add little to our insight.

(7) *As complex as the growth process itself, are the means that keep the various steps of the process, as well as the various growth centers among one another, in mutual harmony.* It cannot be stressed too strongly that growth is regulated by a great multiplicity of factors of chemical and structural nature, no single one of master rank.[1] One potent growth-regulating principle, which we discovered relatively recently, is a "feed-back" equilibration between a growing organ on the one hand, and organ-specific discharges of its own production that restrain the growth of all cells of the homologous type, on the other. Each cell type may be assumed to give off substances specific to its kind which inhibit the multiplication of any protoplasm of the same type in proportion to their concentration in the extracellular environment. As this concentration increases with the growing mass of an organ, growth of each cell type will become self-limiting regardless of how widely dispersed the total mass is throughout the body. This principle explains the "compensatory" growth reactions after partial removal or injury of a given organ, as well as the observation that the presence of crushed cells of a given type in the blood stream (by injection) or in a culture medium enhances the growth of homologous cells; for a more detailed review of the evidence.[12] While this principle operates among homologous members of a cell and organ population, growth effects between heterogenous types are a major function of "hormones."

*   *   *

Since growth processes are so diverse and composite, it would be a miracle if any one hormone were to act on all of them in such fashion as to net always a positive balance, which would make it a veritable "growth hormone." Any hormone affecting any one of the innumerable component steps of growth, is in a sense a "growth hormone," although nothing seems to be gained by naming it so. The obligation remains to find out precisely where and how it acts. This requires more than just measuring over-all changes of size or bulk or composition.

To illustrate the danger of shorthand explanations of the relation of hormones to growth let me conclude with an instructive example from our own laboratory experience. Amphibian metamorphosis from larva to adult is, as you know, dependent upon thyroid secretion. The hormone activates a pattern of proliferation and involution processes, and all organs undergo profound reorganization, including the brain. In this process, a peculiar pair of giant hindbrain cells concerned with larval swimming, so-called Mauthner's cells, atrophy, while other brain parts grow. This could have been ascribed to the loss of their functional terminations, but our experiments[13] proved otherwise. We implanted fragments of thyroid or thyroxin-soaked agar above the 4th ventricle so as to allow the hormone to diffuse into the brain wall; according to earlier results,[14] under such conditions, a circumscribed metamorphosis of the tissue complex within the diffusion field could be expected. This actually occurred, with the following results on brain growth: while all other ganglion cells of the area grew conspicuously, that one pair of cells in their midst which was destined to regress—Mauthner's cells—did not grow, but shrank (Fig. 5). We could show that this reverse behavior had nothing to do with peculiarities of size or position, but was simply an expression of a different biochemical constitution of these cells which predisposed them to react to thyroid hormone with a growth response of opposite sign from that of the other cells of the group. In conventional terminology, one would say that the same hormone in the same dosage at the same time can induce either hypertrophy or atrophy, depending on the kind of cell it strikes. If this holds true for cells so closely related as the different neurons, how much more generally will it apply to more widely

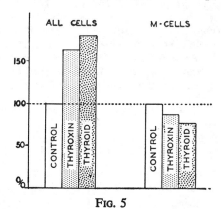

FIG. 5

diversified cell populations. It seems hardly necessary to labor the cautionary lesson contained in this example.

To sum up, what we measure as growth is the resultant of a heterogeneous array of processes of most diverse kinds, and there is no way of telling in advance, without careful analysis, just what component may be affected by any particular agent in any particular tissue in any particular species, and how. As long as we keep this in mind, we are on safe ground even if, for convenience, we resort to such shorthand reference terms as the one heading this conference. Even if the "growth hormone" should turn out not to be just what its name implies, I doubt whether this would in the least detract from the superb factual achievements in its study of which we are to hear an up-to-date account; just as I doubt that progress in X-rays would have been delayed if they had instead been named "death rays" because undeniably they sometimes kill. I also have little doubt that those with firsthand experience in this field are essentially aware of what the real situation is, and how complex it is. Yet, there are also those whom the simple label "growth" might delude into holding complacent, oversimplified and unrealistic notions of its content. My comments were intended to restore the complex problem to plain view—not for discouragement, but simply for clarification of the problems so that research may orient itself toward the real thing, instead of to a verbal symbol. As for my final answer to "What is Growth?", I am tempted to dodge by saying: "Let us go back to work and find out more about it and not pretend we know."

References

1. Weiss, P.: *Chemistry and Physiology of Growth.* Ed. A. K. Parpart. Princeton University Press, 1949, 135.
2. Hamburger, V., and R. Levi-Montalcini: *Genetic Neurology.* Ed. P. Weiss. University of Chicago Press, 1950, 128.
3. Caspersson, T. O.: *Cell Growth and Cell Function,* New York, W. W. Norton & Co., Inc., 1950, 185.
4. Weiss, P., and H. B. Hiscoe: *J. Exp. Zool.* **107:**315 (1948).
5. Fankhauser, G.: *Quart. Rev. Biol.* **20:**20 (1945).
6. Schrader, F., and C. Leuchtenberger: *Exp. Cell Research* **1:**421 (1950).
7. Swift, H. H.: *International Review of Cytology.* Eds. Bourne, G. H., and J. F. Danielli, New York, Academic Press, Inc. **2:**1 (1953).
8. Schneiderman, H. A., and C. M. Williams: *Biol. Bull.* **105:**320 (1953).
9. Harrison, R. G.: *Harvey Lectures, 1933–34* **29:**116 (1935).
10. Weiss, P., and J. H. Overton: *Excerpta Medica* **8:**424 (1954); Overton, J. H.: (in press).
11. Walker, P. M. B.: *J. Exp. Biol.* **31:**8 (1954).
12. Weiss, P.: *Growth Symposium* (in press).
13. Weiss, P., and F. Rossetti: *Proc. Nat. Acad. Sci.* **37:**540 (1951).
14. Kollros, J. J.: *Physiol. Zool.* **16:**269 (1943).

Reprinted from Proc. First Nat. Cancer Conf., 50–60. Copyright 1949 by American Cancer Society

THE PROBLEM OF CELLULAR DIFFERENTIATION*

by PAUL WEISS

What is needed in the study of growth and differentiation is not only the accumulation of more data, but a more precise description and more penetrating analysis of the data in a more rigorous conceptual frame of reference. This need calls for a firmer trend away from obscurant verbalisms toward objective scientific formulations of the problems involved. We cannot hope to develop a better understanding of the phenomena of growth, differentiation, organization, induction, control, harmony, and so on, unless we first obtain a realistic picture of just what factual content these various labels cover. By way of example, such an operational analysis is attempted here for the problem of cellular differentiation. It is a condensed and combined version of results reported and thoughts expressed in three previous publications.

WHAT IS DIFFERENTIATION?

The term "growth" may be reserved to designate the increase in protoplasmic mass, that is, the production, or rather reproduction, of more units of a given kind. This may or may not be associated with a further subdivision (by cell divisions) of the growing mass. As long as the resulting fractions retain essentially the same constitution and appearance, we may speak of pure growth. "Differ-

* Original investigations referred to in this paper have been aided by a grant of the American Cancer Society on recommendation of the Committee on Growth of the National Research Council and by the Abbott Memorial Fund of the University of Chicago.

50

entiation," on the other hand, connotes the appearance of systematic differences among parts that were originally of the same kind. If "growth" means more of a kind, "differentiation" means more kinds. In cellular terms, true "differentiation" then implies the real, not only apparent, diversification (i.e., divergence of character) of cells or cell strains that initially were alike, rather than just looked alike.

DOES TRUE DIFFERENTIATION EXIST?

Whether differentiation in this strict sense really exists, is an empirical question. The answer hinges on the reliability of our testing methods, which furnish the criteria by which to tell the likeness or unlikeness of cells. Historically, undue faith in microscopic criteria has confused the issue. Cells that looked alike were rated as similar, and cells that looked different were considered to be intrinsically different. We must rid ourselves of this ingrained, but utterly fallacious, habit of judging by appearances. A cell is a going concern, in constant interplay with its environment. Its microscopic equipment is merely the cumulative record of its reactions to this environment, reactions of a specifically constituted system to the physicochemical conditions prevailing in the surrounding space. All optically or otherwise discernible characters of a cell are the results and residues of anteceding formative processes. They are indexes, at best, of certain cellular activities only; namely, those that do express themselves morphologically. Since many cellular reactions leave no morphological trace, differentiation of cell character cannot be defined in terms of microscopic criteria. A complete characterization of a given cell would have to include a complete inventory of the molecular species present, their combination and distribution in space, and a list of all possible reactions and manifestations of which the system is capable under any conceivable conditions (the "response repertory"). This seems unattainable in our present state of knowledge. Yet, we can at least exploit to a greater extent than heretofore those tests of cell behavior that are practicable. If we then compare the behavior of two cells or cell strains under identical conditions, e.g., in a common medium, and note constant differences in their behavior in one or more regards, we must conclude that they are of different character, even if they appear alike under the microscope. Conversely, if two strains that differed markedly in appearance while in the organism behave identically when brought into the same medium, this proves conclusively that they have been of one type and had merely displayed different portions of their response repertory in the face of different local environments. The latter process, exemplified by the transformation of fixed histiocytes into macrophages, has been termed "modulation," in contradistinction to "true differentiation" which implies an irreversible change in constitution.

On the basis of such behavioral tests, the occurrence of true differentiation during the development of all higher animals must be affirmed. Tissue culture has shown that cell generations derived from different organs, in spite of assuming similar appearances, retain many of the specific properties of the original strains. This means not only that they had differed in their protoplasmic constitution at the time of explantation, but were able to persist in synthesizing the same specifically different protoplasms without reverting to common type. On the other hand, since the evidence of Experimental Embryology proves that such different cell strains have originated from a common stock, the intrinsic diversification of cell strains during development is an incontrovertible fact. Since this diversification occurs by degrees, it is incorrect to speak of any cell as being "undifferentiated" or "embryonic." Differentiation is not an all-or-none reaction, but a long chain of progressive transformations, so that any cell we are considering has reached a certain point along that line. Also, at each point of the line, the cell is capable of a variety of reactions only part of which are compatible with harmonious development. At any step, an abnormal contingency may provoke a response that may throw the further course of the cell strain off balance and lead to pathological effects.

THE RESPONSE REPERTORY

If, according to the foregoing, visible criteria of shape, arrangement, and so on, are unreliable and incomplete tests of differentiation, what other means of detection do we have available? There are first the chemical products of cells, such as fibers and secretions. Different products are often valid indicators of intrinsic differences in the production plant. Histological stains also sometimes provide sensitive microchemical tests of cellular differences. Histochemical techniques, although still crude, likewise demonstrate specific differences among cells. Further constitutional differences may be revealed by the differential reactions of cells to drugs, hormones, or radiations, provided possible errors due to unequal exposure can be excluded. In this manner, much subtler differences can be detected than are morphologically indicated; for instance, constitutional differences among cells on different branches of the vascular tree, among different types of nerve cells, among different areas of an epithelium, or different regions of the connective tissue.

If this constitutional divergence among cells is based on, or at least associated with, the appearance of distinctive cell proteins, it might be possible one day to trace it by immunological methods. Antiserums against extracts of sperm, lens, kidney, or reticuloendothelial tissue have been shown to have a selective action on homologous organs. We have seen evidence of similar effects in the embryo. We are now testing the possibility of selective absorption of organ antiserums (tagged by C^{14}) by the embryonic precursors of the homologous organs as a means of tracing back the first stages of biochemical divergence. Still other methods are on the horizon. Combined, such methods will give us more pertinent information on when the crucial steps in the differentiation of a cell strain take place. Only then will our attention become more properly focussed on the process of differentiation rather than on the products of differentiation with which we are mostly preoccupied at present.

MOLECULAR ECOLOGY OF THE CELL

The study of cell behavior in development, in immunological reactions, and in the response to drugs, has drawn increasing attention to the cell surface as the seat of specificity of interaction between cell and environment. Similarly, interfaces in the interior appear as seats of specific interactions in the intracellular, intranuclear, etc., spaces. It seems that mere colloid-physical considerations do not provide reaction mechanisms of sufficiently subtle specificity to account for the highly specific and selective interactions recorded in these fields. Interest, therefore, has turned toward intermolecular forces producing bonds of varying strength depending on the configurational fitting ("steric conformance" of a key-lock type) between the respective molecules (e.g., Pauling). Cell relations would be controlled by the interlocking of complementary compounds. The response repertory of a cell would be limited by the number of such key species present in the cell. Not all of these, however, will become effective. In order to operate or combine, conditions for their operation or combination must be favorable. Interfaces offer such favorable conditions by adsorbing, concentrating, and orienting molecular films. The main point is that in this they act selectively. That is to say, depending on the physical and chemical conditions along the interface, certain segments of the molecular population will be selectively attracted to the exclusion of others. Two cells, otherwise identical, confronted with differently constituted interfaces, therefore develop surfaces of qualitatively different composition, and as a result diverge in their subsequent reactions. It should be clear, even from this very condensed comment, that what really counts in determining cell fate is not just the type of chemical compounds present but which of them are in operative condition. And it is in this respect that the physical constellation in the system becomes of paramount importance in setting the stage for the biochemical events. Disposition in space becomes as significant as chemical composition. The field of study investigating this complex but orderly behavior of molecular populations in cells may be termed "Molecular Ecology."

WHERE DOES DIFFERENTIATION OCCUR?

In the light of the concept just outlined, the first step in the differentiation of a cell may be envisaged as consisting of the selective concentration in its surface of certain specific key compounds, which then by virtue of their unique position and orientation act as anchor points for further molecular apposition and also perhaps as catalysts of specific reactions. A period of lability gives way to gradual consolidation, marking the appearance of irreversible features. The evidence of genetics indicates that the genic equipment of the cells of all tissues is and remains the same throughout development, hence, is not subject to differentiation. Differentiation seems confined to the extragenic protoplasm. At the same time, the number and type of differentiations a cell can undergo is strictly limited by the hereditary endowment of the species. Yet, once a cell has attained a given state of differentiation, it can pass this on without attenuation to generations of descendent cells, as is evidenced by tissue-culture experiments. These seemingly conflicting statements can be readily reconciled on the basis of the preceding remarks, leading to the following concept. 1. The numbers and kinds of key compounds that can be synthesized by a given cell are determined by the genic endowment. This assortment is the material basis of what we used to call cell "potency." 2. In any given case, only a fraction of this is "activated," that is, given opportunity to become effective, by being adsorbed to a surface or otherwise enhanced. It becomes the molecular master population of that cell. 3. This master population would then impose its pattern on the further course of synthesis of protoplasm.

A cytoplasmic master compound could perpetuate its kind in one of two ways, depending upon whether the genic apparatus generates the full assortment of terminal products or merely gives rise to more primordial compounds from which the terminal molecular specialties have to be derived by secondary degradations and conversions. In the former case, the cytoplasmic master compound would build on ready-made units of similar kind, while in the latter case, it would impose its own pattern upon the primordial compounds, template fashion. Thus, although at their source in the nucleus, all basic protoplasmic units may be identical in all cells, they would, on contact with the differentiated populations of the cytoplasm, assume the special characters of the latter. The stuff, in this view, is furnished by the nucleus, but reshaped by the differentiated cytoplasm acting as model. The perpetuation of cyto-

plasmic specificity is thereby insured as long as the nuclear production site remains trapped inside the cytoplasm. Suggestive
support for this view is found in the work of Caspersson on the
nuclear production site of proteins, as well as in our own demonstration that the synthesis of protoplasm in nerve fibers occurs
exclusively in the nucleated central portion of the neuron. The
demonstration by Sonneborn of self-perpetuating, although gene-
dependent, cytoplasmic bodies in *Paramaecium* seems capable of
a similar interpretation and may, as he suggests, have a bearing on
the mechanism of cellular differentiation in higher forms.

In conclusion, differentiation is a process in which different parts
of the cell system play different roles, and further research is
needed to identify and clarify the component processes involved.

CONTACT HARMONY

Among the least patent criteria of differentiation is the sum
total of properties that permit a cell to live in harmony with its
neighbors of the same or other types. This is due not merely to the
rapid elimination of all disharmonious combinations if and when
they occur, but to the subtle preadaptation of cells to one another's
prerequisites. One of the most striking examples is the ability of
cells to form tissues by (1) aggregating with their own kind, (2)
combining with complementary types (e.g., epithelium and mesen-
chym; nerve fibers and sheath cells), and (3) rejecting association
with foreign types. That such associations and separations are not
simply the accidental result of proliferation of continuous masses
from common centers, but involve active selectivity, is clearly
brought out by the selective fusion of identical and complementary tissues in regeneration, wound healing, transplantation, and
in the reorganization of cell groups after forcible dissociation. New
investigations on this problem are being carried on in my laboratory. Evidently, cells possess a high degree of discriminatory ability
in recognizing each other. Their means of recognition must be
situated on the surfaces, for this is where they make contact.
Contact may occur between naked protoplasts or through an
intervening coat of exudate. As suggested earlier, the "means of
recognition" may consist of the specific shapes of molecules ex-

posed to the surface. Specific links between conforming molecules could then establish a cohesive union between adjacent cells. Secondarily, such groupings may be consolidated by the formation of fibrous skeletons and membranes. While calcium ions seem to play an important part in promoting adhesiveness between cells, they can evidently not be the determining factor in the selectivity of the associations.

Contact affinities and disaffinities between cells develop in the course of development as corollaries of differentiation (Holtfreter). Thus, two cell strains from different sources can independently develop complementary characters that predispose them for a later union. In other instances, cell types may become mutually adapted after coming in contact. In still other cases, one more advanced cell type may force a less consolidated neighbor into a conforming state, as occurs in the "inductions by contact" to be discussed presently. The final outcome is always harmony of interactions between contiguous cells, as well as between cells and their medium. Establishment of such harmony terminates cell locomotion. Disturbance of the harmonious state sets the cell on the move again. This explains the restlessness at the free edge of an epithelial sheet and similar phenomena. Cells keep moving until all their specific surface contacts are properly matched. As contact harmony depends upon a great many factors, so disharmony may result from a variety of causes. It may originate in a change in the cellular environment or in a change in the cell itself. If the latter change is of such a kind as to reduce the discriminatory acuity that rules in the association among normal cells, inconsistent and abnormal groupings may ensue.

The bearing of these matters on problems of cancer, particularly invasiveness and metastasizing faculty, is evident. To the extent to which these properties mark misdirections of the differentiation process, cancer is a problem of differentiation rather than of growth. The concept outlined in the preceding section explains in principle how a cytoplasmic deviation, once it has occurred, can be perpetuated throughout the subsequent growth of descendent cell generations.

CONTACT INDUCTIONS

The work of Spemann and others has shown that a more mature tissue may influence the course of development of a less differentiated tissue with which it comes in contact. The nature and specificity of this action has long been in the center of interest. That chemical interaction is somehow involved has long since become clear. The underlying mechanism, however, is still as obscure as ever. The immediate effect does not seem to be of the diffusible kind, for it requires that the affected cells be in intimate contact with the inducing cells or, at least, with some cell debris. In the study of one such pair of dependencies, namely the induction of the lens by the eye cup in the chick embryo, we have noted that the first visible trace of the effect consists of a sudden orientation of the prospective lens cells relative to the inducing retina, with the axes of the former becoming perpendicular to the contact surface. Since this reorientation coincides with the area of contact, it must be interpreted as a transcellular contact effect. It is presumably but a sign of the reshuffling and segregation of the molecular population in the epidermal cells in the sense already indicated, that is, attraction of key molecules to the new contact area followed by oriented adsorption, the building on of oriented chains of molecules, and consequent redisposition of the chemical systems of the cell. It is noteworthy that we have seen a similar reorientation of epidermal cells in larval amphibians within a few days after local exposure to an implanted crystal of the carcinogen, methylcholanthrene. Many other instances of contact induction are equally suggestive. Whether or not the particular explanation, attempted here, will prove to be tenable, it shows at least the type of approach from which an eventual resolution of such terms as "induction" into physicochemical realities may be expected. Many pathological processes have long been known to be associated with peculiar cell arrangements, e.g., "pallisading," but little has been done to exploit the descriptive-morphological facts as clues to an understanding of the underlying molecular processes.

A further experimental analysis of the relation between differentiation and contact action seems feasible by exposing cells to

(91)

surfaces of defined constitution. Nageotte has demonstrated the ability of alcohol-fixed cartilage to induce additional cartilage formation in the surrounding tissue. I have described the specific induction of new cartilage along the surface of implanted cartilage that had been devitalized by quick-freezing and drying, as well as induction of cornea and nerve sheath after similar treatment of the corresponding tissues. The specificity of tissue inductions following injection of tissue extracts, as described by Levander and others, remains to be confirmed. Yet, more intensive work along these lines holds promise of valuable data of general significance for the problem of differentiation.

In all such cases, one will have to distinguish clearly between truly differentiating effects, which push a cell into one of several alternate courses, and mere realizing effects, which permit an already single-tracked cell to express some previously latent character. Early embryos mostly furnish examples of the former category, older animals of the latter. A good case in point are the hormones, which in most instances act by merely promoting or repressing in the target cell a course of differentiation the character of which, including hormone-dependence, has been determined by prehormonal influences.

CONCLUSION

This brief survey may suffice to give an idea of the highly composite nature of the phenomena described as "differentiation" and the multiplicity of factors involved. If a cell deviates in its course of behavior from our expectations, we call it pathological. But we realize that the number of points at which such deviations may occur is as great as the number of steps in the process of differentiation. At each step, the deviation may be due to an aberrant change within the cell system or outside of it. Within, it may originate in the cytoplasm, in the nucleus, or in the genes; outside, it may arise in the immediate contact environment (another cell or surrounding matrix) or may come from a distance (as in the case of diffusible agents). It may imply a trivial deficiency easy to repair, or a profound constitutional alteration doomed to permanency. It may affect chemical composition or simply the realization of physical conditions necessary for given chemical systems to become operative. It may act at the surface or in the interior, affect equilibriums of concentration or conformance of configuration, production of compounds or their distribution, electrical or mechanical properties, mobility or adhesiveness, and so on. Realizing this diversity of factors, nothing could be farther off the mark than trying to embrace differentiation—or for that matter, its pathological variations—in a single formula, as do those who search for, or speculate about, "the" mechanism of differentiation, as well as those who speak of "differentiated" and "undifferentiated" cells, as if these were just two sharply delimited stages. This habit of dealing with "differentiation" as a rather vague generalization has seriously handicapped the breaking down of the general problem into concrete and tractable parts which would lend themselves to experimental attack. The purpose of this paper has been to present illustrations of the feasibility and advantages of a less abstract and more factual approach.

REFERENCES

1. WEISS, PAUL: The problem of specificity in growth and development. *Yale J. Biol. & Med.* 19: 235-278, 1947.

2. WEISS, PAUL: Differential growth. *In* Parpart, A. K., Ed.: The Chemistry and Physiology of Growth. Princeton, N. J. Princeton University Press. 1949.

3. WEISS, PAUL: Growth and differentiation on the cellular and molecular levels. (International Congress for Experimental Cytology, Stockholm. 1947.) *Exper. Cell Research.* In press.

These sketchy overviews of the complex content of the phenomena commonly referred to simply as "growth" and "differentiation" should have provided, at least, an inkling of the great diversity of mechanisms involved and of the mounting mass of questions brought to light by their experimental study. The cell being the major agency through which developmental processes are carried out, it becomes even more urgent to learn not just what cells and cell groups do, but how they do it; sheer observation and description of cell behavior to be supplemented by insight into the operative processes. By way of example, the next article delves more deeply into the dynamics and mechanisms by which cells are guided from random ramblings to oriented movements and the orderly assemblies which are the basis of tissue patterns.

GUIDING PRINCIPLES IN CELL LOCOMOTION AND CELL AGGREGATION

PAUL WEISS

INTRODUCTION

THE invitation of the Editor to write a summary comment on the symposium of cell interactions and cell locomotion held at Noordwijk, Holland, made me ponder whether or not the subject matter, as presented, would lend itself as yet to summing up. The conference has been outstanding as an occasion for reviewing on a common platform the fragmentary information bearing on a subject of crucial significance to development, pathology and cellular biology in general. Beyond documenting the fact that here is one of the large blank areas on the map of biological knowledge, it has pointed to a number of constructive analytical approaches which at least promise to fill the vacuum with factual content. It is remarkable that in an age which strives successfully to pinpoint vital activity on tangible mechanisms of molecular interactions (for instance, gene action, contractility, immune reactions, nerve excitation, etc.), one still acquiesces in "explaining" the directiveness of cell locomotion by such purely symbolic and unanalytical labels as chemotaxis, thigmotaxis, and the like, without much evidence of the intellectual discomfort which one would expect to arise from the lack of technological understanding of just how locomotion is produced and guided. After all, a moving cell is a physical body undergoing displacement in space, a process for which there must be tangible mechanisms, that is, a properly timed and spaced sequence of physical and chemical events. The labels we have invented for this mechanism can be no substitute for its description in objective terms, and such an objective description is, in the main, still wanting. This is no minor matter if one contemplates that it implies deep ignorance as to how a cancer cell metastasizes, how a parasite reaches a predestined location in its host after invasion, or how, even in normal development, the primordial sex cells, which originate outside of the gonad, manage to arrive at their eventual functional positions in the erstwhile sterile beds.

[1] The original work referred to in this paper has been supported in part by grants from the American Cancer Society and the National Cancer Institute (National Institutes of Health of the Public Health Service).

Evidently, there has been a growing awareness of both the dearth of knowledge in this area, as well as of the opportunity to do something about it. The Noordwijk Symposium has given proof of this growing realization of the problem and of the effective, if sporadic, current efforts to bring modern experimental techniques to bear on its solution. In collating the scanty and scattered contributions, it has created a nucleus for greater cohesion and concert of future efforts. In documenting the disproportion of speculation over tested facts, it has presented a new challenge to imaginative investigation, and in publishing the proceedings, it will, so we may hope, serve as a sounding board to amplify the call for much more vigorous and disciplined experimentation.

In this sense, the conference may some day be looked back to as an inaugural event. It certainly has been in essence forward-looking, projecting and open-ended, rather than integrating or conclusive, either by tendency or in effect. It was essentially a stock-taking operation, and perhaps the main conclusion I, for one, would draw is that, for some time to come, we shall have to concentrate more on propagating, hybridizing and improving the stock of ideas than on carrying them to the market as if they were ripe for general consumption.

Recognizing this state of flux, I concluded that it might be of greater service if instead of trying to summarize what, for the lack of crucial data, does not as yet add up to a critical sum, I were to limit myself to a brief account of my own and my collaborators' modest efforts over the last nearly forty years to contribute, first, to the clarification of the issues and, second, to their elucidation in terms of tangible processes. Far from any pretense at comprehensiveness or finality, I shall simply state the gist of the facts and ideas that have emerged in decades of preoccupation with phenomena in which cellular locomotion plays a part. I shall do this in reportorial form without attempt at systematic coverage, for the latter task would far exceed the scope of a brief essay.

There is another point that makes me choose the form of reportage, and it is this. No one who has lived through this last half-century of scientific development can have missed the change in the manner of scientific publication that has occurred in this period. It is marked by the progressive bankruptcy of faith and the introduction of legalistic principles of accountancy and documentation, however spurious, for the accreditation of scientific data and conclusions. The printed record has become a measure of validity. Unprinted observations do not count. This tends to bar from recognition that vast store of accumulated experience which an investigator develops in years of concentrated occupation with a given problem and much of which is not precipitated in itemized reports on specific projects. Only a fraction of the work I have ever done in the laboratory has been published in printed detail, while the rest has merely served as a private store of information and judgement. But does the fact that uncommunicated experience has no legalistic standing make it illegitimate? I certainly cannot disown myself of its possession and therefore shall draw on it in the following account whenever pertinent; leaving it to the reader whether or not to give credence to statements not specifically certified by reference to chapter and verse of prior publications.

The problems of locomotion has, as the term indicates, two components—motion and dislocation. Motility refers to the power to move, whereas dislocation means a shift from one place to another. There can be motility and motion with the body remaining in dead center, that is, in stationary position, and conversely, there can be displacement of the body without motility, as in the case of passive convection by external force. Active locomotion, in turn, may be random, that is the number of excursions sampled over a sufficiently long period of time may yield no resultant direction, or there may be directiveness to the total displacement of varying degree and strictness of orientation.

I shall exclude from consideration those cell types which have preformed instruments of propulsion, such as cilia or flagella, as well as the various kinds of blood cells capable of floating and swimming inside a liquid. This leaves those cell types which cannot actively advance in the interior of a liquid medium or, to put it positively, which require a substratum—more correctly, an interface—for their locomotion. This condition is all there is implied in the principle of "contact guidance" to which the first part of this essay will be devoted.

CONTACT GUIDANCE

A naked cell, suspended in a fluid, is essentially spherical. In locomotion, this spherical shape becomes distorted. Our first consideration, therefore, must be given to the deforming forces.

A drop of water suspended in oil, or a drop of oil in water, if wholly undisturbed, tends to assume a spherical shape as a result of surface tension. In groping for models of cell locomotion, Rhumbler pointed out that any local reduction of surface tension on a drop will cause an "amoeboid" deformation comparable to the effect of a local weakening in an elastic membrane around a liquid mass: the intact portion of the contractile surface forcing content to herniate through the aperture of lowered resistance, until the system becomes temporarily equilibrated in some sort of dumbbell shape (for moderate inequalities). If a drop of oil (*a*) is deposited in the interface between two different media (*b*, *c*) with which it is immiscible, the sphere will be flattened to a lentoid of such a contact angle along the circumference that the sum of surface tensions *ab* + *bc* + *ac* becomes a minimum. In other words, the work required to enlarge the surface of the original sphere to that of a lentoid is produced by the potential energy inherent in the combined triple system. Thus, in both of these examples, a sphere becomes deformed as a result of inequalities in its environment.

Since cells, other than those enclosed in rigid envelopes or cell walls, likewise tend to assume nearly spherical shape, when they are unrestrained, they have often been treated as drops subject to the laws of surface tension (e.g. by Rhumbler, d'Arcy Thompson [15], and J. Z. Young [33]), and their flattening out along the interface, for instance, between a slide and a liquid medium has been compared to the spreading of a film of oil along the interface of air and water. In formal regards, the proposition is correct, but closer familiarity with the properties of cell surfaces rules out as oversimplified the notion that the expansion of cell surface in contact with an interface is basically a passive process.

The cell, in fact, is involved quite actively, furnishing some of the energy required to enlarge its surface from its metabolic resources. This is evident from some observations on the "bubbling" of cells freely suspended in liquid media. Not only have rounded-up postmitotic cells long been known to "boil" over their whole surface with little blisters, but the same phenomenon can be seen in many types of ordinary tissue cells enzymatically liberated from their confinement in tissues or organs and suspended in liquid media. The surfaces of such cells are under considerable contractile tension, which manifests itself in the protrusions of numerous little blebs at what must be judged to be temporarily weaker spots along the surface. Taken by itself, this phenomenon of a boiling surface would, of course, only express the statistical inequalities of the surface, making the latter a composite mosaic of patches of different contractile and elastic strengths, for which, in line with our previous comments, surface tension alone could readily account. But there are additional facts that force us to credit metabolic energy for the work involved. One is the fact that this surface activity can be modified by adenosine triphosphate (Lettré [7]), and another is that the contractility which provides the protrusive force appears to move about the cell in a coordinated wave. These and other considerations suggest that the cell expends energy to put its surface layer into a contractile state, yet one which does not result in uniform static compression, but rather in a travelling dynamic oscillation between higher and lower contractile states synchronized over a large fraction of the cell surface and sweeping over it in the manner of a pulse.

We have made numerous observations on this rhythmicity of surface activity in cells isolated from tissues *in vitro*, but have gotten no further than to establishing the reality of the phenomenon. It evidently belongs in the same class as the equally obscure processes of cyclosis in plant cells, radiolarians, and slime molds; of the pulsation of the yolk mass in fish eggs; and perhaps many other propagated slow rhythms in organisms not yet considered under a common viewpoint. Since the substance of the cell is essentially incompressible, the surface necessarily is the region in which regional variations of internal pressure can express themselves; for instance by less intensive "bubbling" in sectors where the crest of the wave passes. This must not be interpreted, however, to mean that the contractile force is confined to the cell cortex, although the extent to which subcortical cytoplasm is actively engaged in the coordinated contractile wave remains to be determined. The whole phenomenon has the aspect of a circling excitatory process which causes those portions of the contractile continuum to contract which have recovered from their refractory condition in the wake of the preceding sweep.

The feature that permits this expenditure of energy to engender protoplasmic motion is the fact that activity is co-ordinated over a large area of the protoplasmic continuum. If the force were produced in random distribution, the result would be an unorganized convulsion, heating rather than moving the cell; but by synchronizing the tension in one large cohesive portion of the system, while at the same time correspondingly relaxing another contiguous portion, a systematic gradient of pumping force results. Various mechanisms invoked to explain amoeboid motion conform in general terms to this principle. Their shortcoming seems to be that they localize the source of the motive force in a circumscribed area of the protoplasmic continuum, albeit in different regions (see Goldacre *versus* Allen in this symposium), whereas a general theory of protoplasmic motion that would embrace under a common principle amoebic motion, plant cyclosis, cell gliding, and perhaps even movements of nuclei and mitochondria within the cytoplasm might have to concede motive power to the whole mass in motion. It should be borne in mind that the effect of such motility is the displacement of cell content relative to a stationary substratum, hence the advance of an amoeba or other naked cell along a solid surface and the streaming of the protoplasm of a plant cell along the inside of the cell wall are essentially the same phenomenon, turned inside out.

When an originally spherical cell flattens out to disc shape along an interface, the contractile wave likewise courses mainly in the plane of flattening and registers as rhythmic fluctuation of activity circling in the protoplasmic fringe of the disc-shaped cell. Depending on the kind of cell, this fringe consists either of a continuous ruffled "undulating" membrane or of separate sectors of such a "membrane"; the term "membrane" in this connection being an historic relic, for one is dealing simply with the thinned-out margin of the cytoplasm itself. If the sectors are relatively narrow, we speak of "pseudopodia", which may end in fan-shaped, knobby or pointed tips, representing increasing degrees of geometric restriction from planar to predominantly linear configuration. Concomitantly, the contractile waves become restricted from their circumferential route into linear courses along the radial pseudopodial extensions, which gives them the configuration of peristaltic waves. We have actually observed such peristalsis in tubelike projections of the character of myelin figures, which are thrust forth from the surface of postmitotic liver cells. In fact, our prior demonstration of a continuous translatory movement of axoplasm in nerve fibers (Weiss and Hiscoe [31]) makes it necessary to postulate such a mechanism.

In conclusion, there is rather striking evidence that metabolic energy is channelled through the cell in coordinated fashion so as to produce rhythmic contractions and expansions of the surface, but the mechanism of this action and the manner of its coordination are still undetermined. Whatever contributions surface tensions and interfacial tensions may make toward the passive deformation of a spherical cell, the cell itself has the power to expand its surface actively beyond any passive deformation by environmental forces.

The described contractile waves deform the spherical shape of a freely suspended cell but little. They lead to some heaving and bubbling of the surface with the protrusion of relatively short projections, but the cohesive and viscous-elastic forces of the system maintain its compact rounded shape. For a cell to expand more extensively, it must be lodged at an interface. Innumerable observations on single cells and nerve fibers in tissue culture have shown unequivocally that active extension requires some adhesion between the peripheral fringe of the cell and an appropriate substratum. This makes the area of contact appear as the effective motor of the cell (note the convincing demonstration of this fact by Ambrose at this symposium). Whereas the unattached protrusions of the freely suspended cell are retracted again by contractile and cohesive forces, these same forces will pull the cell content centrifugally in protrusions whose tips have taken a firm hold on the substratum. The configuration of the substratum thus limits decisively the directions in which a cell may expand.

The expansion of a cell can therefore be understood only in terms of the competition between two opposing sets of forces. Cohesion, viscous-elastic forces and surface tension, including the contractility fibrous networks pervading the cortex of the cell, make for a massive shape of minimal surface, ideally a sphere. Adhesive forces at the margin, contraction in the radial direction and inertia of flow, to be described presently, make for centrifugal expansion, which may be aided in special cases by the formation of crystalline reinforcements in the axial direction—a sort of transient microscopic or sub-microscopic endoskeleton. Whether any particular area of the cell surface will become enlarged or reduced, therefore, depends on the net balance of these forces at that point. This balance naturally varies along the surface and from moment to moment, depending on the local variations in the constitution of the surface itself, on the inhomogeneities of its immediate environment, particularly the substratum, and on the fluctuations of the propulsive force, the latter force becoming greatest for any given point when the crest of the contractile wave is in the antipodal position.

Since, as we said above, expansion or retraction in a given radius depends on whether or not the tip of the projection adheres to the substratum, it is clear that the configuration of the contour of an expanding cell depends on the number and relative strengths of environmental contacts. The eventual outcome of this deformation is what we register as cell shape. Considering the variability of conditions along the border of a cell, both within and without, and the resulting inequalities in the balance of forces from point to point along the border, one realizes that problems of shape cannot be dealt with in terms of *average* surface parameters, but on the contrary, that the very *inequalities* are the critical determinants.

With these facts as background, we can now interpret a wide spectrum of cell shapes in terms of graded deformations of spheres containing motive energy and interacting with interfaces. Let us first consider the simplest case, namely, that of a spherical cell attaching itself to a very smooth surface, such as glass. Adhering firmly to the substratum, the circular line of attachment expands in all radial directions, thus flattening the cell to the shape of a pancake (see the presentation by Taylor at this symposium). Many cell types in tissue culture show this pattern, although the degree of flattening varies with cell type, substratum and medium.

Let us now assume a change, either in the cell surface or in the substratum, such that their mutual adhesiveness would be lowered, which increases the incidence of detachments along the cell margin. The detached stretches become immediately subject to centripetal retractive pull, which forces them to sag in catenary form between the nearest two points at which the margin has remained stuck to the substratum. In this manner, the cell acquires a multipolar shape. Just as the disc-shaped cell can be derived from the spherical cell by the restriction of freedom of radial expansion from three to two dimensions, with all radii in the plane still essentially equivalent, so the multipolar cell can now be derived from the disc-shaped cell by a further restriction of the degrees of freedom of expansion from an infinite to a definite number of radii. The weaker the adhesive force between margin and substratum, the fewer adhesive points for radial elongation will persist. The extreme of this condition, short of total detachment, is reached when there are only two anchor points left between which the cell becomes axially elongated. This yields the bipolar "spindle" cell, which thus marks the ultimate restriction of freedom of expansion to a single dimension.

In this perspective, the problems of cell shape and cell orientation merge into one. Axial orientation is the resultant direction in which the spherical cell has undergone elongation. Reorientation of an established spindle cell, however, requires an additional qualification due to some degree of structural inertia in an already deformed cell. The surface configuration of a cell necessarily affects the movement and arrangement of the macromolecular and particulate populations in the interior, hence in due course produce a dynamic framework which tends to perpetuate with some residual inertia the once initiated cell form. Evidently, in order to be able to change that form, countervailing forces must be the stronger, the longer the prior consolidating phase has lasted.

A related qualification applies to the consideration of a freely suspended cell as essentially isotropic. Any cell has come from a mother cell, and in metazoans, has been a member of a cellular community, hence has had a history of asymmetric exposure to its total environment. How much of the polarized structural residue of this anisotropic exposure endures in a subsequent state of free suspension, is a question which must be settled for each type of cell and for each length of period of isolation empirically.

For most metazoan cells thus far studied, however, polarizing effects of the immediate environment, if of sufficient strength, determine the shape and orientation of the cell. Perhaps the most crucial demonstration of this fact has come from the following experiments (see Weiss [25]). Rounded single cells of various tissues, which on a smooth glass surface would flatten out to disc shape, can be forced to assume spindle shape in a direction imposed by the experimenter by being placed on a glass surface engraved with parallel microgrooves. Such cells at first attach and extend processes in several directions, but extensions along the groove attain a firmer hold than do those on smoother portions of the glass and gradually the former win out in the competitive pull for cell content; eventually, after some tug-of-war, the initially multipolar cell becomes relatively stabilized in the bipolar spindle shape, its two ends pulling in opposite directions along the groove. The concept presented above, reducing cell shape to a problem of differential adhesivity around the free margin of the cell, has thus been substantiated. We do not know as yet whether this differential adhesion is due entirely to the difference in roughness of substratum between the grooved and ungrooved portions of the glass or whether a more subtle oriented feature of the substratum, acquired in the course of the scoring procedure, might be involved; for whereas a number of our scored slides proved consistently successful in orienting all cells of a suspension, others were wholly ineffective.

On the other hand, absolutely reliable results are obtained if one uses a substratum whose oriented inhomogeneities consist of what might be considered the negative of grooves, namely, fibers, The interior of a fish scale, for instance, furnishes a preformed fabric of this kind, as each layer contains a grid of collagen fibers in strictly parallel alignment. Single round cells deposited on such a sheet promptly assume spindle shape in the common direction of the collagen fibers, the whole suspension shortly resembling a school of fish.

Although this may seem to be merely a repetition *en masse* of the original classical experiment of Harrison, in which connective tissue cells in tissue culture were shown to cling to and follow threads of spider web placed in the medium, there is this major difference. Whereas the spider threads traversed a liquid medium and furnished the only possible tracks for cells bound to use a solid substratum, both the grooved glass slide and the fish scale constitute continuous solid systems along which cells could crawl in any direction, as they actually do in some of our glass slides. The explanation of cellular orientation, therefore, can no longer be sought in simple "thigmotaxis" to solids, but evidently involves a directional response to directional properties within that solid.

Moreover these directional cues do not stop on the microscopic scale commensurate to the dimensions of the cell body as a whole, but extend downward into the submicroscopic realm. Historically, this has been the source of my concept of "contact guidance", which implies a more subtle mechanism than the crudely mechanical one for which it has sometimes been misconstrued. Back in 1927, I found that spindle cells in a blood plasma clot would orient themselves in the direction of tension lines prevailing in the coagulum. It was easy to show that tension acted primarily not upon the cells, but rather on the medium, since in a two-step operation, in which a cell-free clot was first subjected to tension and then secondarily, in an unstretched condition, was charged with cells,. the latter would still take courses corresponding to the former tension pattern. The explanation was given in terms of guidance of cells by micellar pathways: tension aligns and orients filamentous fibrin molecules in a common direction, thereby facilitating their aggregation into bundles, and the latter then act as tracks for the moving cells. As has been confirmed later by electron microscopic studies of plasma clots, the network of micellar aggregates is mostly of sub-microscopic dimensions, and yet it has the faculty of drawing cells into its course. The cue being submicroscopic, the initiation of the response of the cell must likewise be an event of submicroscopic scale, which only subsequently is amplified to an effect on the whole larger cell body.

We may visualize the situation as follows. The mobile cellular fringe can be assumed to be covered, like the rest of the cell surface, with a network of long filamentous molecules in the plane of the cell membrane. On contact with an extraneous submicroscopic fiber, this molecular layer would be drawn out along the fiber surface, creeping in the direction of the fiber axis like a wetting substance on the wall of a capillary. A fiber thus creates a momentary outlet for cell content, and if this channel persists long enough, it may be widened gradually to microscopic dimensions by the pumping forces described above. Whether or not such a projection becomes established, will depend not only on the force of thrust but also on the number and distribution of competing surface projections initiated in other directions. A simple hydrodynamic consideration will show that this competition between simultaneous protrusions disappears when they lie so close together in a common direction as to become confluent. Since this is precisely the condition along that part of the cell margin which crosses a set of parallel microfibers or microgrooves, one can understand, at least in principle, how a submicroscopic orientation is translated into the orientation of a microscopic cell.

But even this may be too simple. Electron microscopic observations of single cells of various types in culture have revealed that most of them, when spread out on a plane substratum, are bristling on their surfaces with cylindrical projections of a rather uniform diameter of about 1000 Å and a length of up to several microns, composed of an electron dense core in a thin sheath of ectoplasm, which between neighboring processes forms a web. It is conceivable that an extraneous fibril on contact with the cell surface might align the nearest group of these "tentacles" and thereby create an internal outflow channel for cytoplasm in that direction. In view of its obvious bearing on the problem of selective contact guidance, to which we shall refer below, it would seem promising to pursue this possibility further.

If the fact that a microscopic cell can be oriented by submicroscopic cues reveals the inadequacy of mere "thigmotaxis," that is, of plain surface application, as the principle of cell guidance, the case is further strengthened by observations at the opposite end of the scale, namely, the orientation of microscopic cells by macroscopic bodies. For instance, spindle cells in culture, attached to a macroscopic fiber of glass or plastic, orient themselves in the direction of the fiber axis, although, if nothing more than simple surface application were involved, they could have assumed any other positions and configurations in the cylindrical surface. The actual explanation was found to be as follows (Weiss, [20]). Cultured cells produce macromolecular exudates ("ground mats"), which spread along the interface at which the cells reside. On a cylindrical fiber, the margin of this coat, advancing distally, stretches the meshes of the micellar network behind it lengthwise, and the leading cell processes then trace these longitudinal micellar tracks.

While these studies have stressed the importance of macromolecular exudates as integrating mechanisms in the morphogenesis of cell populations —a feature recently reemphasized by Moscona—little is known as yet beyond the sheer existence of the principle. And yet, it seems plausible that if such exudates are cell type-specific, they would offer a basic clue to the understanding of selectivity in contact guidance and cell association (see below). Recent studies in our laboratory (Rosenberg [11]) have confirmed quantitatively that cells of different types in culture release macromolecular units which coat the surrounding interfaces with monomolecular films, the properties and kinetics of which vary with cell type, substratum and medium. While the relation of these microexudates to the micellar and fibrous ground mats is still undefined, they do caution us not to consider the mechanism of contact relations and contact guidance in over simple terms.

Inasmuch as we are focussing here mainly on the orientation of cells by existing geometric singularities in their environment, the origin of the latter is not really up for discussion. Yet, a few cursory comments may be added to round out the picture. As we have seen, linear fiber tracks for cells can be generated by tension, which aligns chains of filamentous molecules in a common direction. The generating tensions may be imposed upon the medium from the outside, but they may also be self-generated by cellular activity, e.g., in the case of spreading exudates. A particularly potent effect of this latter kind results from strong syneretic activity of proliferating cells, which causes the surrounding colloidal network to shrink considerably. Such local shrinkage gathers the meshes of the fibrous continuum towards the shrinking center, thus setting up a pattern of radial tracks, which orient immigrating or emigrating cells correspondingly. When two such centers arise in a colloidal continuum, their combined contractions lay down a preferential pathway of fibers along the connecting line and thereby generate automatically a straight traffic channel from one center to the other ("Two-center effect"; Weiss [23, 24]). This is a striking example of scalar chemical activity resulting in vectorial, movement- and form-directing effects.

Model experiments *in vitro*, as well as observations on developing tissues in the body, have furnished numerous concrete examples of how chemical inhomogeneities can translate themselves into the physical effects that underlie cell orientation in general. Yet the detailed shape, orientation and fate of any given cell can only be statistically predicted, as the details will vary with the unpredictable fluctuations within the cell itself and with the contingencies of its immediate micro-environment, both substratum and medium. The variability of cell shape and cell orientation in any single tissue culture illustrates this point. Individual cell shape can be treated quantitatively only in terms of probabilities, but not of microprecise determinacy. This proposition has been tested as follows (Weiss and Garber [30]).

In line with our earlier comments, we may assume that contacts of extraneous fibrils with the cell surface create outlets for local protrusions, some of which will be abortive, while others will succeed. Now, since concurrent projections must compete for cell content, the more of them will be able to coexist, the more equal they all are in draining power. On general grounds, larger fibers can be assumed to cause a stronger outflow of cell content, hence to suppress other weaker protrusions in their vicinity. Therefore, the greater the inequality of fiber size and the higher the incidence of larger fibers in the medium, the lower should be the average number of successful processes which cells in that medium could protrude. The fibrin network of the blood plasma clot consists of fibrous aggregates of various sizes. Since the degree of aggregation is greater at lower than at higher pH values, one can produce a graded series of clots of increasing diversity of fiber sizes. Cells reared in them should then show a corresponding gradation in the average number of processes, with a dominance of multipolar forms at the alkaline end of the scale, and of bipolar forms at the acid extreme. A similar series could be expected from cells reared in clots with different fibrin concentrations, the higher concentrations containing larger fibers. Our observations, carried out on thousands of cells, have fully confirmed these expectations. The average number of cell processes decreased linearly with decreasing pH values (during clot formation), as well as with increasing fibrin concentration.

A summary view of our discourse thus far reveals the futility of any attempt to deal with contact guidance by reference to some general and overall "adhesivity". Rather we are faced with a composite mechanism in which three major sets of separate and partly separable variables are involved. These are (1) motive power from metabolic energy of the cell; (2) inhomogeneities in the constitution of the motile fringe of the cell, due (*a*) to random or systematic inequalities in the structure of the immediate environment, which in turn are partly attributable to prior modifications of the environment by cellular activities and exudates, and (*b*) to residual inequalities in the cell stemming from previous environmental influences; and (3) dependence of general adhesivity of the cell surface upon the composition of the medium, the substratum and the outermost cell covering. Given a complete knowledge of these factors, it ought to be possible to predict statistically the shape any given type of isolated cell should assume under given conditions, as long as it has a freely reactive surface. In many instances, shapes freely assumed in a primary reaction to the environment will gradually become consolidated in various degrees by the formation of rigid internal or surface structures. It seems that both fibrous protein systems and lipid lamellae can subserve this harnessing and stabilizing function, of which the mature nerve fiber or the spermatozoa are notable examples. However, in the following we shall continue to concern ourselves only with the free and plastic cell and its behavior. This behavior is subject to major modifications and restraints if a cell does not remain in isolation but encounters other cells with which it can interact. In one regard, it is just such restraints that lead to locomotion, paradoxical though this sounds, it will be documented in the following section.

LOCOMOTION

In the preceding account we have dwelled on the development of cell shape as a result of cellular motility, in the sense that some parts of the cellular content undergo internal shifts relative to other parts, ending in deformation. However, the system as a whole remained stationary. The center of its mass, even though not necessarily static, oscillates about a fixed position without net translocation. For a flattened disc-shaped cell, this appears as an erratic straying about within a relatively narrow range, while for a bipolar spindle cell, it means a shuttling back and forth on a linear track, due to the random inequalities of adhesive and protrusive force between the two mobile ends straining in opposite directions. In other words, motility does not of itself lead to locomotion. Locomotion results only if the center of the mass is in progressive translocation; and if the translocation follows a steady course in a given direction, we designate the locomotion as oriented.

Theories of cell locomotion have in general been classed under four headings; namely, chemotaxis, galvanotaxis, phototaxis, and mechanotaxis (thigmotaxis). Except for mechanotaxis, all of these terms refer to directional signs provided by asymmetric distributions ("gradients") of chemicals, electric charges, or radiations in the environment, while remaining non-committal as to the mechanism by which the external asymmetry is translated into an oriented locomotor response of the cell. Of course, no external asymmetry other than sheer passive convection can serve as cue to orientation unless it is "perceived" by the cell; that is, establishes a corresponding state of asymmetry within the cell itself, beginning with the surface and involving the interior in various degrees. Omitting the trivial and essentially unbiological instances of passive convection by currents, mechanical pull or electrophoresis as well as the reflex orientation of cells having a specialized locomotor apparatus, such as ciliates or flagellates, the proposition is as follows.

Random fluctuations in the local concentration of chemicals and distribution of charges within the immediate micro-environment of a given cell lead continually to corresponding inequalities, hence asymmetries, along the cell surface of the same order as those discussed in the previous section. A temporary gradient of concentration or potential therefore entails a momentary axiation of the cell in the direction of the gradient. However, such an effect cannot become manifest unless the external gradient is steep enough to supersede the internal differentials within the cell and retains its position long enough for the cell to give an effective reaction. For a chemical gradient, this would require that the difference of concentration between the side of the cell facing the source and the opposite side be of such a magnitude that it constantly exceeds any of the internal gradients that arise within the cell from its autonomous activities; and for an electric gradient, it would presuppose a sufficiently steep and steady gradient of electric potential between the two sides.

If one keeps in mind these prerequisites for effective orientation, one realizes immediately that in many situations in which sources of chemical
emanation or electric charges have been considered as either "attractive"
or "repulsive" loci for moving cells, those premises are not fulfilled even in
a medium fully protected against mechanical agitation and perturbation.
The fraction of an external concentration gradient along the short stretch
of the diameter of a given cell, which latter is in itself not homogeneous,
would not seem to be sufficient to serve as a guiding cue, except perhaps
statistically over long periods of time, in which case it would register as a very
gradual drift, rather than an oriented movement. Considering further that
inside the organism fluids are constantly stirred up by muscular contractions, pulse waves, currents, and so forth, and that the motion of the cell
itself stirs its surrounding medium, one realizes that the old primitive concepts
of chemotaxis are far from realistic. And yet, aside from many cases of
misinterpretation, we do know of such phenomena as the migration of
white blood cells toward a focus of inflammation, of slime molds toward a
source of acrasin, and of similar well-attested effects in which a dispersed
cell population was found to be at least eventually aggregated at, if not
necessarily directly guided towards, a chemically distinguished locus in the
environment. In the slime mold, a relay action cell-to-cell, initiated from
a given locus, but then propagated chain-wise by each responding cell
serving as a new amplifying source, and further accentuated by rapid decay
of the product (Bonner [3], Schaffer [12]), offers one type of explanation; but
even here the intervention of some microstructural devices oriented by the
more patent chemical activities (similar to the "two-center effect" mentioned
above) has not been definitely ruled out.

Even so, the possibility that cells can polarize each other directly by
chemical means without any structural intermediation, becomes a very real
one if the distances between the interacting cells are short; for in this case,
each cell forms a physical barrier to the rapid dissipation of the discharged
products of the other, hence these products will accumulate between them
and thus establish the head of a rather steep gradient between the "inner"
and the "outer" sides of the confronted cells. Now, if the products in question
are of the sort that would alter the surface constitution of a cell exposed to
them, whether by causing molecular reorientation (Weiss [26]) or ionic
changes or otherwise, their concentration gradient across the cell would
create a corresponding difference in surface strength on opposite sides,
as a result of which cell content will be protruded on the side that is relatively
weaker; whether this is in the uphill or downhill direction of the gradient

depends on whether the agent is one that loosens or one that tightens surface structures. In the former case, the new protrusions will point toward the other cell, giving the illusion of "attraction," while in the latter case, they will be directed outward. Striking effects of this kind have actually been observed in the protrusion of rootlets from seaweed eggs grouped close together (Whitaker [32]) and in the outgrowth of processes from nerve cell groups in tissue culture (Stefanelli [13]).

Next, if the protrusions have the properties of pseudopods, that is, are adhesive instead of free at their tips, their one-sided extension will, of course, drag the rest of the cell body after them in the same direction. As a result, the two or more cells in interaction will in one case move closer together and in the other case move farther apart. As I have pointed out on earlier occasions, the latter mechanism accounts readily for the observation by Twitty and Niu [16] that pigment cells in a capillary tube tend to recede from each other, without the need of invoking any mutual "repulsion" or "negative chemotaxis".

Electric gradients can similarly give rise to surface asymmetries, which limit the directions in which cell content can be propelled. As colloids on the anodal side become stiffened (Anderson [2]), locomotion in any but the kathodal direction is ruled out; the kathodal drift of nerve fibers in tissue culture (Marsh and Beams [8]) is an obvious illustration of this fact.

In conclusion, no asymmetric condition in the environment can exert any guiding influence on a cell unless it can evoke a corresponding axial differential in the cell, which confines the cell's intrinsic motility to an outlet in a single direction only instead of the all-round expansion open to it in an isotropic space. An isolated cell on an interface can be regarded as having innumerable degrees of freedom of expansion and therefore, being pulled out equally in all directions, remains stationary in the center of the stalemated radial strains. However, as soon as its motility is reduced or totally suppressed in one sector, the remaining portion, now given competitive advantage or true monopoly, has full sway in pulling the cell in its direction. In this sense, the above statement that locomotion results from the restriction, rather than the addition, of degrees of freedom of a motile cell, is no longer paradoxical. And a brief reflection will show that in this light, the problems of cell shape, cell orientation, and now cell locomotion, appear simply as various expressions of a single common principle: the channeling of cellular motility from random into definite courses singled out by physical and chemical differentials in the environment, of which other cells and their products form integral parts.

Contact guidance, as a critical limiting condition for all cells bound to interfacial support, delineates the limited tracks still open to a given cell at a given point in a given environment; in the extreme, on a strictly oriented medium, this leaves the individual cell, now a bipolar one, with only a single track. Yet, even on a single track, there are still two alternative directions left in which to advance, and evidently contact guidance remains ambiguous as to which one will be taken. This to decide, is a matter left to those differentials and gradients just outlined before.

A pertinent analogy is that of a railroad. The rails and switches limit the possible routes that can be taken, while the engine provides the motive power; but even then it still depends on which way the engine is headed whether the train will move forward or backward on the tracks. And if two engines are hitched to the train pulling with equal force in opposite directions, the train will remain standing as did our single bipolar spindle cells on grooves or fiber tracks.

CONTACT INTERACTIONS

Now, as I stated in the preceding section, a cell does not become a significant polarizing factor in the environment of another cell until they both come within close enough range for their discharges (chemical or electric) to sustain telling inequalities in each others' surfaces. The critical distance will vary according to the type and state of activity of the cell and the condition of the environment (composition of medium, configuration of space, degree of perturbation, etc.) but can scarcely exceed the order of magnitude of the diameter of the cell. The short-range extreme of this type of cell-to-cell interaction is reached in cases in which the critical distance is so short as to appear as "contact". We shall take the word here in its primitive meaning on the microscopic scale, unmindful of a certain fuzziness it assumes in terms of molecular dimensions (Weiss [25]). If cells were stated above to be able to paralyze each other's confronted sides as they come within close range, so that thereafter they will move apart again (for example, in the cited experiment of Twitty and Niu), a far more general expression of the partial immobilization which cells can impose on each other's surfaces is observed when cells actually make physical contact. The sequelae of such contact are quite diverse for different cell types, but they all seem to have one feature in common, which I have stressed and illustrated ever since 1941 (see review in Weiss [21]) and which is as follows.

In a freely mobile cell, that part of the mobile fringe which comes in contact with another cell ceases to extend actively. In an epithelial cell, this causes cell content along that border segment to become diverted from its formerly radial trend into a tangential course, remaining available for extension along the still unrestrained part of the edge. That free portion diminishes progressively, as contacts are established with ever more cells, ending with the full loss of mobility, though not of motility, in the completely surrounded cells— with specific qualifications to be outlined presently. This immobilization is by no means due to crude mechanical confinement, but is a biological response to contact. It seems to be of a similar nature to the stabilization of the bubbling surfaces of floating (or post-mitotic) cells when they become attached (or reattached) to a substratum. It must be emphasized, however, that in cell-to-cell contacts, only the fraction of the border touching the other cell is immobilized, but not the whole border, let alone the entire cell. Epithelial cells thus acquire common borders, and if their association endures (see below), they constitute cohesive sheets. Any later disruption of such a sheet creates again a free edge, liberates the cell borders along that edge, hence restores to them one-sided mobility, which automatically leads the free cell front into the lesion; this is how wounds heal (Weiss [27]).

Whereas epithelial cells tend to stay combined, the reaction to mutual contact in bipolar or multipolar cells, especially of mesenchyme, takes a different course. Again, the primary response is one of mutual immobilization at the contact points. But lacking any tendency to stick together, the cells are moved apart by the continuing advance of their free sides. This process has been observed in time lapse motion pictures by both Abercrombie *et al.* [1] and ourselves (Weiss [25]; it has been termed "contact inhibition" by the former—a term which is illustrative provided one keeps in mind that the "inhibition" pertains to a localized fraction of the cell only. In many of our cultures, the immobilized end does not just come to rest, but looses its hold on the substratum and is vigorously retracted towards the main cell body. But whatever the details, the outcome is a temporary asymmetry in the motile apparatus of the cell, giving the lead to the residual uninhibited pseudopodia. In our simile, a railroad train, stalled by being hitched to two engines pulling in opposite directions, can run again if one of the engines is disengaged.

While clarifying the nature of directive interactions between proximate or contacting cells in the manner here outlined, all observations so far have failed to show any trace of direct "attractions" or "repulsions" between cells, which would seem to make the continued loose usage of these terms not only meaningless, but truly misleading and reprehensible. The outward migration of cells from a tissue fragment in culture is not due to any repulsive action of the center, but is again simply the outcome of an environmental asymmetry, namely, the gradient of cell population density; the mere fact that statistically, the freely roaming cells meet more contacts, hence are subject to more contact immobilizations, in the central than in the peripheral directions, leads to a general centrifugal drift.

SELECTIVITY

Without going further into these interesting problems of cellular population ecology, there is one major facet which I have tried to evade so far in this essay, but which is too fundamental to be wholly bypassed, namely, the feature of specificity and selectivity, both in contact guidance and cell inter-action. It signifies that a given cell can distinguish between different kinds of contact substrata, as well as between different kinds of cells, and can respond discriminately.

My preoccupation with this topic dates back to my earliest experimental work (Weiss [17]), in which I noted that a larval amphibian limb trans-planted in place of an amputated limb would suppress the regeneration of the latter only if it was inserted in the correct orientation, in which case it was accepted by the host body as a true substitute. Discovering subsequently the specificity of neuro-muscular relations, the "case of the specific match" as a basic biological principle thoroughly captivated my interest and has held it quite firmly ever since. In 1924 and 1930 [18], I reviewed some of the scanty hints at tissue selectivity under the purely descriptive heading of "affinity," a principle which was soon to receive much more solid factual substantiation by the classical studies of Holtfreter [6] in the 1930's. In 1941 [19], the earlier concept of contact guidance was expanded to encompass "selective guidance," based on "selective adhesiveness," largely on the strength of the demonstration of the selective tracking by different classes of nerve fibers of different preneural pathways, and later of fibers of the cor-responding type (HAMBURGER [5], Taylor [14]). At the same time, I also introduced a hypothetical molecular model of contact selectivity in general, which, though it may not hold the answer to the problem, has led at least to a more rigorous articulation of the questions the facts present to us. In 1946, I summarized these considerations of specificity of cell interactions in growth and development (Weiss [21]), and in 1949 [22] proposed their applicability to the problem of the alienation and metastasis of the cancer cell. This was followed by the demonstration of selective "homing" at their proper destinations of random disseminated embryonic cells (Weiss and Andres [28, 29]) and by the evidence that epithelia will merge only with epithelia of the same or related kinds, but not with unrelated ones (Chiakulas [4]). Meanwhile, the Mosconas [9, 10] perfected the technique of dissociation and reaggregation of cells from embryonic tissues *in vitro*, which made possible the elegant demonstration that scrambled mixtures of cell types sort themselves out rather cleanly according to type (Moscona [9]).

It was a logical step to study the manner of this selective segregation directly by time-lapse cinemicrography, and during the last five years, we have (with A. C. Taylor and A. Bock) compiled a large stock of film records of cell encounters *in vitro* in many different combinations of tissue origin, species, ages, densities, treatments, media, substrata, etc. A sample film was shown at the Noordwijk symposium. However, no more than the most general conclusions can be reported here. They are as follows (see also Weiss [25].

A free epithelial cell on a flat surface, when making chance contact with another cell, may form temporarily a local attachment to the latter. If both are of the same type, they mostly remain associated and gradually enlarge their mutual border line. Even so, their surfaces are by no means firmly bonded to each other, but get detached in spots and reattached in others, so that their conjugation must be explained by a statistical-dynamic, rather than static, principle. As larger numbers of cells of the same type join up, their collective outline tends to assume minimum possible length, i.e. become near-circular. But whether this is the result of a condition of maximum possible internal boundary lengths among the constituent cells or of enveloping action of an exuded ground mat, cannot be decided on existing evidence. On the other hand, if the two meeting cell margins belong to cells of unrelated types, they separate again, much as if the other cell were just part of the ordinary substratum. All this applies to cells freshly liberated from tissues, for after prolonged cultivation some of the discriminative reactions are lost. In this connection it is worth noting that Abercrombie (see this symposium) has found the normal and malignant descendants of mesenchyme to have lost their mutual recognition of kinship, as manifested by the loss of "contact inhibition".

The nature of the mechanisms by which cells recognize each other's kinds as well as the kinds of substrata they want to follow, still escapes us. My suggestion [19] of antigen-antibody-like bonding, even though favored by some, does not seem to be adequate if interpreted statically, although a more statistical and dynamic version of it cannot yet be ruled out definitively.

But one fact stands out clearly: whatever the mechanism of selective "recognition", the response to it by the cell is definitely more comprehensive than a plain surface reaction. The problem is further complicated by the fact that the selectivities in question show gradations, rather than absolutely sharp definition; for instance, in contact guidance, a preference was noted for cells to stay on glass rather than pass on to a fibrin thread [20]. So, taking all in all, it would seem best to leave the matter of specificity open till further analytic work provides some more compelling clues to explanations than we can muster at the present. One cautionary note: some familiarity with the real phenomena that are to be explained is indispensable, for our supply of explanations for imaginary concepts of cell movement and cell interactions is already superabundant.

CONCLUSION

As indicated in the introduction, it would have been presumptious and futile in this essay to attempt a rounded and systematic portrayal of our knowledge, such as it be, of the principles of cell locomotion. The best I could try to do was to record the gist of years of experience with the relevant phenomena, conveying perhaps some semblance of an emerging unifying concept. The field being in flux, any such concept can be considered as no more than *in statu nascendi*, and even then as but a partial contribution to a common goal. Other participants have offered many illuminating contributions of great value to the same cause. The views are starting to converge. No ultimate answers are as yet in sight. But the problems, which pose the questions, have at least gained in sharpness and consistency; and if the conference were to have achieved nothing more, it has scored a major gain as guide post for further research efforts.

REFERENCES

1. ABERCROMBIE, M., JOHNSON, M. L. and THOMAS, F. A., *Proc. Roy. Soc. London B* **136**, 448 (1949).
2. ANDERSON, J. D., *J. Gen. Physiol.* **35**, 1 (1951).
3. BONNER, J. T., The Cellular Slime Molds. Princeton University Press, 1959.
4. CHIAKULAS, J. J., *J. Exptl. Zool.* **121**, 383 (1952).
5. HAMBURGER, V., *Wilhelm Roux' Arch. Entwicklungsmech. Organ.* **119**, 44 (1929).
6. HOLTFRETER, J., *Arch. exptl. Zellforsch. Gewebezücht.* **23**, 169 (1939).
7. LETTRÉ, H., *Cancer Research* **12**, No. 12, 847 (1952).
8. MARSH, G. and BEAMS, H. W., *J. Cellular Comp. Physiol.* **27**, 139 (1946).
9. MOSCONA, A., *Proc. Soc. Exptl. Biol. Med.* **92**, 410 (1956).
10. MOSCONA, A. and MOSCONA, H., *J. Anat.* **86**, 287 (1952).
11. ROSENBERG, M. D., *Biophys. J.* **1**, 2, 137 (1960).

12. SCHAFFER, B. M., *Am. Naturalist* **91**, 19 (1957).
13. STEFANELLI, A., *Acta Embr. Morph. Exp.* **1**, 56 (1957).
14. TAYLOR, A. C., *J. Exptl. Zool.* **96**, 159 (1944).
15. THOMPSON, D'ARCY W., On Growth and Form. University Press, Cambridge, 1942.
16. TWITTY, V. C. and NIU, M. C., *J. Exptl. Zool.* **125**, 541 (1954).
17. WEISS, P., *Wilhelm Roux' Arch. Entwicklungsmech. Organ.* **99**, 168 (1923).
18. —— Entwicklungsphysiologie der Tiere. Steinkopff, Dresden and Leipzig, 1930.
19. —— *Growth* **5**, 163 (1941).
20. —— *J. Exptl. Zool.* **100**, 353 (1945).
21. —— *Yale J. Biol. and Med.* **19**, 235 (1947).
22. —— Differential Growth. *In* Chemistry and Physiology of Growth, p. 135. Ed. A. K. PARPART, Princeton University Press, 1949.
23. —— *Proc. First Natl. Cancer Conf.* **50** (1949).
24. —— *Science* **115**, 293 (1952).
25. —— *Inter. Rev. Cytol.* **7**, 39 (1958).
26. —— *Proc. Natl. Acad. Sci. U.S.* **46**, 993 (1960).
27. —— *Harvey Lectures 1959–1960*, p. 13, Academic Press, New York, 1961.
28. WEISS, P. and ANDRES, G., *Science* **111**, 456 (1950).
29. —— *J. Exptl. Zool.* **121**, 449 (1952).
30. WEISS, P. and GARBER, B., *Proc. Natl. Acad. Sci. U.S.* **28**, 264 (1952).
31. WEISS, P. and HISCOE, H. B., *J. Exptl. Zool.* **107**, 315 (1948).
32. WHITAKER, D. M., *J. Gen. Physiol.* **20**, 491 (1937).
33. YOUNG, J. Z., Growth and Form, p. 41, Clarendon Press, Oxford, 1954.

Such studies as the ones here illustrated, revealing how manifest form and structure can emerge from the orderly play of interactions among cells and between cells and their environments have firmly established the wide range of variability left open to cells for their reactions in accordance to fluctuating circumstances. This realization erases, of course, the notion of a sharp dividing line between the intrinsic soundness of the dynamics of "normal," as against "abnormal" cells; the distinction is revealed as solely a convenient and conventional expression of the degree of closeness or remoteness of a given bundle of cellular properties in regard to a statistical average. This being the case, critical observations of departures from the norm in living organisms—"experiments of nature"—can bring us just as valid disclosures of "causal interrelations" as do controlled experiments in the laboratory. *This is the subject of the next article.*

DEFORMITIES AS CUES TO UNDERSTANDING DEVELOPMENT OF FORM

PAUL WEISS*

Organic form—the architecture and texture of organisms—is better known than understood. Just how and by what mechanisms a mass of cells undergo that typical sorting and ordering in space which gives an organism its shape, is still one of the most obscure problems of living nature. Its study has gained momentum ever since experimentation started to supplement sheer description. Experiments reveal inner workings by establishing causal relations. They do this by decomposing a complex situation into component features and testing one at a time to ascertain just what depends on what. But how is one to know just where to start when one is faced with a perplexing multitude of factors, all of potential relevance, and often, having singled one out for study, finding that it does not lend itself to experimental variation, controllable at will?

It is in this dilemma that acute observation of nature is of immense help; for it can register any departure of observable features from their standard norm, and, if we then succeed in pairing this deviation with a corresponding variation in the external circumstances, we immediately come to suspect a causal nexus deserving closer examination. Although such a pairwise correlation is not of itself proof of a causal relation, it is suggestive and, if coincidence can be ruled out, it can serve as the equivalent

* The Rockefeller Institute. This article is the text of a Lowell Lecture delivered in Boston October 30, 1958. It is reprinted by permission of the publishers from *Disease and the Advancement of Basic Science*, Henry K. Beecher, editor; Cambridge, Massachusetts: Harvard University Press, copyright 1960 by the President and Fellows of Harvard College.

133

of a tentative experiment—in that case, an "experiment of nature."
Of course, the more familiar we are with a class of objects, the smaller
will be the deviations that we shall be able to perceive. Man, as our most
intimate acquaintance, thus becomes the richest source of detectable
distinctions, and the sharpened eye of clinical experience can justly take
credit for having pointed the way to significant advances in the science
of life by having uncovered unsuspected, and having confirmed suspected,
correlations. The study of development has shared extensively in these
benefits. While it repays for them by delivering to clinical practice a
more solid understanding of the growth and repair of tissues as guide
to improved treatment and prevention of disease, it gratefully acknowl-
edges the pointers and stimuli received.

Form is the visible expression of the formative processes that have been
instrumental in its shaping. The end result is but the residual record
of its formative history. Clearly, then, changes in the standard pattern
of formative processes lead to deviations from the standard form: deformations end up as "deformities." In this sense, "deformities" become valuable
clues to the inner workings of formative processes. How instructive
they have been can be documented by a long list of examples, from the
nonviable double-headed or otherwise partially twinned bodies arising
from single eggs, to such less detrimental aberrations as supernumerary
digits, split palates, or fused joints. They have furnished crucial evidence
against the theory of rigid prelocalization of distinct body parts in the
germ and in support of the concept of embryonic development as an
intricate assembly-line process in which the original material endowment
of the egg is progressively transformed by chains of different and complicated interactions proceeding according to a definite inherited production
schedule (1, 2). This schedule has become so blueprinted by evolutionary
experience that, given a standard range of environmental conditions
(climate, nutrition, stresses, and so forth), it will lead to viable and reproductive individuals capable of passing on that pattern and schedule to
successive generations. To yield viable results, these schedules must be
sufficiently flexible to allow for adjustments to the unique and unpredictable fluctuations of conditions prevailing during the developmental
period of any one individual. In other words, the genetic blueprint
provides for tolerances. But the latitude of such tolerances is limited and
narrowly defined, and, in general, the innumerable tributary processes

Paul Weiss · *Deformity Cues to Development*

(117)

feeding into the assembly chain must not be too far off the timing pattern set for harmonious cooperation or else the product will suffer irreparably. If any partial act comes into operation significantly earlier or later than a related process which it is designed to match, they miss each other completely or at least their interaction will be too brief or too inadequate. Depending on the importance of that particular step for further development, the finished product, the developed body, will then bear the mark of that past fault of the construction process, and we shall note a defect.

Whether the defect will be a "more" or a "less" of what we would normally expect to find in the end product depends on the nature of the affected processes. Paradoxically, a lagging link can cause excess production: for instance, when a local growth block causes an early organ rudiment to fork, with two organs resulting instead of one, or when a factor scheduled to stop expansion of an organ at an appointed moment fails to arrive in time to check further growth. Conversely, a local growth process racing ahead at supernormal rate may cause an eventual deficit by obstructing the pathways or preempting the nutrients of companion growth processes. Many such effects of disharmonious development can now be duplicated by experimental procedures (3), but originally it was the study of natural deformities that pointed the direction in which to search.

While there is thus no doubt that understanding of development has been furthered by the study of abnormalities—the science of teratology— the preoccupation with the grossly abnormal has also had the unfortunate side effect of grooving the mental habit of separating the "abnormal" from the "normal" as a distinct and disparate phenomenon, as if the processes themselves were less sound in one case than in the other. It is important, therefore, to restore perspective by emphasizing that even the grossest deformity is produced by the same rigorously lawful molecular and cellular interactions that govern normal development. All that has happened is that the proportions among the component processes, whose harmony is predicated on proper dosing and timing, have become grossly distorted during the course of development because of either some major initial flaws in the (genic) endowment or some disruptive variations in the environment (malnutrition, infection, climatic extremes, and so forth). The point to keep in mind is that these major deviations, though being more spectacular, are no different in kind from the more minor and less conspicuous variations due to the disparities of the gene complexes and the ever-fluctuating environment that we take for granted as the bases of the uniqueness of each individual.

The term "normal" merely circumscribes fuzzily the central range of moderate variation short of those excessive excursions that are no longer safely compatible with continuous survival of the species. Thus, the same process which is "normal" for one group may be highly "abnormal" for another. The principles and mechanisms by which a fish tail is formed are quite the same whether the fish will end up with one tail, as most fish will, or with a double fantail, as is the "normal" feature of some Japanese goldfish. An extra toe, which is a regular occurrence in certain breeds of dogs and fowl, hence is rated there as "normal," is considered quite "abnormal" if it crops out, as it sporadically does, in other breeds. The convergence and fusion of two lateral organs into a single median organ is as rigorous and sound a procedure in its physico-chemical determination as is the coalescence of two drops of water into one. Yet, while this process is the "normal" occurrence in the development of the heart in birds and mammals—two primary halves of heart merging secondarily—it would be utterly "abnormal" for the eyes and the associated brain centers; for if these are combined in the midline—as in the Cyclops of Greek mythology, as well as in some human fetal monsters and their experimental replicas in animals—they render their bearers into nonviable freaks. It is instructive to contemplate that the Cyclopean single eye, after all, is but an extreme point on a scale of developmental variations, the viable portion of which we "normally" see in our midst as people ranging from very wide-set to very narrow-set eyes. And is not the "beauty feature" of a cupid's bow-mouth but a milder degree of hare-lip? Normality thus becomes a purely statistical criterion of no relevance whatsoever when it comes to describing and explaining biological mechanisms in analytical terms. For this reason, it is absurd to maintain—as one can sometimes hear stated—that the "abnormal" is no legitimate source of valid information about the "normal." The example of "deformity as cue to the understanding of form" can well serve as an antidote to such gratuitous assertions.

However, instead of dwelling on the general utility of the lessons of such "experiments of nature" recorded in clinical experience, I shall rather present two specific examples from my own research to illustrate how clinical observations can guide laboratory explorations to the solution of basic biological problems.

The first example links up directly with the topic of deformities. It deals with the problem of the functional sufficiency of those body structures which have mechanical tasks to perform—the bones with their various columns and girders to support weight, exert leverage, and brace soft tissues against collapse; the tendons, which as ropes are to transmit the pull of muscles to the bony levers; and the fibrous connective tissue in general, which is to tie and hold the other tissues together, wrap them in protective sheaths and give the proper combination of firmness and mobility. To serve these mechanical functions, the tissues must satisfy in their construction the most exacting demands of sound mechanical engineering, or else they would tear and break and crumble under the strains and stresses to which they are constantly exposed. And, actually, the more one studies the architecture of the hard tissues and the texture of the soft ones, the more one becomes impressed by their precise fit for the mechanical task at hand, as if they embodied a cunning knowledge of the principles of structural design—a fact clearly recognized already by Galileo. As in bridges, airplanes, or cranes, the solid elements of these tissues are so arranged and jointed that the resulting patterns give maximum resistance to the disruptive forces of tension and pressure with a minimum of bulk.

To build such an efficient structure, it is sufficient to place rigid supports and braces in the directions in which the prevailing stresses are greatest; one need not fill the intervening spaces with material since this would add only bulk but not strength to the structure. The arrangement of parts thus is made to correspond to the "stress pattern." The latter, in turn, is determined by the particular shape and attachment of the structure and by the distribution of the external forces acting upon it, such as load or pull or shear. The architecture of the inner, spongy portion of the long bones is a faithful embodiment of this principle: the fine trabecles of their delicate tracery describe two systems of intersecting lines which coincide rather closely with the trajectories of maximum tension and pressure to which the bone is ordinarily subjected (4).

Now, to determine stress patterns, an engineer can build scale models and test them directly. But how can the organism in its developmental building phase anticipate stress patterns that will not appear until much

137

later, when functional use comes actually into operation? How can an embryo "know" the way the body's weight will bear down on the limbs in that postnatal future when he will have learned to walk?

The answer is, of course, that much of this anticipation really rests on past evolutionary experience; for, in the past, only those animals whose genetic blueprints had turned them out fit to contend with the environmental stresses of free life could have propagated and perpetuated that successful pattern; misfits were automatically excluded. But, as we said earlier, no more than the gross lines of development could have been rigorously fixed in this manner, while flexibility had to be left to each individual to adjust itself to the detailed constellations of unpredictably fluctuating environments, including stresses. For instance, though coming from identical genetic backgrounds, bones bent by the nutritional deficiency of rickets must develop a quite different pattern of internal reinforcements if total collapse is to be averted than will their straight counterparts in the adequately fed individual. Clinical experience has shown that this indeed happens and thereby has revealed the fundamental fact that the grossly adequate genetic predesign of bone structure is elaborated in its finer detailed features by the stresses of actual functional use. Active functional adaptation to the job at hand has thus been established as a reality (5).

Much more dramatic, however, has been the demonstration—again in clinical experience—that this faculty is not confined to the formative years of childhood but extends throughout life. This lesson came from cases of ankylosis, "experiments of nature" in which a diseased joint between two bones is gradually ossified so that the erstwhile separate bony segments become rigidly united, often at an angle. For instance, thigh bone, kneecap, and shin may merge into a single angular piece. Evidently the stress pattern in such a stiffened leg carrying body weight is markedly different from what it was before, when the two parts were separate and mobile. And, actually, in the course of time, the whole pattern of trabecles in the affected portion changes over to conform to the new lines of tension and pressure. It was thus firmly proven that bone can somehow remodel itself to meet, within limits, new functional demands, and that mechanical stress is instrumental in the transformation. But just how this is achieved remained unknown.

It was from this open question that I took my departure in starting, in 1927, a series of experiments intended to reveal the mode of action by which mechanical stresses can mould tissue architecture in general. For guiding clues, I turned again to clinical experience: a simpler instance of adaptation was needed than that of bone. Connective tissue presented itself as a promising candidate, particularly in the form of tendon. Tendon is built like rope. A rope is a bundle of fibers which have great tensile strength in the direction of their axes, but do not resist being teased apart laterally. Tendon is similarly composed of numerous tough parallel collagen fibers oriented in the linear direction of traction from muscle to skeleton, with the formative cells, which are interspersed between the fibers, equally aligned. The way in which this useful orientation comes about in first development was unknown. But it was known that when a tendon had been severed accidentally or experimentally in later life, it healed, and that the reunited structure would again assume the same linear continuity of texture that it had before, all the way across the former gap. Ostensibly, direct functional adaptation was again at play.

Tendon regeneration thus came to be of crucial interest. It occurs in the following series of steps. Owing to muscle pull, the severed ends snap apart. A blood clot fills the gap. Cells from the surroundings invade it and lay down a firm feltwork of extracellular fibers of random orientation, which acts as a temporary link between the stumps and thus restores their mechanical continuity. The linear traction transmitted through this filler from stump to stump then gradually straightens the random orientations of its cells and fibers into parallel courses in the direction of the common pull, aligning and integrating them with the old stumps.

Although the mechanism of this remodeling was not much better understood than that of bone, here was a simple case more suitable for direct analysis. For, since essentially only three items were involved—a blood clot, cells enclosed in it, and tension—it seemed possible to transfer the testing ground from the infinitely complex organism to the much simpler and controllable conditions offered by the technique of tissue culture, which then was still relatively new. In ordinary tissue culture, a bit of tissue, as a source of cells, is planted into a supporting and nutrient clot of blood plasma. From the explanted fragment, cells move out freely into the clot, spreading equally in all directions. Because of their lack of over-all direction they seemed to offer a unique opportunity for a test of whether or not tensions could really orient cells. And, indeed, when

139

cultures were subjected to tensions in defined directions, the streams of outwandering cells were later found to be aligned, like schools of fish, along the lines of stress. The first point was thus satisfactorily demonstrated: tensional stresses actually did have a patterning effect on cell orientation and migration, and thereby on tissue structure. Moreover, having been duplicated in this much simpler setting, the effect could now be analyzed more penetratingly. Without recounting the steps of this analysis (6), the outcome has been as follows.

Blood plasma, like many body colloids, contains rod-shaped or thread-like macromolecules—in this case, fibrin—suspended in liquid serum. When such rodlets make contact with each other, they tend to stick. They thus combine to form a loose network. If their approach to one another has been at random, the resulting spongy framework is quite irregular. But when such a net is then stretched, the chains of molecules are deflected in the direction of stretch, the meshes of the net assuming correspondingly oriented elongation. The same effect is obtained when a population of freely mobile molecular threads is forced into a common orientation before they have become joined; in that event, they aggregate in parallel order right from the start. In either case, the result is a bundling of the parallel units into filaments or fibers running in the direction of the external force.

Now, most tissue cells require some solid support in order to be able to move; very few cell types are equipped to swim. The only firm structures pervading the liquid substance of a plasma clot to which the cells can cling are the nets of fibrin fibers. They act like causeways through swamps. If they criss-cross everyway, the cells on them can stray at random. But, if the fibers are parallel, they provide the cells with pathways oriented in a common direction. Since tension has precisely this effect of creating straight fibrous pathways along the lines of stress, it is readily understood why cells assume orientations conforming to the prevailing stress pattern. The primary step consists of the stress pattern engraving itself in the structure of the intercellular matrix which the cells inhabit; secondarily, then, the cells accentuate this structural pattern by retracing its lines.

In conclusion, the course which plain observations on tendon regeneration had pointed has yielded substantial insight into a general formative mechanism. Besides, it has greatly elucidated the specific object from which it had started, as we now understand more clearly why and how a tendon regenerate acquires the remarkably adapted functional structure that it does. Moreover, these studies were destined to repay their spiritual debt to practical medicine even more handsomely when the same lessons proved applicable to the tactics of peripheral nerve repair. A severed nerve fiber can regrow from its central stump by thrusting its free tip forth ever further into its peripheral surroundings. In their advance, these free tips behave much like the mobile ends of cells of the sort we just described; an observation which prompted Harrison, in his classical studies, to postulate similar mechanisms of guidance for both. Accordingly, it was to be expected that it would be feasible to direct the growth of nerve fibers by the same devices that had permitted us to control the orientation of other cells. Experiments in tissue culture confirmed this expectation. Then, when World War II made the search for improved techniques for the restoration of severed nerves an urgent task, it took only some appropriate adaptations to translate the knowledge of how to control nerve growth into practical procedures of nerve repair (7).

Of the two stumps of a severed nerve, only the proximal one, which is still connected with the nerve centers, retains its complement of live nerve fibers. The distal part, connected with muscle or skin, succumbs to a fatty transformation, but it can readily be repopulated by live nerve sprouts growing forth from the proximal stump, provided these sprouts can manage to span the gap between the cut ends in sufficient numbers. This is often where clinical trouble arises; for the gap tends to be filled quickly with a tough connective tissue scar whose messy tangle of fibers diverts and arrests most of the young nerve fiber branches before they reach the portal of entry to the peripheral stump. A simple manipulation, however, exploiting the lessons of the tissue culture experiments, can turn the scar, which ordinarily would be a barrier and handicap, into a smooth pathway for straight and unimpeded transit from one stump to another. The details need not concern us here. The crucial part is again the blood clot that settles early in the gap between the cut ends. Most any procedure that will prevent this clot from becoming adherent to any of its surroundings except at the two stumps is apt to succeed, for it will cause the tensions, which are engendered by nerve pull as well as by the shrinkage of the clot, to be confined strictly to the linear direction along the connecting line between the stumps—much as in the case of tendon regeneration, which served as a model. As a result, the fibrin of the clot is forced into a corresponding orientation and becomes a parallel pathway system which leads straight from the source of the young nerve sprouts over to the other stump, which is to receive them. This enables them to traverse the usually hazardous scar zone rapidly and in perfect alignment, conducive to good functional recovery.

It was in the course of these experiments that a second important consequence of tensional orientation of fibers was unexpectedly discovered. It was noted that bundles of oriented fibers, presumably because of their larger girth, resist resorption by enzyme action much better than do the disoriented thinner cross links. As the latter are dissolved, the former become more and more prominent, sharpening the correspondence between stress pattern and tissue architecture. This may have a direct bearing on the mechanism of functional adaptation in bone. Bone, it will be recalled, is continuously in the process of both deposition and resorption by its cells. It is conceivable, therefore, that its functional pattern comes about not because bone substance is laid down solely along the lines of stress, but because it is progressively eroded in the stress-free sectors, so that only those parts that are under stress are spared and remain standing.

The basic theme of this chapter on cell and nerve orientation has been the fact that cells follow guide structures and that guide structures in turn can often be created in predetermined directions by deliberate action. It would be interesting to relate how this realization has further led to a stepwise clarification of many features of form in organisms. The fact that, in the quoted experiments, tension had been applied directly as external force, proved to be rather incidental; for, although it is relevant to the case of functional adaptation of tissues to extraneous stress, which was our point of departure, this has turned out to be but a special case of a much broader principle. In the first place, stresses often arise right within the tissues, for instance, as the result of local growth processes and of shearing actions among parts, and these internal stresses are in their patterning effects of course just as potent as are those imposed from the outside. But there are other agents quite aside from tensions which also can alter the fibrous matrix in which the cells reside and, hence, affect the architecture of the tissues. Tension has thus been relegated to a more modest role in the workshop of morphogenesis. The more closely I studied the subtle and complex interactions between the cells and their matrix—cells producing matrix; matrix assuming structure; matrix structure altering form and activity of cells; altered cells modifying matrix; this again rebounding on the cells; and so forth—the more I came to realize the utter inadequacy of any crudely mechanical model of cell behavior.

This does not question the utility of our basic experiment—a grossly mechanical one—which after all has served well not only in explaining functional adaptation to mechanical stress, but in opening new experimental approaches to the more complex and subtler types of interactions. A simple experiment, employing a simple tool to study a simple phenomenon, as in our example, has immense value; pragmatically, as a model, and intellectually, as satisfying our craving for clear and simple conclusions. And, as I said in the introduction, experimental analysis can succeed in disentangling complex phenomena only by virtue of the simplifying technique by which a single component of the complex is picked out for separate investigation, ignoring for the time all the rest of the complex from which the spotlight has been withdrawn. But let us not be deceived by this methodical expedient of blinders into proclaiming any one of the singled-out threads as a fair and representative portrait of the whole fabric. And, following this precept, it would be utterly fallacious to try to generalize our demonstration of the role of mechanics in the shaping of the body into a "mechanical" theory of development; just as it is unwarranted and meaningless to expand the important observations on electric potentials in organsims into a purely "electric" theory, or the measurements of metabolic phenomena into a purely "metabolic" theory. As living systems are enormously complex, drawing upon a most diverse array of mechanisms, their operations cannot be explained solely in terms of any one of the limited aspects according to which we have compartmentalized physical nature.

This had to be stated here explicitly lest the mechanical point of view, which dominated the interpretation of my first example, be unduly expanded, or the illusion be created that surgical success in tendon or nerve repair may be regarded as chiefly a matter of crude mechanics. And, just to balance the score, I have chosen as my second example one from the opposite end of the scale of living complexity, dealing with phenomena of such minute subtlety that they have refused thus far to submit to the strait-jacket of known simple categories and concepts, mechanical or electrical or chemical or others, to which the analytic mind would prefer to reduce them.

The particular phenomena concerned have first been noted, as I said before, in clinical experience. They forced themselves on my attention as I kept reflecting about the ways in which an organism succeeds in maintaining some measure of orderliness in the repair of damaged tissues. Surgeons have long been aware of the fact that in the healing of deep wounds, involving several tissues of different kinds, each tissue tends to rejoin its own kind, shunning nonmatching types. However vague and unanalyzed this notion of a like-to-like reunion was at the time, unmistakable signs of the operation of such a principle could be recognized in a great many observations on growth, embryonic development, regeneration and transplantation (8). And during my early experiments on limb transplantation in amphibians, I came to realize, and stated so (9), that the rule of tissues fusing according to their identities, acknowledged for human healing processes, was just as valid for animals. In a review article slightly later, I referred to this principle as tissue "affinity," which term has retained currency. The origin and role of such affinities in early embryonic development has since been given some pioneering study (10); but the fact that they continue to operate in the establishment and maintenance of the type-specific segregation of tissues has attracted little attention. Yet, since my first dim realization of the significance of tissue affinities as tools of organismic order, I have never been quite able to escape the spell and fascination of the problem. And, after accumulating ever more concurring evidence, I finally embarked with some of my collaborators on a more systematic exploration of this virgin territory.

First, the surgical results were reproduced in the much simpler and experimentally manageable amphibian larva, in which layers from all kinds of tissues can be transplanted into a superficial wound, so that the healing skin will have to face them (11). Invariably, when skin met skin, the edges coalesced and came to rest; continuity and tissue uniformity were restored. When skin met tissues with which it ordinarily had neighborly relations, for instance, cornea of the eye or lining of the oral cavity, it likewise accepted them and acquiesced in a common border. Yet, when the advancing skin sheet met a graft composed of rather alien tissue, such as lung or gall bladder or esophagus, it ignored their presence and kept right on moving, either over or under them, and did not stop until eventually it happened to link up with skin that had advanced equally relentlessly from the other side of the graft bed. This seemed to indicate quite clearly that cells of a given kind can recognize the kinds of cells they encounter and can respond discriminately depending on whether or not they are akin. Having corroborated the empirical findings of surgeons, these results still did not add much to our understanding of how cells effect selective recombinations; especially whether one is actually dealing with subtle discriminative properties of individual cells, or rather with cruder features of mass behavior of large tissue sheets, such as different modes and rates of movement and of growth.

In this sense, another series of experiments, carried out concurrently, proved far more conclusive (12). It was set up to test the fate of single tissue cells set adrift in the blood stream of an embryo. Since, in order to be traceable, the sample cell had to carry an indelible marker, the choice fell on the precursors of pigment cells which would later stand out by their black color. Thus, using as testing grounds embryos of colorless breeds of chicks and injecting into one of their veins a suspension of prospective pigment cells from a dark breed as test cells, any future outcroppings of the latter could readily be identified. The results were quite unequivocal: In a sizeable fraction of cases, the injected white birds actually developed black spots composed of descendants of injected cells. The most note-worthy fact, however, was that such colonies were found exclusively in locations where pigment cells would normally reside in the donor race; not a single cell was ever seen to have lodged in a strange site, where it would not belong. In short, even though these test cells had been dis-seminated and delivered by a wholly atypical and irregular route—the blood stream—they had managed to arrive at their correct destinations. Since the possibility that they may have been guided to those places by attractive forces acting over distances can be safely ruled out, one must conclude that the injected cells had pervaded the tissue ubiquitously, but that when a roaming cell happened upon a tissue environment matching its normal habitat, it settled there and colonized the site; which, as one notes, presupposes that cells possess subtle mechanisms by which to recognize their home bases.

In passing, it is worth mentioning, as a sign of the inseparability of biological and medical progress, that this experiment is the prototype of recently—and presumably independently—developed measures to counter

145

radiation damage in which the blood-forming centers have been destroyed. It has been found (13, 14) that the injection of bone marrow, which is one of the main sources of blood regeneration, from a healthy into an injured animal may lead to long-lasting recovery. This means, of course, that the radiation-depleted production sites of blood cells have become reseeded by viable stem cells contained in the injected suspension, which in turn demonstrates rather convincingly the ability of a given tissue environment to fish out and incorporate quite selectively the corresponding cell types from the blood stream passing in review.

Not so very long ago, biologists might have been satisfied in ascribing such cell behavior to some sort of "homing instinct" and let it go at that. The analytic spirit of modern science, however, aims at deeper penetration and understanding. And the way in which this is being attempted will now be briefly sketched.

Even in the experiments just described, not all injected cells landed in the embryo, where they would have been either incorporated in tissues of matching specificity or else presumably resorbed. Some of them escaped into the yolk sac, where they could find no matching building site. Nevertheless, there they went ahead and multiplied and differentiated into a wide variety of cell types—nerve, muscle, skin, gut, kidney, and so forth (15). But the combination and grouping of their components were by no means as random-scrambled as the initial cell suspensions had been. On the contrary, they formed compact well-organized complexes in rather typical mutual relations. Cells of identical character were mostly solidly grouped together. At first sight, this result could be explained by either of two assumptions: either a more mature cell of an assembly had imposed on its neighbors a like course of differentiation, or, if most cells had been beyond the stage at which they could still be redirected, that they had actively sorted themselves out according to their kinds. The former assumption could be discounted on various grounds. The latter alternative thus gained convincingness; it obviously fell in line with the surgical and experimental results. But this still did not tell anything about the mechanism involved.

Then, one major step forward came with the demonstration that cells in tissue culture are equally selective in forming associations. For instance, if one prepares suspensions of single cells by dissociating kidney and cartilage, mixes both thoroughly and then cultures the mixture in an appropriate nutrient medium, one does not end up with a conglomerate of scrambled kidney and cartilage cells, but rather with large blocks of pure kidney tissue clearly delineated against large blocks of cartilage (16). Even in the neutral territory of tissue culture, therefore, cells remain choosy in their associations, joining their own likes while shunning others —order emerging from disorder outside the body under conditions which permitted continuous unobstructed inspection.

This suggested the next step of analysis as a matter of course. It seemed that inconclusive speculation could be replaced by just that direct and continuous inspection. And so we (with A. C. Taylor and Albert Bock) resorted to taking time-lapse motion pictures of cell encounters under the phase-contrast microscope. The tissue culture chamber was turned into an arena in which single cells in pairs of either like or unlike character were made to confront each other and were photographed during their encounters. Time lapse had to be used because cell movements are too sluggish to be conspicuous at normal cinematographic speeds; phase-contrast optics brought out details of cell contour and structure that would be scarcely perceptible in ordinary light. Cell types used in these tests were epithelia from liver, kidney, lung, skin, and eye; mostly from older embryos of chicks, mice, and rats, but some also from postnatal animals, either freshly prepared or after prolonged cultivation, including human cell strains. The cells were isolated from their tissue compounds by enzymatic (trypsin; pancreatin) treatment followed by washing. As in the earlier experiments, this change of existence from communal to solitary life did not abolish the specific differences among the cells of different tissue origins. Their mutual behavior, as they met, gave proof of this, though not immediately. This is how they behaved (17).

Free single cells move around by sending broad mobile tongues of protoplasm forth along the glass surface to which they cling; now in one direction, then in another direction, like feelers. These movements are quite random. There was no evidence whatsoever in uncrowded cultures that any two cells, whether of the same or of different kinds, exerted attractions or repulsions on each other so long as they were not in direct touch. Contact came about only by chance collisions, the probability of this occurrence, of course, being higher in denser populations. Even after making contact with each other, cells show at first no signs of mutual discrimination. Only after having been in touch for a while do they

147

"recognize" each other and then react accordingly. That is, if they are of one kind, they pull together more closely and remain associated; if they are of nonmatching kinds, however, they break off their mutual contact, pull apart, and continue to roam until they hit other cells, repeating the performance. In this manner, by trial and error, the mixed population sorts itself out into large islands each consisting purely of cells of a single kind. Tissue specificity even overrides species specificity, as liver cells of a mouse will link up smoothly with liver cells of a chick, while liver cells and kidney cells even of the same animal will reject each other (18). Perhaps more refined studies will disclose systematic gradations of strangeness and, conversely, of tolerance among different cell types in accordance with their developmental relations, physiological interdependence, and age. We do know already that satellite types of cells, such as the phagocytic scavengers (macrophages) that keep the lung surface clean, tend to hold themselves within the confines of lung cells even when explanted in tissue culture. But we do not know whether such commensalism is entirely a matter of cellular constitution or whether it can be modified to some extent by habitation.

All these and numerous other questions raised by the discriminatory behavior of tissue cells remain for the future to decide. For instance, what enables a cell to tell its own kind from all others? Vaguely, one might suspect the same sort of chemical sensitivity that enables a parasitic cell to recognize its host, or an olfactory cell to recognize an odor, or an egg to reject foreign sperm. At one time, I supposed the mechanism by which like cells become joined to consist of sterically interlocking surface compounds, in the manner of antigen-antibody complex formation in immune reactions (8, 19). But this view seems much less tenable now that we have watched the cells in action and seen to our surprise that even like cells are not firmly cemented together, but climb rather freely about one another. And how do strange pairs part company? By a direct reaction of their sensitive surfaces, or by a deeper "reflex" response involving the whole cell? And how immutable is this reaction? Can it be dulled or sharpened, the way one can diminish or step up immune responses? And, if so, by what means? And might such studies not give away some clues about the nature of the whole mechanism? Of even more profound medical concern, to what extent is the malignant faculty of cancer cells to metastasize, that is, to emigrate from their originating sites and lodge at inappropriate locations, due to the fact that they have become truly "alienated" from their mother tissue and have lost in varying degrees their sense of discrimination (20)?

It would be idle to keep on listing here question upon question to which there is as yet no answer. But there is comfort in the knowledge that we now possess a practical technique by which the missing answers may be sought. As I hope to have shown, this technique can rightly be regarded as a direct offspring of observations made in surgery; and, if it keeps its promise to illuminate the cancer problem from the novel aspect just referred to, it will have more than repaid its debt.

So much for the examples. Most anyone in biological research could amplify them from his own store of experience. But the lesson would remain the same, and it is this. The study of life processes is, just as life itself, an unbroken continuum. One may enter it from the lowest end of the scale of complexity, for instance, microorganisms and single cells, or from the highest end, at which we find ourselves, or at any intermediate point. But, once inside, one must be able to take excursions, conceptually and factually, in any direction without encountering barriers to comprehension and logical consistency. Life science is a single fabric of interconnected facts and concepts in which, as in all dynamic networks, the structure and strength of every portion depend significantly on the conditions of all others. Thus, even additions and alterations in a limited sector will of necessity rebound on the whole system, and light shed on any part will penetrate and illuminate the rest. Is it surprising, then, to find that in the past illuminating ideas and discoveries have spread over-all enlightenment on life processes no matter whether the original flash appeared in a clinical observation on man or in a laboratory experiment on an amphibian embryo? Or whether the first data and conclusions came from "experiments of nature" or from experiments designed deliberately?

To ready eyes and minds to the spotting and accepting of sound evidence, from whatever quarters it may come, is science's mission; there is no place in it for the parochial point of view. Therefore, if biological investigations are indispensable to the advancement of medicine, effects in the reverse direction are equally true and potent. Indeed, the meaning of setting the two apart, as if they were opposites or even separable, escapes me. Clinical investigation and biological research are integral parts of the same endeavor, as both contribute jointly to the understanding of life.

149

Referring to the special case placed here in focus, the study of deformities has had a share in shaping our concepts of organic form just as the direct exploration of formative processes has helped us, reciprocally, to understand the origin and nature of deformities. The science of life is one, and to promote it we must resolutely counter the ever-mounting tendency to fragment it, by even stronger efforts to hold the fragments together under a common perspective as unified as life itself, with which it deals (21).

Pathology and developmental biology must be reintegrated so that our understanding of the "abnormal" will become but an extension of our insight into the "normal," while, *pari passu*, the study of the "abnormal" will contribute to the deepening of that very insight. Their common problems should provide foci for common orientation so that, as they advance in joint directions, their efforts may supplement and reinforce each other to mutual benefit. If this precept can be made convincing on the strength of examples such as I have presented, and, if it can be made to pervade teaching and thinking in both biology and medicine, then the opportunity accorded me to state the case may turn out to have been more auspicious than if it had been used for a sheer recital of historical facts and technical data. All the more do I appreciate the honor of having been given this opportunity.

REFERENCES

1. C. H. WADDINGTON. Principles of embryology. London: Allen & Unwin, 1956.
2. P. WEISS. Principles of development. New York: Henry Holt & Co., 1939.
3. E. ZWILLING. *In:* Analysis of development, B. H. WILLIER, P. WEISS, and V. HAMBURGER (eds.). Philadelphia: W. B. Saunders Co., 1955.
4. F. G. EVANS. Stress and strain in bones. Springfield, Ill.: Charles C Thomas, 1957.
5. P. WEISS. *In:* Adaptation, J. ROMANO (ed.), p. 1. Ithaca, N.Y.: Cornell University Press, 1949.
6. ———. *In:* Chemistry and physiology of growth, A. K. PARPART (ed.), p. 135. Princeton, N.J.: Princeton University Press, 1949.
7. ———. J. Neurosurg., 1:400, 1944.
8. ———. Yale J. Biol. & Med., 19:235, 1947.
9. ———. Wilhelm Roux' Arch. Entwickl.-Mech. Org., 99:168, 1923.
10. J. HOLTFRETER. Arch. exp. Zellforsch., 23:169, 1939.
11. J. J. CHIAKULAS. J. Exper. Zool., 121:383, 1952.
12. P. WEISS and G. ANDRES. J. Exper. Zool., 121:449, 1952.

13. C. E. Ford, J. L. Hamerton, D. W. H. Barnes, and J. F. Loutit. Nature, 177:452, 1956.
14. P. Urso and C. C. Congdon. Blood, 12:251, 1957.
15. G. Andres. J. Exper. Zool., 122:507, 1953.
16. A. Moscona. Proc. Soc. Exper. Biol. & Med., 92:410, 1956.
17. P. Weiss. Internat. Rev. Cytol., 7:391, 1958.
18. A. Moscona. Proc. Nat. Acad. Sc., 43:184, 1957.
19. P. Weiss. Growth, 5:163, 1941.
20. ———. Proc. Nat. Cancer Conf., 1:50, 1949.
21. ———. J. Mt. Sinai Hosp., 19:716, 1953.

The next article is even more explicit in demonstrating that there is no abrupt discontinuity between the "normal" and "pathological," but that there is a scale of continuous intergradations which leads from insight into the behavior of cells and cell communities to the potential understanding of those extreme aberrations that threaten the survival of the organism—malignant tumors. It points to the cell-biological rationale for a two-directional attack on the cancer problem—both forward from the early phase of tumorigenesis and backwards from the lethal metastatic state to simple neoplasia.

Reprinted from Proceedings Fifth Canadian Cancer Conference. Copyright 1963
by Academic Press

Cell Interactions[1,2]

PAUL WEISS

Introduction

An organism is a system composed of cells and intercellular constituents. Each cell is an organized community of components of various lower orders of magnitudes, from structured cell organelles down to the large and small molecules, solidly arrayed or in solution, all of which in turn are resolvable in last analysis to a selection of the ninety-odd elements of the periodic table in various combinations and interactions. The analytical and resolutionist tendency of our age of science is leading more and more to preoccupation with the lower-order components in this hierarchy of systems, deliberately abstracting from the fact that in so doing one takes the elements out of their context, hence must not expect to be able to reconstruct or even predict from the acquaintance with the isolated pieces the behavior of their assemblies in the higher system. Therefore, lest the basic object of biology, which after all is the *living* organism, or the living cell, be lost sight of, it is important to counterbalance the reductionist's concern about the elements by consideration of their behavior in the integral organic system of which they form parts. Even the most complete knowledge about the elements in isolation need not reveal the rules of coordination and regulation that guide and hold the elemental processes together in the orderly group performance of the organized community (45). I therefore welcome this occasion, like similar past ones (46, 47), to place into full view the complex features of the organized behavior of cells and cell groups.

A normal organism remains viable as long as its constituent cells live in mutual harmony with one another and with their environment. The totality of these integral relations is what we usually refer to as "organization." A cell line emancipating itself from this ordered framework incurs a risk, for ordinarily it will not be able to persist in disharmonious relations with its surroundings. Yet, if in the course of its emancipation, it has coincidentally acquired properties endowing it with an extraordinary range of tolerance and adaptability it will become established; and even then, as in the case of benign tumors, will the survival of the rest of the organism remain unchallenged unless the alienated group has in addition gained properties harmful to the living con-

---

[1] The lecture on which this article is based was illustrated extensively by time-lapse motion pictures of the cellular phenomena described in the text.

[2] The original work referred to in this paper has been aided in part by grants from the American Cancer Society and the National Cancer Institute (National Institutes of Health of the United States Public Health Service).

ditions of the rest by competition or direct interference. In biological perspective, therefore, carcinogenesis appears as a stepwise process to be measured along a sliding scale of degrees of harmony and disharmony among cells and between cells and their immediate environments. The understanding of the nature and origin of pathological disharmonies, therefore, hinges on systematic knowledge about the nature of the working relations between a cell and its microenvironment, which is the topic of "Interactions" assigned to me.

In order to avoid a common semantic trap, let me point out that to designate anything in cell life as "action," rather than "interaction," is really introducing a primitive sort of vitalism by the rear door. When we focus on a gene, or a chromosome, a cell nucleus, a cell, an organism, or a species, we set off a particular fragment of the universe that is of interest to us from the rest of the continuum of universe, which then is called the "environment." This amounts to an abstraction, for in reality they remain always connected. Nothing can change within that chosen boundary unless there are correlated changes outside of it. Only the limitations of our powers of observation and detection may give us the illusion that the "within" acts independently from the "without"; especially if we confine our consideration of a process to a limited time segment that we have arbitrarily dissected from the uninterrupted time continuum of processes in organisms that goes clear back to when life started. For then, the illusion of spontaneous "action" merely reflects the fact that we have not traced the particular process back far enough to recognize its "interactive" source.

Accordingly, even though in everyday parlance it may be passable and indeed unavoidable to speak of genes or hormones "doing" this or that, the scientifically correct picture to bear in mind is the one diagrammed in Fig. 1. It represents the organism with its environment as a system of concentric and interacting shells, each outer one being "environment" for the next inner one (37). Since every shell serves as potential transmitter, converter, and modifier of effects between the shells to either side, which it divides, the network of conceivable interactions to be identified in such a system (indicated in Fig. 1 by arrows) becomes, indeed, most complicated—quite in contrast to the mental pictures of extreme oversimplification evoked by our conventional shorthand terminology, which places "actors," as it were, into each shell.

Failure to take cognizance of this intricacy of interactive relations has encouraged the uncritical acceptance of all sorts of unrealistic and often purely verbal shortcuts to "explanations" of cellular behavior and thus has obscured the need of finding out first more penetratingly and precisely just what the real facts are that were to be explained. It is hardly my task here to list the crude mechanical or electric models for cell shape, cell locomotion, cell surface interaction, etc., that have been put forward as "explanations" in the past, including various abstract notions of cell "tropisms," blissfully unmindful of such facts as the impenetrability of bodies or the thermal agitation in liquids—all of them valid, if halting, steps in the groping for understanding in the face of so much that is still unknown. But I do intend to document that the era of acquiescing in that sort of thing has passed and that it has become not only essential, but quite feasible, to take a closer look at the true complexity and subtlety of conditions of cell behavior and cell interactions with each other and their environments. A major lesson derived from such studies is that cellular interactions are

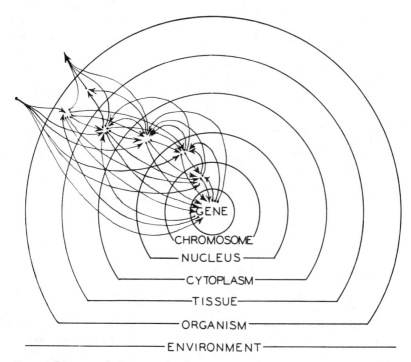

Fig. 1. Diagram of the network of relations and interactions in the hierarchy of subsystems within an organism.

not only complex, but engage mechanisms of the most diverse kinds—electric, mechanical, enzymatic, some operating through solid macromolecular arrays, others through short-range or long-range diffusions, etc.—so that one may give up once and for all the wasting of effort on the illusory search for any single monopolistic master agent. In fact, the complexity is so great that even in trying to portray it as in the following examples, one still must indulge in a considerable measure of oversimplification.

Since the purpose of this exercise is the illustration of a principle, rather than of any specialized subject, the choice of illustrative examples could be made arbitrarily. For reasons that will be self-evident, I have chosen them largely from research that has been carried out in my own laboratory, as much of our work is particularly pertinent in the present context. Realizing that the problem of cellular interactions cannot be dealt with practically in that generality, we have tried to break it down for purposes of investigation into a number of tangible components. There are three major experimental variables: (1) the *cell* at the time when it is tested; meaning the cell type at the stage of differentiation attained during its previous ontogenetic history;[3] (2) the *substratum* to which the cell is applied; for most cell types of a higher organism require an interface, i.e., a phase boundary between two immiscible media, for support;

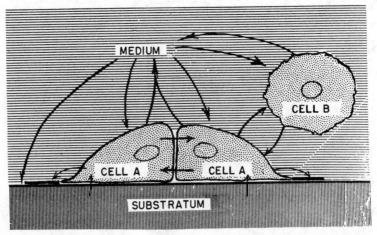

Fig. 2. Diagram of the major types of interactions between a cell and its environment.

and (3) the *ambient medium* bathing the free portion of the surface of the cell with all kinds of molecules in solution. For brief, we shall refer to these three variables as (1) the cell type, (2) the substratum, and (3) the medium. The network of interrelations between them is symbolized in Fig. 2 by arrows. No valid statements can ever be made for any one component of this triple system except in reference to the other two. In other words, in singling out either the cell or the substratum or the medium for separate discussion, it is tacitly implied that the other two are likewise involved, but kept relatively invariant.

The technique of tissue culture is most suitable for the separate study of these three variables. The substratum to which the cells are to attach themselves can be chosen at will, and so can the liquid medium. As for the cells them-

---

[3] We shall not deal here with the differentiative process as such, but will accept the cell of a given organ in the state in which we find it when and as we test it. [Regarding differentiation, see (39).]

selves, many kinds can be separated from the compounded tissues and tested as single individuals. Rous and Jones in 1917 were the first to liberate cells of higher animals from their tissue enmeshment by the use of trypsin, and this technique has recently been rediscovered and exploited most successfully by Moscona (17), but other ways of separation, either by physicochemical agents (13) or mechanical action (48) had also been practiced. The test cells used in the experiments to be described below have been obtained as single-cell suspensions by dissociating embryonic organs or cultured tissues by enzymatic (trypsin, pancreatin) or chelating (Versene) agents.

The shape assumed by isolated single cells in suspension is essentially spherical, if we confine ourselves to the tissue types of higher animals and disregard habitually free single cells (erythrocytes; spermatozoa). Even the freely floating cell isolated from vertebrate tissues, however, does not really present the smooth surface of an ideal sphere, but shows various degrees of bubbling by cytoplasmic herniations which incessantly bulge forth and recede again through weaker spots of the mechanically inhomogeneous cell membrane. Only statistically can this shape be defined as spherical. The phenomenon of bubbling is indicative of the fact that the cell surface varies locally in its dynamic state, patches of greater tensile strength alternating with weaker ones, this mosaiclike distribution fluctuating rather than being structurally fixed. Contractile surface forces in the more rigid parts drive the cell content out in transitory protuberances in the more yielding sectors (13, 43). There are indications that the contractile force is generated by the metabolic energy of the cell and sweeps over the cell surface in the form of waves of rhythmic alternations between states of contraction and relaxation (13, 47). In other words, cellular metabolism itself furnishes the energy that can enlarge the cell surface beyond the minimum size characteristic of a smooth static sphere.

Contrary to free blood cells and ascites cells, most isolated tissue cells do not thrive in suspension, but require contact with an interface referred to as the substratum. Both in suspension and along an interface, the power of motility resides primarily in the metabolic machinery of the cell. However, whether it results in the random bubbling of the surface, as in suspension, or in the roaming of the whole cell about dead center, as in a nondirectional interface, or in actual directive locomotion and displacement, depends on the nature of the conditions facing the cell surface. Let us consider first the interaction between a free cell and a substratum offered to it for attachment.

The Substratum

COMPOSITION

The first perceptible reaction of a floating cell to contact with a solid substratum is that of attachment. Despite attempts to reduce this reaction to terms of simple stickiness as in adhesive inorganic systems, our results thus far cannot support any such simple explanation. An extensive series of experiments to determine the time it takes for cells of a given type to attach to various surfaces of different composition, leaving the medium and all other circumstances equal, has shown a considerable range of characteristic attachment times for different substrata, but without any clear-cut recognizable relation to any graded scale of known physicochemical properties of those substrata (24). Figure 3 gives an example. It shows the proportion of cells that have settled firmly from suspension on a variety of sample surfaces at the indicated sampling times, ranged in the declining order of promptness of attachment. But if we then rate the respective substrata according to their hydrophilic or hydrophobic properties,

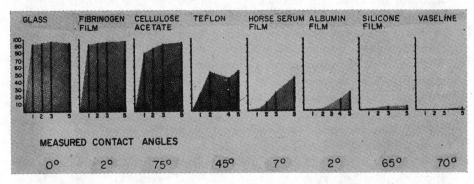

FIG. 3. Rates of attachment of a single cell type on eight different substrata. The ordinates give the percentages of cells which have become firmly attached after the intervals given in hours on the abscissa. (From Taylor (25).)

as expressed by the low or high contact angle of the meniscus of an aqueous medium, we note that the facility of attachment of a cell seems totally unrelated to the affinity of the substratum for either aqueous or lipid componens in the cell surface.

The role of divalent ions, particularly calcium, which often has been demonstrated as instrumental in the binding of cells to other surfaces (7), is likewise not so simple as sometimes envisaged (30) because under the conditions of our experiments it manifests itself exclusively in the presence of serum in the medium whereas in protein-free salt solutions the presence or absence of calcium and magnesium does not seem to affect the rate of attachment (24).

The matter is further complicated by the finding that the mode and rate of cellular activities after attachment are not automatic sequelae of the attachment process, but are governed by other sets of factors. Some cells upon attachment retain their spherical shape and continue to bubble for some time, while others rather promptly begin to spread out along the interface. This spreading is an active process, again sustained ostensibly by expenditure of metabolic energy, rather than being a mere passive expansion by interfacial creep, as I had supposed in earlier days (34). In spreading, the bubbling activity of the formerly near-spherical cell becomes confined to the free edge along which the cell and the substratum are in contact. This line is at first circular, and its expansion in all radial directions flattens the cell along the plane of contact.

The rate of this spreading and flattening is different for each cell type for a given substratum, and it likewise varies for different substrata. Moreover, to add to the complexity, the rate for a given cell type on a given surface also varies with the composition of the ambient medium. An example of this dependence is illustrated in Fig. 4. It shows that for a given cell population on given identical substrata, the average rate of spreading may be ten times as slow in the presence of a trace of serum than it is in a pure salt solution.

The instructive value of such model experiments on artificial substrata depends, of course, on how closely the conditions simulate contact relations in the organism. For artificial substrata which have been coated with monomolecular films of organic substances, either transferred from Langmuir trays or adsorbed from the medium (24), the pertinence of the model is self-evident. However, even for inorganic substrata offered to the cells by the experimenter cleanly, the relation to natural conditions is closer than may at first appear. This is due to a further complicating step in the cell-substratum interaction. As I had pointed out some time ago (35), cells in tissue culture tend to give off exudates which seep out ahead of the cells along the fibrous or planar surfaces to which the cells are attached, rolling out a molecular carpet of their own making, which from then on serves as their true substratum for spreading. A systematic series of experiments carried out in our laboratory (18) has now revealed that all cell types release such material in the form of microexudates which creep along the interfaces at rates (and perhaps compositions) depending upon the type of cell, as well as on the nature of both substratum and medium (Fig. 5). It is evident that such coatings, if they are cell-specific, can exercise not only a binding and guiding function between substratum and cell but even effect the establishment of connections and communication between formerly unconnected cells. Moreover, if they are further fortified by macromolecular recruiting, the resulting firm network can, as previously demonstrated (16, 35) tie dispersed cells into a cohesive and integrated mechanical continuum. The role of such networks in intercellular relations will be discussed further below.

In all of these experiments, the interaction has been one between the cell surface and the surface layer of the substratum in direct contact with it; contact to be defined as sufficiently close range between the two boundaries to permit strong molecular interactions and exclude an intervening liquid space subject to thermal agitation (41). It came as quite a surprise when it was discovered

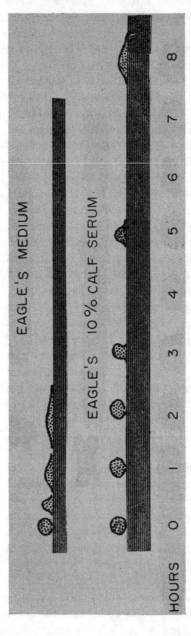

Fig. 4.   Profiles of cells spreading on glass in two different media at the indicated times. (After data from Taylor (24).).

(19) that the interaction between cell and substratum involves influences extending considerably in depth beneath the surface layers that are in immediate contact. The respective experiments are illustrated in Fig. 6. As stated above, the average rate of spreading of a cell of a given type on a given substratum in a given medium is of fairly constant value. Thus, when a suspension of cultured cells from a human conjunctiva strain is allowed to settle on a quartz

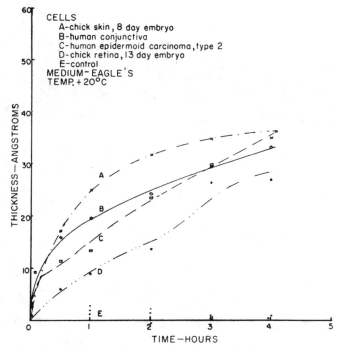

FIG. 5. Development of deposits of exudates from four different cell types, measured by ellipsometry. The control points, E, refer to a cell-free medium; the curves recorded in the presence of cells give *average* thickness of the microexudate films at the indicated times; their asymptotic increase expresses approach to saturation coverage of the intercellular area by a monomolecular layer of exudate. (From Rosenberg (18).)

slide, the average spreading time, determined for instance by the average degree of flattening reached after a standard period of time, is known. If then one treats quartz slides by coating them with stacked-up double layers of stearate and stearic acid molecules, transferred from Langmuir trays, and tests the spreading rate of cell suspensions deposited on top of these layers in a standard medium, one finds that the affinity reaction of the cells to the subjacent bulk substratum of quartz is not abolished immediately but declines gradually with the thickness of the intervening coat (Fig. 6,A).

In other words, the interposition of a dense gasket of stearate layers between quartz and cell does not immediately isolate the former from the latter dynamically. The grading off of the interaction has been measurable up to a thickness of about 80 layers of stearate, corresponding to a distance of the cell from the original bulk base of about 2000 Å. Evidence for the fact that this is a true interaction between the cell and the distant base lies in the fact that

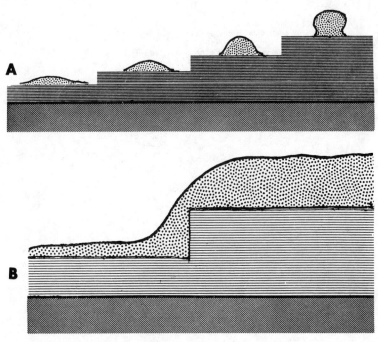

Fig. 6. Average degree of spreading of cells on stacks of different heights of double layers of stearate and stearic acid (horizontal striation) deposited on a given bulk base (diagonal striation). A, effect on whole cells; B, differential effect on different cell sectors on terraced substratum. In the diagrams, cells and substratum are out-of-scale by a factor of approximately 100:1.

the intensity of the effect has been found to vary characteristically with the nature of the bulk material, being different for glass, Teflon, and stainless steel for identical numbers of interposed lipid layers.

The basis of this unexpected long-range interaction is still wholly obscure and not even a hypothetical explanation can be offered pending further analytical experiments. But the reality of the effect is well established and is most conspicuously illustrated by the behavior of cells on terraced surfaces as diagrammed in Fig. 6,B (20). The substratum is a slide coated with double layers of lipid in such a manner that one part is covered to a greater height than the other, the step between them being rather sharp. When cells are then deposited on the slide, those that happen to overlap the step collect rapidly at the lower level, evidently because of the difference between the intensities of "attractive" interaction to which the lower and the higher sectors of the cell surface are subjected. If one considers that this differential has been found to be effective for steps of no more than 500 Å in height for a cell which covers an area of a diameter of 200,000 Å, the sensitivity of the cellular response can be appreciated. Not only is the phenomenon as such still unexplained, but its potential occurrence in the living organism is even more conjectural. But even so, it does dramatize the ignorance that still beclouds our familiarity with cellular properties.

Given the proper combination of medium and flat substratum most favorable to cell spreading, the motility of the free cell border will draw out the cell mass rather uniformly into a nearly circular disc. If conditions, however, become less favorable to spreading, then owing to the statistical inhomogeneities of the cell surface, the border will become serrated, with the less adhesive portions becoming detached and sagging between the adhering and advancing radii (49). A circular cell thus becomes lobulated, and in more extreme cases, just multipolar star-shaped. Each momentary shape marks an equilibrium state determined by the energy of thrust of cell protrusions, the ability of the mobile tips of the protrusions to adhere to the interface, the visco-elastic and cohesive forces of the cytoplasm and the cohesive and contractile forces in the cell membrane, further modified by surface coats and exudates; the distribution of all of these factors varying statistically from moment to moment in accordance with the local inhomogeneities along the cell border and with the stresses and strains within the cell (43). Adding to this the fact that the external medium likewise is never ideally homogeneous, one realizes the high degree of indeterminacy inherent in the concept of cell shape. The same considerations, however, furnish in logical consequence also the key to the explanation of cell shapes of more definite character such as, for instance, that of the bipolar spindle cell. This form can be readily derived as the reaction of an erstwhile disc-shaped cell to a substratum containing linearly disposed inhomogeneities. We are thus led to shifting our attention from the general composition and physical properties of the substratum to its structural features.

STRUCTURE

If we let a planar interface in which a cell is spread out radially in all directions shrink in one dimension, so that eventually it becomes essentially a linear strand, the cell covering it will obviously likewise be deformed into a ribbon. Similarly, a cell that later happens to make contact with such a fiber in a liquid medium would become linearly extended along the fiber axis, spreading as if on a trellis. Fibers in the environment thus can turn into pathways

for cells. This fact, established first by Harrison, has since been amply demonstrated and explained as underlying not only the orientation, but also the
morphology, of mesenchymal cells, such as fibroblasts, myoblasts, or sheath cells
of nerve (e.g., 36, 42, 49). Its fundamental significance for the orderly behavior of cells in morphogenesis, histogenesis, and healing processes stems from
the fact that developmental mechanisms to generate such oriented fiber pathways in the cellular environment have become rather well known. By the
application of external factors, for instance tension, it was possible to fashion
at will fibrous paths which afterward served as guides for cells (31, 32). This

FIG. 7. Aligning action of tension (lower portion of picture) on a network of
threadlike macromolecules.

principle has become known as "contact guidance." Since it has been dealt
with on many previous occasions, only those elements will be repeated here
which are essential to the understanding of some later sections of this article.

Contact guidance is a two-step process. It is based on the ability of filamentous macromolecules to assume parallel orientations and aggregations in a
field of mechanical or electrostatic potentials, plus the secondary retracing of
such oriented tracks by cells in contact with them. The threadlike macromolecules of proteins in animals and of cellulose in plants tend to aggregate
to cohesive networks, the meshes of which can respond in their orientation to
the directions of strains and stresses imposed upon them by external forces or
arising locally from within the fabric. Figure 7 indicates schematically the
effect of oriented stretch. According to what we said before, cells entering an

oriented matrix of this sort, of course, have no choice but to align themselves with the underlying structure. The less defined the orientation of the macro-molecular network, the more indefinite will be the shape and orientation of the cells bound to its interfaces (Fig. 8). The apparent dimensional disparity between the submicroscopic trellis and the microscopic cell processes has been resolved, but a detailed account lies beyond the scope of this paper (43).

The fact that the familiar phenomenon of functional adaptation to mechanical stresses in connective tissues (tendons, fasciae, scars, etc.) is a two-step response, rather than a direct primary reaction of the cells to stress, is plainly demonstrated by the fact that if a group of randomly oriented mesenchyme cells is presented with a preformed mat of parallel fibers or grooves (e.g., the parallel collagen fabric on the inside of a fish scale or parallel microgrooves scored in

FIG. 8. Shape and orientation of cells in a fibrous matrix of various degrees of orientation, graded from randomness (on top) to stretch-engendered alignment (at bottom).

a glass slide), the cells assume the linear orientation of those external guide-lines (42). At first each cell spreads out all around, but gradually those points of its motile margin which are in contact with the linear structure of the sub-stratum adhere more firmly, proceed in opposite directions and pull the cell out into an elongated spindle or ribbon as the less adhering lateral processes are competitively retracted (41). Since in a cell having thus become bipolar, the two opposing ends strain in opposite directions, the cell remains essentially stationary without making any net advance. Actual locomotion becomes possible only if the equilibrium between the opposing tractions is upset, an instance of which will be cited further below.

To complicate matters still further, there is evidence that besides the general physicochemical properties of the contact surfaces and the role of their physical structure, specific chemical properties of the guiding surfaces are a key factor in leading cells discriminately to different destinations. For instance, in early development, the pioneering tips of the outgrowing motor and sensory nerve fibers follow each a separate preneural fibrous pathway system (11, 23), a feature which could hardly be understood except by assuming differential chemical clues in the fibrous surfaces ["selective contact guidance" (33)].

In conclusion, it will be seen that what has formerly appeared as a relatively simple relation, namely that between a cell and its substratum, lumped under terms like thigmotaxis or stereotropism, and often enough ascribed summarily to surface tensions, is by no means such a simple and uniform phenomenon. In fact, it is far too complicated to hold much promise that it will ever yield to any unifying single formula; but if it does, it will have to be on the basis of new evidence, and not just by proclamation.

The Medium

COMPOSITION

By comparison with the extensive research that has been done on nutrient and other chemical requirements supporting the growth and maintenance of cells bathed by a liquid medium, relatively little is known about effects of the chemical composition of the medium on the locomotor behavior and the resultant configuration of cells and cell groups. This is not the place to review the general nutrient requirements or even the specific requirements of individual cell types (for instance, iodine for thyroid cells), including such spectacular effects as the alternative switching of epidermal cells *in vitro* into a keratinizing or mucus-producing course in accordance with a low or high vitamin A level in the medium (8, 50). But a few examples of more direct bearing on the problem of cell shape and intercellular relations may be cited as follows (25, 46).

If monkey kidney cells are settled on a glass surface in a medium of balanced salt solution containing horse serum, they flatten out and move with rather broad lobular extensions; in this condition, as much as about half of the aggregate circumference of the cell may at any one time be in contact with the glass, the remaining unattached sectors of the contour sagging (Fig. 9,A). However, if the same cells, under otherwise identical conditions, are kept in the same salt solution, but with the omission of the serum component, only minute fractions of the margin succeed in attaching themselves to the substratum as motile tips, while the rest of the cytoplasm contracts much more strongly than in the former medium; as a result, the cytoplasmic bridges between the advancing tips and the great mass of the cell body become stretched out into long, straight, wiry filaments, which incidentally on cursory inspection may suggest to some a superficial resemblance to young nerve fibers (Fig. 9,B). If one did not know the conditions under which these two extreme forms of the same cell can be made to materialize, one might easily mistake them for different cell types, which goes to show the unreliability of purely morphological criteria as diagnostic for cell character.

A similar transformation has been obtained by adding adenosinetriphosphate (ATP) to a medium containing multipolar cells flattened on glass surfaces. While the free tips of the cell processes remained attached, the suddenly increased contractility of the cell surface collects most of the cell substance in a central lump, leaving the connections to the free tips standing only as thin varicose strands, like fibers of a spider web. Upon washing the ATP out with fresh medium, the centrally accumulated cytoplasm streams out again centrifugally into the shrivelled strands, restoring the cell to its former shape and motility.

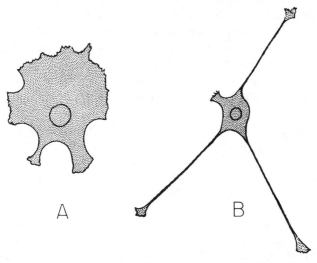

FIG. 9. Morphology of two cells of identical type on identical substrata bathed by two different fluid media. A, in Eagle's medium with horse serum. B, in pure Eagle's solution.

It is evident from these examples that the configuration of a cell at any one moment is signally dependent upon the local distribution of the ratios of centrifugal thrust and peripheral adhesivity as numerators over contractility and detachment from the substratum as denominators, with the sign of the net balance between the two opposing forces varying from spot to spot and from moment to moment as one scans the cell contour.

PHYSICAL PROPERTIES

One can easily extrapolate from Fig. 9, B the configurations into which the cell would be forced if its surface contraction were to be intensified even further so that even its terminal holdfasts would lose their grip. The cell then would obviously resume the original near-spherical shape which it had immediately after attachment from free suspension. This effect can actually be produced by raising the pH in the medium from its normal value of 7.4 to about 8.0 and above. Formerly spread out cells then retract their margins and round up (26). The effect is the same whether the change of pH has been produced by buffering or by reducing the carbon dioxide content in the medium or by a combination of both. The condition is fully reversible and the cell resumes its spread-out flattened shape as soon as the medium is returned to its normal pH value. Lowering of the pH in the medium below a level of about 6.0, produced by buffering or increased carbon dioxide concentration, has an equally drastic effect (26). Cells which have been moving in the ordinary manner then become frozen in the position and configuration in which they happen to be; the cytoplasm becomes gelated and all internal mobility ceases, and whenever a mitotic process has been under way, it is likewise stopped in its tracks. This stage of rigor is again fully reversible within a few hours after its inception: returned to normal pH, the cell reacquires its internal mobility and the interrupted locomotor and mitotic activities proceed from the points where they had been arrested.

DIFFERENTIAL EFFECTS

These experiments intimate that pH changes might be a major device by which cells can influence one another through alterations of their local microenvironments. For instance, lactic acid released from a given cell during a phase of high metabolic activity might be expected to have a temporary paralytic effect on the surrounding cells, as well as perhaps a regulatory feedback effect on the originating cell itself. This concept assumed even greater promise when we found that the pH effect on the cell is local rather than all-or-none (47), as follows. Single bipolar cells in tissue culture were subject to a pH gradient along their length. This was done (Fig. 10) by having two submerged micropipettes direct two streams of the culture medium against the motile tips, one stream of normal pH for control, and the other of either higher or lower pH. As mentioned before, the two motile ends of a bipolar cell strain in opposite directions, thus holding the cell in a relatively equilibrated position. In the present experiment, however, the one end exposed to an increased pH, lost its hold on the substratum and retracted, thus leaving the cell under the towing force of the opposite, unaffected, process (Fig. 10,A). As a result, the cell moved away from the alkaline stream. If the test stream was acid (Fig. 10,B), the locomotor effect was in the same direction, although for different reasons: the acid-flushed end did not retract, but simply became paralyzed, thus likewise giving the opposite, still motile, end an opportunity to move the cell in the latter direction.

It can easily be seen that inequalities of this kind within the medium can yield differential effects on a cell only provided the difference is still of suffi-

cient magnitude when it reaches the cell surface itself; that is to say, for agents
of diffusible nature the sources would have to lie within close range of the cell,
for the farther apart they are, the more will their differential become equalized
by thermal agitation and turbulence. This is as true of pH gradients as it is
of the gradients of concentration of chemical compounds and imposes rather
narrow restrictions on any explanations of the orientation of cells by diffusing
chemicals.

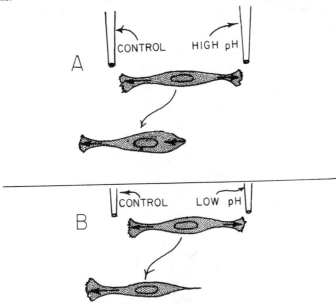

FIG. 10. Locomotor effects of local exposure of one pole of a bipolar cell to high (A)
or low (B) pH values. (Original: Weiss and Scott.)

In summary, the model experiments, which have revealed major modifications of cell behavior in response to artificial changes of the ambient medium,
have at the same time opened the much wider prospect that, under natural
conditions, the cells themselves may take the place of the experimenter and by
altering each other's local environments, may produce critical local effects up
and above the general effects commonly associated with body fluids.

Cell to Cell Interactions

INTERACTIONS IN LIQUIDS

For close-range interactions, the experiments just cited have, therefore, given
us the proper transition from single-cell behavior to interactions of cells in the
group. The link is illustrated by a classic precursor to our pH gradient experi-

ment. The first differential step in the development of the egg of the seaweed, *Fucus,* is the localized protrusion of a rootlet. Whitaker (29) has shown that the point at which the rootlet will emerge from the egg surface can be determined by a variety of external gradients, including pH gradients, imposed as

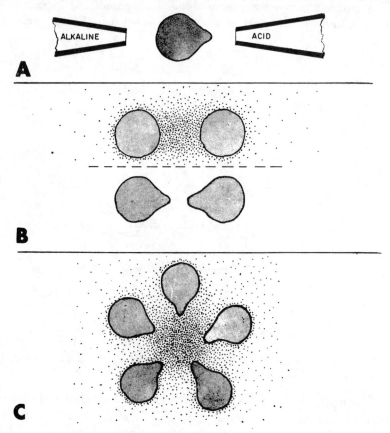

FIG. 11. Polarization of rootlet formation in seaweed eggs. A, Polarization of single egg in pH gradient. B, Mutual polarization in pairs of eggs within close range (top, concentration gradient; bottom, morphological response). C, Resultant polarization in multiple groups. (After Whitaker (29).)

shown in Fig. 11,A, where one can see the rootlet issue on the acid side. The exact mode of action on the membrane of the egg is not yet known, and as one can see by comparison with Fig. 10, is evidently of a different nature than that observed in our tissue culture cells. However, for our present purpose this difference is irrelevant, the main point being that in both cases a definite polarity relative to a polarized environment has been established in the responding cells.

Of course, even if left alone, the seaweed egg would still have protruded a root-let, but this would have appeared in a random location decided by accidental inequalities in both the egg surface and the medium, for no natural system is ever ideally homogeneous. The crux of the experiment is that the indeterminacy of randomness could be replaced by the localization of the event at a predeter-mined spot. In line with our previous conclusions, this then presents a model of one mode of interactions by which cells could determine each other's mutual relations. The model proved to be valid. If two seaweed eggs are made to face each other at close range and then are left alone, each sprouts its rootlet from the point that is nearest to the opposite cell, as if by reciprocal "attraction" (Fig. 11,B). The explanation is, of course, that each egg must be credited with giv-

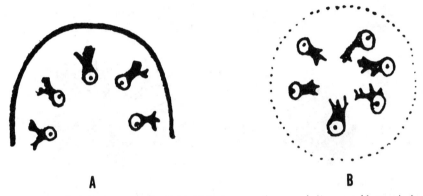

A   **B**

FIG. 12. Polarized outgrowth of dendritic processes from cerebellar neuroblasts. A, in a confined medium near the edge (either *in vitro* or in the embryo) ; B, inside the medium, far from the edge. (From Stefanelli (21).)

ing off certain surface-active substances, perhaps comparable to the exudates discussed before, and that these substances will, in the earlier stages of diffusion, accumulate in higher concentrations at the near sides of the confronted sources than they would at the far sides, with the resulting gradient of each determining the axis of outgrowth (Fig. 11,B). That this is the correct interpretation, rather than any reference to "attractive forces," is evidenced by assemblies of more than two eggs (Fig. 11,C), in which each egg issued its rootlet from a point facing the center of the concentration gradient of the common pool of exudates, rather than facing the neighboring eggs.

The relevance of these experiments to the explanation of ordered cell group behavior in tissues is demonstrated by the fact (21) that the point of outgrowth of dendrites from neuroblasts in groups obeys similar rules (Fig. 12) ; the site at which the nerve process emerges from the cell body is determined by differ-entials in the medium, set up either by the experimenter deliberately (Fig. 12,A) or by the collective products of the clustered cell groups (Fig. 12,B). An analogous response has been described for pigment cells within confined spaces (27). Polar surface inequalities recorded in cells placed in electric fields (e.g., 4) suggest that this may be still another mechanism by which the cells generating such potentials might influence each other.

These first examples of organized interactions between cells have in common the fact that they were exerted across unstructured liquid spaces. To make clear that this is one, but by no means the only, mechanism of group interaction, let us now turn to a second type, in which the interaction is mediated through structural connections.

STRUCTURAL INTERACTIONS

Let us return to the example illustrated in Fig. 8, representing cells applied to a continuous and cohesive fibrous network pervading a liquid medium. Many

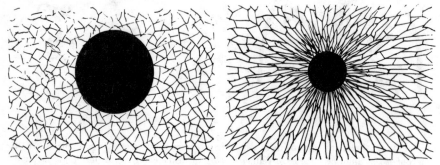

FIG. 13. Structural effect of shrinkage of a local area (black disc) of a cohesive fibrous network: radial puckering of meshes.

of the colloidal systems to which cells and tissues owe their firm consistency contain this kind of two-phase configuration. Now, whereas our earlier comments gave one-sided attention to the contact guidance of cells by their substratum, the facts of the matter are that the relation between the cells and the fibrous network in which they are enmeshed is a reciprocal one—a true interaction. We have discussed the effect the orientation of the network exerts upon the shape and orientation of the cells. As for converse effects by cells upon their matrix, we have already referred to the exudates which spread from cells along surface structures, including fibrous pathways (35). However, in addition there are cell products which can profoundly alter the composition and structure of the colloidal systems in the cellular surroundings. For instance, one finds that actively proliferating cell cultures, embedded in a clot of blood plasma, produce a strong syneretic "dehydratization" of the coagulum in the vicinity. That is, the fibrin micels become more densely aggregated, while formerly bound water is released into the interstices. In other words, the fibrous portion of the matrix around the cells is shrunk, which local shrinkage, since the whole system is continuous, creates a pattern of tensions radiating toward the center of the contraction, resulting in a corresponding puckering of the meshes (Fig. 13). In a colloidal matrix of the appropriate composition, cell groups can thus, by a peculiar chemical activity attending cell multiplication, give rise to physical tracks radiating from and toward the proliferating source. This is the outcome in the presence of a single growth center (31, 36).

However, if there are two separate growth centers present in a common matrix, the same activity exerted simultaneously by both creates a preferential pathway system along their connecting line (Fig. 14). This is due entirely to the fact that meshes in the space between the two shrinking foci are subject to

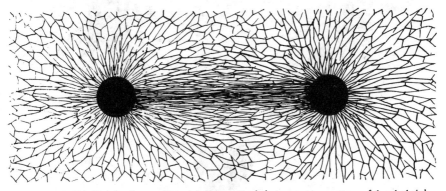

Fig. 14. Formation of a preferential fibrous track between two centers of local shrinkage in a common fibrous matrix ("two-center effect").

pull in two opposite directions, hence to much greater stretch and orientation than are the more outlying meshes (36, 38). It can readily be seen then that cells that happen to move out from either center will find, as a result of their prior structuring effect upon the common substratum, a preformed bridge to lead them straight from one focus to the other. And if there are three such centers growing simultaneously, they will become interconnected by fibrous bridges, and later by cells, in a triangular pattern (Fig. 15).

These processes have actually been observed both in tissue culture (38) and in the living animal (33). They demonstrate in a simple, but highly instructive, instance a principle of morphogenesis in which unoriented and erratic cell groups, embedded in an irregular matrix, will through a sequence of identified interactions give rise to an emergent pattern of a much higher degree of regularity and orientation. At the same time, it will be recognized that the geometric order attained in these last examples is totally different from the one illustrated in the two previous examples (Figs. 11 and 12), which dealt with interaction by diffusion. Three centers of growth, placed on a rigid substratum in a common liquid medium devoid of an interconnecting fibrous network, would presumably have achieved, if any preferential orientation of outgrowth

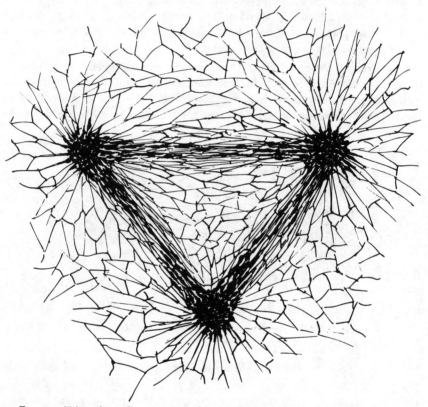

Fig. 15. Triangular cell connections forming between three separate growth centers as a result of the triangular deformation of the fibrous structure of the matrix.

at all, only one directed toward the interior of the triangular area, much as the rootlets in Fig. 11, C, rather than orientation along the sides of the triangle as in Fig. 15. In conclusion, these examples should have made it abundantly clear that interactions at a distance between cells and cell groups can only be defined if one takes into full account all three essential components of the situation—the cell, the substratum, and the medium—and specifies their mutual interactions, the distances involved, and the structure of the resulting fields of forces.

CONTACT INTERACTIONS

All the interactions discussed so far between individual cells and their environment, including other individual cells, had one general feature in common. They all involved the imposition of certain restrictions of the degrees of freedom in the behavior of the cell in the direction from greater randomness to greater definition. Still greater restraints are imposed upon cells when they come into direct contact, as in the formation of tissues and organs. Contact, let us recall, has been defined above as approximation between two solid surfaces close enough to prevent free thermal agitation in the space between the surfaces. The systematic investigation of contact interactions, although started half a century ago with invertebrate cells, has not hit its stride until comparatively recently with the development of techniques for the artificial separation of cells from the community of tissues, followed by studies of their subsequent reaggregations (see above). These studies have concerned themselves with two related, but rather separable, aspects of the integration of dispersed single cells into complexes of a higher degree of order (40). One aspect pertains to the manner in which cells come together and behave upon their encounters; that is, the conditions under which they join to form multicellular complexes and their reactions toward each other in the process. The other aspect is the subsequent behavior of the various constituent cells in the freshly established or reconstituted assembly. In both regards, the behavioral reactions were found to vary characteristically and consistently according to the stage of development of the organism from which the cells were taken, whether taken from an earlier embryo or a later embryo or a juvenile or an adult donor; according to the type of organ or tissue; according to their history prior to testing; and again according to the environmental conditions in which their encounters and subsequent activities were being tested. We shall first consider the cell responses following immediately upon contact.

Encounters of Mesenchyme Cells

As pointed out earlier, cells of mesenchymal tissues are rather polymorphic, assuming a great variety of forms, depending on the environmental conditions, particularly the substratum and medium (see Fig. 8). Under certain conditions, as in the formation of mesothelia, they will combine into cohesive membranes, whereas under other conditions, they form dispersed populations with each cell moving independently or only tenuously connected with others. Much as their configuration, so their mutual reactions upon contact vary according to circumstances. The reactions which I am about to exemplify pertain to the dispersed or loose distributions; for instance, the common types of spindle cells in tissue culture.

As mentioned previously, such cells have a few pseudopods with mobile

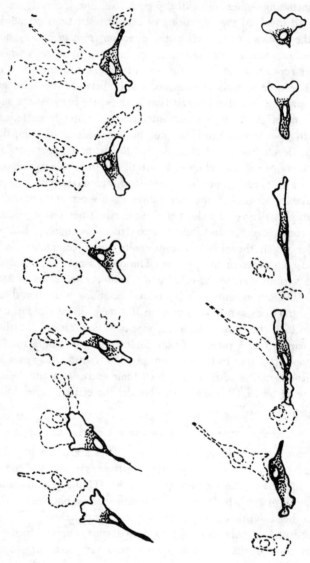

Fig. 16. Eleven stations in the moves of a single stroma cell (solid contour) making various contacts with other cells of the same type (broken contours). Read from left to right; first the upper row, then the lower row.

tips, which, as they extend in different directions, keep the mass of the cell body essentially stationary. Figure 10 presented an example of upsetting that stationary equilibrium by an external factor, thus permitting the cell to be actually displaced in the direction of the resultant motile force. A similar effect without external intervention results when two mesenchyme cells make contact with their mobile tips. These tips either just cease to move (3) or become actively detached from the substratum and retract (41), although both of these phenomena seem to be just variants of the same principle, which Abercrombie has termed "contact inhibition." As a result of their mutual contact, then, such cells move apart (Fig. 16) until the immobilized part of the margin of each recovers from its paralysis, protrudes a new pseudopod and thus stalls the advance of the cell once more. It can be seen that by this mechanism cells have a means of spacing themselves out as a relatively thin population, maintaining automatically a standard density determined by the average range of their random probing excursions (that is, the inverse probability of mutual collisions).

It is highly significant that contact inhibition of this kind has not been observed between sarcoma cells and mesenchyme cells from normal tissues under otherwise identical conditions (2). A further study of these differences promises valuable clues as to the general surface properties of the malignant cell, which may be plausibly related to their loss of "co-aptation" (see below) and assumption of migratory and invasive activities (6).

Encounters of Epithelial Cells

As pointed out in the introductory remarks, motility of a free cell is a primary expression of expenditure of metabolic energy. When cells join to form compact tissues, mutual interactions restrain or fully suppress this indigenous activity of the constituent members of the group. Contrary to rather naïve contentions, ascribing this suppression to crude mechanical force, such as turgor and pressure from crowding into limited space, there is conclusive evidence to show that far subtler and specific relations are involved—a principle to which I have given the purely descriptive name of "co-aptation" (37). The evidence has been assembled from a variety of observations and experiments. In brief, the principle is this. Cells suspend free active mobility and enter group associations only provided the new collective grouping possesses a higher degree of stability than does the dispersed population. Such a stabler equilibration presupposes that adjoining cells be harmoniously adjusted and compatible with each other in their neighborly relations (surface configurations, physiological manifestations, etc.). Disharmonious associations cannot persist and lead automatically to dissociation. In this manner, cells of different types, having different properties, possess an automatic device for self-ordering into homologous groups, the active principle being not a primary seeking and joining of like to like, but rather a random roaming, temporary joining and mutual testing, followed by the disjunction of disparate, and hence, not durable associations. Extensive experimental work in recent years has largely verified and strengthened this general principle. Its detailed manifestations, however, vary greatly in accordance with the variables outlined above.

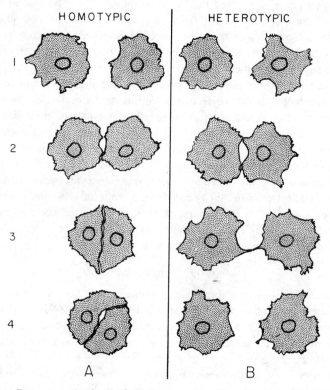

HOMOTYPIC   HETEROTYPIC

A   B

FIG. 17. Four stages in the confrontation *in vitro* of pairs of identical (homotypic) cells (A) and of unrelated (heterotypic) cells (B).

Let us consider, for example, the behavior of a loose suspension of epithelial cells, freshly isolated from embryonic organs at a rather advanced stage, and containing several different cell types (41). These cells spread out on the substratum as described earlier, and roam rather freely [Fig. 17(1)]. Upon accidental contact with another cell [Fig. 17(2)], their behavior is at first about the same regardless of the character of the latter. Those sectors of the motile cell margins which have met cease to move on, establishing thus for a while a common border. This might well be the same phenomenon as the mutual immobilization of contacting mesenchyme cells described in the foregoing. Within a fraction of an hour, however, further developments take place which differ crucially depending on whether or not the two adjoining cells belong to the same or to nonmatching types (Fig. 17,A and B). If they are of identical character ("homotypic"), they draw more closely together [Fig. 17,A(3)], enlarging their common boundary, and remain henceforth associated, though not physically cemented to each other [Fig. 17,A(4)]. Contrarily, if they belong to different kinds ("heterotypic"; for instance, liver and kidney, or kidney and lung, or liver and epidermis), they gradually move on in different directions [Fig. 17,B(3)], and as they pull apart, rupture any physical attachments they may have formed in the interim [Fig. 17,B(4)]. Large and varied series of experiments have firmly established the fact that cells possess in their surfaces some means of recognizing each other's kinds and, upon identification of a partner as belonging to the same or a related kind, effect a more intimate junction, whereas if the identification reveals an alien type, each goes its own way, leading to disjunction.

There is no evidence either for cells "attracting" each other even within close range, nor for their actively "repelling" each other in heterotypic combinations. Moreover, both the criteria of recognition and the discriminatory responses vary according to the type and previous history of the test cells. Connective tissue cells and stroma, in general, are multivalent, as it were, capable of attaching to different kinds of epithelia, thus serving as a mediating and binding agent between them (12). Macrophages have great affinity for lung cells, roaming freely over an island of lung epithelium, but rarely and only with difficulty straying beyond its borders (46). Schwann cells and nerve fibers likewise combine preferentially (1); and it obviously becomes an empirical task of the future to establish a natural tree of such tissue kinships, comparable to a tree of taxonomic relations. It should be emphasized that in the tissue culture tests, tissue specificity overrides species specificity, so that the homotypic cells from different species will readily associate, while heterotypic combinations of the same individual will not endure (15).

Upon prolonged culture *in vitro,* however, the self-segregation of heterotypic cells, originally derived from different organs, begins to fade (46). To what extent this reflects a loss of surface criteria of cell character, or a loss of the discriminatory response, or a gradual change in the composition of the descendant cell populations concerned, is quite uncertain. It is becoming increasingly evident that on prolonged cultivation certain segments of the original mixed cell population outbreed and eventually replace other segments (22); therefore, any final interpretation of what superficially looks like a progressive acclimatization and equalization of originally incompatible strains must be deferred to the future.

A similar reserve seems indicated at present in the interpretation of the mechanism underlying the specific recognition and subsequent discriminatory behavior between cells. It is certainly not farfetched to assume that the identifying criteria consist either of specific steric properties of individual type-specific key molecules in the cell surface, or else of certain regular mosaic configurations in the array of groups of molecules in the cell surface. My earlier suggestion (33), later adopted by Tyler (28), that matching cells might bind each other by the interlocking of complementary molecules, as in antigen-antibody combinations, does not seem tenable in view of the fact that during the crucial phase of the interaction the apposed cells do not maintain stable mutual positions (46, 47). If one considers furthermore that electron-micrographic close-ups of the cell borders have shown that contact is made not in a broad front, but through filamentous tendrils, about one-tenth of a micron in diameter [see Fig. 7 in (45)], the idea of a direct molecular bonding between homologous cells meets with almost insuperable difficulties, even if one were to change the static bonding to a purely statistical one.

In view of the stress laid earlier on the role of cellular exudates, which has recently been re-emphasized (16), it is important to keep in mind that homotypic association and heterotypic disjunction might very well be based not on activities of the respective cell membranes themselves, but rather on the confluence or nonconfluence of their respective chemical discharges, which if confluent would hold the constituent cells together like in a common envelope. In this connection, the observations on the reduction of surface coats in malignant cells (9) would assume increasing significance.

A further fact to take into account is that primary associations among cells based on mutual recognition are secondarily sealed and fortified by various mechanical devices, such as desmosomes, intercellular cements or fibrous networks.

In conclusion, despite the extreme brevity of this description, the examples will have given some idea of the great subtlety and specificity of contact interactions among cells which follow their mutual encounters. In those cases in which close contact relations are then maintained, opportunities arise for further specific interactions among the associated cells which manifest themselves in group operations not demonstrable in cell populations kept in the dispersed state. These further group interactions, more fully discussed in earlier papers (5, 37, 39), can be but briefly exemplified here in the following section.

SELF-ORGANIZATION

It has long been known that embryonic cell groups, explanted *in vitro* prior to the stage of overt microscopic signs of their future morphological and physiological specializations, will in many cases go ahead and produce those criteria of advanced differentiation in the new and artificial surroundings. After it had been shown that they could do this, even if they had been explanted as a completely dispersed population (17), the stage was set for testing mixed populations. A scrambled mixture of precursor cells of future cartilage and future kidney, thus tested in tissue culture, however, did not give rise as one might have expected, to a correspondingly random amalgamate of tissue but yielded solid blocks of pure cartilage and of pure kidney tissue cleanly separated (14). In short, the mixed cell types had not only succeeded in sorting themselves out like-to-like, as exemplified above, but then had continued each in developing its appropriate type of histological structure as a collaborative performance of the newly formed homotypic assemblies.

Even though such cell clusters in tissue culture can under appropriate conditions attain organlike organization (10), their morphogenetic faculties *in vitro* are limited. More optimal conditions can be offered to dissociated and reaggregated cell clusters by transplanting them to the extraembryonic membranes *in vivo*. When this was done, the random assortments of cells reconstituted themselves into quite typical miniature organs of the types from which the cells had originally been taken (51). The cells in these experiments had been obtained from embryonic organs of chicks in rather advanced and fully functional stages. The donor organs were dissociated, the freed cells were scrambled at random, reaggregated by mild centrifugation, and bits of the resulting hash were then incorporated in the chorioallantoic membrane of the host egg for vascularization and further nursing.

Under these conditions, random mixtures of liver cells eventually became reconstituted into well-organized functional livers, with typical cords, bile capillaries, collecting into canaliculi, confluent in typical branching patterns into a bile duct, with hematopoietic sites, Kupffer cells, and venous sinuses. Suspensions of original kidney cells formed functional kidney, with perfect glomeruli filtering into collecting and secretory tubules, radiating toward an imitated pelvis. Skin regrouped cells formed appropriate appendages, such as feathers.

The history of these developments is rather complex and cannot be reviewed here. Moreover, most of the many steps of interactions in this remarkable organogenesis have not yet been identified. What is certainly involved, is the sorting out of homologous cells; the recruiting of less mature cells by more mature ones; inductive interactions, evoking conforming differentiation in adjacent cells; migration of cells and cell groups into appropriate positions; secondary coalescence of patches of homologous tissue into larger complexes; differential cell proliferation according to location within the group; and many more of the kinds of processes which form the subject of study of experimental embryology. All that needs to be said in the present context is that continued interactions among originally isolated and self-sufficient cells can lead to this amazingly high degree of organized and harmonious performance.

These highly organized results, however, were obtained only if the dissociated and scrambled tissue components were given an opportunity to reassemble and reorganize themselves within a day or so after their removal and dissociation. If, on the other hand, the dissociated cells were first nursed for a number of days in tissue culture as independent individuals, then reassembled and transplanted to the chorioallantoic membrane, they gave totally different results. Instead of typical organs, they formed only unorganized and loosely structured nodules of cells of rather nondescript character. Since there is binding evidence that the cells could not within a few days of culturing have been stripped wholly of their original specificities and on the other hand, it also has been shown (16) that during a stay in culture, cells do lose their clustering tendency, or rather acquire a greater tendency to stay apart, we must attribute the gradual loss of the faculty for orderly reconstitution to the progressive failure of isolated cells to get close enough together to establish the intimacy of contact interactions that are essential for histogenesis.

Lest this description rest wholly on symbolic terms, I am adding here a model of how one could conceive of the nature of such histogenetic prerequisites in which intimate association between the cells would be a physical necessity. The example concerns the formation of a kidney tubule; it is partly based on concrete observations, partly still on conjecture. It does, however, indicate a trend of thought and of research amenable to further practical investigation. When isolated cells of kidney are kept in culture, one often sees a vacuole, evidently of secretory nature, forming in the cytoplasm, which as it increases, indents the nucleus, bulges against the cellular contour, and eventually is extruded into the medium (Fig. 18,A). If the cells are embedded in blood plasma, the extruded liquid creates an open space between that side of the cell surface and the clot. In a statistically isotropic environment, no preferred direction of the extrusion was noted. However, when cells became closely associated, even if only in small numbers, the configuration depicted in Fig. 18, C was observed. It is easy to interpolate the intermediate stage of Fig. 18, B, which has not yet been observed, but links up logically with such group interactions as were portrayed in Fig. 11. That is to say, that if, for instance, three cells came within very close range, their products would set up a gradient field of properties distinctly polarized from the inner space between the cells as center toward the outer medium. Assuming further that this would impose corresponding polar differences upon the cell membranes, followed perhaps by internal cytoplasmic rearrangements, the extrusion process would become rigorously oriented toward the common center, in contrast to the random dissipation by cells in the dispersed state. As long as there are free channels between the cells, the extruded liquid would, of course, escape from that central pool. However, as soon as the cells become tightly joined, as in Fig. 18, C, the extruded liquid would remain locked in: a lumen would be formed, with the extruding cells serving as wall. Continued polarized secretion into this lumen would distend this primordial cyst, while the cells of the wall could go on to proliferate. As a result of the new basal-apical polarity imposed upon the wall cells, a new interaction with the environment (in the presence of stroma cells) would lead to the formation of a confining basement membrane at the basal surface (Fig. 18,D). If in analogy with other basement membranes, this sheath were to have a definite submicroscopic architecture (44), in this case predisposing a cylindrical extension, the original cyst would, in the course of further proliferation of cells and further dilation of the lumen by continued secretion, automatically become fashioned into a tubule.

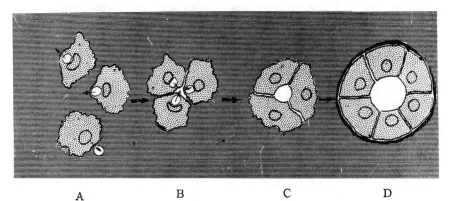

A   B   C   D

FIG. 18. Schematic representation of the formation of a kidney tubule by reaggregating isolated kidney cells (see text).

We know enough way stations in this course of development to make the formation of a kidney tubule from isolated reaggregating cells according to this concept appear quite plausible; but we do not yet have all the data necessary for full confirmation. Even so, it can be seen that any such mechanism would be contingent upon a tight apposition among the member cells so as to prevent the leakage of internal fluid, whose turgor constitutes the lumen. Evidently, if cells in days of *in vitro* culturing develop a bristly surface, as we have seen in our electron micrographs, they have deprived themselves of the faculty for such smooth and tight surface closure. This could explain, therefore, why they could no longer manage to constitute a tubule. But whether or not the matter is as simple as that remains to be seen.

Cancer

I indicated at the beginning that the purpose of my presentation would be an exposure of the complexity of interactions that must be understood and taken into account in the explanation of even the simplest problem of organization.

In looking back over the examples presented, it should be possible to get at least a feeling of the multiplicity and diversity of component tasks into which our general groping for insight into the interactions of cells with their environment and with one another must be broken up if we are to replace purely verbal and noncommittal formulations by concrete factual knowledge. It will have become equally clear, however, that if the behavior of the *organized* system offers so many different facets relevant to the harmonious interplay of its component members, problems of *disorganized* and *disharmonious* behavior can hardly yield to a single unifying formula, either. It therefore would be not only presumptuous, but wholly counter to the purpose and spirit of my presentation, if I were to add some general comments about the cancer problem, which could only be either platitudinous or else denying my cell-biological conviction that the cancer problem cannot possibly be of *one* piece.

Yet, by implication and indirectly, a number of statements throughout this text have obviously a close bearing on the behavioral distinctions between malignant and nonmalignant cells. This is particularly evident for that feature of malignancy which manifests itself in the alienation of a cell from its mother tissue and in its subsequent emigration, invasiveness, and inability to become reintegrated into harmonious co-aptation, as in metastases. I hope to have been sufficiently explicit in indicating that I see no reason for presuming that even this metastatic power is gained by the neoplastic cell in one fell swoop. In fact, the evidence points to the notion that many of the diverse factors on which the harmonious existence of a cell in its environment hinges may have to be upset before the crucial malignant crisis is attained. Which ones of the mentioned interactions, and of the many others either not quoted or not yet known, are relevant to a particular facet of the cancer problem, can only be determined by empirical research, although a hard look at what we already know might give such research some plausible direction.

At any rate, it is not for me, and certainly not on this occasion, to indulge in such predictions. I merely repeat the conclusion which I presented in the First National Cancer Conference in the United States in 1949 and which I summarized (37) in the diagram here reproduced in Fig. 19. In order to exist, survive, and function properly, a cell called "A" (assumed here to be epithelial) must be adjusted harmoniously at least threefold. It must be compatible with neighboring cells, A; with its substratum, C, which also may consist of a complementary cell type, such as stroma; and finally, with the liquid environment, B, either bathing it or brought to it in capillary spaces of blood and lymph. Not only must these harmonious interactions, indicated by arrows A, B, C, prevail, but resistance to disharmonious interrelations, Y and Z, is likewise a condition for the maintenance of organization, although one that is not equally patent and often can only be determined indirectly by appropriate tests. Any disruption of any one of these relations between a cell and its environment must lead to a change of cell behavior. The degree to which such change jeopardizes the existence of that particular cell or its descendants, or even imperils others, is a matter for practical determination; except that the general prediction seems clear enough that many such disruptions, cumulatively imposed upon the same cell strain, are necessary to produce the critical summation that yields an overtly pathological condition.

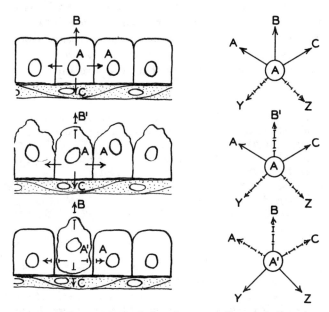

FIG. 19. Diagram of "co-aptive" relations between cells and their environment (solid arrows) and of the effects of disruption (broken arrows) of those relations.

If the bathing medium changes from B to B^1, the exposed part of the cell surface may become restless, its permeability properties may change, and the metabolic equilibrium may for a while suffer. On the other hand, if a cell by cumulative damage during its history, by mutation, by virus infection, by radiation damage, or by various chemical insults, becomes sufficiently alienated from its sister cells, so that its character changes from A to A^1, and if, as a result of this alienation, it becomes detached from C, loses contact with its neighbors and is rendered disequilibrated with its medium B, it would resume motility and take an independent course. Yet, unless it loses at the same time its resistance to living in other surroundings, Y and Z, it still would not become a seed for metastatic trouble.

The principle of *co-aptation,* crudely diagrammed in the schematic picture of Fig. 19, is simple, but it remains meaningless unless a whole corps of investigators gets busy through detailed work to fill with concrete sense the various arrows standing here as symbols. The way in which some progress toward this goal can be made has been, at least modestly, indicated by our examples. This is a mere beginning, while infinitely more still lies ahead. But you will note that whatever may be the source of the change from A to A^1 in our diagram— and I have listed quite a few origins which have already been invoked—it does not of itself directly explain the rupture of the arrows symbolizing harmonious relations, nor the acquisition of other arrows symbolizing disharmonious ones. If cancer *prevention* may have to concentrate on the change from A to A^1, perhaps concern with cancer *cure* might advantageously direct some more attention and investigative effort to the study of the co-aptive arrows.

REFERENCES

1. Abercrombie, M., Johnson, M. L., and Thomas, G. A. The influence of nerve fibres on Schwann cell migration investigated in tissue culture. *Proc. Roy. Soc.* **B136**: 448-460 (1949).

2. Abercrombie, M. Behavior of normal and malignant connective tissue cells *in vitro*. *Proc. Can. Cancer Research Conf.* **4**: 101-117 (1961).

3. Abercrombie, M. The bases of the locomotory behaviour of fibroblasts. *Exptl. Cell Research, Suppl.* **8**: 188-198 (1961).

4. Anderson, J. D. Galvanotaxis of slime mold. *J. Gen. Physiol.* **35**: 1-16 (1951).

5. Andres, G. Experiments on the fate of dissociated embryonic cells (chick) disseminated by the vascular route. Part II. Teratomas. *J. Exptl. Zool.* **122**: 507-540 (1953).

6. Coman, D. R. Mechanisms responsible for the origin and distribution of bloodborne tumor metastases: A review. *Cancer Research* **13**: 397-404 (1953).

7. Coman, D. R. Cellular adhesiveness in relation to the invasiveness of cancer: electron microscopy of liver perfused with a chelating agent. *Cancer Research* **14**: 519 (1954); **15**: 541 (1955).

8. Fell, H. B., and Mellanby, E. Metaplasia produced in cultures of chick ectoderm by high vitamin A. *J. Physiol. (London)* **119**: 470-488 (1953).

9. Gasic, G., and Gasic, T. Removal of sialic acid from the cell coat in tumor cells and vascular endothelium, and its effects on metastasis. *Proc. Natl. Acad. Sci. U.S.* **48**: 1172-1177 (1962).

10. Grover, J. W. The enzymatic dissociation and reproducible reaggregation *in vitro* of 11-day embryonic chick lung. *Develop. Biol.* **3**, No. 5: 555-568 (1961).

11. Hamburger, V. Die Entwicklung experimentell erzeugter nervenloser und schwach innervierter Extremitäten von Anuren. *Wilhelm Roux' Arch. Entwicklungsmech. Organ.* **144**: 272-363 (1928).

12. Holtfreter, J. Gewebeaffinität, ein Mittel der embryonalen Formbildung. *Arch. exptl. Zellforsch.* **23**: 169-209 (1939).

13. Holtfreter, J. Observations on the migration, aggregation and phagocytosis of embryonic cells. *J. Morphol.* **80**: 25-26 (1947).

14. Moscona, A. Development of heterotypic combinations of dissociated embryonic chick cells. *Proc. Soc. Exptl. Biol. Med.* **92**: 410-416 (1956).

15. Moscona, A. The development *in vitro* of chimeric aggregates of dissociated embryonic chick and mouse cells. *Proc. Natl. Acad. Sci. U.S.,* **43**: 184-194 (1957).

16. Moscona, A. Patterns and mechanisms of tissue reconstruction from dissociated cells. *In* "Developing Cell Systems and Their Control" (D. Rudnick, ed.), pp. 45-70. Ronald Press, New York, 1960.

17. Moscona, A., and Moscona, H. The dissociation and aggregation of cells from organ rudiments of the early chick embryo. *J. Anat.* **86**: 287-301 (1952).

18. Rosenberg, M. D. Measurements of microexudates from cells grown in tissue culture. *Biophys. J.* **1**, No. 2: 137-159 (1960).

19. Rosenberg, M. D. Long-range interactions between cells and substratum. *Proc. Natl. Acad. Sci. U.S.* **48**: 1342-1349 (1962).

20. Rosenberg, M. D. In preparation.

21. Stefanelli, A. Sul comportamento sociale di neuroni in speciali condizioni sperimentali. *Acta Embriol. Morphol. Exptl.* **1**: 56-64 (1957).

22. Syverton Memorial Symposium: "Analytic Cell Culture." *Natl. Cancer Inst. Monograph* **7** (1962).

23. Taylor, A. C. Selectivity of nerve fibers from the dorsal and ventral roots in the development of the frog limb. *J. Exptl. Zool.* **96**: 159-185 (1944).

24. Taylor, A. C. Attachment and spreading of cells in culture. *Exptl. Cell Research Suppl.* **8**: 154-173 (1961).

25. Taylor, A. C. Cell adhesiveness and the adaptation of cells in surfaces. *In* "Biological Interactions in Normal and Neo-Plastic Growth" (M. J. Brennan, ed.), pp. 168-182. Little, Brown, Boston, Massachusetts, 1962.

26. Taylor, A. C. Responses of cells to pH changes in the medium. *J. Cell. Biol.* **15** No. 2: 201-209 (1962).

27. Twitty, V. C., and Niu, M. C. The motivation of cell migration, studied by isolation of embryonic pigment cells singly and in small groups *in vitro. J. Exptl. Zool.* **125**: 541-573 (1954).

28. Tyler, A. An auto-antibody concept of cell structure in growth. *Growth* Symposium **6**: 7-19 (1946).

29. Whitaker, D. M. The effect of hydrogen ion concentration upon the induction of polarity of Fucus eggs. I. Increased hydrogen ion concentration and the intensity of mutual inductions by neighboring eggs of Fucus furcatus. *J. Gen. Physiol.* **20**: 491-500 (1937).

30. Weiss, L. Studies on cellular adhesion in tissue culture. III. Some effects of calcium. *Exptl. Cell Research* **21**: 71-77 (1960).

31. Weiss, P. Erzwingung elementarer Strukturverschiedenheiten am in vitro wachsenden Gewebe. Die Wirkung mechanischer Spannung auf Richtung und Intensität des Gewebewachstums und ihre Analyse. *Wilhelm Roux' Arch. Entwicklungsmech. Organ.* **116**: 438-554 (1929).

32. Weiss, P. *In vitro* experiments on the factors determining the course of the outgrowing nerve fiber. *J. Exptl. Zool.* **68**: 393-448 (1934).

33. Weiss, P. Nerve patterns: The mechanics of nerve growth. *Growth* **5**: 163-203 (1941).

34. Weiss, P. The technology of nerve regeneration: A review. Sutureless tubulation and related methods of nerve repair. *J. Neurosurg.* **1**: 400-450 (1944).

35. Weiss, P. Experiments on cell and axon orientation *in vitro*: the role of colloidal exudates in tissue organization. *J. Exptl. Zool.* **100**: 353-386 (1945).

36. Weiss, P. Differential growth. *In* "Chemistry and Physiology of Growth" (A. K. Parpart, ed.), pp. 135-186. Princeton Univ. Press, Princeton, New Jersey, 1949.
37. Weiss, P. Perspectives in the field of morphogenesis. *Quart. Rev. Biol.* **25**: 177-198 (1950).
38. Weiss, P. "Attraction fields" between growing tissue cultures. *Science* **115**: 293-295 (1952).
39. Weiss, P. Some introductory remarks on the cellular basis of differentiation. *J. Embryol. & Exptl. Morphol.* **1**: 181-211 (1953).
40. Weiss, P. The compounding of complex macromolecular and cellular units into tissue fabrics. *Proc. Natl. Acad. Sci. U.S.* **42**: 819-830 (1956).
41. Weiss, P. Cell contact. *Intern. Rev. Cytol.* **7**: 391-423 (1958).
42. Weiss, P. Cellular dynamics. *Rev. Modern Phys.* **31**, No. 1, 11-20 (1959).
43. Weiss, P. Guiding principles in cell locomotion and cell aggregation. *Exptl. Cell Research Suppl.* **8**: 260-281 (1961).
44. Weiss, P. The biological foundations of wound repair. *Harvey Lectures Ser.* **55**: 13-42 (1961).
45. Weiss, P. From cell to molecule. *In* "The Molecular Control of Cellular Activity" (J. M. Allen, ed.), pp. 1-72. McGraw-Hill, New York, 1961.
46. Weiss, P. Cells and their environment, including other cells. *In* "Biological Interactions in Normal and Neoplastic Growth" (M. J. Brennan, ed.). Little, Brown, Boston, Massachusetts. In press.
47. Weiss, P. Structure as the coordinating principle in the life of a cell. *In* "Welch Foundation Symposium 1961." In press.
48. Weiss, P., and Andres, G. Experiments on the fate of embryonic cells (chick) disseminated by the vascular route. *J. Exptl. Zool.* **121**: 449-487 (1952).
49. Weiss, P., and Garber, B. Shape and movement of mesenchyme cells as functions of the physical structure of the medium. Contributions to a quantitative morphology. *Proc. Natl. Acad. Sci. U.S.* **38**: 264-280 (1952).
50. Weiss, P., and James, R. Skin metaplasia *in vitro* induced by brief exposure to vitamin A. *Exptl. Cell Research Suppl.* **3**: 381-394 (1955).
51. Weiss, P., and Taylor, A. C. Reconstitution of complete organs from single-cell suspensions of chick embryos in advanced stages of differentiation. *Proc. Natl. Acad. Sci. U.S.* **46**: 1177-1185 (1960).

In reading, in this article, that cells can recognize each other's kinds and can associate or disengage in accordance with their degrees of mutual affinity or disaffinity, one will at once become aware of many similar manifestations of specificity in other biological interactions. This raises the question of whether we might not be dealing here with just a special manifestation of a much more general principle, namely, that of biological communication through pairwise matching specificities. *This question is explored in the following chapter.*

Reprinted from Differentiation and Immunology (Ed. K. Warren), Symposium of International Society for Cell Biology, Vol. 7. Copyright 1968 by Academic Press

MOLECULAR SPECIFICITY—LINK BETWEEN IMMUNOLOGY AND DIFFERENTIATION[1]

PAUL WEISS

Like organic evolution, progress in science draws on two sources. On the one hand, there is the progressive specialization and refinement within individual disciplines, comparable to the selection of adaptive mutations within species, and, on the other hand, there is the emergent novelty resulting from the crossing of formerly isolated lines to yield fertile hybrids, often endowed with hybrid vigor. Cross fertilization has been the intent of this symposium. Studies on *differentiation* and on *immune reactions* in organisms have been running in parallel and relatively independently until rather recently when signs of confluence became apparent. Although the first hybridization attempts between the two antedated the era of modern molecular genetics and macromolecular biology in general, the upsurge of these latter branches presages a firmer union between the studies of development and of immunology into a new hyphenated scientific discipline. The symposium, the major contributions to which are presented in this volume, was organized to give expression to this fact. It had a precursor in a symposium on "Immunology and Development," held twelve years ago [1]. A comparison between these two events is quite instructive. It shows that, whereas advances in technical sophistication and understanding have been made in both lines, though perhaps more in matters of immunology than of differentiation, mutual interaction has remained on a minor scale. Hopefully, this symposium will give it impetus.

Let us look briefly at what to expect from such an interaction. In the first place, since the ability to form antibodies is confined to certain cell types only, the development of the distinctive characteristics of those cells is in itself a prototype of cell differentiation, singularly suitable for rigorous analysis. Many examples of progress in this field will be found throughout the chapters of this book. Conversely, immune sera, prepared against specific tissue types, can serve, by their localized and target-specific effects, to distinguish features of differentiated tissues not dis-

[1] Original work referred to in this introductory chapter was supported in part by Grants CA 10096 and NB 07348 from the National Institutes of Health (U.S. Public Health Service) to Dr. Paul Weiss as principal investigator and by a grant from the Faith Foundation of Houston.

ix

tinguishable by any other criteria. Moreover, as more is becoming known about the genetic basis of antigenic differences and a correlation is beginning to be made with the data of molecular genetics in their bearing on protein synthesis, further pursuit of this relationship might also yield valid models for the molecular correlates of cell differentiation in general. The prospect of success for such an explanatory extrapolation, of course, hinges on how broadly one conceives of that particular phenomenon of "differentiation" that one undertakes to explain.

For instance, one serious difficulty, not generally taken into account in current attempts to establish a cogent link between the total genic endowment of cells, on the one hand, and the typically disparate expressions of that endowment in the diverse cell types of higher organisms on the other, stems from an unwarranted confinement of interest to the phenomenon of *cytodifferentiation*. This focuses on a given cell *individual* during its conversion from a morphologically or otherwise rather undistinguished appearance into a state in which overt structural or cytochemical characters enable an observer to identify the tissue type to which the particular cell individual belongs. Thus, primitive embryonic myoblasts, chondroblasts, and melanoblasts may be almost indistinguishable until they develop their visible signal flags of muscle fibrils, cartilage matrix, or melanin granules, respectively. Various theories have been proposed to explain this process of cytodifferential expression in terms of the masking or derepression of appropriate stretches of the gene string. Yet, however adequate such theories may turn out to be as explanations of the fate of a given cell individual, they do not seem able to account for the major problem of development in higher forms, at least of animals, which is that different somatic cell types, once they have become established in their various differential characters, will keep on breeding true to their acquired characters despite the fact that they all retain essentially the same genic endowment.

Thus, *strain differentiation* gives rise to cells the offspring of which continue to breed true for generations even if reared in a common environment different from, and unrelated to, the original sites and environments in which they attained their primary differentiation [2, 3]. For instance, when cultured *in vitro*, descendants of the various explanted cell types may change considerably in their morphological and functional expressions, but the *differentials* between the progenies of the different strains continue to remain demonstrable, perpetuated without attenuation, let alone abolition. Bacteria, the prime test objects of molecular genetics, can hardly furnish us with models for the self-perpetuation of differentiation of somatic *cell strains* since the generative cell and the somatic cell in bacteria are one and the same. The magnitude of the problem of strain differentiation becomes staggering if one takes account of the great number of intrinsically diversified cell species in a higher animal organism, detectable by cytochemical and physiological differentials, far in excess of the gross distinctions discernible under the microscope.

The categorical distinction between cytodifferentiation and strain differentiation need not imply that some common denominator for both might not eventually be demonstrated. In fact, I have in the past favored the hypothesis that the bifurcation of a single cell line into two distinct true-breeding subspecies might be inaugurated by an erstwhile reversible step of "modulation" of the common ancestral cell from which they stem in one or the other of two alternative directions. But just how the subsequent fixation of the self-perpetuating limitation could be derived simply from an automatic extension of the current molecular vocabulary proposed for cytodifferentiation is to me still quite obscure.

It is in this direction that the lessons of immunology present us with a parallel which might turn out to hold a key to the understanding of strain differentiation in a much wider sense. It lies in the phenomenon of acquired immunity (or conversely, acquired hypersensitivities), in which a cell strain, induced to produce antibodies against a given foreign antigen, continues to yield progeny matching the alien antigen long after the latter has ceased to be physically present. If the term "alien" were to be expanded to include mutually alienated (i.e., disparately differentiated) cell strains of the same organism in contact or interaction, the linkage between theories of immunology and differentiation might become close enough to serve as a point of departure for a more general theory encompassing both. Without prognosticating the eventual outcome, the pursuit of the idea, if only by the juxtaposition of parallelisms of the indicated kind, as in this symposium, seems to be worthwhile in the almost trackless wilderness in which we still find ourselves in the problems of differentiation.

Yet, the potential benefits of close association between immunology and cell biology extend way beyond the problems of differentiation. A few examples of this projection into the future, picked at random, might serve to justify this note of optimism.

Even before the days of modern molecular biology, the crux of the immunological response as symbolized in the key-lock analogy of Paul Ehrlich has been sought in the complementarity of structural (i.e., steric) properties of matching macromolecules. The course of analytical studies since has amply justified that premise. Moreover, it is becoming ever more patent that the principle of molecular complementariness extends far beyond the range of immunological phenomena, being in fact one of the most fundamental properties of biological mechanisms. In my own attempts at finding broad common denominators and explanations for biological phenomena in areas seemingly as disparate as development, immunology, wound-healing, endocrine regulation, growth control, and the functioning of the nervous system, I have been increasingly impressed by the likelihood of reducing many puzzling problems to a single principle of steric matching, key-lock fashion, among molecular systems of *complementary structure* [4], or more generally, *complementary dynamic specifications*. Immunological interactions would merely represent one special manifestation of the same principle, perhaps more intensively studied because of its practical significance, but otherwise a co-equal beneficiary of a universal biological principle which in another version, for instance, appears in all those cell biological and developmental interactions which I have lumped under the label of template-antitemplate processes.

The factual foundations and the rationale underlying this broad generalization have been illustrated in a recent book [5], but can, of course, not be detailed here. However, since the matter, in a way, supports the rationale of the present conference, some spot examples might be briefly cited. In speaking of structural complementarity between interacting macromolecules, for instance, in the rather static structural terms originally formulated by Linus Pauling, in which the strength of bonding among molecules along two closely fitting molecular surfaces, comparable to a mold and its cast, result in the *selective* interaction between two systems, we may for the moment ignore whether the matching configuration was imposed by one partner upon the other in the manner of a true "induction" or whether the interlocking systems had been prematched coincidentally. Even if translated into modern terms of molecular conformation, this phenomenological duality in the origin of conformity remains.

However, as I indicated previously, the static concept of selectivity based on purely configurational complementarity may have to be amended further by adding complementarity of *dynamic* specifications as a candidate for key-lock mechanisms. This addition seems called for in view of the general need for loosening up some of the rather rigid static thinking that cell biology has inherited from its microscopic past, now sometimes even reaching two orders of magnitude farther down into the realm of electron microscopy. The growing isotopic evidence of very rapid turnover of macromolecular populations in the cell, denoting limited stability and durability of any one particular molecular unit per se (other than perhaps DNA) seems to demand a major shift of attention from individual molecules to molecular collectives contributing conjointly and cooperatively to ordered group performances. In the terms of what I once outlined as "molecular ecology," the existence, survival, and operation of any one macromolecule is a critical function of the peculiar constitution and constellation of its immediate local environment, which, in turn, includes other, equally interdependent, molecular species. Macromolecular communities, therefore, are in a sense complex symbiotic groupings of members subtly harmonized to mutual coexistence, as well as to the more general pool of their metabolic requisites. Thus, if one were to consider the surface of a given cell as a metastable mosaic of such macromolecular communities (including among their members lipoproteins, glycoproteins, mucopolysaccharides, etc.) in equilibrated proportions and activity states, perhaps even yielding a resultant periodicity of their group kinetics, one could ascribe specific interactions of that cell with another cell through surface contact to the presence of matching molecular domains of reciprocal kinetic activity patterns in mutual resonance.

As one can see, the regular coded fine structure of macromolecules would then form only part of the true "information content and transmittal" in a cell; partial in that it could become effective only in combination with, and through the agency of, the pulsating or otherwise temporally structured force fields generated by group activity. I mention this highly speculative, but by no means wholly unsubstantiated, scheme merely because in the light of growing realistic acquaintance with the properties of living cells, the empirical concept of "active sites" in the cell surface for intercellular transactions would seem to be more readily amenable to some such solution as here ventured than by sole emphasis on individual macromolecules as solitary agents. At any rate, whatever the precise mechanism of selective cell interactions may turn out to be, and it may indeed operate through a variety of mechanisms employing a common principle, the ubiquity of its use in the coordination of living processes is unmistakable. It is readily documented by the following list of typical examples.

(a) *Selectivity on the molecular scale.* Specificity between antigen and antibody, both in their mutual recognition and selective interaction; selective relation between enzyme and substrate.

(b) *Selective interactions between macromolecule and cell.* Selectivity of cells for food substances, drugs, and products of other cells, such as hormones; selectivity of chemoreceptors for gustatory and olfactory stimulants.

(c) *Selectivity of cells for particles.* Selective phagocytosis; ingestion of food particles by invertebrate cells; selective virus penetration into cells.

(d) *Selective cell-to-cell interactions.* Species-specific impregnation of eggs by sperm; selective conjugation of protozoans; selectivity in the association of cells with like and complementary cell types in tissue formation; selectivity of sensory or motor nerve fibers in either making or shunning synaptic connections with receptor or effector cells, respectively; selectivity of cells, as well as of their processes (e.g., nerve fibers), for matching types of pathways in their migrations ("selective contact guidance"); selectivity of parasites for corresponding hosts.

These examples could be vastly amplified. It will be noted that almost all those listed exemplify the wide variety of biological mechanisms that rely for their target-specificity on prearranged key-lock correspondence between missile and target. Save for the example of antigens determining the configuration of the corresponding antibodies, there is little in the list that would bear directly on one of the salient questions in the differentiation problem: whether there are cases in which there is an actual "induction" of matching specificity in a more plastic cell by a more firmly structured one, implying a veritably "instructive" process, comparable to the molding of a lock to fit a given key. In general, influences of this kind have been suspected whenever a definite criterion of differentiation in a given cell type x known to be normally associated with the presence of a cell type y, failed to develop in the absence of y, but could still be brought out by the timely restitution of y. The pertinence of this simple formulation, however, is belied by the heterogeneity of processes that fit the formula. Again, only a cursory illustration of the complexity of the problem is feasible here, as follows.

The simplest cases deal with ordinary trigger effects that merely release, or rather disinhibit, a preformed further step in an intrinsic cellular reaction sequence, the trigger bearing no specific relation to the pattern of the ensuing event; in cases of this kind, the course of differentiating steps had already been single-tracked in the particular cell strain. Then there are the more strictly differentiating actions in which the "inductive" effect may result from some graded environmental conditions "tipping the scales" in a bivalent cell that is still capable of proceeding in either of two alternative, but mutually exclusive, courses. The favored course gradually monopolizes the synthetic pattern of the cell, and thereby also sets the course of its progeny. In some cases, the decisive environmental threshold might be a simple function of the inorganic content of the medium bathing the cell surface. In other cases, the triggering key action is exerted by special types of molecules (e.g., the switching of secondary sex characters in the male or female direction by the corresponding sex hormones; or the switching of the progeny of an epidermal cell into either a keratinizing or a mucus-producing cell type [6], depending on the concentration of vitamin A in the environment). Only in a minority of instances has it been possible to link the nature of a specific course of differentiation to an "instructive" interaction with a molecule of specifically matching properties, and evidence for an actual transfer from cell to cell of "information-carrying" molecules (e.g., RNA) is even scarcer.

The last-mentioned category is, of course, the only one on this list for which the antigen-antibody type of induction could serve as a model. In the past, I have suggested schemes in which the configuration of molecules facing the outer surface of a cell, in the form of either an adjacent cell surface or of a layer of macromolecules attracted and adsorbed from the medium, could call forth inside the cell a conforming or complementary course of differentiation [7]. I explained this in terms of a selection of favored species of molecules of prematched fitness from among the mixture of templates in the macromolecular population of the cell, rather than as an actual imposition of a new impress on moldable molecules. However, in the light of developments in molecular and cell biology since then, it would seem that, if correct at all, such schemes would have to be carried one step backwards, from the static bonding between molecular entities to the dynamic patterns of synthesis and assembly according to which such macromolecules are constantly being regenerated in the cell. (The reference to "macromolecules" in this generality deliberately avoids any gratuitous specification of their unknown mode of interaction; for instance, as enzymatic, structural, complexing, etc.)

I have extended the hypothesis of a rather universal role of macromolecules of complementary configurations, conducive to pairing, into an explanation of organ-specific or cell type-specific growth control by proposing a feedback regulation of the generation of templates in the cell by the inhibitory action of complementary antitemplates, arising as byproducts of the generative process itself [8]. Although increasingly advocated in current literature, this model is nevertheless still far short of conclusive verification. Even so, the mere fact that the extract of cells of a given type, when offered to a mixture of cell types, *in vitro* or *in vivo*, acts selectively and discriminately on the donor cell type [9, 10], seems reasonably well established, as is, for instance, documented in one of the chapters of this symposium. On the other hand, the nature of the intracellular reactions unlocked by such molecular key-lock mechanisms is still entirely in the realm of speculation and full of uncertainties. Its clarification is evidently a matter of crucial moment for the assessment of any possible scientific basis for the various clinical procedures which refer to "organ-specific" effects, generally lumped under the label of "cellular therapy" [11].

As one may sense after this brief review, as soon as one tries to delve beneath the rather vague and equivocal term "differentiation," one gets entangled in a maze of suppositions and contentions projected from an as yet insufficient background of data. The resultant muddle can perhaps in part be blamed on the common and pardonable tendency of investigators, not excluding myself, to cover the gap from facts to theory in one big leap, instead of filling it more solidly and systematically with the missing links of factual evidence; modern biological verbiage lends itself readily to such saltatory feats. But in the main, the dearth of concrete information on the processes of differentiation stems from the tremendous complexity and intricacy of epigenetic development in higher organisms, the disentanglement of which is an indispensible undertaking, however tedious and unglamorous it may be.

Nevertheless, some general principles are beginning to emerge. Judging from critical evaluation of whatever spotty evidence we have available, it now appears that the progressive diversification (differentiation) among cell strains in higher animals proceeds in long sequences of numerous dichotomous steps, each branching point presenting the cell with only two possible alternatives left over from the series of prior restraining steps the cell strain has already negotiated. The binary choices at each of those road forks are partly made by those extraneous influences impinging upon the cells from their environments that were listed above, but partly the choices are also functions of the field patterns generated by the group dynamics of large cell communities; this latter mode evidently can receive no elucidation from the analytical exploration of only single cells. Each step then sets the stage for the next dichotomy, and so forth, until in the end some cell strains become single-tracked (e.g., erythroblasts, melanoblasts, neuroblasts) while others still retain multiple reactive capacities throughout life (e.g., the cells of connective tissues).

As one can see, the development of the hematopoietic system, including the immunologically competent cell, furnishes us with an exemplary model of such stepwise differentiative divergence among cell strains. This fact, in combination with the involvement of molecular recognition and molecular complementarity in the immunological phenomena, and the further fact that the underlying molecular mechanisms are beginning to be unraveled, make a strong case for closer collaboration and collation of results between students of differentiation and of immunology. To motivate collaborative work and to promote the incipient synthesis is therefore an eminently timely and useful task. To serve it has been the aim of this symposium. Its scope is indicated by the wide variety of interrelated topics presented at the meeting and published herein. As was to be expected, the spirit of convergence and the prospects for more concerted progress in the future became more evident in the unpublished free and frank discussions than in the formal printed presentations. However, even the sheer juxtaposition of these papers will further the cause. One point will not have gone unnoticed. I am referring to the fact that the program has been more heavily weighted toward the immunological end than toward the discussion of differentiation. The reason is simply that there is so much more known about the former than about the latter. If perusal of this book stimulates some readers to help redress that imbalance, the symposium will have more than served its purpose.

A debt of deep gratitude is due to the Oak Ridge National Laboratory, especially to Drs. Fuller and Kimball for providing help in the arrangements for the conference, to Drs. Makinodan and Papaconstantinou of the staff for assistance in the preparatory phase, and particularly to Dr. Papaconstaninou for his exceedingly effective contribution to the successful conduct of the meetings. Moreover, on behalf of the International Society for Cell Biology, I want to express as its President most grateful appreciation to the Editor, Dr. Katherine Warren, who has selflessly undertaken the job of collecting, editing, and chaperoning the manuscripts into print.

REFERENCES

1. Edds, M. V., Jr., ed., "Immunology and Development," 59 pp. Univ. Chicago Press, Chicago, Illinois, 1958.
2. Weiss, P., Some introductory remarks on the cellular basis of differentiation. *J. Embryol. Exptl. Morphol.* 1, 181–211 (1953).
3. Defendi, V., ed., "Retention of Functional Differentiation in Cultured Cells," 66 pp. Wistar Inst. Press, Philadelphia, Pennsylvania, 1964.
4. Weiss, P., The problem of specificity in growth and development. *Yale J. Biol. Med.* 19, 235–278 (1947).
5. Weiss, P., "Dynamics of Development: Experiments and Inferences," 624 pp. Academic Press, New York, 1968.
6. Fell, H. B., and Mellanby, E., Metaplasia produced in cultures of chick ectoderm by high Vitamin A. *J. Physiol.* (*London*) 119, 470–488 (1953).
7. Weiss, P., Perspectives in the field of morphogenesis. *Quart. Rev. Biol.* 25, 177–198 (1950).
8. Weiss, P., and Kavanau, L., A model of growth and growth control in mathematical terms. *J. Gen. Physiol.* 41, 1–47 (1957).

9. Weiss, P., Specificity in growth control. *in* "Biological Specificity and Growth" (E. G. Butler, ed.), pp. 195–206. Princeton Univ. Press, Princeton, New Jersey, 1955.
10. Andres, G., Growth reactions of mesonephros and liver to intravascular injections of embryonic liver and kidney suspensions in the chick embryo. *J. Exptl. Zool.* **130**, 221–249 (1955).
11. Schmid, F., and Stein, J., eds., "Zellforschung und Zellulartherapie," 579 pp. Huber, Bern, 1963.

Once recognized as the common means of biological communication, it was rather obvious to examine macromolecular specificity *as the possible key to the understanding of* organ-specific growth control *by chemical feedback. Some of the widely scattered data that support that notion rather compellingly are summarized in the next article.*

Reprinted from Biological Specificity and Growth (Ed. E. G. Butler). Copyright 1955 by Princeton University Press

SPECIFICITY IN GROWTH CONTROL

BY PAUL WEISS[1]

IN ESSENCE, this chapter is a sequel to the general discussion of "Specificity in Development and Growth" given before the Society for the Study of Development and Growth in 1945 (P. Weiss, '47). Of the problems raised then, that of growth control will be singled out here for special consideration. The account will be confined to illustrative examples, with no attempt at reviewing the subject comprehensively.

"Specificity" is understood here as that property of two interacting systems, A and B, which permits A to react to B with some degree of selectivity. Biological specificity, as previously outlined, is a basic property of living systems and is most prominently displayed in drug responses, hormone actions, gene effects, immunological reactions, host-parasite relations, and developmental mechanisms. A common denominator in biochemical, presumably stereochemical, terms is indicated. Translated to these terms, specificity in growth confronts us with four separate issues: (1) the fact that the various cell strains of the body are different biochemically; (2) the possibility that biochemical distinctiveness may be not only a by-product of differentiation but also an instrumental factor in growth; (3) the possibility that this may constitute a mechanism for the humoral coordination and regulation of growth processes throughout the organism; and (4) the hypothesis that this regulatory function presupposes the generation in each cell strain of paired compounds of complementary configuration, after the antigen-antibody scheme.

I. THE BIOCHEMICAL MOSAIC

It has been stressed on previous occasions (Weiss, '49) that cells are "speciated" into biochemically diverse strains, indeed strains of much greater diversity and subtlety than are morphologically discernible. My attention was first drawn to this fact by the discovery of the

[1] Department of Zoology, University of Chicago. Present address of the author is: Rockefeller Institute for Medical Research, New York, N.Y. This chapter is dedicated by the author to Professor F. Baltzer of the University of Bern, Switzerland, on the occasion of his seventieth birthday. It represents a condensed version of the paper of the same title presented at the 1953 Growth Symposium.

Original work referred to in this chapter has been aided by grants from the Wallace C. and Clara A. Abbott Memorial Fund, University of Chicago; the American Cancer Society upon recommendation of the Committee on Growth of the National Research Council; and the National Institutes of Health, Public Health Service.

[195]

strict constitutional specificity of individual muscles and skin territories (Weiss, '52), but all the localized effects of hormones and drugs on different predisposed cell groups point to the same conclusion. Different organs are thus composed of cell strains of specifically different biochemical constitutions. On the other hand, organs occurring in pairs or other multiples may be assumed to be composed of biochemically similar cells. Such similarity of composition might provide a means of selective chemical communication between homologous cell groups regardless of spatial separation.

The existence of some such active interrelation between paired structures is indicated, for instance, by the observation that injury to a given nerve is often followed by an involvement of the symmetrical nerve (Greenman, '13, Nittono, '23, Koester, '03, Tamaki, '36). It is more definitely evinced by the compensatory growth reactions of one of a pair of organs after removal of the other.

II. HOMOLOGOUS COMPENSATION

A "spontaneous" spurt of growth of the residual parts of a partially removed organ system has been described for many objects : contralateral appendages in annelids (Zeleny, '02, '05) ; claws in Crustacea (Przibram, '07) ; kidneys in mammals (Golgi, 1882, Ribbert, '04, Arataki, '26, Rollason, '49) ; testes in mammals (Ribbert, 1895) and fishes (Robertson, '54) ; lungs (Haasler, 1891) ; and orbital glands (Teir, '51). Liver regeneration following partial ablation (e.g. Brues, '36) and blood cell regeneration after hemorrhage are in the same category. In all these cases the response is essentially confined to the homologous tissue and consists primarily of intensified reproduction of homologous protoplasm, which may take the form of cellular hypertrophy, hyperplasia, or regeneration. Necrosis may produce similar effects as extirpation.

The explanation of such compensatory growth has often been sought in the excessive functional load placed upon the remaining fraction of the organ system. However, neither the invertebrate cases nor the testes and orbital glands of the above list fit such an explanation. I, therefore, considered it more likely that these phenomena are manifestations of a much more general principle, namely the active maintenance of the total mass of each organ system in an equilibrium state and the return to that state after disturbance by virtue of a chemical communication system in which specific releases from each cell type, circulating in the body, would inform the homologous cell types of the state of their total mass. A test of this theory requires the demonstration that, (1) compounds produced by

[196]

a given cell type have some selective effect on the same cell type, and (2) that this homologous effect is instrumental in the regulation of growth.

III. HOMOLOGOUS ORGAN-SPECIFIC EFFECTS

Evidence for the first point is contained in the observations of Danchakoff ('16) and of Willier ('24), who found enlarged spleens in chick embryos whose chorio-allantoic membranes had received spleen grafts. Weiss and Wang ('41), unaware of these results but corroborating them fully (see Weiss, '47), found that minute fragments of liver incorporated in the extraembryonic area of a chick embryo caused the host liver to grow to excessive dimensions. Implants of other tissues either had no effects or their effects were much less marked. The results with spleen were later confirmed and expanded by Ebert ('51). Along the same line, balancers implanted into the body cavity of urodele larvae affect the resorption of the host balancers specifically (Kollros, '40), as shown by the absence of a similar interference from implanted gills. Thus, there are definitely specific chemical effects transmitted humorally from a given type of organ to other cell groups of the same type, and these effects entail alterations of growth and size. Contrary to the inference from compensatory growth after partial removal, however, the experimental addition of tissue in these experiments produced no decrease, but rather a further increase of the homologous host tissue. Therefore, while the specificity of the growth reaction was clearly demonstrated, the sign of the reaction was paradoxical. This in itself was a significant revelation and we shall return to it below.

IV. IMMUNOLOGICAL REVERSAL OF ORGAN-SPECIFIC COMPOUNDS

My original concept had been that: (1) cell populations of a given type keep their total mass in check by producing, as they grow, compounds which would repress the growth process in proportion to their concentration ("feed-back" fashion); (2) this self-inhibition would be due to steric complementariness between these inhibitor compounds and the specific catalysts of growth in each cell type; and (3) the assumed complementariness might be of the antigen-antibody type. On this assumption a series of experiments was started in 1938 to test the effects that antibodies to organ-specific compounds, rather than the compounds themselves, might exert on the embryonic growth of the homologous organs (Weiss, '39; see Weiss, '47).

The fact that antibodies to organ extracts may affect corresponding

[197]

organs selectively, mostly by damaging homologous cells, has been clearly demonstrated for the lens (Guyer and Smith, '18), the kidney (Smadel, '36, Pressman, '49), and others. Our injections of anti-liver and anti-kidney sera into chick embryos, however, entailed again larger sizes, rather than damage, of the homologous host organs. This could of course be ascribed to an initial damaging effect followed by repair with overcompensation. At any rate the specificity of the effect, if not its sign, seemed to have been ascertained, and the demonstration that organ-specific compounds did not lose their specific effectiveness by immunological (steric?) reversal seemed to give validity to the concept that these experiments were intended to test.

Although war work had interrupted this investigative program, its main premises and theoretical foundations were summarized in my discussion of specificity at the Growth Symposium in 1945. Purely as a guide in planning further research and in trying to reconcile the paradoxical results of the past, I have adhered to the particular concept of growth control that I had outlined previously (Weiss, '47, p. 272-273; '49, p. 180-181). Its pragmatic value has proven itself by bringing disparate results to a common denominator and by suggesting the design of new experiments reported further below.

V. A CONCEPT OF SPECIFIC GROWTH CONTROL

This concept is based on the following suppositions.

(1) Each specific cell type reproduces its protoplasm, i.e. "grows," by a mechanism in which key compounds that are characteristic of the individual cell type act as catalysts. The postulated cell-specific diversity of compounds is the chemical correlate of the "differentiation" of cell strains. Growth rate is proportional to the concentration of these intracellular specific catalysts (or "templates") in the free or active state. Under normal conditions these compounds remain confined within the cell.

(2) Each cell also produces compounds ("antitemplates") which can inhibit the former species by combining with them into inactive complexes. These may be turned out as direct by-products in the process of protoplasmic reproduction or be secondary differentiation products. They may be steric complements to the former or matched to them in some other fashion. The only prerequisites are: (a) that, contrary to the specific templates, they are released from the cell and get into the extracellular space and into circulation; (b) that they carry the specific tag of their producer cell type which endows them with selective affinity

[198]

for any cell of the same type; and (c) that they are in constant production so as to make up for their extracellular decomposition and final excretion.

(3) As the concentration of "antitemplates" in the extracellular medium increases, their intracellular density, hence inactivation of corresponding "templates," will likewise increase; in short, growth rate will decline in all cells belonging to that particular strain bathed by the common humoral pool. When stationary equilibrium between intracellular and extracellular concentration is reached, growth will cease. This mechanism results in a sigmoid growth curve for the total mass of each organ system (see Morales and Kreutzer, '45), and the familiar sigmoid curve for the whole organism would essentially be an aggregate of similar curves for the individual constituent organ systems.

This general concept offers a rational explanation for both the self-limiting character of growth in a confined medium (organism or culture) and the homologous organ-specific growth reactions after experimental interference. As can readily be seen, each interference will have to be examined in a dual light as to its effects on the concentration of both "templates" and "antitemplates," since it is the ratio of both that determines growth rate. The following conclusions can immediately be deduced from this scheme.

(a) Removal of part of an organ system removes part of the sources of the corresponding types of "templates" and "antitemplates." Since the former, according to our premise (1), have been in intracellular confinement, neither their former presence nor their recent loss are perceptible to other cells of the system. This is not so for the "antitemplates," which are in circulation and a reduction of whose production source would promptly be recognized by their lowered concentration in the extracellular pool. According to points (2) and (3) this would shift the intracellular ratio of "templates" to "antitemplates" temporarily in favor of the former, causing automatic resumption of growth till a steady state is restored—to all intents a "compensatory" growth reaction.

(b) Addition of a part should have opposite effects depending on whether or not its cells survive, or rather on the ratio of surviving to disintegrating cells. If all cells survive, the net effect would be an increased concentration in the circulation of the particular "antitemplates," hence a reduction in growth rate of the corresponding host system, provided it is still in a phase of growth (actual regression after growth has ceased need not be expected). On the other hand, cells that disinte-

[199]

grate release into the extracellular space a complement of specific "templates" that would otherwise never have escaped. Assuming that these, according to point (2), combine with or otherwise trap homologous "antitemplates," their presence in the pool will entail a temporary lowering of "antitemplate" concentration—hence again a spurt of growth in the homologous cell strains of the host. The simultaneous release of "antitemplates" from the disintegrating cells would have to be assumed to be insufficient to cancel this effect because of their faster metabolic degradation (see point 2c). An alternative possibility is that "templates" freed from cracked cells are directly adopted by homologous cells, where they would temporarily increase the intracellular concentration of growth catalysts—hence growth rate. In either scheme the release of cell content would accelerate homologous growth by increasing the intracellular ratio of "templates" to "antitemplates"—in the former case by reducing the denominator, in the latter case by increasing the numerator. It can be seen that in terms of this interpretation partial necrosis of an organ will have the same effect as partial removal, and that implantation of a fragment followed by some degeneration, as well as the injection of cell debris, are merely further variants of the same procedure.

To test the validity of this concept the following series of experiments were undertaken. In contrast to our earlier attempts, the assay of growth responses by measurements of size attained after a given period was abandoned as too unreliable; not only do such measurements fail to distinguish between the specific components of an organ and its content of connective tissue and blood, but also initial growth reactions can easily be missed due to secondary regulations or even overcompensations. Instead the mitotic index was introduced as a more sensitive and reliable criterion. A large series of experiments on the stimulation of mitotic activity in amphibian skin (Weiss and Overton; mostly still unpublished) has conclusively shown that cell division is secondary to cell growth; hence, if present it can be used as an index of protoplasmic increase. The same conclusion can be drawn from the precession of the increase of mass over that of cell number in liver regeneration (Brues, Drury, and Brues, '36).

VI. COMPENSATORY HYPERPLASIA WITHOUT FUNCTIONAL OVERLOAD

One of the inferences from our theory is that the "compensatory" growth of one member of a pair of organs after the removal or destruction of the other would be attributable to the disturbance of the described

[200]

chemical equilibrium rather than to the burden of augmented functional activity. In view of the well-established compensatory hypertrophy of the remaining kidney after unilateral kidney removal, this experiment was repeated with the embryonic metanephros of the chick at a stage prior to the onset of its excretory function, the latter function being still fully exercised by the mesonephros. Wayne Ferris in our laboratory cauterized one metanephros in 12- to 13-day embryos and counted the mitotic response in the undamaged residual kidney fixed within 2 days after the operation. On the basis of a total count of 12,000 mitoses in 12 controls and 15 experimental cases, 4 of them sham operations, an average increase of 70 per cent was noted on the unharmed side that could be definitely identified as a response to the destruction of kidney tissue rather than to injury as such. In fact the effect was confined to the specific epithelium while the connective tissue stroma remained unaffected.

This demonstration of direct compensatory growth reactions resulting from disturbance of the intracellular-extracellular balance of complementary organ-specific compounds in no way rules out the occurrence of true "functional" hypertrophy as a result of overload; the relative roles played by the two processes will presumably vary from object to object. Moreover, in the endocrine system additional compensatory regulations arise from the reciprocity of hormone relations between different glands.

The direct chemical balance reaction illustrated above may turn out to be a ubiquitous and general principle to which functional and hormonal effects would be merely superimposed. Several considerations indicate its general validity. For instance the observation of an increase in the undamaged liver of one partner of a pair of parabiosed rats following partial removal of the liver of the other partner (Bucher, Scott, and Aub, '51; Wenneker and Sussman, '51) lends itself to the same interpretation.[2] In fact the correlation of liver regeneration rate with blood flow (Flores, '52) and the increase of this rate when the blood is diluted (Glinos and Gey, '52), thus reducing the concentration of our hypothetical liver-"antitemplates" in the circulation, add further support to our interpretation.

[2] Further confirmation has recently been produced by Friedrich-Freksa and Zaki (*Ztschr. Naturf. 9b*, 394-397) who found mitotic spurts in the livers of normal rats injected intraperitoneally with serum from partially hepatectomized animals.

[201]

VII. INJECTION OF CELL DEBRIS

Homologous growth effects were also obtained by the direct injection into the embryonic blood stream of triturated cell masses from kidney or liver, either fresh or after freezing and thawing. These experiments, carried out by Gert Andres in our laboratory (in press in *Journal of Experimental Zoology*) and involving a count of 86,000 mitoses, demonstrated that the mitotic ratio of host kidney to host liver is within a day significantly ($P < 0.001$) raised by the injection of kidney material, and lowered by liver material, each organ debris exerting an homologous effect.

Comparable results on a smaller scale have been reported for the orbital glands of rats following intraperitoneal injection of homologous extract (Teir, '52).

VIII. HOMOLOGOUS ORGAN EXTRACT IN TISSUE CULTURE

In the light of our theory, the common observation of a "growth-stimulating" effect of embryo extract on the proliferation of tissue cultures would be accounted for by the fact that, since embryo extract contains cell debris of all organs, the growth of any tissue explanted in it would be favored. In order to put this contention to a test, large series of tissue cultures of kidney and heart were set up in paired media, one containing extract of the complete embryo, the other, extract from which the homologous organ was omitted. The experiments, carried out with Ilse Fischer, showed remarkable differences between the two sets of conditions.

In the kidney experiments (6,300 cultures of 12-day mesonephros and 2,335 cultures of 9- or 17- to 20-day metanephros), the frequency of tubule differentiation was used as a criterion. In the presence of kidney extract this frequency was greatly reduced. Since differentiation in tissue culture is generally conceded to be in some inverse relation to the intensity of proliferation, this result could be interpreted as an homologous growth stimulation by the kidney debris in the medium.

In the heart cultures the differentiation of new myofibrils, evidenced by continued pulsation in successive transfers with subdivision, was used as a sign of depressed growth. In a first series of 978 paired cultures, with and without extract of 5- to 6-day hearts, a large preponderance of pulsation was found in the absence of heart extract, signifying presumably reduced growth. In a later reinvestigation (with Margaret W. Cavanaugh) it was noted, however, that the effect could not be

[202]

definitely established unless the embryo extract was from embryos older than about 9 days. After this time it made a great deal of difference for heart cultures whether or not heart extract was present in the medium. Such an age effect was previously reported by Gaillard for tissue cultures in general and by Ebert ('51) for the growth stimulation of spleen by chorio-allantoic spleen grafts. Possibly the "growth-promoting" potency ascribed by Hoffman and Doljansky ('39) to heart extract can be related to the fact that their standard assay objects were heart fibroblasts.

An extension of our experiments to tissue cultures of skin and thyroid has thus far given no comparable results, presumably because of the lack of sharp criteria. Even so, the use of tissue culture for the further analysis of these homologous growth interactions between specific cell types and corresponding cell constituents in the culture medium seems to hold much promise. Whether cell compounds in the extract promote homologous growth by being directly incorporated into the corresponding cells, or by neutralizing homologous growth inhibitors in the medium, is still unresolved.

IX. IMMUNOLOGICAL EXPERIMENTS

After these varied reconfirmations of the effect of cell extracts on homologous growth, it became particularly intriguing to resume our original attempts to secure similar effects with antibodies against specific organ extracts. As mentioned above, we had found livers and kidneys of chick embryos, treated with liver- or kidney-antisera, respectively, to be significantly larger than after treatment with non-homologous antisera. A repetition of the liver experiments confirmed the size increase but proved it to be due to hemorrhages from specifically damaged liver vessels. The homology of the action is still evident but its relation to growth is unsubstantiated. Injection of anti-lens serum likewise failed to produce any appreciable effect on the growth of the host lenses (work with Audrey Peterson).

After these failures to detect specific growth alterations from anti-organ sera, it seemed necessary to turn back one step and ascertain whether or not at least the preferential incorporation of anti-organ sera in homologous embryonic organs could be proved. Immumological reactions of specific embryonic tissues to homologous antibodies have been demonstrated (Burke et al., '44; Ebert, '50; Grunwalt, '49), and it was rather obvious to try to demonstrate the selective absorption directly by using isotope-tagged antibodies. Unfortunately five years of continued efforts in that direction have failed to produce the expected re-

[203]

sults (immunological work with the aid of D. H. Campbell, California Institute of Technology, and Robert Petzold; experiments and isotope assays aided by Gert Andres, Howard Holtzer, Margaret W. Cavanaugh, Evelyn R. Mills, and James Lash).

Antibodies tagged with C_{14}-glycine injected into the yolk sac were concentrated in the embryo, but proved to be of too low titer and radioactivity for a test of selective distribution. We then turned to purified antibody preparations (gamma globulin fraction) tagged with I_{131} according to Pressmann and injected directly into embryonic veins by the technique of Weiss and Andres ('52). Radiation assays proved that the injected material was differentially distributed throughout the embryonic tissues, with blood, heart, and kidneys showing the highest concentrations and other organs following in a certain order. However, there was no evidence of greater absorption of a given organ-antibody by the homologous embryonic organ. It remains undecided whether these failures are due to technical imperfections or actually prove that organ anti-sera are not absorbed in demonstrably larger quantities in the homologous cells of the embryo. It is quite possible, of course, that if growth promotion by these antibodies were of a catalytic nature, even amounts too small to be detectable could exert potent effects.

X. CONCLUSIONS

From this brief survey it seems that the existence of a cell-type specific chemical mechanism of correlating growth processes among homologous cell types must not only be postulated but also also may be regarded as conclusively demonstrated. As for the nature of this mechanism, my own concept or theory, advanced on previous occasions and reiterated here, has proved its value as a guide but must not be taken to have been either proved or disproved. In its current form it is probably too simple to be wholly correct; further work will amend or even replace it. But the general idea of selective chemical communication among cells of identical types by direct exchange of protoplasmic type-specific compounds can hardly be questioned in view of the large evidence in its favor. My earlier detailed suggestion that the complementary systems of growth-catalyzing and growth-repressing compounds are of the antigen-antibody class has found no direct support in our further immunological studies; but it has not been definitely ruled out. Immunoembryology has made vigorous strides of late, but most of that work has been devoted to the detection and tracing by immunological techniques of the appearance of certain antigens during differentiation, e.g. Cooper

[204]

('50), Woerdemann ('53), ten Cate ('50), Schechtmann ('52), and Clayton ('53), rather than to the possible instrumental role of these systems as determining and regulatory factors, as I had originally proposed. This latter view, also adopted by Tyler ('47) in an extension of his earlier ideas on "autoantibodies" to problems of growth, therefore remains open to question, but it still deserves to be kept in mind, if only as a model.

BIBLIOGRAPHY

Arataki, M. 1926. *Am. J. Anat. 36,* 437-450.
Brues, A. M., D. R. Drury, and M. C. Brues. 1936. *Arch. Path. 22:* 658-673.
Bucher, N. L. R., J. F. Scott, and J. C. Aub. 1951. *Cancer Res. 11,* 457-465.
Burke, V., N. P. Sullivan, H. Peterson, and R. Weed. 1944. *J. Infect. Dis. 74,* 225-233.
ten Cate, G., and W. J. Van Doorenmaalen. 1950. *Proc. Kon. Ned. Ak. Wetensch. 53,* 894.
Clayton, R. M. 1953. *J. Embryol. Exp. Morph. 1,* 25-42.
Cooper, R. S. 1950. *J. Exp. Zool. 114,* 403-420.
Danchakoff, V. 1916. *Am. J. Anat. 20,* 255-327.
Ebert, J. D. 1950. *J. Exp. Zool. 115,* 351-378.
Ebert, J. D. 1951. *Physiol. Zool. 24,* 20-41.
Flores, N. 1952. *C. R. Soc. Biol. 146,* 589-591.
Glinos, A. D., and G. O. Gey. 1952. *Proc. Soc. Exp. Biol. Med. 80,* 421-425.
Golgi, C. 1882. *Arch. ital. biol. 2.*
Greenman, M. J. 1913. *J. Comp. Neurol. 23,* 479-513.
Grunwaldt, E. 1949. *Texas Reports on Biol. Med. 7,* 270-317.
Guyer, M. F., and E. A. Smith. 1918. *J. Exp. Zool. 26,* 65-82.
Haasler. 1891. *Centralbl. allg. Path. path. Anat. 2,* 809.
Hoffmann, R. S., and L. Doljanski. 1939. *Growth 3,* 61-71.
Kollros, J. J. 1940. *J. Exp. Zool. 85,* 33-52.
Köster, G. 1903. *Neurol. Centralbl. S. 1093.*
Morales, M. F., and F. L. Kreutzer. 1945. *Bull. Math. Biophysics 7,* 15-24.
Nittono, K. 1923. *J. Comp. Neurol. 35,* 133-161.
Pressman, D. 1949. *Cancer 2,* 697-700.
Przibram, H. 1907. *Roux' Arch. 25,* 266-343.
Ribbert, H. 1895. *Roux' Arch. 1,* 69-90.
Ribbert, H. 1904. *Arch. f. Entwicklgmech. 18,* 267-288.
Robertson, O. H. 1954. In publication; personal communication.
Rollason, H. D. 1949. *Anat. Rec. 104,* 263-285.
Schechtman, A. M., and H. Hoffman. 1952. *J. Exp. Zool. 120,* 375-390.
Smadel, J. E. 1936. *J. Exp. Med. 64,* 921-942.
Tamaki, K. 1936. *J. Comp. Neurol. 64,* 437-448.
Teir, H. 1951. *Commentationes Biol. 13,* 1-32.
Teir, H. 1952. *Acta pathol. et microbiol. Scand. 30,* 158-183.
Tyler, A. 1947. *Growth 10* (suppl.), 7-19.

Weiss, P. 1939. *Anat. Rec. 75* (suppl.), 67.
Weiss, P. 1947. *Yale J. Biol. Med. 19,* 235-278.
Weiss, P. 1949. *Chemistry and Physiology of Growth,* pp. 135-186, Princeton Univ. Press.
Weiss, P. 1952. *Publ. Ass. Res. Nerv. Ment. Dis. 30,* 3-23.
Weiss, P., and G. Andres. 1952. *J. Exp. Zool. 121,* 449-488.
Weiss, P., and H. Wang. 1941. *Anat. Rec. 79,* 62.
Wenneker, A. S., and N. Sussman. 1951. *Proc. Soc. Exp. Biol. Med. 76,* 683-686.
Willier, B. H. 1924. *Am. J. Anat. 33,* 67-103.
Woerdeman, M. W. 1953. *Arch. Neerland. Zool. 10* (suppl.), 144-162.
Zeleny, Ch. 1902. *Roux' Arch. 13,* 597-609.
Zeleny, Ch. 1905. *J. Exp. Zool. 2,* 1-102.

The discussion of growth control *as one of the mechanisms by which the organism tends to maintain stability and equilibrium, and to restore them after non-disruptive disturbances, leads logically over to the consideration of one of the most common instances of the recuperative power of the body*—wound healing.

---

[206]

THE BIOLOGICAL FOUNDATIONS OF
WOUND REPAIR*†

PAUL WEISS

TO present a Harvey Lecture is not only a privilege, but a real opportunity: an invitation to take leave from the minutiae of laboratory work and to present instead, in bold perspective, a synthesis and forward projection of trends of research and thought. The boldness—or crudeness—of such a bird's-eye-view of a field of study is in direct proportion to either our power of abstraction or our blurred vision in not having perceived the details to begin with. Valid abstraction brings great intellectual and esthetic satisfaction, compared to which the mere correction of defective vision seems an uninspiring task. Nevertheless, in dealing with the living organism, the more we learn about it, the more we realize that a view from ever greater distance only too often leads to generalities, rather than useful generalizations; that there is no alternative to a realistic study of its detailed mechanisms; and therefore, that progress often will hinge on taking a closer, rather than a more distant, look. In this presentation, I mean to document this fact; foregoing thus the tempting opportunity to treat myself to an exposure of the broader and bolder generalizations in which I have at times indulged.

A living organism is an immensely complex machinery. Merely to state this is a platitude. Yet, to resolve that complexity remains the perennial challenge and task of analytical research; resolve it, not just obliterate it or gloss over it by physical or mental homo-

* Lecture delivered October 15, 1959.

† Elements of this lecture were previously presented in a Litchfield Lecture at the University of Oxford, and in lectures at Albany Medical College and at the Istituto Superiore di Sanità in Rome. Some of the experimental investigations referred to have been aided by grants from the American Cancer Society and the National Institutes of Health (United States Public Health Service).

13

genization. Success with disentangling the complicated machinery of the organism is rapidly advancing our knowledge of its composition, structure, and functioning. Compared with this, our insight into the mechanisms of development—the understanding of just how that complex machinery elaborates itself in orderly fashion from the infinitely simpler egg, and once matured, keeps itself continuously in renovation and repair—is still in a most fragmentary state. Perhaps there has been too much of a monopoly of attention given to the egg and early germ. Development continues throughout life, and many of its components appear in more elementary form, hence lend themselves more readily to analysis, in later stages. The repair of tissue damage by healing and regeneration is one of these.

Not only is wound healing an important source of knowledge about development, but what we learn about development, in turn, furthers the medical practices of wound repair. Which brings me to a major thesis of my talk: that in essence, biology and clinical medicine are but the two ends of a continuous spectrum, inseparably connected and interacting to mutual benefit. I shall try to illustrate this thesis by samples of experimental work from my own laboratory, some new, some old, touching on several basic problems of development. In reviewing this work, I think with deep gratitude of the integral part that my collaborators and students have played in its execution, foremost among them my long-time colleague, A. C. Taylor, with his unbounded resourcefulness. But whatever interest the factual results may command, my prime purpose in presenting them is to convey a message of overriding importance in the scene of contemporary biology and medicine, and it is this:

Let us ever be on guard lest we glibly accept a generality for knowledge, or an appealing term for insight. Developmental biology is full of general terms—"induction," "genic control," "hormonal integration," "correlative differentiation," and what not—which name the problems, but do not solve them and are no substitutes for disciplined and realistic analysis. A machine is built not by a string of words, but by the stepwise assemblage of real things. Consequently, no real understanding of the construction process can be gained except by reconstructing, step by step and factually, the true chain of events. There is no short cut to knowledge. To come to the point, just contrast some of the labels attached to wound healing with the dearth of factual information about their content. We speak of "trauma," "wound hormones," "metabolic products," without specifying and identifying any of them. We invoke "healing tendencies" and "tropisms," unmindful of their mechanisms, and end up in doctoring a lesion with tinctures and salves empirically, without much of a notion of why and how they are supposed to work. My plea is that in the study of mechanisms—and development works through mechanisms—concreteness take precedence over abstraction.

The surgeon, like the rest of us, is faced with organs and tissues on a macroscopic scale. Skin looks not too different from leather; a tendon or a nerve looks like a string. But when a bruised or burned skin is to heal, or a cut tendon or nerve is to be mended, the relevant events take place not in the macroscopic, but in the microscopic and submicroscopic realm. The sole performers in the reparative process are the microscopic cells. For them to cross a gap of a few centimeters between the retracted ends of a cut nerve or tendon is about the same feat as is to us the crossing of a mile-wide range with rivers, lakes, and mountains. Therefore, to understand and improve wound healing, we must scale ourselves down to the dimensions of the cells and acquaint ourselves with their world in their own terms, as Gulliver had to do with the Lilliputians. This we shall now attempt.

For simplicity, we turn to an elementary kind of skin—that of larval amphibians. It consists of a smooth epithelial sheet, just two or three cells high, resting on a tough, fibrous cell-free membrane (Fig. 1). Yet even in this simple structure, repair of injury involves a combination of processes and maneuvers almost as complex as a military campaign. This is what happens after an injury (Fig. 2) (see Weiss, 1959). The wound edge retracts, and a colloidal exudate covers the lesion. Then the epidermal cells, which had been firmly attached to the basement membrane, become detached and mobilized. They then start spreading over the wound. As they advance, the next rank of cells behind them is mobilized, then the next one, and so forth, until the whole marginal area is on the march. It is this migration, rather than growth, that establishes the primary closure of a skin wound. The converging fronts finally meet head-on and almost instantaneously stop in their tracks. Growth with mitotic cell division continues and makes up for the loss of emigrated cells. This likewise drops back to normal as tissue continuity is restored. There follows then a phase of functional adaptation, during which earlier irregularities and scars are remodeled in harmony with the mechanical and physiological conditions of the old skin. There are many more chapters to this story—e.g., the so-called wound contracture (see Grillo *et al.,* 1958) or the rebound of a lesion on the general metabolic and endocrine state of the body, which in its turn then affects the various local components of the healing process (see Moore, 1958)—but these few may suffice to indicate the composite nature of the healing process. We shall now look at each one of these separate steps somewhat more closely. Each one presents peculiar problems, defying any attempt to embrace them all in a single general formula.

First, as for the early exudate, not much is known about it. Save for a few beginnings (e.g., Friedenwald *et al.,* 1945), no one seems to have studied it effectively. Presumably it is a mixture of coagulated tissue juice, blood, cell debris, and cell discharges. The presence of blood fibrin and other fibrous units in this primary wound cover is important because, as I shall explain shortly, such fibers act as pathways for the moving cells.

The second major step is cell detachment. In stationary skin, the epidermal cells are rather firmly applied to the underlying membrane. This attachment used to be considered a simple matter

---

FIG. 1. Survey section through dorsal crest of amphibian larva, showing the simple skin coat (*e*) over the enclosed gelatinous connective tissue (*c*). (Original: J. Overton.)

FIG. 2. Schematic representation of sequence of main steps in the healing of a skin wound in amphibian larvae.

FIG. 3. Electron micrograph of underside of epidermal cell attached to basement lamella by "bobbins." From Weiss (1958).

FIG. 4. Electron micrograph of epidermal cell (*e*) detached from underlying basement lamella (*b*), 1 hour after wounding of neighboring skin. Note the free "bobbins" in the detached surface. (Original: Weiss and Ferris.)

FIG. 5. Diagram of tissue culture in hanging drop of blood plasma.

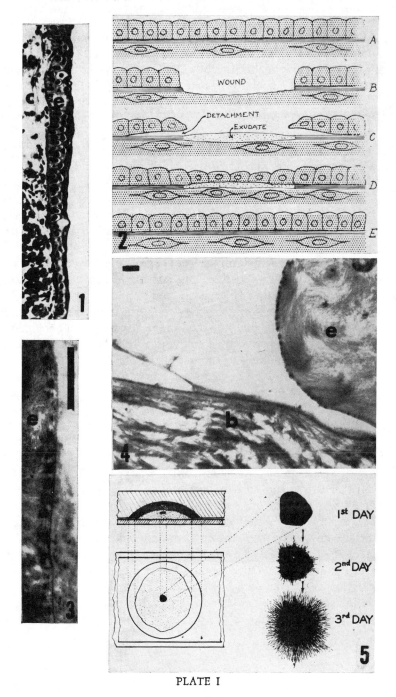

PLATE I

of adhesion in terms of general colloid-physical properties of the contacting surfaces. Electron microscopy, however, suggests a much more elaborate mechanism. It shows (Fig. 3) the underside of the epidermal cell to be dotted with submicroscopic bodies in the shape of "bobbins" about 2000–2500 Å high (Weiss and Ferris, 1954a). Combining chemical and enzymatic treatments with electron microscopy, we could dissect these bodies into two disks rich in lipids, separated by a hydrophilic belt, the outer disk lying in the cell surface (Weiss, 1958). This cell surface rests on a granulated layer, about 500 Å thick, which binds the cell to the basement membrane (Weiss and Ferris, 1954b). Being readily dissolved by salivary amylase, it presumably contains much carbohydrate. When an epidermis cell is made to shrink—for instance, by hypertonic solutions or formalin fixation—all its basal surface retracts from the substratum with the exception of the lipid-rich bobbins: they remain firmly stuck (Weiss, 1958). From this we judge that they are veritable hold-fast mechanisms. The devices for attachment are thus quite special and elaborate.

Now, when skin is injured, the bobbins of cells near the wound give up their hold (Fig. 4), the binding layer becomes free, and the whole cell, deprived of its moorings, rolls and glides off in a sort of ameboid motion. Its migratory phase begins.

This makes us ask at once, what actuates these cells to change from sedentary to migratory life? One used to think in terms of a positive stimulation, perhaps by wound hormones released from damaged cells. As I shall prove later on, this view is incorrect. In fact, the whole concept behind it is fallacious. Cells do not have to be stimulated in order to move. On the contrary, motility, as an expression of cellular instability, is a primary feature of any cell that is free and unrestrained. Motion pictures of isolated cells *in vitro* show them in a state of permanent agitation. The metabolic energy of the cell finds outlets in the ever fluctuating cell surface now here, now there, protruding mobile pseudopods in incessant restlessness. The question, therefore, is not what makes a cell move, but, on the contrary, what causes such autonomous movements ever to stop. For epithelial cells, the answer seems to lie in contact with other cells of like character. Only the free portion of the cell surface is mobile. Thus, when an epithelial cell is completely girded by fellow cells, it becomes immobilized. And the cells at the edge of a wound resume motion for no reason other than that their surface has been deprived of its former contact with fellow cells (Weiss, 1950).

Now, one may ask, is this mobilized cell front at the wound border the only active motor in wound closure, dragging the cohesive epithelial sheet passively along? The answer is, no. Close observations in our laboratory (Lash, 1955, 1956) have shown that in their movement over the wound, the epidermal cells do not hang together but move individually, each of its own accord, much as a herd of animals. Then, what is it that orients their advance, so that they will not just crawl off in all possible directions, but move straight into the wound? This raises the more general problem of cell orientation, to which I have applied myself for more than thirty years, endeavoring to fill symbolic terms like "chemotaxis" and "thigmotaxis" with concrete meaning. Time will allow only a very brief summary. Most of this work was done in tissue culture (Weiss, 1929, 1933).

The now familiar method of tissue culture consists of transferring a small group of living cells into a medium containing nutrients and other life necessities in some sort of glass chamber, sealed for protection and transparent for optional microscopic inspection. A culture of the older standard type is shown in Fig. 5. The medium here consists of coagulated blood plasma. In this medium, cells from an explanted piece of embryonic tissue move out promptly, migrating, growing and dividing, surrounding the original fragment with a dense corona of emigrated cells. The margin of the explant behaves quite like the margin of any wound in the body.

Left alone, the outwandering cells move essentially at random. The locomotor apparatus of a free cell consists of blunt or pointed protrusions from its surface. These are the engines that drag the cell body around. Without directional cues, their numbers and directions are wholly a matter of chance. Figure 6 shows this lack of orientation near the margin of an ordinary tissue culture. Free cells are as erratic as Brownian motion.

However, one can readily and at will turn such randomness into rigorous orientation. One recent example is shown in Fig. 7

(Weiss, 1958). A suspension of isolated cells was deposited in liquid nutrient on a glass slide scored with microscopic grooves. The disk-shaped cells have become elongated in the direction of the grooves, the cell body being drawn out into spindle shape by its two mobile ends proceeding in opposite directions. The shape of these connective tissue cells thus results from their deformation along an axis imposed by their environment.

A study of this morphogenetic event in time-lapse films made under the phase microscope by my collaborators, Dr. Taylor and Mr. Bock, has indicated the mechanism of this elongation: it seems that the mobile cell contour clings more firmly to the rough groove than it does to the smooth surface of the glass (Fig. 8). In this manner the cells are bound to preformed tracks or pathways. Since they move blindly, guided solely by contact, I have named this principle of orientation "contact-guidance."

Of course, the grooved glass in tissue culture serves merely as a model of many similar linear track systems provided in the body by the reverse of grooves; namely, fibers. My earlier experiments in plasma cultures have made this clear. A blood plasma clot is a sponge of fibrin fibers imbibed with serum. Figure 9 is an electron microgram of dried blood plasma (Hawn and Porter, 1947). The fine, cross-striated elementary filaments of fibrin form bundles of various sizes, but without any definite orientation. It is these solid fiber systems that serve as climbing ropes to moving cells. Evidently, having to cling to such a tangled mess of fibers, as in this picture, cells would be lost like wanderers in a dense jungle.

FIG. 6. Stroma cells near the margin of a culture, in random orientation. (Original: A. C. Taylor.)

FIG. 7. Orientation of free cells in the direction of microgrooves of scored glass. From Weiss (1958).

FIG. 8. Four stages from motion picture of spherical stroma cell elongating on grooved glass support. From Weiss (1958).

FIG. 9. Electron microgram of dried blood plasma, showing fibrin net. From Hawn and Porter (1947).

FIG. 10. Diagram of orientation imposed by tension upon a net of filamentous molecules.

FIG. 11. Diagram of progressive orientation of a fibrous medium by stretch (in the direction of the arrows) and the conforming orientation and configuration of the cells contained therein. From Weiss (1949).

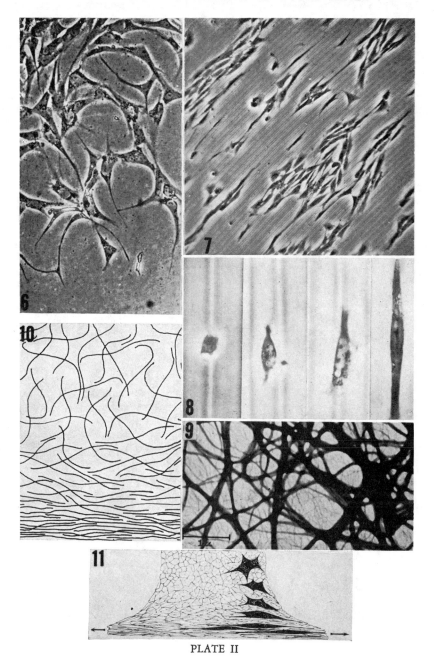

PLATE II

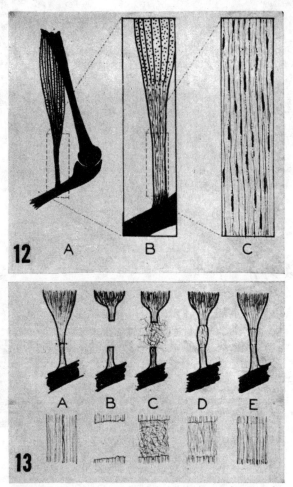

PLATE IIIA. FIGS. 12 and 13. See facing page for legends.

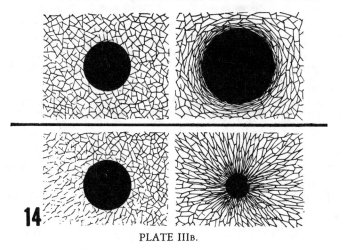

PLATE IIIв.

FIG. 12. Diagram of linear (ropelike) arrangement of tendon cells and fibers along tension lines.

FIG. 13. Diagram of tendon regeneration, indicating structural ordering of tissue linking the stumps.

FIG. 14. Patterns of tension in network developing around centers of expansion (upper row) and contraction (lower row). From Weiss (1949).

But rod-shaped macromolecules, like fibrin or collagen, can be forced into alignment by a variety of external forces. For instance, if an irregular network of filamentous molecules is stretched, as in the lower portion of Fig. 10, the molecules are straightened in the direction of the stretch. Aligned, they tend to aggregate into submicroscopic, and eventually, microscopic fibers.

Thus, tensions orient fibers, and fibers orient cells. Figure 11 shows the results. The better oriented the medium, the more rigorously are the cells aligned. Since the tips of nerve fibers likewise follow contact guidance, the direction of nerve growth can be similarly controlled (Weiss, 1934, 1945). All this has been found out by experimental work motivated by nothing but the urge to understand developmental mechanisms.

But here we also come upon a direct link between basic research and surgical practice. For these experiments are a fair, if simplified, model of the way a cut tendon is restored. A tendon (Fig. 12) is a rope of countless parallel fibers, interspersed with equally aligned slender cells, embedded in a ground substance. The ropelike structure is essential for the safe transmission of pull from muscle to skeleton. When a tendon is cut (Fig. 13), the ends snap apart, and a clot of blood and tissue juice fills the gap between them. This clot then serves as matrix for regrowth, just like the plasma clot in tissue culture. Subject to linear stretch by the contractions of the muscle, a fibrin bridge is soon established along the tension lines, connecting stump to stump, and the invading cells, of course, assume corresponding alignment. The new link thus gradually becomes integrated in its structure with the old tendon—a messy scar transformed and fittingly assimilated into functional tissue.

Let us now go one step further: In tissue culture, I, as the experimenter, had furnished pathways or pathway-forming tensions, to which the cells submitted. In tendon regeneration, the muscle was the source of tension. But what orienting force is there in a skin wound converting the underbrush of a wild scar into converging pathways to lead cell streams toward the center? Perhaps the following considerations can guide our thinking.

The fibrous network pervading a tissue is a continuum. That is to say, tensions originating or released at any point can affect the stress pattern of the whole net. The two most elementary cases are exemplified in Fig. 14. The black disks on the left represent a piece of tissue enmeshed in fibers. When it expands, as in the upper half, it deforms the surrounding meshes circumferentially. This may explain, for instance, why tunics of connective tissue around growing or dilated ducts and organs, as well as capsules around foci of inflammation, assume concentric patterns. On the contrary, if an area shrinks, as in the lower half of the diagram, the meshes are gathered in radial directions toward the center of contraction.

Now paradoxically, such shrinkage happens in the body matrices around areas with a high rate of cell proliferation. Proliferat-

---

FIG. 15. Model of tensions (indicated by distortion of meshes of net) engendered by two centers of contraction.

FIG. 16. Structural effect of two growing centers on fibrous matrix. From Weiss (1949).

FIG. 17. Cell and fiber bridge formed automatically between two spinal ganglia grown in thin blood plasma membrane. From Weiss (1934).

FIG. 18. Cell bridges formed automatically between three growing cultures in thin blood plasma membrane. From Weiss (1949).

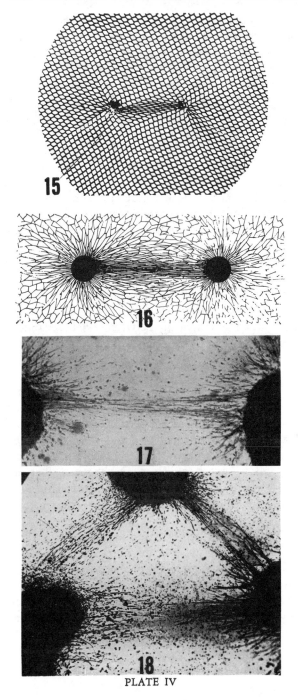

15

16

17

18

PLATE IV

ing cells liberate substances which dehydratize the colloids in the surroundings (Grossfeld, 1934; Weiss, 1929, 1934). As interstitial fluid is lost, the solid components become condensed, and since this nucleus of condensation and contraction exerts centripetal pull on the rest of the net, the meshes are gathered into a radial pathway system for moving cells. By this device, an erstwhile unoriented growth process can itself create patterns of orientation (Weiss, 1949a).

Even more striking is the effect produced by a pair of centers growing in a common clot, where they introduce two separate points of shrinkage. What to expect, is shown by a model of netting gathered in at two points (Fig. 15): the meshes between the two points have become conspicuously stretched in the direction of the connecting line. Similarly, two proliferating cell groups establish automatically a fibrous bridge between them (Fig. 16) so that outgrowing cells are conducted straight from one group to the other. In short, the orientation of the cells is the result of contractions engendered by their sources, and not of any chemotactic attractions by their destinations. Figures 17 and 18 show such cell bridges formed automatically between widely separated growing cultures without any outside direction. I shall refer to this as the "two-center effect" (Weiss, 1952).

The "two-center effect" is another instance where laboratory experience offered itself for ready translation into surgical practice—in nerve repair. When a nerve is cut, the distal stump degenerates, and reconnections between the centers and the muscles or skin can be effected only by the outgrowth of new nerve fiber sprouts from the proximal stump. Such nerve sprouts, as I said before, follow contact guidance. Degenerated fiber segments of the distal stump can serve as tracks. Yet, to reach these tracks, the growing sprouts must first traverse the trackless gap between the stumps—in cellular dimensions, an immense space in which to get lost. To minimize the distance, the surgeon sews the stumps together, achieving what macroscopically looks like neat apposition. But viewed in the dimensions of microscopic cells, the landscape there appears as a confounded wilderness: Crushed fiber ends caked with extravasated blood, create a maze of crisscrossing guide ropes—the notorious nerve scar—in which the blind new nerve sprouts get hopelessly tangled up and trapped. A volume of new nerve sprouts that would be fully adequate for functional reconnections, if it were properly guided, thus exhausts itself in the futile meandering through this trackless jungle.

However, the lessons of tissue culture have shown us how to turn futility into success. We simply have to imitate the two-center effect by letting the two nerve stumps themselves create their own connecting bridge. Ramón y Cajal had shown (1928) in classic experiments (Fig. 19) that regenerating nerve sprouts indeed tend to converge upon a distal degenerating nerve stump as if attracted chemotactically by its orifice. His observation was correct, but the explanation was not. What actually is involved, is a two-center effect. When we explant two pieces of adult rat nerve, side by side, into a thin plasma clot, as in Fig. 20 (Weiss, 1952), Schwann cells proliferate from the open ends, and these two growing points produce again quite automatically a fibrin, and consequently, cell bridge between them. Nerve fibers, if present, would thus be guided straight from stump to stump. It is precisely this automatic self-orientation that one must try to facilitate in nerve repair, and here is how it can be done (Weiss, 1943; Weiss and Taylor, 1943; Weiss, 1944).

Instead of forcing the nerve ends together by suturing, we join them by an elastic tube of some material to which blood will not adhere (Fig. 21). In practice, we have used arterial segments, fresh or frozen, or cuffs of tantalum. The point is to let the blood clot in the gap adhere to the nerve ends, but not to the sleeve, so that tensions can act in only one direction, namely, along the line connecting the two stumps—the nerve axis. The tensions involved arise from the retraction of the stumps and the syneretic shrinkage of the clot itself. As a result, a perfectly oriented linear pathway system of parallel fibrin tracks forms in the blood bridge between the two stumps, which guides the outwandering Schwann cells and new nerve sprouts straight across the gap toward their destinations. Figure 22 illustrates the drastic contrast between an ordinary and a tubulated union in two branches of a rat nerve, 5 days after transection, the lower one left untreated, the upper one reunited by an arterial sleeve. The former shows already an irregular scar, with cells and nerve fibers crisscrossing at random,

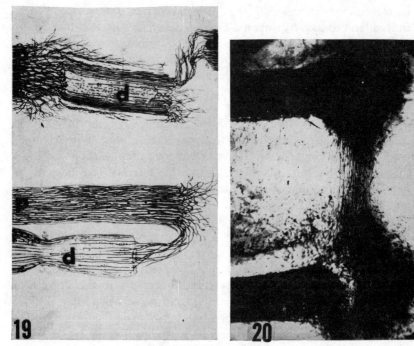

PLATE VA. FIGS. 19 and 20.

FIG. 19. Deflection of nerve fiber regeneration from proximal stumps (*p*) "toward" degenerated nerve fragments (*d*). From Ramón y Cajal (1928).

FIG. 20. Mushroomlike proliferation of Schwann cells from open ends of two rat nerve stumps in blood plasma clot, with bridge of cells connecting the two centers. From Weiss (1952).

FIG. 21. Diagram of progression of orienting effect of splicing nerve stumps by nonadhesive sleeves. From Weiss (1944).

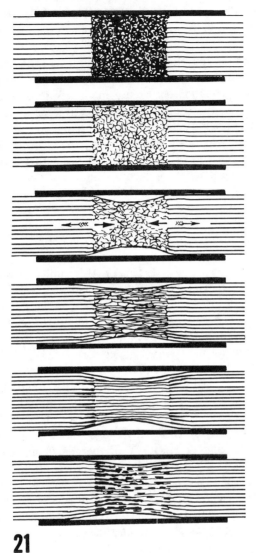

21

PLATE Vᴮ. Fɪɢ. 21. See facing page for legend.

whereas the sleeve has led to an orderly straight connection, with nerve fibers and cells passing directly and unimpeded from end to end.

By contrast, if the blood clot in the gap is subject to the least lengthwise compression, rather than extension, as shown in Fig. 23, which is a common occurrence in tight sutures, the fibrin net forms crosswise, constituting a most effective barrier to the transit of regenerating nerve sprouts from stump to stump. A comparison between these two cases gives an impressive demonstration of how supposedly inconsequential details of manipulation may be of the most crucial consequence for eventual success or failure.

In applying these lessons now to skin wounds, one could assume that it is the gradual contracture of the primary colloidal wound exudate or granulation tissue that generates radial fiber tracks by which the cells invading from the perimeter would automatically be made to converge upon the wound center. Unfortunately, there are no actual data on this fundamental problem. If our conjecture is correct, it is evident that relatively subtle variations in the mechanical and chemical configuration can make all the difference between whether a mobilized cell mass will either radially invade a raw wound and cover it or, on the contrary, circle around it, leaving an open sore (cf. Fig. 14).

Eventually, the invading wound margins meet head on. This rather promptly makes them stop and settle down. One could conclude that as soon as equilibrium of tissue continuity is restored, migration and further growth are automatically suspended. But what counts as "tissue continuity" in complex lesions involving more than one kind of tissue? Will merger among any two tissues, even foreign ones, satisfy the provision? It has long been the experience of surgeons that there is a tendency for each tissue to heal with its own kind, avoiding nonmatching combinations. Biological experimentation has proved this discriminatory behavior to be a general property of tissues, usually referred to as

FIG. 22. Regeneration of two adjacent rat nerves, 5 days after transection; the upper one with ends sheathed in arterial sleeve (*a-a*), the lower one with ends simply apposed but unsheathed. From Weiss and Taylor (1943).

FIG. 23. Transverse fibrous block between two nerve ends in arterial sheath, but pressed together. From Weiss and Taylor (1943).

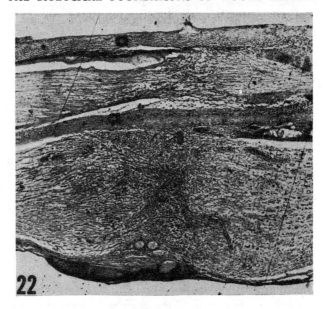

PLATE VI

tissue "affinity." Holtfreter (1939) has shown its embryonic origin, and experiments in our laboratory have tried to clarify its nature.

In one test (Weiss and Andres, 1952), embryonic precursor cells of pigment cells, injected into the blood stream of young chick embryos of an unpigmented race, cropped out as black colonies in the precise locations typical as residences for pigment cells, and nowhere else (Fig. 24). Obviously, after their random dissemination throughout the body, they had been fished out and lodged selectively at their matching sites. This broadcasting of cells through the blood stream, followed by selective lodging, has since assumed great practical promise, as it forms the basis of the reseeding of radiation-damaged bone marrow by injected healthy stem cells.

In another test, more directly bearing on wound healing (Chiakulas, 1952), various epithelia were grafted into a surface wound of skin. If the graft was likewise skin or tissue normally adjoining skin, such as cornea, the two advancing wound margins merged smoothly. However, if the graft was foreign to epidermis —for instance, esophagus or gall bladder or lung—the edges did not join, but the epidermis kept on moving either over or under the graft, not satisfied until it met another epidermal edge. Similarly, cartilages from a common source, either mesoderm or neural crest, will fuse, but cartilage from either of these sources will not join with cartilage from the other (Chiakulas, 1957).

Cells thus establish a high degree of structural order by their own discriminative associations. To study the phenomenon more closely, we have used the technique of dissociated cells in culture, designed by Moscona (Moscona and Moscona, 1952) and later elaborated by him in our laboratory. He observed that when a scrambled mixture of cells from different embryonic organs, for instance, kidney and cartilage, was explanted, the cells would sort themselves out according to kind, forming separate clusters of pure kidney and pure cartilage (Moscona, 1956). Just how they did this, was not clear. To find out, we have now taken direct cinematographic records of cell encounters *in vitro*. They show how an epithelial cell behaves when it meets another epithelial cell of either the same or a different type.

Here are the main conclusions (Weiss, 1958): After settling on the glass surface, the epithelial cells move about at random. They show no conspicuous reactions to other cells, either attractive or repulsive, so long as there is no direct contact interaction. As soon as two cells do collide perchance, they join at first. But having done so, a crucial difference appears, depending on whether they are of matching or nonmatching tissue origins. If of a matching kind, they draw together and remain associated; if of nonmatching kinds, they withdraw the apposed margins and thus become disengaged from each other. In other words, unlike cells do not shun mutual contact, but after having perceived each other's strangeness, they actively separate. The active principle is not the junction of like cells, but the disjunction of unlike ones. The nature of the discriminatory reaction is still under investigation, but the phenomenon as such is spectacularly clear.*

We evidently are faced here with a very basic biological principle, instrumental in maintaining order in the organism. It not only explains the self-ordering of complex tissues in the healing process, but also has a direct bearing on the cancer problem. For the emigration of the metastasizing malignant cell from its mother tissue and its invasion and lodging in foreign locations must surely be related to its having become so alienated that its surface no longer matches that of its sister cells (Weiss, 1949b). But to dwell on this would be going far beyond the scope of this lecture.

We should go on next to discuss the problems of compensatory cell multiplication, which returns the reduced cell population to its normal density. Basically, the problem is the same for wound healing as for growth control in general, which manifests itself, for instance, in the compensatory hypertrophy and hyperplasia of kidney, liver, and other organs after partial removal (see Weiss,

---

* The behavior here described has been observed in the following cell types in various combinations, freshly dissociated: embryonic chick liver, epidermis, lung, heart, kidney; embryonic mouse liver, lung; neonate rat liver. Embryonic chick and mouse livers merge, but embryonic and neonate livers do not. Cells from cultured strains of human conjunctiva, human liver, or rabbit kidney do not coalesce with any of the fresh tissues listed above, but do associate with one another. Macrophages show complementary affinity to lung epithelium. Mesenchyme cells, on the other hand, retract from each other on contact (Abercrombie and Heaysman, 1954; Weiss, 1958).

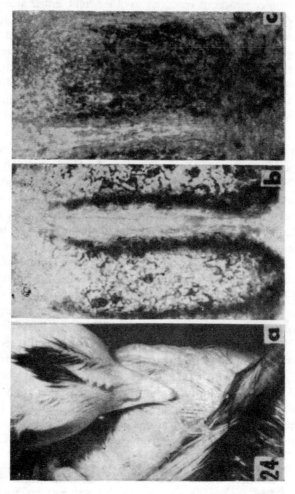

PLATE VIIA. Fig. 24. See facing page for legend.

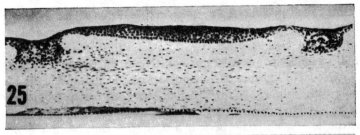

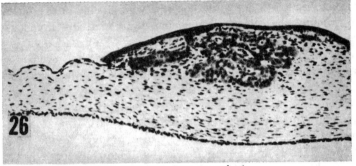

PLATE VIIB. FIGS. 25 and 26.

FIG. 24. Colonization of unpigmented chick host embryo by prospective pigment cells from colored donor disseminated after injection into the blood stream. a. Pigment islands in skin and feathers on head and leg. b. Specific localization of pigment cells at base of young feathers of control donors. c. Precise localization of disseminated donor cells at feather bases of unpigmented hosts. From Weiss and Andres (1952).

FIG. 25. Embryonic chick cornea healed 4 days after wounding on sixteenth day of incubation; former wound margins marked by epidermal plugs. From Weiss and Matoltsy (1959).

FIG. 26. Margin of wound unhealed 4 days after wounding on ninth day of incubation, showing denuded stroma on the left and adenomatous penetration of proliferating epidermal border into the underlying stroma on the right. From Weiss and Matoltsy (1959).

1955). But this is such a complicated problem that it would require a separate lecture (see Weiss and Kavanau, 1957). Instead, let me just briefly report some recent results which have revealed that the activation of cell multiplication in wound healing is, in any event, not dependent upon the act of cell migration, as either can go on quite well without the other (Weiss and Matoltsy, 1959).

We found that the chick embryo in its early stages conveniently dissociates growth from migration after the wounding of skin or cornea. Any wound made at any time after the tenth day of incubation, whether in the embryo or in the hatched bird, is promptly closed by epithelial cells moving across the lesion and dividing mitotically. Figure 25 for instance, shows a corneal wound completely covered, even hyperplastically, 3 days after an injury made in the later embryonic period. Yet, if the same wound is made prior to the tenth day (Fig. 26), the wound edge grows, but fails to migrate: the cells proliferate into the underlying stroma, with cystic adenomatous extensions, while the wound area remains an open sore. Both skin and cornea behave alike. Yet, even in such stationary wounds, as soon as the injured embryo reaches the critical tenth day, migration sets in spontaneously, whereupon the wound is rapidly covered. These results prove not only that growth is independent of migration, but also that the act of wounding itself, with all its traumatic byproducts, cannot be held responsible for the initiation of the migratory process. Just why the epithelium of skin and cornea in the early embryo fails to heal, is still a mystery, for we have found that even the youngest stages can heal quite promptly when transferred from the embryo into tissue culture. We have reason to suspect that the deficiency in the early embryo is related to the absence of functioning endocrines prior to the critical age, but we have no proof. At any rate, the case surely epitomizes the composite nature of the healing process.

Let me now add to this a final complication. Not only must we learn to gauge macroscopic situations on the microscopic scale of

---

FIG. 27. Section through skin of urodele amphibian larva, showing (from right to left) epidermal cells, basement lamella, and underlying loose connective tissue.

FIG. 28. Electron microgram of stratified basement lamella under the epidermis of urodele amphibian larva.

FIG. 29. Electron microgram of section through basement lamella. From Weiss and Ferris (1956).

FIG. 30. Diagrammatic representation of two phases in the restoration of the basement lamella (*l*) after wounding (left: earlier phase; right: later phase). *e*, Epidermal cell; *f*, fibroblast.

PLATE VIII

cell behavior, but cell behavior itself must be projected downward to the ultramicroscopic, macromolecular, realm. This leads me to my last example.

I mentioned in the beginning the fibrous membrane of the amphibian skin (Fig. 27). The electron microscope (Weiss and Ferris, 1954b) shows it to be laminated (Fig. 28), and higher magnification (one micron corresponds to sixteen mm.) reveals an amazing regularity (Fig. 29): There are about twenty layers, each containing a set of cylindrical collagen fibrils, 500 to 600 Å. wide, in strictly parallel array. But from each layer to the next, this orientation changes by 90 degrees.* Therefore, in Fig. 29, proceeding from layer to layer, one sees the fibers alternately in profile and in cross section.

How does such a masterpiece of fine-structural architecture arise? We approached the problem by studying whether and how damage is repaired (Weiss and Ferris, 1956). Briefly, a hole made in the membrane is mended as follows (Fig. 30): After the epidermal cells have covered the wound, fibroblasts of the connective tissue underneath shed immature collagen fibrils into the gap at random, like trucks dumping building material for a house. These young fibers form a messy tangle. Within the second week, however, a new order begins to spread over this tangle, from the epithelial sheet downward, orienting the young fibers progressively into the mature layered arrangement: the erstwhile disoriented fibers are now given their definite orientations alternating between layers by right angles. Figure 31 shows the initial deposit of immature collagen units devoid of order. But just a few days later (Fig. 32), a tangential section through the skin shows the

---

* Clear indications of this orthogonal texture had already been observed under the light microscope by Rosin (1946) and Mizuhira (1951) in amphibians and by Fauré-Fremiet (1938) in fishes.

FIG. 31. Electron microgram of unoriented collagen mat in early stage of restoration of wounded basement lamella. From Weiss (1956).

FIG. 32. Electron microgram of beginning orthogonal ordering of collagen fabric in later stage of healing wound of basement lamella. From Weiss (1956).

FIG. 33. Hypothetical lattice of ordered alignment and stacking of collagen fabric in the restoration of the orthogonal structure of the basement lamella. From Weiss (1956).

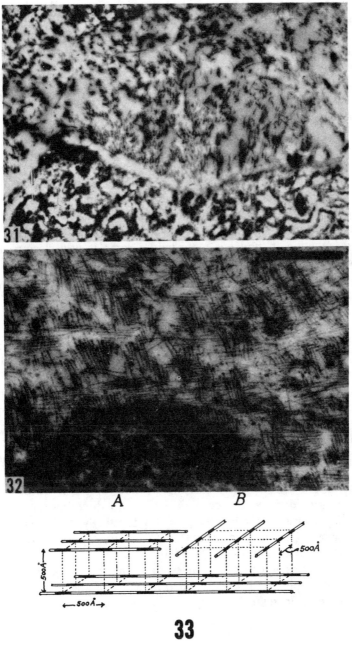

A   B

33

PLATE IX

beginning of the rearrangement of the fibers in a regular checker-
board pattern, anticipating the final mature structure of the re-
woven fabric. The ordering of the filamentous units seems to
occur in a space lattice of cubic structure with 500- to 600-Å
spacing between nodal points (Fig. 33). We witness here living
organization in its workshop, but this is not the right occasion
to dwell on the fascinating vistas of macrocrystallinity in biological systems which these results open and which may bring
biology and modern solid state physics into close conceptual relation.

Our round trip has returned us to the ultramicroscopic realm
from which we had started. Every step brought unforeseen disclosures: new facts, new concepts, modified expectations. Does
this not counsel modesty, restraint, and recognition of the fragmentary state of current knowledge about life, and a more fervent
determination to find out more before complacently closing our
accounts? If I were to sum up the experience of my forty years of
scientific work in one sentence, I would say that my ignorance
has grown faster than has my knowledge. We shall never see the
end; science is unending approximation.

Wound healing had seemed like a simple phenomenon, amenable to simple explanations. I have tried to show that it is neither
simple nor will submit to any sweeping formula. Of course, we
all appreciate broad generalizations; as I said at the outset, I have
contributed my share of them, like "biological field theory" or
"molecular ecology." But as thermodynamics does not tell us how
to go about repairing a stalled automobile, so the great biological
principles of evolution, gene action, homeostasis, and the like,
don't tell us how to repair a damaged tissue. To repair an engine,
we must know its mechanism, part for part. I hope to have shown
that insight into the mechanisms of wound healing is within our
grasp, provided we approach the task with disciplined realism,
looking painstakingly hard at how things actually work; and that
the practice of medicine stands to gain tangibly from such an
analytic course. The profusion of the medley of examples that I
presented was intended to convey some impression of the enormous multiplicity, diversity, and complexity of the processes involved even in reputedly simple vital mechanisms—as antidote to

our contemporary impatience and flair for oversimplified magic formulas and verbal trappings.

REFERENCES

Abercrombie, M., and Heaysman, J. E. M. (1954). *Exptl. Cell Research,* **6,** 293–306.

Chiakulas, J. J. (1952). *J. Exptl. Zool.* **121,** 383–417.

Chiakulas, J. J. (1957). *J. Exptl. Zool.* **136,** 287–300.

Fauré-Fremiet, E. (1938). *Arch. anat. microscop.* **34,** 219–230.

Friedenwald, J. S., Buschke, W., and Crowell, J. E. (1945). *J. Cellular Comp. Physiol.* **25,** 45–52.

Grillo, H. C., Watts, G. T., and Gross, J. (1958). *Ann. Surg.* **148,** 145–152.

Grossfeld, H. (1934). *Wilhelm Roux' Arch. Entwicklungsmech. Organ.* **131,** 324–332.

Hawn, C. van Z., and Porter, K. R. (1947). *J. Exptl. Med.* **86,** 285–292.

Holtfreter, J. (1939). *Arch. exptl. Zellforsch. Gewebezücht.* **23,** 169–209.

Lash, J. W. (1955). *J. Exptl. Zool.* **128,** 13–28.

Lash, J. W. (1956). *J. Exptl. Zool.* **131,** 239–256.

Mizuhira, V. (1951). *Arch. Histol. (Okayama)* **2,** 445–462.

Moore, F. D. (1958). *Harvey Lect. Ser.* **52,** 74–99.

Moscona, A. (1956). *Proc. Soc. Exptl. Biol. Med.* **92,** 410–416.

Moscona, A., and Moscona, H. (1952). *J. Anat.* **86,** 287–301.

Ramon y Cajal, S. (1928). "Degeneration and Regeneration of the Nervous System." Oxford Univ. Press, London and New York.

Rosin, S. (1946). *Rev. suisse zool.* **53,** 133–201.

Weiss, P. (1929). *Wilhelm Roux' Arch. Entwicklungsmech. Organ.* **116,** 438–554.

Weiss, P. (1933). *Am. Naturalist* **67,** 322–340.

Weiss, P. (1934). *J. Exptl. Zool.* **68,** 393–448.

Weiss, P. (1943). *A. M. A. Arch. Surg.* **46,** 525–547.

Weiss, P. (1944). *J. Neurosurg.* **1,** 400–450.

Weiss, P. (1945). *J. Exptl. Zool.* **100,** 353–386.

Weiss, P. (1949a). *In* "Chemistry and Physiology of Growth" (A. K. Parpart, ed.), pp. 135–186. Princeton Univ. Press, Princeton, New Jersey.

Weiss, P. (1949b). *Proc. Natl. Cancer Conf. 1st Conf. 1949,* pp. 50–60.

Weiss, P. (1950). *Quart. Rev. Biol.* **25,** 177–198.

Weiss, P. (1952). *Science* **115,** 293–295.

Weiss, P. (1955). In "Hypophyseal Growth Hormone, Nature and Actions" (R. W. Smith, O. H. Gaebler, and C. N. H. Long, eds.), pp. 3–16. McGraw-Hill, New York.

Weiss, P. (1956). *Proc. Natl. Acad. Sci. U.S.* **42,** 819–830.

Weiss, P. (1957). *J. Cellular Comp. Physiol.* **49** Suppl. **1,** 105–112.

Weiss, P. (1958). *Intern. Rev. Cytol.* **7,** 391–423.

Weiss, P. (1959). *In* "Wound Healing and Tissue Repair" (W. B. Patterson, ed.), pp. 1–9. Univ. of Chicago Press, Chicago, Illinois.

Weiss, P., and Andres, G. (1952). *J. Exptl. Zool.* **121**, 449–487.
Weiss, P., and Ferris, W. (1954a). *Exptl. Cell. Research* **6**, 546–549.
Weiss, P., and Ferris, W. (1954b). *Proc. Natl. Acad. Sci. U. S.* **40**, 528–540.
Weiss, P., and Kavanau, L. (1957). *J. Gen. Physiol.* **41**, 1–47.
Weiss, P., and Matoltsy, A. G. (1959). *Develop Biol.* **1**, 302–326.
Weiss, P., and Taylor, A. C. (1943). *A.M.A. Arch. Surg.* **47**, 419–447.

Although the powers of the body to maintain, and when necessary to restore, vital integrity are immensely wide and resourceful, they are, at any rate, neither unlimited nor inexhaustible. Extrinsic "wear and tear" inexorably makes them run down with time. All the more crucial, therefore, becomes the mandate to develop to the utmost and to keep in practice the intrinsic faculties for adaptation and resilience to stress, *with which the organism and its tissues are endowed. This is the focal topic of the following article.*

Reprinted from
THE ART OF PREDICTIVE MEDICINE
By WEBSTER L. MARXER, M.D.
and GEORGE R. COWGILL, PH.D., SC.D. (HON.)
CHARLES C THOMAS, PUBLISHER
Springfield, Illinios, U.S.A.

DETERIORATION IN CELLS*

PAUL WEISS†

W E REALLY DON'T KNOW enough about cells to talk conclusively about deteriorative trends in them. But we *do* know enough about cells to know that some of the things said about them with regard to their true nature and mechanisms are quite unrealistic. Some of the naive notions current in present thinking, and partly also in research, could readily be, if not put back on the right track, at least blocked on the wrong track. In that regard I could give you a long list of misconceptions that can already be rectified in the light of what we do know about cells and an infinitely longer list of what we don't know about cell life.

In an essay which I sent in prior to this meeting, I put down a brief summary of generalizations to prove that the "generalized" cell of which we carry a rigid mental picture does not exist. Cells, just like individuals, fall into different classes possessing crucially different properties, which one must learn empirically and can't deduce. We can't deal with cells across the board as if they were

---

* Work supported in part by Grant No. CA-06375 from the National Cancer Institute (National Institutes of Health of the United States Public Health Service).

† At the time of the Symposium, Dr. Weiss was a member and professor of the Rockefeller Institute, New York, New York. On October 1, 1964, he became Dean and University Professor of the Graduate School of Biomedical Sciences of the University of Texas, Houston, Texas.

1

all identical, like tin soldiers. Cells differ constitutionally according to the types to which they belong. Moreover, one and the same cell changes from moment to moment; and furthermore, every cell individual of a given type is somewhat different from every other individual cell, even of the same type. Therefore, there is a three-dimentional scale of variability implied in the abstract *cell.*

Among the changes of cells from moment to moment, some are repetitive and cyclic. Such fluctuations are only ripples on a basic carrier wave which is not cyclic and recurrent but which leads steadily, definitely and inexorably to the eventual termination of the life of that individual cell, either by death or by dividing.

Enlarging on these premises, we arrive at the following conclusions.

1. Since constitutional properties are totally different among different cell types, no single cell type can automatically serve as a model for the rest.

2. It is particularly important to distinguish between the cells that are permanent individual residents of the mature body (e.g., nerve cells, muscle cells, bone cells) and those that are being continuously or periodically reproduced (e.g., bone marrow, skin, intestinal epithelium). Progressive changes in the former class afflict cell *individuals,* in the latter class, cell *strains.*

3. All cell classes may undergo changes which impair the optimal functioning of the body. Whether such changes originate in single cells, cell groups or systemically throughout the body, whether they are due to extraneous influences or to the inevitable internal wear-and-tear, and whether they remain locally confined or involve ever-wider areas, in no instance will their effects on the organism become detrimental unless and until they have added up to a critical momentum at which the *harmony* and *coordination* within the cell *population* of the body is seriously disturbed. In short, except for irreparable genetic deficiencies, the organism suffers telling damage only from critical *disharmonies* in intercellular *relations.*

4. Short of that critical level, there is so much plasticity and power of compensation, adaptation and repair latent in cells and

tissue systems that the equilibrium of the organism is essentially safeguarded and preserved despite the innumerable deviations caused by internal and external contingencies to which the members of the cell population are continually subjected.

5. In view of these facts, positive anti-deteriorative measures must center on *optimizing the multiple natural conservative and restorative devices of the body.* This implies: (a) the development and widening of the adaptive range of each body constitutent by constant practice within stress limits; (b) the detection and identification of potentially hazardous tissue disharmonies early enough to be averted or counteracted; (c) after irreversible impairment of one part or function of the system has occurred, the maximizing of the faculties of substitution, vicariousness and compensation of the remaining parts and functions of the system.

Aside from these generalities, the type of measure will vary not only from tissue to tissue, but also with the degree of our knowledge of the properties of the various cells, tissues and organs and of their interrelations. This is at present the most serious bottleneck. Pathology deals chiefly with those later stages of tissue alterations which are detectable by the relatively crude means at our disposal, that is, with those late stages which countless adverse modifications arising from subtle fluctuations of "normal" cells have piled up to the point where they yield a grossly disharmonious situation. The statistical emergence of the "abnormal" from "normal" variability is largely still a twilight zone in which more research is urgently needed. For it is in this area that we can learn how to exploit "normal" variability selectively for the opportunities it offers for improving the body's resistance to deterioration, in contrast to letting them build cumulatively toward pathological results. The full range of our power to influence the fate of the various cell populations for better or worse is barely realized, let alone taken advantage of.

To quote examples from three different cell types, let us first look at the nonreproductive cells of the central nervous system—the neurons. Even though in higher mammals, including man, multiplication of nerve cells ends shortly after birth, each nerve cell renews its own substance constantly at a very fast rate—the cell body synthesizing a mass of nerve substance equal to its own volume about once every day. The cell individual is continuously regrowing itself around the nucleus, moving the newly synthesized products into its nerve fiber, in part to replenish metabolic loss, in part for export into muscles and sense organs. We know and we understand now that the rate of synthesis in these cells varies quantitatively with the load of functional requirements placed upon it in both the ascending and descending directions; it can, perhaps, even adjust itself qualitatively to specific influences, as in the phenomena of learning and of neural sensitization and idiosyncrasies. The reader should realize that the nerve cell is not a static body built by the embryo once and for all, to function henceforth statically like Atlas carrying the globe on his shoulders, but is in a state of constant dynamic renovation. Also many nerve cells wear themselves out and die during the life of the individual. We are losing about 10^3 nerve cells every day, irreparably, for post-embryonic nerve cells can no longer reproduce; they do not undergo mitotic division. But, since we have 10^{10} or 10^{11} cells in our brain, the total loss in a lifetime remains well below 1 per cent. Since the rate of internal self-renewal, and hence the vigor of the nerve cell, has been shown to vary with the functional load to which the neuron is exposed, the degree and even kind of activity with which we utilize our nervous system assumes major importance as a deterrent to the degenerative decimation of its cell population.

There are other cell types, however, in which it makes no sense to talk about the aging of the cell as an individual. The intestinal cell has an average lifetime of about a day or two, and then it is shed. With such rapid population turnover, it doesn't make any difference how long it would take for the individual cell to die. The skin epidermis has a somewhat longer life expectancy, but still one that measures only in terms of weeks. Again, blood cells of hemopoietic organs in general have different life spans, but still of limited duration. In those cases, therefore, deteriorative trends pertain not to single cells but to the whole lineage, the whole strain.

Now, in a proliferating strain of this kind, there occur changes that remain confined to a given cell individual; they are not necessarily harmful, because that individual won't live long, and they may be wiped out as soon as it divides into daughter cells. But there are other changes that may leave behind residual alterations. If there is such a residual change, then it may in turn be cancelled out in the next cell division by a change of opposite sign. However, if there is a buildup of synergic changes in successive cell generations, of which there are hundreds and thousands in our lifetime, as a result of which minute, almost infinitesimally small deviations become cumulative and pile up, then there may come a time when trouble arises. Such trouble may arise from a cell becoming nonfunctional, hypo-functional or hyper-functional, so that it no longer matches other cells that depend on it reciprocally. So it is a breakdown, not necessarily of the vitality of a given cell strain, but of the *harmonious relations among the various cell strains* of the body, which causes the detectable trouble.

Another illustration is the cellular basis of the immunological defense mechanisms of the body. Even though the individual antibody-forming cells have limited life spans, the phenomena of both acquired immunity and acquired tolerance have demonstrated the perseverance of chemical "memory" traces in the respective proliferating cell strains, which again emphasizes the importance of appropriate cell training (e.g., the epidemiologically demonstrated value of subclinical infections).

The third example pertains to intercellular products, which form the bulk of the connective and skeletal tissues. They consist of a fabric of collagen fibers embedded in mucopolysaccharide ground substances, with or without calcareous incrustations. Subserving mainly the mechanical functions of transmitting and withstanding pressures and tensions, their architecture is qualitatively and quantitatively adapted to the patterns of strains and stresses operating upon them. The molecular and cellular mechanisms involved in their adaptive reactions are among the best understood "functional adaptations." Excessive stress may entail rupture. But failure to exercise them contributes demonstrably to their atrophy and disorganization. Stress, mechanical stress, is absolutely essential, not only for the production of the tissue matrix, but particularly for its organization, for its orderly texture and architecture. The same amount of tissue mass can appear in a functionally useful pattern or in a wholly inadequate form. A rope that has flaws will break, and this is precisely what can happen in the connective tissues if a tendon, for instance, isn't constantly kept in a certain moderate state of activity. Here, likewise, we know that both over- and under-action will be equally harmful. The normal structural properties of the tissue are designed for an intermediate range, beyond which lie the hazards of harm by too little or too much.

At this juncture, let me again call your attention to the mutuality of relations among cells. Earlier in this Symposium, the trophic effects of the peripheral nervous system on tissues were mentioned. There is also an unexpected reciprocal effect of connective tissue on nerves but with an opposite sign. That is, hypertrophy of the connective tissue can encroach on the health of nerve fibers. It can clamp down on them and interfere with their functioning and survival, so the hypertrophy of one type of tissue can lead to the atrophy of another type. It is this kind of reciprocal relations which, given time, I could illustrate by numerous examples. Fortunately, our body has also built into it innumerable mechanisms that stabilize the relations among the tissues.. We are beginning to learn about them, but as we still don't know much about them, an enormously wide field is open for future research.

All of these examples, which could be amplified, carry one basic lesson. This is: Regardless of the specific manner in which cells react to their environment and to each other according to their types, they are all endowed with a certain adaptive latitude which represents the margin between superior and inferior performance, vitality and endurance. To learn to keep the net balance of the total complex network of cellular activities as potent as possible within that range is the most natural method of minimizing the deteriorative trend in tissues; the trend itself, however, is a natural and inescapable phenomenon which can only be retarded and mitigated but never abolished. Intensive study of cell biology will have to reveal how individual cells can be stimulated or trained to display their maximum desirable potentialities and how cell strains in continuous proliferation can be influenced so that the more desirable combinations of their offspring will be given a selective advantage over the less desirable ones.

Some practical studies involving cell biology occur to me as worthy of mention here. If we knew a little more about the subtle long-range changes in cell populations with age—and this may come soon—then we could do more in the way of using sample cells from the body of a patient for actual diagnostic assays. To some extent we do this now, but we could do much more. One could, for instance, easily scrape cells from the mucous membranes of the oral cavity, as well as from various other parts of the body, without harm. Studies of such cells, in addition, of course, to determinations of the composition of the blood plasma etc., might furnish data valuable as indices of general deteriorative status. In the longitudinal study-project which we have been asked to consider, storage of such information from presumably healthy people in a computer-setup would permit it to be used later for comparison along with data pertaining to many other parameters. This information could prove to be very significant in the detection of important "predictive parameter patterns." This is a completely undeveloped field.

Similar external tests are provided by the characteristic ridges of fingernails, which are beautiful recorders of rhythmic or arhythmic fluctuations in our metabolic and hormone activity. This field is likewise waiting for systematic investigation. It seems to offer hints of things to come. A large amount of information might presumably be read from these self-registering records. Perhaps it too could prove useful for the "parameter patterns" we hope to discover.

In mentioning these possibilities, I am simply calling your attention to the fact that here lie areas which are not the ambitious glamorized fields in the life sciences, but which are perhaps infinitely more useful in the practical sense and which should be entered by investigators with imagination. I wish we could persuade more of the young people to go into these fields; they would reap an immensely rich yield of useful knowledge.

In conclusion, I would like to point out that an organism does not live in a vacuum but in a changeable environment, of which the balance sheet of optimal conditions cannot be stated except in relation to man's actual environment, both physical and social. Therefore, to combat deteriorative trends in the body rationally and methodically, the conclusions and lessons of cell biology, organismic biology and environmental biology will have to be drawn upon conjointly. This calls for immensely intensified work in all these branches and for continued integrated evaluation of their results. This endeavor is still in its infancy.

Yet, even with the most ideal countermeasures, that is, by the maintenance of the most propitious balance between efforts at reducing environmental stress and at increasing stress resistance by invigorative exposure to tolerable amounts of stress, the overall deteriorative trend in life cannot be blocked. The word for its unrelenting course is "ageing." Here is another cover term, like "growth" and "differentiation" above, which badly needs filling with more concrete sense and content if it is to serve as realistic guide to the scientific search for ameliorative, or at least palliative, measures. The following paper is one such attempt at resolving the phenomenon of ageing into more specific terms.

Reprinted from, PERSPECTIVES IN EXPERIMENTAL GERONTOLOGY, SHOCK
CHARLES C THOMAS · PUBLISHER

AGING: A COROLLARY OF DEVELOPMENT

PAUL WEISS

PREAMBLE

THIS ESSAY is written in full realization of its inadequacy. Yet a request to contribute to a volume commemorating the eightieth birthday of a friend committed to the study of gerontology, whose very youthfulness belies the stigma of the aging process, could not be declined simply for lack of qualification. A commentary by one who has never studied specifically the later part of the life span may seem presumptuous. Yet, it may not be wholly unwarranted to try to raise the sights from specific factual data to the broad overall perspective of biological processes in general from which they must be viewed and rated. And viewed from that perspective, the *aging* process, so called, appears but as a conveniently, but arbitrarily, delineated aspect of the process of *development*. The purpose of the following brief essay, therefore, is to place it back into that context.

Development consists of a continuous succession of processes of change and transformation, going on incessantly in uninterrupted sequences throughout the life span of an individual from egg until death. True, the rate of change varies markedly for different periods, and from tissue to tissue, and the *average* of these kinetics taken over the body as a whole can be said, in general, to decline with time. However, those changes of kinetics which strike the superficial observer or the self-observing subject as sudden and abrupt, reveal themselves on closer inspection as continuous and gradual, without the sharpness of demarcation which our conventional terminology seems to denote.

In this light the aging process appears as an integral facet of the continuous progress of development of an organism. It cannot be

311

dealt with as if it were a separate and separable encumbrance, superimposed upon the ordinary processes of life—a sort of extraneous contamination, like a bacterial infection, that could be stripped off film-like once it has formed, or hopefully, be totally averted. Aging is not only with Minot (1908) the price we pay for our developmental differentiation: it *is* differentiation. On these grounds, I have given it at least "honorable mention" in my text on *Principles of Development* (1939, pp. 27-35), and nothing discovered in the quarter of a century and more since has weakened the argument.

A BRIEF SYNOPSIS OF DEVELOPMENT

The more we learn about development, the harder it becomes to compress its essence into a brief essay. The following synopsis, therefore, is crude and sketchy. Its main objective is to give concrete meaning to the loose term "differentiation," the substance of which is the source of "aging."

The egg, as the link between successive generations, reflects this role in its dual constitution: as both a highly specialized cell of the somatically differentiated maternal gonad and the germinal primordium of the new offspring. It carries over, accordingly, two sets of properties. One is the set of chromosomes containing the genome, now identified with specifically arrayed sequences of nucleotide pairs in strands of DNA, which at fertilization are combined with the paternal genome. The other set is the map of cytoplasmic organization which the egg derives directly from its residence in the ovary. Although this cytoplasmic pattern has often been eclipsed by monopolistic attention to the genome, it is important to restore it to its determinant role as a primordial framework of organization with which the genome is bound to interact. Its firm physical bearings lie presumably in a surface mosaic in the egg cortex, in which fields of different chemical composition and physical constitution are mapped out in typical configuration. During the subsequent cleavage of the egg by cell division, the various blastomeres thus receive disparate portions of this surface mosaic while all of them receive nuclei possessing the same full genic complement. As a result, nuclei that are erstwhile equivalent and interchangeable come to lie, from the very first, in different cytoplasmic environments. This sets the stage for *differential* nucleo-cytoplasmic interactions in different regions of the germ. Each cell genome thus is exposed from the very start to a system of different conditions arrayed in a specific pattern which is as much a part of the basic blueprint of the new organism as is the orderly array of genes. In further consequence, the interactions between the two systems yield different products and diverse effects in the different regions of the germ.

The evidence that the genome as such remains throughout life essentially identical in all cells of an organism (except for sporadic somatic mutations) is compelling. Yet, despite this essential constancy of their genic content, cell lines diverge progressively in the development of higher organisms. It is this process of diversification—"differentiation" in the strict sense—which is basic to our understanding of aging, as follows.

The brilliant progress of molecular cytogenetics, resting heavily on microbial evidence, has led to the concept of a direct transcription and subsequent translation of the DNA code, through various RNA intermediates, to the orderly sequence of amino acids in the synthesis of cell proteins. Since in bacteria the generative and somatic cell is one and the same, bacteria obviously cannot furnish a model for the puzzling problem of differentiation in higher forms. For in the latter, a great diversity of qualitatively different cell types emerge during ontogeny. Just how many, is indefinite. The only sure fact is that estimates based on morphological criteria vastly underrate the real magnitude. For a realistic perspective, the reader may be referred to an earlier summary account (Weiss, 1953). A sharp distinction must be made between the differentiation of an individual cell ("cytodifferentiation") and the differentiation among cell *strains*. Cytodifferentiation refers to the elaboration by a given cell, mostly the terminal descendant of a cell line, of specialized characters or products by which we have come to identify that cell as belonging to a given type; such critical products are, for instance, myofibrils, secretions, blood pigments, antibodies, pigment granules, and so forth. *Strain* differentiation, by contrast, denotes the splitting of the progeny of cells of common origin into branch lines of different "potencies," that is, restricted repertories of performance and production faculties differing qualitatively from branch to branch. The fact that the branch lines are capable of passing on their differentials, once established, to their descendants indefinitely even in a common indifferent environment (e.g., in tissue culture) proves that strain differentiation connotes some indelible change which can be propagated through many cell generations without attenuation.

Admittedly, we still miss the key to the explanation of either cytodifferentiation or strain differentiation, although the former is beginning to yield. In each cell, only a selected fraction of the full complement of genes which it contains is supposed to be active in a given instant, the rest being effectively blocked (the blocking effect recently ascribed to histones). This evidently presupposes a rather well-structured *extragenic* machinery to do the proper "activating" and "blocking." Such a view is perhaps conceivable as long as one focuses on a single *individual* cell in cytodifferentiation. But its extension to *strain* differentiation presents difficulties. Consider that a thyroid cell can either grow and divide, giving rise to another thyroid cell, or alternatively switch to manufacturing thyroxin and colloid. The same extragenic models (or "templates," as I have termed them) would therefore at one time have to induce the genomes to fashion more of their own kind needed for further self-perpetuation of that special cell line while at another time, they would have to trigger the machinery for the synthesis of a special product. It seems that cytoplasmic RNA units are somehow involved in the extragenic template systems, but if so, one must postulate that they come in as many distinct molecular forms as there are self-perpetuating types of differentiation. The immense diversity of differentiations seems to militate against explanations of differentiation in terms of somatic mutation or of induced enzyme synthesis.

To put it candidly, the detailed mechanisms of differentiation are still wholly conjectural. Nevertheless, some general rules which bear on the aging problem have emerged. They can be summarized roughly as follows.

1) The Egg Mosaic

For brevity, we lump all intracellular, but extragenic, matter into a single compartment. The primary topographic pattern of cytoplasmic egg districts, outlined above, places the equal genomes of cleavage nuclei into preformed unequal intracellular environments. The ensuing "epigenetic" interactions between each genome and its local environment elaborate these primordial differences. Thus, from the very start, the genome is a captive of its intracellular environment. Both are in "cross talk": the various environments "demand" and each genome "responds" with a matching answer provided for in its "code," thus altering its own intracellular environment. Where this process is slow relative to the rate of cell division, a multitude of cells of comparable constitution—identical genomes in identical environments—arise. The subsequent, strictly "epigenetic," differentiation among their progeny, however, poses a new problem.

2) Epigenetic Differentiation

The answer lies in the group dynamics of the cell population, which creates secondary inequalities among the erstwhile equal members of a group. As the extragenic *intra*cellular environment determines the genic response, so the *extra*cellular environment, in turn, affects the intracellular system in various degrees of specificity. For any given cell, all other cells are part of the "extracellular environment." The interactions between contiguous cells (by contact) or distant cells (through diffusing products) thus introduce a new major diversifying principle. When interactions between two cell types, though in theory mutual, are conspicuously unilateral, they are often referred to as "inductions."

3) Nature of Cell Interactions

The kinds and modes of operation of cell interactions are too varied to submit to any common formula (Weiss, 1963). They may involve transfer of substances, electric polarization, mechanical deformations, osmotic or pH changes, activation or stoppage of movements or of energy delivery, redistribution of cell content, and above all, such specific changes in the *intracellular* environment as may evoke an altered response from the genome.

4) Progressive Dichotomous Differentiation

Schematically, therefore, if we designate the genome as **G**, its intracellular environment as I, and the extracellular environment (e.g., a cell of another type) as E, the following chain of events takes place:

$$I_1 \rightarrow G \rightarrow I_1; \quad E \rightarrow I_1 \rightarrow I_2; \quad I_2 \rightarrow G \rightarrow I_3; \quad E \rightarrow I_3 \rightarrow I_4; \quad I_4 \rightarrow G \rightarrow I_5; \text{ etc.}$$

Note that E and G can communicate with each other only indirectly through the mediation of I, in which G lies entrapped. If, in addition, we let E go through a series of modifications E', E'', E''', $\cdots$, we gain a realistic, if diagrammatic picture of differentiation as a stepwise process of progressive diversification inasmuch as the internal changes in one cell create a changed external environment for its neighbors. The stabilization of self-perpetuating cell types $I_n \rightarrow G \rightarrow I_n \rightarrow G \rightarrow I_n \cdots$, mentioned earlier, further complicates the picture.

This mode of development contains several potential sources of aberrations. 1) G in a particular cell line may suffer a somatic mutation to G'; the whole descendant cell generations will then show altered behavior. 2) The process $I_1 \rightarrow I_2$ might deviate to $I_1 \rightarrow I_2'$, leaving two possibilities: a) $I_2' \rightarrow G \rightarrow I_3$ (the genome failing to discriminate between I_2 and I_2' as if $I_2 \sim I_2'$); the error would then remain confined to the affected single individual cell without entailing lasting effects on the descendants. b) $I_2' \rightarrow G \rightarrow I_3'$; consequently, $I_3' - G \rightarrow I_3' \rightarrow G \rightarrow I_3'$, etc.; the error would thus be perpetuated throughout subsequent cell generations. c) $E \rightarrow I_3' \rightarrow I_4'$; this would in general aggravate the deviation. d) $E \rightarrow I_3' \rightarrow I_4''$, where $I_4'' \sim I_4$; this would correct the error and bring the cell line back on the track. Net error relevant to strain differentiation thus is the sum of self-perpetuating deviations of positive and negative signs. Since the probability of each positive deviation being offset by one of opposite sign is very low, errors of types (b) and (c) are apt to become compounded as cells continue to proliferate.

5) *Developmental Variance*

The outlined sequential origin of terminal "characters" of the body through numerous seriated interactions, in each of which the genome functions as reactor, but never as an autocratic actor, rules out any concept of the developmental course as following rigidly and microprecisely laid out linear tracks. In contrast to the high degree of precision in the specific array and reproductive duplication of the genes, the extragenic system, with which they must continuously interact, is far more variable due to the random fluctuations of both the outer and inner environments. Consequently, the respective interactions and their results are equally variable. Development thus becomes a probabilistic, rather than micro-deterministic, phenomenon. The range of variability—the margin for

error—is held within tolerable bounds a) by the evolutionary erad-
ication of non-viable excesses; b) by stabilizing dynamic devices of
cells and organ systems, such as the regulatory functions of the
nervous system, of hormones, of "homeostatic" mechanisms, of
growth correlations, and so forth; and c), above all, by the composite network character of living systems, as follows.

6) *Network Dynamics*

Development does not proceed as a bundle of separate linear
single-tracked courses. Rather, the program of development calls
for many secondary linkages and cooperative interactions between
cells (and products) of diverse origins and different prior histories.
As developmental diversification increases, so does the number
and intricacy of interdependencies. But the outlined variations of
erstwhile independent component courses and kinetics also become compounded as time goes on. Thus, while mutual dependence grows, the probability of the actual occurrence of the scheduled linkages declines. This would seriously jeopardize development, were it not for the provision in the developmental program
of *multiple pathways* converging toward common unified results.
Instead of linear deterministic chain reactions, we discover a mul-
tidimensional network system of dynamic interactions, intricately

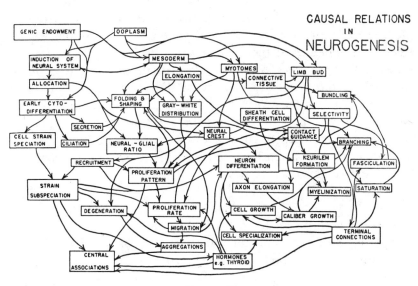

FIGURE 1

(237)

branched and anastomosed. As illustration, I reproduce in Figure 1 from an earlier publication (Weiss, 1955) the network of dynamic interactions and dependencies involved in the development of the nervous system. Every arrow represents an activity for which a physical or chemical effect upon another branch has been experimentally demonstrated. For intracellular events likewise, the linear chain reaction concept must be replaced by network theory, as is clearly reflected, for instance, in the diagram by Nicholson (1963) showing the net of alternative pathways in an intracellular metabolic system (Fig. 2). The point is that such networks endow the respective systems with high degrees of elasticity; if any one branch line lags or fails, the remaining bypasses can still produce a viable. if slightly modified, result.

7) *Commentary*

All the preceding principles from (2) to (6) continue to operate throughout life, even though with increasing restrictions. The programming of the different courses of differentiation leads to the terminal variety of tissues with radically different properties, each continuing to grow, to react and to produce according to its own type and rate. Many cells remain in pre-terminal "bipotential" conditions, in which they can either reproduce more cells of their own kind or transform by cytodifferentiation into sterile workers of shorter or longer life expectancies. Times from reproduction to death vary from a few days (e.g., intestinal mucosa) to weeks (e.g., epidermis; blood elements) to years (e.g., bone cells). Other cell types grow continuously without dividing (e.g., neurons, which burn and discharge what they grow). None of them truly rest. And as they keep being exposed to the fluctuations of the internal and external milieu, the harmony of their dynamic and material interdependency relations continues to be subject to the danger of disruption by excessive deviations from the range of tolerable divergence.

AGING

There is nothing in this picture of development to suggest any abrupt discontinuity, whether initiation or cessation, from which one could date the onset of "aging." *Growth* goes on steadily. Its

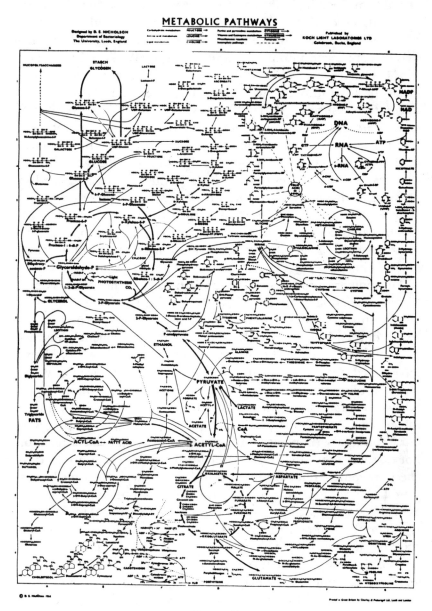

FIGURE 2

rate declines gradually but not necessarily because the reproductive units become less efficient, but chiefly because differentiation progressively reduces the generative compartments of cells and tissues by conversion into products (e.g., fibers) (Weiss and Kavanau, 1957). Conversely, *cell degeneration* and *cell death* are by no means peculiar of older ages; they occur extensively in embryonic stages (Glücksmann, 1951). Progressive changes in *composition and physical properties* of tissues, particularly of the more inert extracellular components, (e.g., the fiber-to-ground substance ratio in tissue matrices) are likewise traceable to early life. So, really all the *elemental* attributes of what in later life one is accustomed to consider as the aging syndrome, are common attributes of the entire developmental process. It is correct, therefore, though commonplace, to describe aging in terms of common language, as simply a function of age. But then, what is aging in terms of developmental biology?

To summarize the answer, let us turn back to the seven criteria of differentiation enumerated in the preceding section. In (4) I have pointed to the sources and the compounding of errors, as life —i.e., development—proceeds. Each body component thus accumulates its own unique history of deviations. These of themselves need not be detrimental to the organism as a whole. What really troubles the organism is rather the increasing disharmony of *mutual relations* among the various component activities, a loss of integration. As pointed out in (6), numerous component processes must constantly cooperate for conjoint effects, and like a team of horses, some slow, some fast, hitched to a carriage, they are held in check by control reins as hinted at in (5,b). Now, if the same horses were to be released, they would disperse according to their speeds, as in a race and cease to act as a team. The same happens in the body if either the component processes get too far out of step or the checking devices lose their hold on them. The independent variance of the components discussed under (5) tends to have just such an effect. It cumulatively magnifies what were initially innocuous discordances (e.g., of timing or chemical specificity) to that critical degree of discrepancy where the erstwhile conjugated components will cease to mesh. The coordinating systems, as body parts, must share this fate. If, following our earlier analogy, we compare the system of interdependent component processes to an elastic network, more and more meshes will thus be strained beyond the stress limit and snap. More and more of the alternate bypasses formerly available to vicariate and compensate for lost interaction pathways will thereby be put out of commission. This then is the crux of the phenomenon which manifests itself to introspection, observation and measurement alike as *decline of plasticity, adaptability and efficiency* with age.

Aging, in biological perspective, therefore, must be regarded as basically a matter of disturbed normal *relations;* and not as a product of *"agents,"* such as "aging factors," "aging substances," "metabolic slags," etc., as it has at times been pictured. The latter misconception would not only, with Ponce de Leon, cruelly mislead public thinking, but misguide research. In my opinion, research on the biology of aging will always be auxiliary to research in *developmental biology* in general. Since time magnifies the effects of critical disturbances of interactive relations, the study of the aged will favor the discovery of such relations; this then will stimulate and guide the backtracking of those relations through their prior life history, when their ever present fluctuations and distortions had not yet become grossly disruptive, hence were accepted as "normal." Our dismally deficient knowledge of "normal" development, aggravated by our ready acceptance of words as substitutes for knowledge, might well receive as much enrichment through the tracing back of change from old to young as through the customary tracing forward from the egg.

Regardless of which end he chooses to proceed from, the searcher will be disappointed if he looks naively for "single causes" and strictly "deterministic" models. As development is a *probabilistic network of multifactoral dynamics,* so is aging. Szilard (1959) has correctly recognized the probabilistic nature of the aging process, although his specific model, derived from microbial concepts, is far too monotonic—indeed, too fatalistic—to fit the highly diversified developmental dynamics of metazoan organisms, including man. For unpreventable though the statistical deterioration of individual cell lines be, the network character of their interrelations enables the higher organism to stem impending disintegration within limits by appropriate compensatory and substitutive counter measures. To keep the latter faculties in training by practice throughout life is therefore the biologist's rational design for living: if aging is inevitable, we can at least retard its pace.

REFERENCES

GLÜCKSMANN, A.: Cell deaths in normal vertebrate ontogeny. *Biol. Rev., 26:*59, 1951.

MINOT, C. S.: *The Problem of Age, Growth, and Death.* New York and London, Putnam, 1908.

NICHOLSON, D. E.: Metabolic pathways. Colnbrook, England, 1963.

SZILARD, L.: On the nature of the aging process. *Proc. Nat. Acad. Sci., USA, 45:*30, 1959.

WEISS, P.: *Principles of Development.* New York, Holt, 1939.

WEISS, P.: Nervous system (neurogenesis), Eds. B. H. Willier, Paul Weiss, and Viktor Hamburger. In: *Analysis of Development.* Philadelphia, Saunders, 1955, pp. 346-401.

WEISS, P.: Cell interactions, In: *Proc. Fifth Canad. Cancer Conf.,* New York, Academic Press, 1963.

WEISS, P., AND KAVANAU, L.: A model of growth and growth control in mathematical terms. *J. Gen. Physiol., 41:*1, 1957.

IV. THE LIVING-NERVE CELL AND THE NERVOUS SYSTEM

AN INTRODUCTION TO GENETIC NEUROLOGY[1]

PAUL WEISS

PREAMBLE

THE function of the chairman of a conference is to serve in the catalytic role of moderator. As organizer and chairman of the Conference on the Development, Growth, and Regeneration of the Nervous System my primary task was, therefore, to put the problems in focus and steer the discussion. The unique pattern of publication of the proceedings, however, according to which each participant had to write a contribution in retrospect, implies an obligation to record my own version of the content and achievements of the conference. This can best be done by following the topical organization of the conference, illustrating the various subjects discussed under each heading, pointing to the present state of their exploration, and supplementing information wherever necessary. This will add up to a random sample of genetic neurology, with a running commentary. Familiar facts will be referred to without further documentation. Items discussed in greater detail in other chapters of the book will be so identified. Many a minor problem, neglected and ill explored in the past, will be accorded more attention and space than some of the major problems on which more adequate information is available. Such arbitrariness of selection, together with the pardonable temptation to illustrate points at issue by examples from one's own experimental experience, is bound to distort the proportions of the total picture. Yet, since the other articles are similarly slanted, and quite deliberately and desirably so, from other angles, their totality ought to present a fairly sound perspective.

If the analytical study of development during the first half of this century has taught any general lesson, it is the realization of the composite and enormously complex nature of the processes involved. As we now view it, development is an assembly-line process in which

1. Original research referred to in this article has been aided by the Wallace C. and Clara A. Abbott Memorial Fund and by a research grant from the National Institute of Health, Public Health Service.

1

countless component events are brought together in orderly patterns in regular succession and are interwoven with one another by innumerable specific interactions (89). Thus the closely knit fabric of any organ, structure, or function, which in its mature stage impresses us by its purposeful unity, when traced back in its developmental history resolves itself into numerous separate threads of different origins, different characters, and different dependencies. In this sense, each component process contributes a share to the final assembled product, but the unity of the assemblage is an emergent unity. Although all developmental processes are under some common control from the very first, the composition and the grouping of the operative units change progressively as cell groups give up old and enter new associations, and the various organs acquire their final identity and functional adequacy only by degrees through the co-ordinated commingling and interplay of originally unrelated contributions.

This conclusion of developmental theory finds a natural corollary in the demonstration by genetic theory that any single terminal character may depend on any number of genes and, conversely, any one gene may affect any number of terminal characters. However, while current genetic theory favors the view that all primary gene action is of a single kind, namely, control of enzymatic reactions, developmental theory proves that, at least by the time the various morphogenetic assembly lines are in operation, both the source materials and the tools are of a wide diversity, much as the materials and manufacturing procedures in the making of, let us say, an automobile vary from step to step. The complex engineering performances of technology are a much more pertinent model of the nature of morphogenesis than are the more elementary phenomena dealt with in basic physics and chemistry.

Viewed in this light, the mature nervous system is the terminal product of many convergent chains of processes with cellular contributions from many sources, with incessant interactions among the units and between the units and their environment. In studying the nature of these interactions, we encounter the widest variety of biophysical and biochemical phenomena, with electrical, chemical, thermal, and mechanical factors participating in various combinations. If in some not too remote past the question as to whether a given component of nerve development was exclusively an electric or a chemical or a mechanical phenomenon was pardonable on grounds of a general lack of familiarity with the principles of development, the same question repeated today would be a sign of lack of comprehension, if not of disregard, of known facts. The oversimplified past theories of nerve development ("electric" or "chemical," etc.) were useful historically as stopgap measures. However, if perpetuated, they will become an intolerable drag on the progress of knowledge, since in their failure to formulate the real problems and in glossing over the complexities of the latter, they hide, rather than reveal, practicable lines of approach. It is not so much that they obstruct experimental analysis as that they divert it to rather fictitious tasks.

Consequently, in order to be realistic in our research, we must accept and face the assembly-line character of the nervous system, the multiplicity and heterogeneity of agents that enter into its manufacture, and give up the hope of embracing the whole process in a single, simple formula. We must take the complex fabric as we find it; try to resolve it into its constituent threads, that is, individual chains of causal linkages; and determine their mode of action without the narrow preconception that they must all belong to a single category. Perhaps it has been the most important result of this conference that it engendered and reinforced such an attitude of sober analytical realism. It is remarkable how grandiose concepts often melt away when brought face to face with hard-and-fast facts which they were purported to explain and how the removal of a verbal smoke screen opens exciting new vistas for research. In this spirit of analytical dissection, we shall now proceed to single out a few of the main contributory processes to the development of the nervous system in the order in which they were taken up by the conference.

The six main sessions of the conference were devoted to six relatively separable topics, as follows: (I) the differentiation of the central nervous system and of its units; (II) the outgrowth of nerve fibers and the establishment of nerve connections; (III) the growth and trophic relations of neurons; (IV) the regeneration of nerves, including its implications for the clinical problems of nerve repair; (V) the problems of specificity and selectivity in the development and operation of the nervous system; and (VI) the development of behavior and its neural foundations.

I. NEURON DIFFERENTIATION

The composition and size of any organ depend on the initial allocation of materials for its formation from one or several sources in the embryo and the modifications to which these materials are subsequently subjected. Such modifications include migrations, spatial re-

grouping, recruitment of cells from the surroundings, growth, proliferation, loss of cells by destruction or emigration, and differentiation.

A. ALLOCATION

In the nervous system the initial allocation is under the control of
influences generally referred to as "inductions" and extensively studied in experimental embryology (69). The allocations seem to bear,
from the very first, certain general regional characteristics, which,
since they can express themselves in atypical locations, are evidently
manifestations of early qualitative differences among different primordial groups of nerve cells (see below, Sec. IF). The early neural
system consists of a number of interacting fields (17, 54) which operate in the manner of morphogenetic fields in general (89), that is,
by outlining their respective domains through competitive interaction and by initiating further diversifying processes, or subfields,
within their respective territories. Local processes thus become progressively more restricted, more firmly fixed, and more autonomous.
Depending on how far this course has advanced, injuries to the
embryonic nervous system are either wholly or partially or not at all
reparable. Many abnormalities of accidental, experimental, or genetic
origin, such as cyclopia (2), anophthalmia (14), anencephaly (134),
etc., are explicable in reference to the time scale of development, with
its progressive loss of regulatory faculties.

B. TRANSFORMATIONS

The early transformations of the neural system are brought about
mainly by shifts of cells and cell complexes and changes of mechanical
configuration, while growth plays only a subordinate role (27). The
mechanics of neurulation are still not yet fully understood, but the
formative forces seem to be intrinsic to the neural plate (9), perhaps
aided by the differential composition of the media along its inner and
outer surfaces. Changes in cell adhesivity (8), as well as the contractility of a surface coat (47), seem involved. Fluid secretion into the
central canal and the ventricles (80) serves to keep the brain walls
from collapsing, and postero-anterior propulsion of this cerebrospinal
fluid by the cilia of the canal may add to the necessary turgor. The
mechanics of the formation of fissures, folds, and evaginations in the
early brain are not yet well understood but may be due in large
measure to mechanical yielding of weaker or more pliable portions of
the wall, which expands faster than the capacity of the skull (15).
Evidently, the pattern of lines of least resistance along which these

caveins occur is the systematic result of previous developmental events, and its causation, in turn, remains to be explained.

The slit-shape of the central canal depends on the presence of the notochord (37) and is due to the fact that a rigid fiber system spanning the ventral thickness of the neural plate remains inserted on the notochord as a hinge about which the lateral halves fold upward (110). The tangential stresses to which this median strip of the plate is subjected in the folding process are presumably responsible for a corresponding ultra-structural pattern running crosswise in the floor of the tube as a later guide for the ventral commissures (see Sec. II).

Fibers laid down along the surfaces of the original medullary cells, hence radially oriented, are evidently preferential guide lines for the displacement of the cells of the tube. Consequently, all intrinsic growth will lead to expansion in the radial direction. The embryonic tube seems to have little intrinsic tendency to grow in length. Elongation must, therefore, be produced by outside forces, the active agent being presumably the notochord (39, 40). Its elongation confers passive stretch upon the adhering neural tube. Very likely these longitudinal stresses in the margin of the tube furnish, at the same time, the structural foundation for the later longitudinal fiber-tracts.

The spinal ganglia arise as an unsegmented mass, moving down from the neural crest on either side of the cord. The cell columns tend to break up into clusters, but the segmental regularity of this subdivision in normal development is imposed upon them by the segmentation of the surrounding mesoderm (44, 19).

These are merely a few examples of steps in the morphogenesis of the central system. If some of them seem crudely mechanical, it must not be forgotten that they only lay the foundation for many much subtler events to follow and, moreover, that the mechanical events in themselves are conditioned by the differential behavior of cell groups governed by subtle biochemical and colloid-physical differences.

C. PROLIFERATION

From its early transformations the nervous system emerges endowed with differential properties which soon express themselves in differential proliferation, migration, growth, and differentiation, elaborating further the initial differences established in the preceding stages of allocation and transformation. The nature and causes of these differentials are still almost wholly obscure. Transplantation and defect experiments have revealed at least the time when certain differences arise and the extent to which they are based on properties

(249)

intrinsic to the cell groups concerned and on properties of the cellular environments.

The total size of any given central district is the resultant of the following factors: the proportion of cells in proliferative activity, the rate of their multiplication, the duration for which they continue to proliferate, the enlargement of cells without further division, the immigration of cells from the vicinity, the loss of cells, and the differentiation of nerve fibers. The classical experiments of Detwiler (20) have shown that the quantitative development of a nerve center is determined both by its own growth potential and by extraneous influences emanating partly from other central regions and partly from the periphery. But it has remained for the painstaking research of Hamburger and his collaborators to reveal the full complexity of these interrelations and to begin to unravel them. For details we refer to the comprehensive article by Hamburger and Levi-Montalcini in this volume.

The factors maintaining mitotic activity in characteristic distributions are practically unknown. The concept of mitogenetic radiations (28) is generally regarded as unsubstantiated. We have recently discovered that nervous substance contains a diffusible, strongly mitogenetic principle not found in most other organs (55). It will be interesting to explore the relations of this agent to the proliferative activity of the nervous system itself. The only clue regarding the mitogenetic stimuli in the nervous system is the preferential confinement of mitoses to the lining of the central canal and ventricles. The fact that, after injury to cord or brain, cells of the mantle promptly enter into mitosis (21, 33) proves that mantle cells are not incapable of dividing but normally fail to divide merely because of their insulation from the mitotic stimulus, which after injury becomes available to them.

D. MIGRATION

The fact that cells of the central nervous system migrate extensively has long been recognized. Ontogenetic movements recapitulating phylogenetic shifts have been described and labeled as "neurobiotaxis"; but the factors at work have not yet been elucidated. We are faced with essentially the same problems as those presented by the outgrowth of cell processes (see further below). The radial migration of the cells of the neural tube is clearly correlated with the presence of a radial gliding system of guide fibers constituted by the primordial cells of the tube; but this establishes a limiting, rather than a determining, condition for the final cell distribution. A pathway permits movements in opposite directions, and, since both have been observed (see article by Hamburger and Levi-Montalcini), the question remains as to which cells move in one sense and which in the other. Cells first scattered at random gradually accumulate in specific locations, as, for instance, in the formation of the columns of the ventral horns or the various neatly spaced strata of the brain, which adds to the problem of orientation that of the termination of the various movements. Why do cells aggregate at certain sites and not at others? Moreover, since the cells of a given nucleus or a given stratum eventually exhibit common functional properties, the question arises as to whether those properties were imposed upon them by local factors of the zone they occupy or whether they had already been differentiated when they left their sources and merely become selectively attracted or selectively retained in the appropriate environments. (This problem of the origin of specificity of neurons will be taken up later.)

To judge from observations in tissue culture, cell migration is sometimes merely simulated by the fact that the nucleus shifts its position along the drawn-out cell processes without the latter's changing their locations (45). Such a change of nuclear position within a neuron is obviously not the same thing as the displacement of a whole neuron.

For the study of these problems, the derivatives of the neural crest may be more suitable than the intra-central neuroblasts. It has been shown, for instance, for the pigment-producing components of the neural crest that their migratory urge, direction of migration, and final localization are determined by separate sets of factors (74); by analogy, we may assume that the factors causing the ganglionic elements of the crest to migrate are also different and less specific than those that cause them to settle at specified sites as spinal ganglia, sympathetic ganglia, and myenteric plexus. Noting further the regular association of sheath cells with nerve fibers (see article by Speidel), it is difficult to escape the conclusion that these various derivatives of the crest are gathered into their final locations not by mechanical accidents but by selective affinities to the respective local environments. Such affinitive associations, as well as disaffinitive dissociations, play prominent parts among developmental mechanisms in general (38). A possible explanation on a molecular basis has been suggested (105), but factual information on the subject is very scarce.

E. RESORPTION

Just as the growth of an individual cell is the balance of synthesis over breakdown of protoplasm, so the growth of a tissue depends on the ratio of the proliferation of new cells over the destruction of old ones. In the nervous system, regression has been known to attend the disappearance of body parts during metamorphosis; but, as a component of normal development, resorption of nerve cells has only recently been given prominence, as described in the subsequent article of Hamburger and Levi-Montalcini. Such resorption may be simply the terminal stage of progressive atrophy, which it undoubtedly is after nerve section in later life (see article by Bodian), or it may be due to an active lytic effect of the environment. Whatever the mechanism, it is instructive to realize that, as in so many other phenomena of life, equilibrium is maintained by the proper dosing not merely of a single process but of two opposing principles, one making for production, the other for destruction, operating through different mechanisms.

F. DIFFERENTIATION

Differentiation is frequently understood in too narrow a sense, as the production of *visible* differences among cells. This residue of a pictorially oriented era of microscopic anatomy has given way to a more pertinent concept, according to which differentiation connotes the appearance of *constitutional* differences among cells, presumably always based on biochemical differences but frequently demonstrable only indirectly by the fact that such cells behave differently under otherwise identical conditions (107). Such different behavior may or may not lead to visible distinctions. In this sense, early neuroblasts, spongioblasts, etc., are differentiated relative to one another as well as relative to their own common precursor stages, although the microscope shows no sign of these differences. Differentiation is not a single event but a course of events. Many cells never run the full course of which they are capable but are arrested part way, without "expressing their full potencies," in the usual phrase. On the other hand, many cells are capable, at any one stage of their differentiation, of assuming a variety of appearances, depending on local conditions. Such adaptive modifications of a given cell type have been called "modulations" (89, 107), in contradistinction to the progressive chain of transformations for which the term "differentiation" ought to remain reserved.

For these reasons, the number of truly differentiated cell types in the mature nervous system and the times when they arise cannot be told from morphological observations but must be ascertained for each case by appropriate empirical tests. Just as sheath cells, both embryonic and adult, can modulate into a wide variety of morphological forms, depending on their physicochemical environment (100,

130), so nerve cells may be assumed to be able to appear in a variety of forms in different locations without inner divergence of character. Conversely, nerve cells of different kinds may hide their constitutional diversity behind a similar guise. One would hardly interpret the microscopic similarity of secretion granules in two different glands as implying biochemical identity of either the products or the producing cells. Yet nerve cells, because they all have certain morphological characters in common, are readily assumed to consist of the same protoplasm without specific distinctions relevant to either development or functioning. It is in rectifying this erroneous view that the conference has perhaps made one of its most significant contributions.

The evidence that neuron classes differ in kind and that these differences are instrumental in maintaining both developmental and functional order is based on crucial observations on development, specific reaction to drugs, differential susceptibility to infectious agents, staining reactions, metabolic studies, and functional properties. It is especially mentioned in the articles by Schmitt, Bodian, and Sperry. We shall return to it in Section V.

The ontogenetic history of nerve-cell differentiation is complex and still rather obscure. As will be explained in the article of Hamburger and Levi-Montalcini, the neural epithelium is presumably a mosaic of areas the developmental qualities of which have become specifically restricted at very early stages. A good example is the early localization of Mauthner's neuron in amphibians, more fully treated in the article of Stefanelli. While Mauthner's cell presents a uniquely favorable case because of its distinctive size and configuration, the story is likely to be the same for other cell types for which we have as yet found no distinguishing criteria. There certainly exist many more different species of neurons than those at present identifiable as cholinergic, adrenergic, and so forth.

G. ELABORATION

Cells emerge from their progressive differentiation not only with different overt equipments but also with different response patterns. Consequently, all later local modifications of growth patterns, migration, and association are conditioned by the earlier steps of differentiation. By bringing cells into novel combinations and interactions, these secondary changes, in turn, set the stage for the next step of differentiation, which will further alter the subsequent distribution of the units, and so on. Thus the pattern of the nervous system is gradually elaborated in an ever increasing complexity of interactions. As a corollary of such differentiation, cells acquire the above-mentioned affinities and disaffinities with regard to other units (105), properties that regulate not only the association between neural and peripheral units (see Sec. II) but perhaps also the relations among neural units.

Genetically, the developmental processes in the nervous system are so timed and dosed that under normal conditions they fit into the developmental pattern of the surrounding body. Whenever this harmony is disrupted, incongruous combinations result. For instance, a normally growing nervous system in a retarded spine and skull will herniate or cave in, with severe functional consequences (133). Evidently there must be all gradations from such crude disharmonies, which are easily spotted, down to the most subtle deviations, detectable only by the closest functional examination. It will be an important task to study the extent to which minor genetic aberrations or nutritional deficiencies during early development leave their marks on the nervous system and hence affect the behavior of the individual (64).

II. THE DEVELOPMENT OF NERVE PROCESSES
AND NERVE CONNECTIONS

Ever since the experimental confirmation by Harrison of the outgrowth theory of His, the mechanism of the formation of nerve fibers and the factors controlling their course have been in the foreground of interest. What had at first seemed to be a relatively simple process has presented us with an ever increasing number of facets, each posing a separate problem. For instance: What determines the points at which the axon and later the dendrites will sprout from the cell body? By what forces do they become elongate, and what determines the direction in which the elongation will occur? How do they manage to perforate the limiting membranes of cord and brain, and why do only certain types of fibers emerge? What determines whether they remain simple or become branched and how profuse the branching is to be? Why do they associate with sheath cells and with other nerve fibers to form nerve bundles, and what controls the order, if any, in such associations? Why do they commingle and separate again, as in the formation of plexus, and what determines the final groupings in which they become sheathed by connective tissue? What sets their course in the periphery and what determines where they will end? What controls their density in a given territory and the number of central and peripheral functional connections? And so forth.

To many of these questions the conference has given definite, if sometimes provisional, answers or at least plausible suggestions of answers. When brought together from all sides, the scattered bits of information composed a body of knowledge of impressive consistency. In the end a rather sharp picture emerged. It is amusing to reflect on how, only a short time ago, it was deemed perfectly satisfactory to answer all those specific questions by reference to one all-inclusive term—"neurotaxis."

A. ULTRA-STRUCTURE

Marked advances in the study of the ultra-structure and physiology of protoplasm, some on nerve, have constrained our speculations on neuron growth. The article by Schmitt presents an up-to-date account of the ultra-structure of the mature neuron. The article of Flexner establishes the bridge to the embryonic phase. It seems hardly questionable that the capacity to form a nerve process is predicated on the production in the nerve cell of long filamentous protein chains which form the ultra-structural basis of what in the fixed preparation and occasionally in the living (129, 46) appears as a neurofibril. Presumably, the elementary fibrillar units are at first rather mobile and become linked and consolidated into stabler formations only as the axon matures. It would be incorrect to visualize these units as a rigid axis skeleton which, by its crystallization, would protrude the axon. On the contrary, it is rather the streaming forth of the axoplasm from the cell body which orients and aligns the filamentous units contained in it.

B. MECHANISM OF AXON GROWTH

Observations on living, growing nerve fibers, both in transparent tissues of the body and in tissue culture, have produced a rather unified view of their locomotion. The splendid cinematographic records of Lewis, described in his article, as well as those of Speidel (67), have fully corroborated the original observation by Harrison that the tip of the sprout is a highly agile part. Elongation results from the deposition of new substance at the tip. This substance originates in the far-off cell body, from which it drains toward the tip in a constant axial stream. According to Lewis, the axis cylinder is comparable to an extremely elongated amoeba. As in the amoeba, the fluid core of endoplasm would gelate upon coming to the surface and thus build up the more consolidated outer layer of the axon. Contrary to the amoeba, the rear of the cell, being anchored at the central end, cannot, of course, follow the advancing process. As a result, the distance between tip and base increases as more and more substance is drained into the periphery from the nerve cell. The motive force of the elongation is not quite understood. While Lewis ascribes it generally to the contractility of the superficial gel layer, it may become necessary to assume a rhythmic alternation between contractility and relaxation residing in the axon surface and moving the axoplasm forward in the manner of a peristaltic wave. The neuron seems to possess a peculiar pumping mechanism by which material from the cell body can be forced distad all the way to the tip; evidently, this is the same mechanism which, after the fiber has ceased to elongate, continues to pump in axoplasm, which then accrues to the width of the fiber (see Sec. III). At any rate, the elongation of the nerve process is essentially a phenomenon of protoplasmic motion rather than of true growth.

C. ORIENTATION

In nerve elongation the driving mechanism does not of itself determine the direction of the advance. What determines the latter has variously been ascribed to a number of none-too-well-defined tropisms, such as stereotropism, chemotropism, galvanotropism, and hodogenesis. All existing evidence makes it clear, however, that the fiber is guided not by a single factor but by a combination of factors not represented by any one of these simple theoretical categories. The acting principle can best be characterized as "contact guidance" (95), operating through a combination of physical and chemical properties. The following facts seem to be firmly established:

1. Nerve tips cannot extend into a structureless, homogeneous medium but can move only along interfaces (32, 81). Linear interfaces are furnished by the surfaces of all fibrous structures of the surroundings. Even in a planar interface (glass slide, membrane, etc.), there are usually enough inhomogeneities to mark out linear pathways within the plane. Frequently, fibrous exudates coating surfaces appear in the role of pathways (104). The nerve tip is drawn out along such linear threads as if by capillarity. The actual cause of this adhesivity is not known, but it does not seem to reside in simple surface tension and wetting properties, or at least not exclusively so. It exerts a certain pull at the tip of the fiber, thus giving direction to the push of the pumping mechanism discussed before. Because of this dual action, I have termed this a "pull-push mechanism" (103). Guidance by fibrous interfaces is an active principle and not a passive one, such as "least resistance" (95).

2. If nerve fibers advance on a substratum whose fibrous pathways run nearly parallel, all nerve tips are bound to follow the common direction as the only possible one (81, 104, 109, 123).

3. If a nerve fiber advances upon an unoriented network of intersecting fibrils, its tip will become divided at each intersection, with the various branches competing for the inflow of axoplasm. Aside from a factor of inertia favoring maintenance of direction, chance will decide which branch the fiber will follow at each fork. However, the bending of fiber courses observed in the presence of transversal electric fields (50) indicates that electrical asymmetry at the innumerable intersections weights each decision slightly in favor of the cathodal side (109). This does not produce oriented, but merely deflected, nerve growth and operates in combination with, rather than to the exclusion of, contact guidance.

4. If fibrous substrata of different chemical constitutions intersect, a nerve tip exposed to both may choose one kind of pathway to the exclusion of the other. Evidence of such preferential choice between pathways has been obtained *in vitro*, but only on a very elementary scale (104). Much more refined selectivity of adhesion must be postulated to supervene in the organism where nerve fibers of a given kind show definite predilection for corresponding types of pathway systems, either pre-neural, as in the development of primary innervation (73, 95), or neural, as in larval regeneration (see the articles of Speidel, Piatt, and Stefanelli.

5. Contact guidance is thus a necessary, but not a sufficient, condition for nerve orientation and becomes sufficient only in the special case that all pathways are strictly oriented in a single common direction so as to leave the fibers no choice. Much of the problem of nerve orientation in development actually resolves itself into the production in the nerve environment of just such definite pathway systems. A great variety of experiments has demonstrated that this is achieved by oriented tensions and that such tensions, in turn, are generated by the growth processes of the body itself, through differential expansions and contractions resulting from localized chemical activities as they affect the colloidal substrata (81, 95, 107).

6. Where the structural pathways are indefinite and lack an overall resultant orientation, nerve growth is either correspondingly random, e.g., in the neuropil, or, if it follows a more definite course, does so because of additional limiting factors, as, for instance, chemical selectivity. It seems evident, however, that such chemical guidance, where it occurs, is a matter of contact affinity (105) and not of distance action, as was originally implied in the theory of "chemotropic"

nerve conduction. Nerve fibers are definitely guided to their destinations rather than "attracted" by them (124, 109).

The principle of contact guidance, as here presented, can account for most of the known facts of nerve-fiber orientation. It comes closest to the concept of hodogenesis of Dustin (24), or, more correctly, it translates this principle into concrete and analytical terms. Yet fiber orientation is only part of the problem of nerve patterns. There are other contributory features, one of which is "towing" (95). As long as it roams freely, the tip of the nerve fiber determines the course of the fiber. But, once the fiber has attached itself to another unit (muscle fiber, sensory element, or another neuron), its further course becomes subject to passive shifts resulting from the movements and the growth of its terminal organs. Nerves are often dragged over very great distances in the body.

Whether contact guidance, towing, and selective fasciculation (to be described presently) are all that is needed to explain the formation of nerve patterns cannot be decided until certain as yet ill-understood phenomena have been resolved. One such phenomenon is the tendency of nerves innervating limbs with aberrant developmental histories to assume, nevertheless, fairly typical distribution patterns. This was first shown for the nerve patterns in regenerated limbs (128, 57) and then was confirmed for the delayed innervation of originally nerveless limbs (60). Despite minor deviations, the major nerve courses were typical in all these cases, which indicates that the normal chronological succession of events in the ontogeny of the limb cannot be too relevant for the final configuration of the nerve pattern.

D. NERVE FORMATION

Attention has been focused in the past mainly on the orientation of the early pioneering fibers, which grow out singly. In peripheral nerves and central nerve tracts, however, nerve fibers do not remain single but are joined by other fibers that use the pioneers as pathways and thus gradually build up nerve bundles ("fasciculation"). In studying this process experimentally, it was found that fasciculation of significant magnitude occurs only if the nerve finds adequate peripheral terminations (109). Presumably, pioneering fibers which have attained a successful peripheral connection thereby become selectively adhesive for newly outgrowing nerve fibers. Thus nerve cables are established in response to peripheral conditions. This adds another phenomenon to our list of examples of controlling influences exerted by the periphery upon the development of the nerve centers.

The roles of sheath cells and connective-tissue cells in fasciculation and the elaboration of the final architecture of peripheral nerves are practically unexplored. In view of the fact that there is orderly fluid traffic in the spaces between nerve fibers (98, 131), the organization of the nerve as a whole deserves greater attention than if it were a mere package of nerve fibers; hence the development of that organization should receive intensive investigation in its own right and in relation to nerve pathology.

E. BRANCHING AND PLEXUS FORMATION

Terminal branching of nerve fibers can be understood as a statistical consequence of the repeated splitting of fiber tips on a highly intersected pathway system with no specific directional guides (95, 103). Collateral branches, on the other hand, result when the consolidated stem portion of a fiber becomes locally remobilized by some local stimulus (95).

Plexus formation will occur when fibers, arriving from different sources over separate routes, are deflected into a single-track pathway structure (81), such as is furnished, for example, in the dorsal funiculi for the incoming dorsal root fibers, in the various horizontal strata of brain and retina for their radial fiber tracts, in the girdle region for the peripheral nerve fibers, and the like.

F. PERIPHERAL CONNECTIONS

As a rule, nerve fibers of a given kind are found connected with corresponding end-organs. As indicated above, end-organs can exert no specific "attraction" on their corresponding neurons but receive their proper neuron consignments already in the right order because of the selective character of the pathway systems leading to the end-organs. However, when fibers arrive in mixed assortments or are forced into the wrong type of periphery by experimental means, the end-organs fail to accept functionally incongruous neurons. Thus cutaneous sensory fibers can be made to grow into muscles, but they will effect no transmissive neuromyal junctions (115, 30). Whether the peripheral matching is any more discriminative than for merely general sensory or motor character is uncertain, since motor fibers connect indiscriminately with any muscle (58) and even intra-central fiber tracts can be brought to innervate muscles adequately (109).

G. SATURATION FACTORS

The number of nerve branches available to a given peripheral area is a function of (a) the number of mature nerve cells in the corresponding centers; (*b*) the number of processes that have been drained into the periphery by fasciculation; (*c*) the rate of peripheral branching, which is high in muscle but low in sensory fibers; and perhaps (*d*) the eventual resorption of unconnected fibers. However, from the incoming pool of nerve fibers, only a definite quota is admitted into each peripheral district, the amount being under the direct control of the peripheral tissues. Thus each muscle fiber, as a rule, accepts only a single nerve ending (25), and sensory areas likewise have characteristic saturation densities. Nerve fibers seem to invade a given territory only in proportion to its mass. This has been quantitatively demonstrated for the penetration of regenerating fibers into mature or regenerating limbs of varying sizes (86, 49). In nerve regeneration the peripheral stump itself limits the number of fibers it will carry (48, 113, 114). In sensory territories the self-regulation of innervation density has been directly observed (68). There is no reason to believe that the principle of saturation is in all cases served by the same mechanism. The regional differences of saturation quotas are highly important in their functional implications, since they determine, for instance, the different sensory acuity in different parts of the skin.

III. NEURON GROWTH

Thus far we have dealt only with the numerical development of the nerve centers and the establishment of their topical relations with one another and with peripheral organs. However, in the nervous system the final number of units is established long before the organism has attained its final size, and all further adjustment to the increasing demands is achieved by the continued enlargement of the individual units. Fiber diameter and size of the cell body increase in a certain general proportionality. The final size differential among neurons is based partly on constitutional differences among the nerve cells and partly on influences imposed upon them from their own peripheral organs or from other neurons or, more indirectly, by the degree of functional activity. Studies of neuron metabolism promise deeper insight into the factors regulating neuron growth.

A. METABOLIC REQUIREMENTS

The realization that morphological features are merely the outward expression of the behavior of a cell of given biochemical organization in response to its environment is increasingly turning attention from the microscopic signs of differentiation toward the more fundamental biochemical and metabolic criteria. It is only natural that a tissue, even though developed in abnormal surroundings, which has the morphological aspects of neural tissue has also its biochemical properties, such as the production of cholinesterase (6).

Significant progress has been made in tracing some of the biochemical events attending nerve differentiation, as reported in the articles of Flexner, Bodian, and Hydén. These studies are particularly interesting, in that they demonstrate definite correlations between the development of certain biophysical and biochemical properties and the inception of functional operation in the respective nerve centers.

B. THE GROWTH OF THE NEURON

The growth of the individual neuron has in recent years become a favorite object of investigation. Neurons are uniquely suited for such studies because of their large size and the ease with which the nucleated and nonnucleated portions of the cytoplasm can be separated from each other. The results, obtained by morphological, experimental, and biochemical methods, are in good agreement. They are repeatedly referred to in the articles of Young, Bodian, Hydén, and Flexner. The present state of the field may be summarized as follows:

1. The mass of the neuron, as expressed in the size of the cell body and the caliber of the axon, is not a fixed static character but represents a steady-state equilibrium between continuous growth and concurrent degradation.

2. The site at which the neuron grows is confined to the vicinity of the cell nucleus (perikaryon). Active growth is revealed by increased protein synthesis, enlarged nucleolus and nucleus, and high concentrations of nucleic acids (see Hydén).

3. From the perikaryon the newly produced neuroplasm is conveyed to the axon, where it becomes available both for additional length—during the phase of extension—and for increase in width of the fiber (117). The mechanism through which the proximodistal convection is effected is unknown, but it may be the same as the one discussed in Section IIB as the motive force behind the elongation during outgrowth. Cell turgor (136) does not seem to qualify as motile mechanism.

4. While the rate of central synthesis determines the rate at which new axoplasm becomes available for distribution to the periphery, the width of the channel, that is, the caliber of the nerve fiber after it has acquired a fibrous tube, sets an upper limit to the amount of axoplasm that can actually be conveyed to more peripheral levels. Any marked reduction in the width of the channel by constriction of the fiber causes all farther distal parts of the fiber to assume and re-

tain correspondingly undersized proportions (125). At the same time, excess axoplasm piles up proximally to the constriction because the amount delivered from the cell exceeds the amount that can be carried off through the narrowed passage (117).

5. The amount of myelin produced is a direct function of the caliber of the producing segment of the fiber, so that the wider parts of a fiber have a proportionately thicker sheath than the narrower portions (125).

6. The rate of central synthesis of neuroplasm, which determines the stationary size of the axon, appears to be a constitutional property of the neuron acquired during its differentiation but subject to upward and downward adjustments, depending on a variety of conditions. Lack of adequate peripheral connections entails reduced synthesis, bringing the whole neuron into a lower size class. This effect was first discovered in the reduced calibers of the nerve fibers concerned (124, 116, 62); but, as has later been demonstrated, the primary action is on the cell body (13), in which nucleus and nucleolus are the first to lose size, with the cytoplasm following suit. The proportion of neurons in which atrophy after peripheral disconnection comes to rest at a lower size level seems to vary with the kind of neuron and the species. A certain proportion shrinks to the point of nonviability and is resorbed. Perhaps the difference between peripheral and central neurons in the ability to regenerate axons, discussed in Section IVF, is an expression of the different degrees of regression suffered by different cell types upon the amputation of their processes. These problems are ably dealt with in the work of Bodian.

7. Conversely, when a neuron is overloaded peripherally by excessive branching, it undergoes a certain degree of hypertrophy (see the article of Young). A similar increase is also obtained as a result of intensified physiological activity (see Hydén's article).

The size fluctuations of the central cell body and its peripheral fiber in response to varying demands for growth and physiological activity are of far-reaching importance for the general understanding of neural functions (see Young's article). Let it be remembered, for instance, that with the size of a nerve fiber are correlated such physiological properties as threshold, sensitivity, and conduction velocity, and that the size of the cell surface, in combination with some saturation factor as discussed in Section IIG, will determine the number of synaptic endings on that unit. Above all, the realization that the neuron is a system in a constant state of flux must have a profound influence on our thinking about the integrative action of the nervous system, including the phenomena of learning and memory, which presuppose a certain amount of plasticity of the underlying substratum.

In view of the capacity for continued growth of the neuron, borne out by its faculty for repeated regeneration (see below), it would be wholly inconsistent to assume that any axon has a predetermined length. The fact that intra-central fibers terminate at definite sites must therefore be ascribed to the fact that their free tips have been arrested by junction with local cells rather than by exhaustion of growth potential.

C. TROPHIC EFFECTS

Not only is the metabolic state of neurons regulated by influences from other units, including the terminal organs, but the trophic relation is mutual. Lacking proper innervation, peripheral tissues will atrophy. The time for the deterioration to become apparent varies greatly with the type of tissue and the species, but, as outlined in Speidel's article, it will occur eventually. Whether the atrophy is produced through increased susceptibility of the denervated organs (10) or through the loss of a positive complement normally provided by the nerve fibers has not yet been definitively settled. The trophic influence of innervation on tissue repair and regeneration, while conclusively demonstrated, is also still unexplained.

The trophic control which the nucleated cell body holds over the axonal process has long been deduced from the fact that severed distal fragments of the axis cylinder succumb to degeneration (56). This is easily understood, not only in terms of general physiology but particularly on the basis of what we have now learned about continued protoplasmic replacement from the nuclear center. Pertinent comments on this problem will be found in the article by Gerard.

IV. NERVE REGENERATION

The session on nerve regeneration dealt chiefly with the application of the lessons of primary nerve growth to the processes of secondary regrowth occurring after injury to the mature nervous system. Since ontogenetic and regenerative nerve growth have most of their basic mechanisms in common, it is not surprising that experimental evidence obtained in one field can often be directly applied to the other. Yet the vastly different scope and dimensions of regeneration in later life, as well as its implications for problems of nerve surgery, justify a treatment in its own right. In this treatment the conference dwelt as much on the basic similarities to ontogeny as on the distinguishing features, which in some respects, particularly that of numerical control and of specificity of pathways, are quite marked.

A. MECHANISM OF PERIPHERAL NERVE REGENERATION

The cut end of a proximal nerve-fiber stump establishes a new growing point which advances by the same type of amoeboid motion that characterized the first outgrowth. There seem to be the same mechanisms at work, and even the rate of advance is of the same order as in first development, namely, at best, several millimeters per day in warm-blooded animals. As in first development, fibrous pathways of the surroundings act as guides to the advancing tips, and the abundant branching and extensive straying of young sprouts near the wound is definitely attributable to the irregular and confused arrangement of the pathway system in the fibrous scar that forms over the nerve end. As in first development, it has been possible, by the application of longitudinal stresses, to orient the fibrous pathway system along the nerve axis, thus giving the outgrowing sprouts a straight trellis that guides them over the gap to the distal stump (97, 101, 103, 123). The orientation of the fibrous substratum under the influence of stress is reinforced by proteolytic resorption of all fibrous cross-links that do not lie in the direction of major stress (123).

Since such fibrous pathways serve as guides for sheath cells as well as for nerve fibers, the association between these two elements remains close. In the distal stump the nerve fibers likewise find ample sheath cell tracks to associate with; and there seems little doubt that these two tissue elements are predisposed by their mutual affinities for a true symbiotic relationship (1). This matter is treated from the classical histological point of view in the article by Boeke. If the Schwann cell contributes any nutriment for the formation of the axon, it is obvious from Section IIIB that this could not be incorporated at the place of intake but would have to be moved centrad for assimilation. The main function of the Schwann cell seems to be to coat fibrous interfaces with its substance, which is peculiarly suited for the application of nerve fibers, and, moreover, to provide the stimulus and perhaps some complements needed for the formation of the myelin sheath.

B. REGENERATION RATE

Nerve fibers can regenerate repeatedly with undiminished vigor and unreduced rates (23). Since the advance of the tip is physical motion rather than true growth, the so-called "regeneration rate" is presumably determined chiefly by the physical properties of the system, such as contractility, viscosity, elasticity, etc. It is interesting to note that the rate of advance (31) is of the same order as that which has been calculated for the rate of protoplasmic replacement in the continuously growing neurons (117). Emphasis on the physical properties does not mean, however, that these processes could go on in the absence of the necessary metabolic, i.e., biochemical, resources.

Maximum rates of advance of *ca.* 4 mm. or more per day are obtained when the free tip can proceed on a straightaway, either along a column of Schwann cells (29) or in a well-oriented fibrous matrix with large liquid interstices (123). Wherever these optimum conditions are not realized, the regeneration rate is reduced, evidently in proportion to the frequency of temporary arrests, which, in turn, is a function of the intersectedness of the fibrous reticulum along which the fiber tip must proceed (104). An apparent stimulation of the rate of nerve-fiber regeneration after systemic administration of certain nerve extracts, reported in the literature (53), is clearly to be explained as an effect of the agent on the consistency of the scar, reducing resistance to nerve-fiber penetration, rather than as a speedup of fiber "growth." Since we are not dealing primarily with a process of "growth," it is rather obvious that any attempts to improve nerve regeneration by applying so-called "growth stimulants" miss the mark, and actually every single one made in the past has failed.

C. SELECTIVITY

As in first development, the principle of contact guidance has been found fully valid for nerve regeneration, essentially as defining the possible routes rather than the actual courses of a given fiber. Only if the substratum is strictly oriented (see above, Sec. IVA) will this provision also define the actual course of the nerve. Otherwise, the problem of additional factors selecting one pathway to the exclusion of others raises itself. In this, however, regeneration of mature nerves is significantly different from first development. Thus far, no evidence of specificity of pathways has been found in regeneration. Sensory nerve fibers travel as readily and as rapidly along former motor nerve paths as along their own (115, 30), and motor fibers grow with equal ease through sensory stumps (114). Likewise, a denervated muscle is as ready to accept innervation from a foreign nerve as from its own former nerve (118, 25). Since some degree of selectivity has been reported for the regeneration of nerves in larvae (73; see also Speidel's article below), we are evidently dealing here with a property that is only gradually lost in the course of development and maturation.

Contrary to the lack of selectivity during regenerative outgrowth, peripheral connections are established only between nerve fibers and end-organs that match. Thus sensory fibers will pervade a muscle but will fail to establish transmissive connections (115, 30). The fact that the presence of such regenerated fibers cannot be demonstrated by functional tests formerly led to the erroneous interpretation that fibers fail to regenerate into nerve stumps of a different kind (18).

D. NERVE GRAFTS

Nerve grafts are intended to reduce the gap between separated nerve stumps which regenerating fibers must span before entering the protective and guiding channels of the distal Schwann tubes. In animal experimentation such grafts often serve the intended function admirably (61), even after devitalization (122, 99) that does not transform them into foreign bodies. However, the usefulness of grafts in peripheral nerve surgery in man is still seriously questioned (65).

E. CLINICAL ASPECTS

The emergency of the second World War brought a new upsurge in interest and research to improve methods of surgical repair of injured nerves. While the urgency of the situation dictated for the most part an empirical approach, attempts to broaden and strengthen the factual and theoretical foundation on which all nerve repair rests have not been neglected. By applying the knowledge of the mechanisms of nerve regeneration to practical problems, some distinct advances have been made (66, 101, 103, 126, 51, 4, 71). However, the technics thus developed on laboratory animals have not always proved applicable to clinical practice, and, even where application was feasible, the results in man did not equal those obtained in the laboratory. This is due to the fact that, despite the fundamental identity of the processes of nerve regeneration in man and other mammals, differences of size and degree often prove of crucial importance. Some comments on the problem of nerve regeneration from the viewpoint of a clinical investigator are reported in the article by Sunderland.

Even when morphologically adequate peripheral nerve regeneration can be obtained in satisfactory volume, the functional result can never measure up to the normal condition as it existed prior to the injury. This is due to the fact that, because of the lack of specificity in nerve regeneration, a majority of the fibers enter into more or less foreign paths. Channels leading to incongruous endings are thus wasted on functionally irrelevant regeneration, while channels leading to functionally related, but still aberrant, destinations will cause a corresponding confusion in motor co-ordination. Some of this can be corrected by functional adjustments in the central patterns of co-ordination; but the range within which such reorganization is possible is definitely limited and much more modest than former sweeping generalization concerning the plasticity and regulability of central nervous functions would have made one believe (111, 70).

On the other hand, further improvements in the technics of nerve repair can be safely predicted if systematic research is continued. In this pursuit it would seem profitable to go beyond the mere reiteration of the fact that there are certain crucial differences in nerve regeneration between man and experimental animals and to find out just what those differences consist of and how to make proper allowances for them in extrapolating from laboratory mammals to man.

F. CENTRAL REGENERATION

Peripheral nerve regeneration is essentially a phenomenon of cellular physiology, inasmuch as it concerns the self-repair of a mutilated cell, the neuron. In contrast to this highly developed faculty, the nervous system has no regenerative capacity on the tissue level, that is, it cannot replace whole neurons that have been lost. There is some capacity for central regeneration during embryonic stages' and in later life, at least in the lower vertebrates such as fishes and amphibians (see the article on central regeneration by Stefanelli), but in mature higher forms any loss of neurons is permanent. Reparative processes in the centers remain confined to proliferation of scar tissue, largely composed of glia.

As for the capacity of central neurons to regenerate lost cell processes, it seems rather definite that such ability is less widespread and relatively minor in degree as compared to the peripheral system. A discussion of this point will be found in the articles of Gerard and Hooker summing up succinctly the present status of the problem. More concerted research along these lines may bring more conclusive solutions, which would be eminently important in order to assess the possibility, however remote, of repairing central lesions in man. If the poor regenerative display in the centers is due to unfavorable conditions in the neuronal environment, there may be hope for a solution. If, on the other hand, as indicated in Section IIIB6, the incapacity is based on constitutional properties of the central neurons themselves, then there would indeed be much less reason for optimism.

V. SPECIFICITY AND SELECTIVITY

One of the serious defects of most modern neurological and neurophysiological theories is their patent neglect of the qualitative diversity of the neural elements. Psychology is forced to postulate specific differences in neural activities, and experimental biology can demonstrate them *ad oculos*. Yet most physiological concepts of central nervous activity proceed from the assumption that all neurons are essentially alike in character, that is, are all constituted of essentially the same kind of protoplasm, and that the only parameters relevant to central nervous activity are quantitative variations of the metabolic state of this protoplasm, of the electric properties of its surface, and of the geometric configuration of the network. This thesis of the uniformity of the neural network has found its most explicit expression in the current comparisons of the brain to an electronic calculating machine (132).

In this situation it becomes doubly important to stress the evidence that has accumulated in favor of the inner qualitative diversity of the nervous system. It was interesting to note that the conference repeatedly took occasion to emphasize this fact of specific differentials among neurons, to which direct reference is made in the articles by Schmitt, Bodian, Speidel, Young, and particularly Sperry.

The problem of specific differences among neurons has, of course, several aspects. The first question is whether such intrinsic differences exist; the second, whether they are demonstrable; the third, whether they play a role only in the developmental process; the fourth, whether they are instrumental in establishing functional order; and the fifth, whether they can be described in terms of known physical and chemical properties.

A. CONSTITUTIONAL SPECIFICITIES

The evidence for the existence of constitutional differences among neurons beyond the crude subdivisions into cholinergic and adrenergic neurons has already been referred to above, in Section I. The embryological evidence alone is quite conclusive. In addition, there are the differential reactions to drugs, stains, viruses, and other agents already mentioned. It is interesting to note that many students of the physiology of the nervous system are still so strongly dominated by the spirit of a strictly morphological era, in which only visible images were rated as valid criteria, that they are willing to concede biochemical specificity to a nerve cell in the pre-optic nucleus of a lower vertebrate, in which certain secretion granules can be seen under the microscope, but would be reluctant to admit the existence of similar specificities in other neurons with no directly visible distinctions, even though behavioral tests of those neurons contain conclusive proof of their distinctiveness in development and response.

B. SELECTIVITY IN NERVE GROWTH

The case for selectivity with regard to pathways and end-organs during the primary outgrowth of nerves has already been presented in Section II. There is no need to restate the case here, but it is necessary to point out the full meaning of its acceptance. It should be borne in mind that acknowledging the selectivity of a given neuron type or a given pathway or a given end-organ implies nothing less than the following: that different neuron types are fundamentally and critically different in their composition; that a similar critical diversity exists among pathways and terminal organs; and that the neuron must possess means to identify or recognize, as it were, the appropriately matching specificity of its predestined pathway or terminal. These are logical inferences which are cogent, irrespective of whether or not we find any explanation of the underlying differentials in the realm of known physical and chemical phenomena. In an effort to show at least the feasibility of such an explanation, I have proposed a stereochemical model of the type of affinities involved (95, 105), which, pending more precise information, gives us at least a formal picture of selectivity. Its pertinence remains to be proved. At any rate, let us remember that the failure of a sensory neuron to connect with a muscle fiber lies in subtle discordances on the molecular level which the microscopic picture is too crude to reveal. This being the case, one should not expect that looking through the microscope at a synaptic ending in the central nervous system would reveal with any greater degree of certainty whether or not the particular contact is transmissive.

C. MODULATION

Perhaps the most astonishing, though incontrovertible, evidence of specificity not only in nerve growth but in the establishment of functional order in the nervous system has come from the so-called "resonance" phenomena, through which particular peripheral areas put themselves into the proper response relations with the corresponding centers in the central nervous system. The evidence has been recounted on past occasions (77, 84, 94, 92) and most recently in a brief review (108). It is dealt with rather concisely in the article by Sperry in this book.

In a long series of experiments it could be shown that each muscle has a specific biochemical differential, that it projects this differential into the motor nerve fibers that come to innervate it and thus tunes ("modulates") the motor ganglion cells to a specificity appropriate for the particular muscle. The central nervous system, in turn, employs in its co-ordination corresponding sets of specificities, so that central activity destined for, let us say, a gastrocnemius muscle is selectively picked up by the gastrocnemius-specific ganglion cells to the exclusion of all others ("myotypic function" [94]). The significant point to remember is that these ganglion cells have received their specificity by a retrograde influence ("modulation") from the muscle itself. This is proved by the fact that, upon reconnection with another muscle at a sufficiently early period of life, their specificity and central response relations will change in accordance with the new termination (75, 78, 85).

The same type of specific relationship, based not on stereotyped connection patterns but on secondary modulation, has also been demonstrated within the proprioceptive field. It was discovered that the central nervous system identifies, as it were, an excitation coming from a particular muscle according to the name of the muscle rather than according to its place in the system or according to the mechanical, physiological, or biological effects of its contractions (127). A further example of specific modulation was found in the establishment of the cornea reflex (96). The most remarkable demonstration of subtle specificities in the sensory field has certainly been furnished by the experiments of Sperry on the visual sense. These and other related experiments are reported in greater detail in his article.

It would seem idle to speculate on how far the continuation of this line of research will lead us. That these resonance relations are at present wholly outside the sphere of physiological thinking is evidenced by the simple fact that, obviously, no one could have predicted the results from existing theories. It is perhaps equally idle to speculate about the reason why these phenomena, which were first described nearly thirty years ago, have remained essentially unassimilated by the body of neurological concepts. It would seem that additional research, employing a combination of the classical technics of nerve physiology with the experimental technics of transplantation used in experimental embryology and morphology, could go far in removing the existing inconsistencies.

VI. DEVELOPMENT OF BEHAVIOR

It is a healthy sign that the sharp separation once advocated between a purely phenomenological study of behavior, on the one hand, and the physiological study of its possible neurological foundations, on the other, has not been generally adopted. The pursuit of any one scientific field under an injunction against trespassing into another is neither rational nor productive, especially if both have common objects. It simply is not true that nothing can be learned about the "organism as a whole" by studying its constituent parts and their interrelations. On the other hand, it would, of course, be equally erroneous to assume that mere preoccupation with the elements will tell the full story of their collective behavior (76). In the light of developments, it would seem unwarranted to subscribe to either a purely holistic or a purely elementarian theory of neural functions and behavior to the exclusion of the other, or to pursue studies on behavior alone or on its neurological foundations alone without the benefits that each field can derive from the advances of the other. Regardless of the pertinence of his detailed propositions, it certainly has been the historical merit of Coghill (16, 34) to have made a strong case for the conjoint attack on the problems of behavior and against the separatist trends of technical disciplines.

The realization that much can be learned about behavior by the study of its development is of relatively recent date. But, as frequently happens in the history of science, the formation of theory outraced the acquisition of factual knowledge, and soon students of the development of behavior were found to be rallied around two opposite doctrines, one stressing the primacy of the holistic, the other the elementarian, viewpoint. Each centered its arguments on certain objects, observations, and technics different from those of the other, and evidently each party felt justified in considering its particular niche as a fair sample of the behavioral universe. Thus what in sober evaluation would have become a fruitful stimulus to further clarification of the issues assumed the dogmatic aspect of an irreconcilable antithesis. Again, as often happens in the course of scientific history, the conflict is turning out to be a matter of one-sided viewpoints and undue generalizations rather than of facts. The articles of Windle and Hooker give a brief account of some of the recent history, and the article of Barron illustrates well the healthy tendency to escape from the dilemma and reconcile contradictions based partly on interpretation but partly also on a real diversity inherent in the various objects. It was highly encouraging to the conference to see how the spirit of exploration overcomes doctrinary ties and how research on the development of behavior and of its neural basis is proceeding with renewed vigor.

Valuable facts have come to light in the study of chemical systems known to be indispensable for functional activity in the mature nervous system. The appearance of the cholinesterase system, as well as its quantitative development, is closely correlated in time with the appearance and maturation of the functions of the central nervous system (118). Similar and even more subtle correlations between the appearance of chemical and functional properties have been summarized in the subsequent article of Flexner. Perhaps many of these facts prove no more than that the nervous system, in order to operate properly, must be in possession of all the physical and chemical properties known to be requisite for such functioning. But some future refinements of tests may lead to a more differential diagnosis by which the simultaneous appearance of a particular compound and of a particular functional complex would reveal specific causal links that could not be isolated from the fully developed nervous system in which all the chemicals and all the functions coexist. The study of development may thus be used on a larger scale in the same analytical sense as the study of deteriorating functions in mental patients has been used to identify certain biochemical correlates of central activity (35).

The phenomenology of behavioral development is actually an old discipline. It started with the recognition of the fact that behavior does have a stepwise ontogenetic history, and it went on to describe the steps involved. Only in the second instance did it proceed to test the significance of the steps as instruments or causal links in the development of the whole sequence. However, ever since the demonstration that embryos raised in narcosis would develop behavioral patterns of normal organization (11, 52), even though the overt expression of the whole series of precursor steps had been suppressed, it has been clear that the behavioral steps are merely external manifestations of underlying intrinsic developments rather than practice steps. The complex performances of later stages cannot possibly be founded upon the tested success of their simpler precursors, since they seem none the worse for the omission of the intermediate functional tests due to narcosis. Again, undue generalizations must be avoided, and what is said here for the early and fundamental steps of behavioral development does not apply equally to the terminal phases, in which the inherent developmental patterns are polished and perfected by actual practice and adjustment.

The phenomenological study of the development of behavior has revealed that, like all development, it follows a trend from the general to the specific and from more widespread involvement of elements to more restricted and differential activation. Coghill's principle of "individuation" from a background of mass reaction is based on this realization. It still holds true as designating a trend of events, even if the initial performance under consideration has never been a total activity of the whole body. In some cases and for some functions the primordial activity undoubtedly involves all the neural apparatuses capable of functioning at the same time (see subsequent articles by Hooker and Barron), while in other cases and for some other functions it seems equally clear that activity is territorially localized from the beginning (see the article by Windle).

To give a clear-cut example of the latter type, we need only refer to the appearance of the lid-closure reflex in amphibians studied extensively in our laboratory (41, 43). This reflex appears only at metamorphosis after having been completely absent in the otherwise fully functional larva. Both the sensory and the motor innervations required for the reflex are present in the larva and are individually capable of functioning, but the necessary central relations are not established until a certain state of maturation is reached. As soon as these relations are established, the reflex makes its appearance as a strictly localized and circumscribed act, which has never been part of a "total pattern" of central functions. Evidently, individuation from mass action does not apply to this type of response, but this, in turn, does not invalidate the principle for other performances. The sobering lesson from all this work has been that we cannot find a key formula for the development of behavior which will save us the trouble of investigating each component of behavioral development in its own right.

C. THE NEURAL BASIS OF INDIVIDUATION

The development of behavior shows clearly two phases—an early expansive and a later restrictive one (12). During the expansive phase, wider and wider areas of the body come under neural control. This sequence has been clearly correlated by Coghill and others with the gradual expansion of intra-central nerve connections and pathways (16). In a sense this correlation is obvious, as it merely expresses the fact that where there is no neural pathway there can be no neural function. Reactions during this early phase are remarkably stereotyped, indicating absence of discriminative response mechanisms. However, the more the nervous system approaches structural completion, the more prominent becomes its ability to activate restricted portions and patterns of the existing network independently in selected and co-ordinated combinations. It is this restrictive "individuation" for which the proper neural correlate is still to be revealed.

Coghill and others believed to have discovered a general neural model of "individuation" in the development of limb innervation. Amphibian limbs were described as being moved at first only in association with trunk movements, which was explained by the fact that their early innervation consists of collaterals from the motor neurons of trunk muscles. Later "dissociation" from the trunk appeared linked to the development of a secondary separate fiber system from the limb segments of the cord (137). Closer study (72), however, suggests that the so-called "primary" associated limb movements are, in reality, passive movements effected through the trunk muscles of the shoulder, while the intrinsic true limb movements do not appear until after the limb muscles have received the independent set of segmental neurons which was called "secondary" but which, as far as these muscles are concerned, is really primary. Hence the intrinsic limb function arises as a separate and individualized activity from the very first rather than as an "individuated" offshoot of an earlier mass response. There being no individuation, the attending neural changes cannot possibly serve as a model to explain individuation, and the search for the neural correlate of individuation must continue. The progressive refinement of the control of movements within the limb, which constitutes "individuation" on a smaller scale, can be accounted for, at least in part, by the progressive muscle-specific modulation of the limb neurons, establishing more discriminatory central relations (see Sec. VC and the article by Barron.

D. CENTRAL ORIGIN OF CO-ORDINATION

Many modern concepts of neurophysiology attempt to derive the properties of the output of the nervous system directly from the pattern of the sensory input. Such a concept is clearly contradicted by the studies on development. The fact that the appearance of motor performance antedates sensory control has often been stressed (16). Even more striking is the evidence of animals in which the development of the sensory nervous system had been experimentally suppressed. The basic patterns of motor co-ordination in such anesthetic areas develop without major impairment, and limbs lacking sensory innervation from the beginning function co-ordinately without sensory control having ever had a chance to play a constructive part in the development of the motor patterns (93, 135, 22).

E. THE ORIGIN OF CENTRAL CO-ORDINATION

Since neither learning nor patterns of sensory stimuli have any part in the development of orderly central functions, we must look to the autonomous processes of central development itself as the source of co-ordination. Experimental evidence indicates that the substratum of co-ordination is not spread diffusely over the nervous system but is restricted to sectors related to the corresponding organs; for limb movements, for instance, it resides in the limb segments of the cord. Detwiler was the first to show that a limb innervated from trunk segments cannot function properly (20). Limbs innervated from cranial nerves are similarly incapacitated (59). On the other hand, trunk segments incorporated in the limb level of the cord at an early embryonic stage will acquire the functional organization requisite for limb co-ordination (20).

We must recognize, therefore, the existence of specific regional differences in the establishment of co-ordination patterns, but the nature of those differences has not yet been disclosed. The only fact that has been shown conclusively by experimentation is that the central nervous system develops a finite repertory of behavioral performances which are pre-functional in origin and ready to be exhibited as soon as a proper effector apparatus becomes available (92, 94).

F. SPONTANEITY

A clear distinction must be made between the generation of a central discharge and the pattern of its distribution (co-ordination). Contrary to a widespread belief, a central discharge does not depend for its generation upon afferent influx but can originate within the centers. Many instances of rhythmic automatisms of nerve centers have been reported (3, 7, 36) and referred to underlying fluctuations in the metabolic and electric state of the neurons (26). The discovery that any isolated and deranged fragment of medulla or spinal cord will permanently exhibit trains of spontaneous rhythmic discharges (90, 91, 109) suggests that such activity is a basic property of pools of neurons rather than a specialty of certain centers only (92).

G. HORMONE EFFECTS

One of the most interesting and practically unexplored chapters of genetic neurology is the extensive change in neural functions and behavior that accompanies the transition from the larval to the adult stage in amphibian metamorphosis. During this phase many new structures and functions arise, while old ones disappear, and the nervous system undergoes a thorough remodeling so as to fit the reorganized system. It has been shown that the thyroid hormone, which actuates the bodily transformations, has also a direct and local effect on the nerve centers that are to be transformed (42). This may be a pertinent model of the hormone dependency of neural and behavioral changes in other instances, such as the activation of sex behavior at the time of sexual maturation (5). It appears that hormone action has no constructive or pattern-determining influence on the functional performance but operates merely by releasing certain patterned responses the distribution of which is determined by differential susceptibilities acquired during previous phases of differentiation.

H. CONCLUSION

The points chosen here for special comment were to be merely illustrations of how the analytical technics of experimental embryology and experimental morphology can be profitably applied to the study of the development of behavior, resulting in clarification of our concepts of behavior and its neural basis in general. Here the achievements of the conference acquire higher meaning. Just as the application of nerve regeneration to the problems of surgical nerve repair in the fourth session, so here, again, the demonstrated bearing of biological research on problems with which human neurology, psychology, and psychiatry are still grappling presents a strong case for the inseparability of fundamental research and human welfare. While scientific workers are more and more constrained into narrower and narrower confines in which to pursue their specialties, science as a whole cannot develop as a healthy and proportionate organism unless specialists will leave their burrows on periodic occasions and meet on common ground, take stock of their common inventory, sort out and interrelate their discoveries, survey the perspective of the whole, and develop the habit of keeping one another's problems and concepts in view while working toward a common goal, albeit through separate channels. It would seem that this conference has been eminently successful in achieving just this informal integration of viewpoints. It has brought clarification of old concepts as well as the formulation of promising future research, but, above all, it has given all participants a lively awareness of the interdependence of their various specialties, resulting in the determination to combine their efforts wherever possible in a conjoint attack on the vast unsolved problems of genetic neurology.

REFERENCES

1. ABERCROMBIE, M.; JOHNSON, M. L.; and THOMAS, G. A. 1949. The influence of nerve fibers on Schwann cell migration investigated in tissue culture. Proc. Roy. Soc., London, s.B, **136**:448–60.

2. ADELMANN, H. B. 1936. The problem of cyclopia. Quart. Rev. Biol., **11**:161–82 and 284–304.

3. ADRIAN, E. D. 1937. Synchronized reactions in the optic ganglion of *Dytiscus*. J. Physiol., **91**:66–89.

4. ALEXANDER, EBEN, JR.; WOODS, ROBERT P.; and WEISS, PAUL. 1948. Further experiments on the bridging of long nerve gaps in monkeys. Proc. Soc. Exper. Biol. & Med., **68**:380–82.

5. BEACH, FRANK A. 1947. Hormones and mating behavior in vertebrates. Recent Prog. Horm. Research (Proc. Laurentian Conf.), **1**:27–63.

6. BOELL, E. J., and SHEN, SHIH-CHANG. 1944. Functional differentiation in embryonic development. I. J. Exper. Zoöl., **97**:21–41.

7. BREMER, FREDERIC. 1944. L'activité "spontanée" des centres nerveux. Bull. Acad. roy. de méd. de Belgique, **9**:148–73.

8. BROWN, M. G.; HAMBURGER, V.; and SCHMITT, F. O. 1941. Density studies on amphibian embryos with special reference to the mechanism of organizer action. J. Exper. Zoöl., **88**:353–72.

9. BURT, AGNES S. 1943. Neurulation in mechanically and chemically inhibited *Amblystoma*. Biol. Bull., **85**:103–15.

10. CANNON, W. B., and ROSENBLUETH, ARTURO. 1949. The supersensitivity of denervated structures: a law of denervation. New York: Macmillan Co.

11. CARMICHAEL, L. 1926. The development of behavior in vertebrates experimentally removed from the influence of external stimulation. Psychol. Rev., **33**:51.

12. ———. 1933. Origin and prenatal growth of behavior. In: A handbook of child psychology, pp. 31–159. 2d ed., rev. Worcester, Mass.: Clark University Press.

13. CAVANAUGH, MARGARET W. 1950. Quantitative effects of the peripheral innervation area on nerves and spinal ganglion cells. J. Comp. Neurol. (in press).

14. CHASE, H. and E. 1941. Studies on an anophthalmic strain of mice. I. Embryology of the eye region. J. Morphol., **68**:279–301.

15. CLARK, W. E. LE GROS. 1945. Deformation patterns in the cerebral cortex. In: Essays on growth and form, pp. 1–22. Oxford: Clarendon Press.

16. COGHILL, G. E. 1929. Anatomy and the problem of behavior. Cambridge: At the University Press.

17. DALCQ, ALBERT. 1946. Recent experimental contributions to brain morphogenesis in amphibians. Growth, suppl., **10**:85–119.

18. DALE, H. 1935. Pharmacology and nerve endings. Proc. Roy. Soc. Med., **28**:15–28.

19. DETWILER, S. R. 1934. An experimental study of spinal nerve segmentation in *Amblystoma* with reference to the plurisegmental contribution to the brachial plexus. J. Exper. Zoöl., **67**:395–441.

20. ———. 1936. Neuroembryology: an experimental study. New York: Macmillan Co.

21. DETWEILER, S. R. 1944. Restitution of the medulla following unilateral excision in the embryo. J. Exper. Zoöl., 96:129–42.

22. ———. 1947. Further observations on the function and posture of limbs following removal of the trunk neural crest in *Amblystoma*. J. Exper. Zoöl., 106:299–312.

23. DUNCAN, DONALD, and JARVIS, W. H. 1943. Observations on repeated regeneration of the facial nerve in cats. J. Comp. Neurol., 79:315–27.

24. DUSTIN, A. P. 1910. Le rôle des tropismes et de l'odogénèse dans la régénération du système nerveux. Arch. de biol., 25:269.

25. FORT, W. B. 1940. An experimental study of the factors involved in the establishment of neuromuscular connection. Dissertation, Chicago.

26. GERARD, R. W. 1941. The interaction of neurones. Ohio J. Sc., 41:160–72.

27. GILLETTE, ROY. 1944. Cell number and cell size in the ectoderm during neurulation (*Amblystoma maculatum*). J. Exper. Zoöl., 96:201–22.

28. GURWITSCH, A. G. 1937. Mitogenetic analysis of the excitation of the nervous system. Amsterdam: N.V. Noord-Hollandsche Uitgeversmaatschappij.

29. GUTMANN, E. 1942. Factors affecting recovery of motor function after nerve lesions. J. Neurol. Psychiat., 5:81–95.

30. ———. 1945. The reinnervation of muscle by sensory fibers. J. Anat., 79:1–8.

31. GUTMANN, E.; GUTTMANN, L.; MEDAWAR, P. B.; and YOUNG, J. Z. 1942. The rate of regeneration of nerve. J. Exper. Biol., 19:14–44.

32. HARRISON, R. G. 1935. The Croonian lecture on the origin and development of the nervous system studied by the methods of experimental embryology. Proc. Roy. Soc., London, s.B, 118:155–96.

33. ———. 1947. Wound healing and reconstitution of the central nervous system of the amphibian embryo after removal of parts of the neural plate. J. Exper. Zoöl., 106:27–84.

34. HERRICK, C. J. 1949. George Ellett Coghill, naturalist and philosopher. Chicago: University of Chicago Press.

35. HOAGLAND, HUDSON. 1947. Enzyme kinetics and the dynamics of behavior. J. Comp. & Physiol. Psychol., 40:107–27.

36. HOLST, ERICH VON. 1937. Vom Wesen der Ordnung im Zentralnervensystem. Naturwissenschaften, 25:625–31 and 641–47.

37. HOLTFRETER, J. 1935. Formative Reize in der Embryonalentwicklung der Amphibien, dargestellt an Explantationsversuchen. Arch. f. exper. Zellforsch., 15:281–301.

38. ———. 1939. Gewebeaffinität, ein Mittel der embryonalen Formbildung. Arch f. exper. Zellforsch., 23:169–209.

39. HÖRSTADIUS, SVEN. 1944. Über die Folgen von Chorda-Exstirpation an späten Gastrulae und Neurulae von *Amblystoma punctatum*. Acta zool., 25:75–87.

40. KITCHIN, IRWIN C. 1949. The effects of notochordectomy in *Amblystoma mexicanum*. J. Exper. Zoöl., 112:393–416.

41. KOLLROS, J. 1942. Experimental studies on the development of the corneal reflex in Amphibia. I. The onset of the reflex and its relationship to metamorphosis. J. Exper. Zoöl., 89:37–67.

42. ———. 1943. Experimental studies on the development of the corneal reflex in Amphibia. II. Localized maturation of the reflex mechanism effected by thyroxin-agar implants into the hindbrain. Physiol. Zoöl., 16:269–79.

43. ———. 1943. Experimental studies on the development of the corneal reflex in Amphibia. III. The influence of the periphery upon the reflex center. J. Exper. Zoöl., 92:121–42.

44. LEHMANN, F. E. 1927. Further studies on the morphogenetic role of the somites in the development of the nervous system of amphibians. The differentiation and arrangement of the spinal ganglia in Pleurodeles waltli. J. Exper. Zoöl., 49:93–129.

45. LEVI, G. 1934. Explantation, besonders die struktur und die biologischen Eigenschaften der in vitro gezüchteten Zellen und Gewebe. Ergebn. d. Anat. u Entwcklngsgesch., 31:125–707.

46. LEVI, G., and MEYER, H. 1937. Die Struktur der lebenden Neuronen. Die Frage der Präexistenz der Neurofibrillen. Anat. Anz., 83:401–56.

47. LEWIS, WARREN H. 1947. Mechanics of invagination. Anat. Rec., 97:139–56.

48. LITWILLER, R. 1938. Quantitative studies on nerve regeneration in Amphibia. I. Factors controlling nerve regeneration in adult limbs. J. Comp. Neurol., 69:427–47.

49. ———. 1948. Quantitative studies on nerve regeneration in Amphibia. II. Factors controlling nerve regeneration in regenerating limbs. J. Exper. Zoöl., 79:377–97.

50. MARSH, G., and BEAMS, H. W. 1946. In vitro control of growing chick nerve fibers by applied electric currents. J. Cell. & Comp. Physiol., 27:139–57.

51. MATSON, DONALD A.; ALEXANDER, EBEN, JR.; and WEISS, PAUL. 1948. Experiments on the bridging of gaps in severed peripheral nerves of monkeys. J. Neurosurg., 5:230–48.

52. MATTHEWS, S. A., and DETWILER, S. R. 1926. The reactions of Amblystoma embryos following prolonged treatment with chloretone. J. Exper. Zoöl., 45:279–92.

53. MURALT, ALEXANDER VON. 1946. Die Signalübermittlung im Nerven. Basel: Birkhäuser.

54. NIEUWKOOP, P. D. 1946. Investigations on the regional determination of the central nervous system. J. Exper. Biol., 24:145–64.

55. OVERTON, JANE. 1950. Mitotic stimulation of amphibian epidermis by underlying grafts of central nervous tissue. J. Exper. Zoöl. (in press).

56. PARKER, G. H. 1932. On the trophic impulse so-called, its rate and nature. Am. Naturalist, 66:147–58.

57. PIATT, J. 1939. A study of nerve-muscle specificity in the forelimb of Triturus pyrrhogaster. J. Morphol., 65:155–85.

58. ———. 1940. Nerve-muscle specificity in Amblystoma, studied by means of heterotopic cord grafts. J. Exper. Zoöl., 85:211–41.

59. ———. 1941. Grafting of limbs in place of the eye in Amblystoma. J. Exper. Zoöl., 86:77–85.

60. ———. 1942. Transplantation of aneurogenic forelimbs in Amblystoma punctatum. J. Exper. Zoöl., 91:79–101.

61. SANDERS, F. K. 1942. The repair of large gaps in the peripheral nerves. Brain, 65:281–337.

62. SANDERS, F. K., and YOUNG, J. Z. 1945. Effect of peripheral connexion on the diameter of nerve fibers. Nature, 155:237.

63. SAWYER, CHARLES H. 1943. Cholinesterase and the behavior problem in Amblystoma. J. Exper. Zoöl., 92:1–29 and 94:1–31.

64. Scott, J. P. 1949. Genetics as a tool in experimental psychological research. Am. Psychologist, 4:526–30.

65. Seddon, H. J., and Holmes, W. 1944. The late condition of nerve homografts in man. Surg., Gynec. & Obst., 79:342–51.

66. Seddon, H. J., and Medawar, P. B. 1942. Fibrin suture of human nerves. Lancet, p. 87, July 25.

67. Speidel, C. C. 1933. Studies of living nerves. II. Activities of ameboid growth cones, sheath cells, and myelin segments, as revealed by prolonged observation of individual nerve fibers in frog tadpoles. Am. J. Anat., 52:1–79.

68. ———. 1942. Studies in living nerves. VII. Growth adjustments of cutaneous terminal arborizations. J. Comp. Neurol., 76:57–73.

69. Spemann, H. 1938. Embryonic development and induction. New Haven, Conn.: Yale University Press.

70. Sperry, R. W. 1945. The problem of central nervous reorganization after nerve regeneration and muscle transposition: a critical review. Quart. Rev. Biol., 20:311–69.

71. Tarlov, I. M. 1944. Autologous plasma clot suture of nerves: its use in clinical surgery. J. Am. Med. Assoc., 126:741–48.

72. Taylor, A. C. 1943. Development of the innervation pattern in the limb bud of the frog. Anat. Rec., 87:379–413.

73. ———. 1944. Selectivity of nerve fibers from the dorsal and ventral roots in the development of the frog limb. J. Exper. Zoöl., 96:159–85.

74. Twitty, V. C. 1949. Developmental analysis of amphibian pigmentation. Growth, suppl., 9:133–61.

75. Weiss, Paul. 1924. Die Funktion transplantierter Amphibienextremitäten. Aufstellung einer Resonanztheorie der motorischen Nerventätigkeit auf Grund abgestimmter Endorgane. Arch. f. Entwcklngsmechn. d. Organ., 102: 635–72.

76. ———. 1925. Tierisches Verhalten als "Systemreaktion." Die Orientierung der Ruhestellungen von Schmetterlingen (Vanessa) gegen Licht und Schwerkraft. Biol. generalis, 1:168.

77. ———. 1928. Erregungsspezifität und Erregungsresonanz. Grundzüge einer Theorie der motorischen Nerventätigkeit auf Grund spezifischer Zuordnung ("Abstimmung") zwischen zentraler und peripherer Erregungsform. Ergebn. d. Biol., 3:1.

78. ———. 1931. Das Resonanzprinzip der Nerventätigkeit, dargestellt in Funktionsprüfungen an transplantierten überzähligen Muskeln. Arch. f. d. ges. Physiol., 226:600.

79. ———. 1933. Functional adaptation and the role of ground substances in development. Am. Naturalist, 67:322–40.

80. ———. 1934. Secretory activity of the inner layer of the embryonic midbrain of the chick, as revealed by tissue culture. Anat. Rec., 58:299–302.

81. ———. 1934. In vitro experiments on the factors determining the course of the outgrowing nerve fiber. J. Exper. Zoöl., 68:393–448.

82. ———. 1935. Homologous (resonance-like) function in supernumerary fingers in a human case. Proc. Soc. Exper. Biol. & Med., 33:426–30.

83. ———. 1936. A study of motor coordination and tonus in de-afferent limbs in Amphibia. Am. J. Physiol., 115:461–75.

84. ———. 1936. Selectivity controlling the central-peripheral relations in the nervous system. Biol. Rev., 11:494–531.

85. ———. 1937. Further experimental investigations on the phenomenon of homologous response in transplanted amphibian limbs. I. Functional observations. J. Comp. Neurol., 66:181–209.

86. ———. 1937. Further experimental investigations on the phenomenon of homologous response in transplanted amphibian limbs. II. Nerve regeneration and the innervation of transplanted limbs. J. Comp. Neurol., 66:481–535.

87. ———. 1937. Further experimental investigations on the phenomenon of homologous response in transplanted amphibian limbs. III. Homologous response in the absence of sensory innervation. J. Comp. Neurol., 66:537–48.

88. ———. 1937. Further experimental investigations on the phenomenon of homologous response in transplanted amphibian limbs. IV. Reverse locomotion after the interchange of right and left limbs. J. Comp. Neurol., 67:269–315.

89. ———. 1939. Principles of development. New York: Henry Holt & Co.

90. ———. 1940. Functional properties of isolated spinal cord grafts in larval amphibians. Proc. Soc. Exper. Biol. & Med., 44:350–52.

91. ———. 1941. Further experiments with deplanted and deranged nerve centers in amphibians. Proc. Soc. Exper. Biol. & Med., 46:14–15.

92. ———. 1941. Autonomous versus reflexogenous activity of the central nervous system. Proc. Am. Phil. Soc., 84:53–64.

93. ———. 1941. Does sensory control play a constructive role in the development of motor coordination? Schweiz. med. Wchnschr., 71:591.

94. ———. 1941. Self-differentiation of the basic patterns of coordination. Comp. Psychol. Monog., 17:1–96.

95. ———. 1941. Nerve patterns: the mechanics of nerve growth. Growth, suppl., 5:163–203.

96. ———. 1942. Lid-closure reflex from eyes transplanted to atypical locations in *Triturus torosus:* evidence of a peripheral origin of sensory specificity. J. Comp. Neurol., 77:131–69.

97. ———. 1943. Nerve regeneration in the rat, following tubular splicing of severed nerves. Arch. Surg., 46:525–47.

98. ———. 1943. Endoneurial edema in constricted nerve. Anat. Rec., 86:491–522.

99. ———. 1944, Functional nerve regeneration through frozen-dried nerve grafts in cats and monkeys. Proc. Soc. Exper. Biol. & Med., 54:277–79.

100. ———. 1944. *In vitro* transformation of spindle cells of neural origin into macrophases. Anat. Rec., 88:205–21.

101. ———. 1944. Sutureless reunion of severed nerves with elastic cuffs of tantalum. J. Neurosurg., 1:219–25.

102. ———. 1944. Evidence of perpetual proximo-distal growth of nerve fibers. Biol. Bull., 87:160.

103. ———. 1944. The technology of nerve regeneration: a review. Sutureless tubulation and related methods of nerve repair. J. Neurosurg., 1:400–450.

104. ———. 1945. Experiments on cell and axon orientation *in vitro:* the role of colloidal exudates in tissue organization. J. Exper. Zoöl., 100:353–86.

105. ———. 1947. The problem of specificity in growth and development. Yale J. Biol. & Med., 19:235–78.

106. ———. 1949. Growth and differentiation on the cellular and molecular levels. Exper. Cell Research, suppl., 1:475–82.

107. ———. 1949. Differential growth. In: Chemistry and physiology of growth, pp. 35–186. Princeton, N.J.: Princeton University Press.

108. WEISS, PAUL. 1950. Experimental analysis of coordination by the disarrangement of central-peripheral relations. Cambridge: At the University Press.

109. ———. 1950. The deplantation of fragments of nervous system in amphibians. I. Central reorganization and the formation of nerves. J. Exper. Zoöl., 113: 397–461.

110. ———. Unpublished observations.

111. WEISS, PAUL, and BROWN, P. F. 1941. Electromyographic studies on recoordination of leg movements in poliomyelitis patients with transposed tendons. Proc. Soc. Exper. Biol. & Med., 48:284–87.

112. WEISS, PAUL, and BURT, AGNES S. 1944. Effect of nerve compression on Wallerian degeneration in vitro. Proc. Soc. Exper. Biol. & Med., 55:109–12.

113. WEISS, PAUL, and CAMPBELL, C. J. 1944. Nerve fiber counts and muscle tension after nerve regeneration in the rat. Am. J. Physiol., 140:616–26.

114. WEISS, PAUL, and CUMMINGS, J. B. 1943. Regeneration of the lateral line nerve of Amblystoma from different nerve fiber sources. Anat. Rec., 87:119–25.

115. WEISS, PAUL, and EDDS, M. V., JR. 1945. Sensory-motor nerve crosses in the rat. J. Neurophysiol., 8:173–93.

116. WEISS, PAUL; EDDS, M. V., JR.; and CAVANAUGH, M. 1945. The effect of terminal connections on the caliber of nerve fibers. Anat. Rec., 92:215–33.

117. WEISS, PAUL, and HISCOE, HELEN B. 1948. Experiments on the mechanism of nerve growth. J. Exper. Zoöl., 107:315–96.

118. WEISS, PAUL, and HOAG, ANN. 1946. Competitive reinnervation of rat muscles by their own and foreign nerves. J. Neurophysiol., 9:413–18.

119. WEISS, PAUL, and LITWILLER, R. 1937. Quantitative studies on nerve regeneration in Amphibia. I. Factors controlling nerve regeneration in adult limbs. Proc. Soc. Exper. Biol. & Med., 36:636–38.

120. ———. 1937. Quantitative studies on nerve regeneration in Amphibia. II. Innervation of regenerated limbs. Proc. Soc. Exper. Biol. & Med., 36:638–39.

121. WEISS, PAUL, and RUCH, T. C. 1936. Further observations on the function of supernumerary fingers in man. Proc. Soc. Exper. Biol. & Med., 34:569–70.

122. WEISS, PAUL, and TAYLOR, A. C. 1943. Repair of peripheral nerves by grafts of frozen-dried nerve. Proc. Soc. Exper. Biol. & Med., 52:326–28.

123. ———. 1943. Histomechanical analysis of nerve reunion in the rat after tubular splicing. Arch. Surg., 47:419–47.

124. ———. 1944. Further experimental evidence against "neurotropism" in nerve regeneration. J. Exper. Zoöl., 95:233–57.

125. ———. 1944. Impairment of growth and myelinization in regenerating nerve fibers subject to constriction. Proc. Soc. Exper. Biol. & Med., 55:77–80.

126. ———. 1946. Guides for nerve regeneration across gaps. J. Neurosurg., 3: 375–89.

127. WEISS, PAUL, and VERZÀR, FRITZ. 1930. Untersuchungen über das Phänomen der identischen Bewegungsfunktion mehrfacher benachbarter Extremitäten. Arch. f. d. ges. Physiol., 223:671.

128. WEISS, PAUL, and WALKER, R. 1934. Nerve pattern in regenerated urodele limbs. Proc. Soc. Exper. Biol. & Med., 31:810–12.

129. WEISS, PAUL, and WANG, H. 1936. Neurofibrils in living ganglion cells of the chick, cultivated in vitro. Anat. Rec., 67:105–17.

130. ———. 1945. Transformation of adult Schwann cells into macrophages. Proc. Soc. Exper. Biol. & Med., 58:273–75.

131. WEISS, PAUL; WANG, H.; TAYLOR, A. C.; and EDDS, M. V. 1945. Proximodistal fluid convection in the endoneural spaces of peripheral nerves, demonstrated by colored and radioactive (isotope) tracers. Am. J. Physiol., 143: 521–40.

132. WIENER, NORBERT. 1948. Cybernetics, or control and communication in the animal and the machine. New York: John Wiley & Sons.

133. WOLBACH, S. BURT. 1946. Vitamin A deficiency and excess in relation to skeletal growth. Proc. Inst. Med. Chicago, 16:118–46.

134. WRIGHT, SEWALL, and WAGNER, K. 1934. Types of subnormal development of the head from inbred strains of guinea pigs and their bearing on the classification and interpretation of vertebrate monsters. Am. J. Anat., 54:383–447.

135. YNTEMA, C. L. 1943. Deficient efferent innervation of the extremities following removal of neural crest in *Amblystoma*. J. Exper. Zoöl., 94:319–49.

136. YOUNG, J. Z. 1945. The history of the shape of a nerve fiber. In: Essays on growth and form, pp. 41–93. Oxford: Clarendon Press.

137. YOUNGSTROM, K. A. 1940. A primary and a secondary somatic motor innervation in *Amblystoma*. J. Comp. Neurol., 73:139.

If the preceding article served in the manner of an overture to the appreciation of the orchestrated symphony of the development of the nervous system, the following article gives in greater detail the scores of some of the component instruments that it has been possible to single out from the total harmonious performance. The bearing that better insight into the mechanisms of neural development has on steadiness of progress in neurology and the behavioral sciences is so intimate that the following account of the infant field of neurogenesis represents a sort of primer for the rationale on which the practical applications to neurosurgical problems, reported in Section V, are based.

Nervous System

(Neurogenesis)

PAUL WEISS

THE OBJECT AND THE PROBLEMS

WE ARE to deal here with the causal analysis of "the development of the nervous system." In that generality, the task is simply unmanageable. Of the innumerable aspects the mature nervous system offers to the observer, each one has had its characteristic ontogenetic history, hence raises separate questions as to time and manner of its origin and as to mode and means of its ontogenetic transformations. This points us to the only practical approach, which lies in resolving the confusing complexity of the system into simpler components and addressing our questions to the more elementary events thus singled out. Most of the following account will be essentially a sample exercise in phrasing and sorting such questions of sufficient concreteness as to offer hope for precise answers. The answers themselves are mostly still in a very fragmentary state and will be presented without glossing over their often provisional character. I have chosen topics and examples chiefly in the spirit of the guiding theme of this book, which is to illuminate, rather than cover, the processes of development. This also explains the argumentative, rather than reportorial, manner of presentation. It reflects the effort to give a coherent and consistent picture, in which facts and data are rated not as isolated items, but as tools for the clarification and solution of problems—not as sheer statements, but as answers to questions; which makes the text useful as a guide more to the understanding, than to the literature, of the field.

Some familiarity with the main morphological, physiological, and embryological features of the nervous system will be taken for granted. Yet a brief listing of the most prominent ones may help to keep our analytical questions properly focussed from the start. Somewhat arbitrarily we shall separate the discussion of the central nervous system, which serves intercommunication among its constituent units, from that of the peripheral nerves, which serve communication between the former and the nonnervous tissues of the body.

THE PERIPHERAL NERVE

Nerves are composite structures, containing bundles of nerve fibers of different classes, associated in variable numbers, proportions, and groupings, and held together and sheathed by connective tissue, in which course blood and lymph vessels and endoneurial fluid. In the so-called plexuses, nerves regroup or exchange some of their fibers. Farther peripherally, they branch by successive dichotomies and distribute their branches over the periphery according to patterns characteristic of the given peripheral sector or organ, with considerable latitude for individual variation.

The component nerve fibers themselves are composite (Fig. 125), with the axis cylinder (axon or neurite, a)—a protoplasmic extension of the centrally located cell body (perikaryon)—at the core; covered by a membrane or medullated sheath (m) consisting of alter-

346

nating layers of myelin and protein; surrounded by the thin protoplasm of the sheath cells of Schwann (*s*), arrayed in tandem and (in medullated fibers) corresponding each to an internodal segment (between two nodes of Ranvier); the whole enclosed in a collagenous tube (*t*). Axons vary in diameter (caliber) according to the classes to which they belong (sympathetic, somatic motor, tactile sensory, etc.) and, within each class, according to length and peripheral distribution; the thickness of the myelin sheath and usu-

different types of neurons differ substantially in their constitution (molecular content), as evidenced by selective reactions to poisons, drugs, histological stains, hormones, and the production of specific secretions (neurosecretions). This specificity of neurons may be assumed to extend into the axis cylinders, which are true protoplasmic extensions of the cell. Many more items could be added to this list. In their totality, they make up what may be described as the "functional architecture" of the CNS.

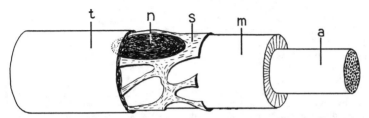

Fig. 125. Diagram of composition of single nerve fiber (explanation in text).

ally also the length of internodes vary proportionately. These parameters are importantly related to functional properties (conduction velocity, threshold, susceptibility, etc.). Fibers remain single or branch out, either by terminal flaring or by side shoots (collaterals), in accordance with functional needs. Each branch ends either blindly or on a specific end-organ with which it forms transmissive and trophic connections ("innervation"). Nerve fibers of a given class generally are found connected with the appropriately matching type of end-organ. The density of innervation varies regionally and with the type of innervated organ.

THE CENTRAL NERVOUS SYSTEM (CNS)

The CNS and its outpost ganglia contain the cell bodies (perikarya) of the peripheral neurites, and the former also a host of intracentral fibers, either in orderly bundles (fiber tracts, funiculi, commissures) or irregularly dispersed as "neuropil." In addition, these neural masses are interlaced with various types of glia cells, blood vessels, and, according to some, ground substance of ill-defined nature. Morphologically, the cell bodies vary characteristically in size, location, grouping, number, distribution of processes, and mode of interconnections, all of which may be called "geometrical" criteria. In addition to these distinctions, however,

NEUROGENESIS

Every feature thus singled out raises a separate question as to its origin. We have noted the finished products; but how have they come about? This circumscribes the task of neurogenesis. Our goal is to reconstruct the whole causal chain of events that leads from the properties of the egg cell to each particular item on our list. These events include complex molecular interactions with the emergence of new molecular species and the loss of others; displacements and rearrangements of substance on a molecular, micellar, cellular, and supracellular scale; metabolic energy production and consumption; electric, thermal, hydrodynamic, and mechanostatic (pressure-tension) phenomena, etc.; at any rate, processes that are in principle observable, measurable, and describable in terms of the substances, forces, interactions, and conditions actually present at each step. This is the object of ontogenetic analysis. Phylogenetic (evolutionary) considerations, introducing past history, do not enter into this causal (or operational) analysis at all; they only explain why of the infinite conceivable number of possible causal chains of events, only a very limited selection has found materialization.

Causal analysis must be preceded by a complete description of the events that are to be explained; description, of course, in objective and, wherever possible, quantitative terms. Much of the current research in neurogenesis is still in this descriptive phase, even though, in order to get the necessary data, it makes extensive use of experiments. The mode of the formation of a nerve fiber is a case in point. At the turn of the century, there were two opposing schools of thought given to different interpretations of inconclusive static observations. The one maintained that the axis cylinder is produced in fractions by tandem chains of peripheral cells, which are then secondarily joined together into a single strand, drainpipe fashion; while the other contended the axon to be a protoplasmic sprout of a single central neuroblast cell. The ingenious experimental feat of Harrison ('07a, '10) in isolating the supposed neuroblasts in extraneous media devoid of peripheral cells to test whether or not they could still form axons, settled the issue: they could. A descriptive datum had been ascertained by an experimental method. Then, passing on to explore the reaction of cells in vitro to solid fiber substrata, Harrison ('14) carried his research into the strictly analytical sphere, where one examines why things happen as they do—in the given case, why the nerve fiber follows one course rather than another. The Hows and Whys of our questions are thus intimately related and often enough blend into one. With this in mind we may now attempt to carve out some specific neurogenetic questions from the body of neurological data presented above. Evidently, this can only be a crude and fragmentary sample.

Why and where does the axon arise from the neuroblast? What causes its elongation? What gives it its course? Do the trunks and branches of the mature nerves reflect the orientation of early outgrowth? Is that outgrowth strictly oriented or is it haphazard, followed by selective abolition of unsuccessful connections? What determines deflections or other changes of course? What causes branches to arise, and where? Are tissues flooded with nerve fibers, or is admission selective? If the latter, how is invasion held in check? And is penetration tantamount to functionally effective innervation? What causes the association of sheath cells and nerve fibers, and what is the mechanism of myelin formation? How do fibers group into bundles—by active aggregation or by the enveloping action of connective tissue? And what determines the places and proportions in which the various tissue elements combine to form nerves? How does it happen that fibers of similar function are often grouped together, and how do they each reach their appropriate destinations? Or do they? And, if not, how can central functions fail to be confused? How does a nerve fiber gain in width, and what decides its final caliber? And does it change with body growth? What controls the number of fibers available for a given area—size of the source, frequency of branching, overproduction followed by terminal screening, or all of these? And if the size of the source is a factor, what determines it? This points us to the centers.

How does the neural plate transform into primordia of brain, spinal cord, and ganglia? How does it grow? How do its cell groups specialize for their respective formative tasks, how early, in what places and what sequence? What makes them divide or cease to divide? What causes them to migrate and in what directions, and what to assemble in defined locations? What sets the numbers and quotas of the different neuron types, and adjusts them to the functional needs of the individual? How do they achieve selective interconnections on which their later functioning will depend? And which ones of these are really relevant to the specific patterns, rather than just the general execution, of central functions? What provides the neuron population with the proper contingent of supportive, protective, and nutrient cells and structures of other origins, in varying combinations according to the local needs? And how much interdependence and interaction in growth and differentiation is there between different central regions before and after they have become segregated? If there are interactions, what is their nature and how are they transmitted? Does exercise and practice have a constructive, or at least modifying, effect on central pathways or central size? Are fluctuating peripheral demands taken into account in the development of centers, and, if so, by what means? Can growing centers adjust to lesions or deformation, and how—by regeneration, compensatory growth, or substitutive functional corrections? And can the development of overt behavior be correlated with, or even explained by, the stepwise emergence of neural apparatuses?

Specific questions like these, rather than noncommittal generalities about "the development of the nervous system being a matter of metabolic processes, gradient fields and enzymatic reactions," are effective guides to useful research.

NERVE REGENERATION

Since our insight into nerve development and growth has been greatly aided by studies on nerve regeneration, the essentials of this phenomenon may be briefly recapitulated here for later reference; for fuller reviews, see Cajal ('28), Nageotte ('22), and Boeke ('35).

freezing, chemical damage, etc.), the segment lying distally to the lesion (the "distal" or "peripheral" stump), within a few days loses conductivity, and the individual nerve fibers in it become converted into non-conducting plasmatic strands ("Schwann cords" or "Buengner's cords"); myelin and axis cylinder remnants break down (o, Fig. 126B), and as they are being resorbed, their place

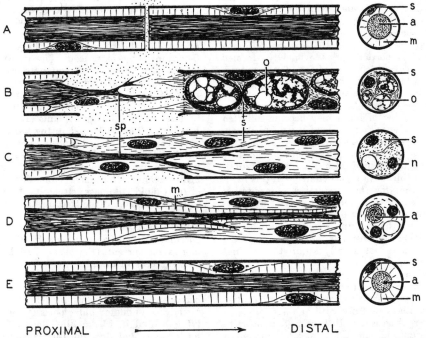

PROXIMAL   DISTAL

Fig. 126. Diagram of regeneration of single nerve fiber after transection (explanation in text).

Nerve regeneration is the restoration of morphological and physiological continuity in a transected nerve. The older supposition that this may take place *per primam fusionem* of the severed ends has proved untenable; the observation that cut ends of axons in tissue culture that lie within a distance of a few micra may merge during the first hours after severance (Levi, '34), does not apply to nerves in the body, where this condition is practically never realized. In the body, the nerve is restituted by renewed outgrowth of fibers from the proximal stump, repeating with some modifications the process of embryonic outgrowth. Briefly, the events are as follows (Fig. 126).

After a nerve has been severed or otherwise locally disrupted (e.g., by pressure, wise locally disrupted (e.g., by pressure,

is taken by the hypertrophying and multiplying sheath cells of Schwann (s, Fig. 126C). This combination of regressive and proliferative processes is generally referred to as "Wallerian degeneration." In the "proximal" or "central" stump, it remains confined to the immediate vicinity of the lesion, and although the whole injured neuron, including the central perikaryon, shows some traumatic reaction, the part that has retained its continuity with the central cell body soon becomes the source of the regenerative process.

The free tip of each proximal axon stump assumes amoeboid activity and extends into the surroundings much the same as in the first development (sp, Fig. 126B). Branching is frequent, but many of the branches are arrested in their course and remain abortive. While the outgrowing axon branches roam about the wound area, Schwann cells spill from the cut nerve ends, notably from the "degenerating" peripheral stump. When an advancing axon tip meets such a Schwann cord, it follows it and is thus guided into the peripheral stump (Fig. 126C), and through it to the peripheral tissues, where new transmissive connections can be established if the arriving nerve branch is of the proper type.

The highly irregular connective tissue that seals the cut nerve ends, commonly referred to as "scar," causes the dissipation of a large proportion of the newly formed branches, which may form dense tangles called "neuromas." Nerve regeneration thus involves a great deal of overproduction and wastage of sprouts. Eventually, a near-normal number of fibers may become collected in the deserted channels of the distal stump. The new branches, small at first (1μ or less), gradually gain in width and develop on their surface a new myelin sheath (m, Fig. 126D), which thickens proportionally. In this manner, lines for the conduction of excitation between centers and periphery are reestablished. However, owing to the misdirection of many fibers into wrong channels, the physiological control restored by regenerated nerves does not usually attain the original perfection.

In contrast to the practically unlimited power of regeneration observed in peripheral nerves, regenerative growth of intracentral nerve fibers declines with age and phylogenetic rank so as to be little more than abortive in brain and spinal cord of adult mammals under ordinary circumstances. Whether this is due to an intrinsically lower growth potential of the neurons or to less favorable growth support, perhaps even greater active obstruction, by the central, as compared to the peripheral, environment, is still a matter of debate.

ANALYSIS OF THE DEVELOPMENT OF A NEURON

OUTGROWTH OF AXIS CYLINDER

Mechanism of Elongation. As was indicated above, it is now indisputably established that the neurite (axon) develops as a direct protoplasmic extension of the nerve cell. At a given point along the circumference of the neuroblast, cytoplasm is protruded to form a short thread with a highly mobile tip. Presumably any breach in the cell surface may serve as outlet. The fact that in the

embryo the sprouts tend to emerge from the same sides in all neuroblasts of a given group must be ascribed to certain polarizing factors in the cellular environment, analogous to the determination of rootlet formation in Fucus eggs by the polar action of electric fields, ultraviolet light, pH gradients, etc. (Whitaker, '40).

The young sprout of axoplasm has no rigid axis skeleton, no firm sheath, nothing to propel it in a predetermined direction. The sprout continues to elongate by virtue of forces residing chiefly within the cell of origin, but the course of the elongation is determined by extraneous factors. In his classic observations on axon outgrowth in tissue culture, Harrison ('10) correctly identified the mode of advance as of the amoeboid type, which view has been fully borne out by later observations in explants (Lewis and Lewis, '12; Levi, '34) and in the living tadpole (Speidel, '33). Adopting and partly amplifying Lewis' ('50) interpretation, we may conceive of the sprout as a cylinder of firmly gelated ectoplasm surrounding a core of more fluid entoplasm streaming from the cell body distad. At the free tip, this central stream would erupt in numerous pseudopodial processes, which then compete among one another hydrodynamically for the common axial current (Fig. 127). The branch that succeeds in draining the inflow into its own channel thus automatically obliterates the weaker pseudopods, and as its surface becomes gelated, it adds its length to the already consolidated older parts of the fiber lying behind it. Meanwhile, the tip bursts forth anew, and thus the fiber advances in a continuous series of steps of protrusion of pseudopods, competition, and consolidation. Evidently, the protoplasm for the fiber is produced in the cell body, but it is added at the tip to which it is conveyed by the central stream. The motive mechanism of this convection is still obscure, but it may consist of peristaltic contraction-relaxation waves of the fiber surface. It provides some sort of "pumping" action, which after the fiber has ceased to elongate, continues to supply protoplasm for its further growth in width (see p. 363). In contrast to true amoeboid locomotion, however, the rear end of the nerve cell remains anchored to its surroundings so that instead of dragging the bulk of the cell after it, the advancing tip merely spins out a thread of increasing length between itself and the cell body.

The described active advance ends as soon as the free tip of a fiber attaches itself permanently to a peripheral receptor or effector cell. Further elongation becomes essentially a matter of passive extension, the fiber being in tow by the terminal tissues, which are subject to considerable migrations (e.g., muscle buds) and displacements during the subsequent phases of growth (Fig. 128). Because of this "towing" process, the primary growth pattern of nerves becomes greatly

problem, and a variety of "tropisms" and "attractions" of chemical, electrical, mechanical or undefined physiological nature have been suggested as the orienting agents (see Harrison, '35a,b). At present, we are approaching a rather unified concept of the mechanism of nerve fiber orientation, which is summarized in the following account (condensed from Weiss, '41c, '44, '50c).

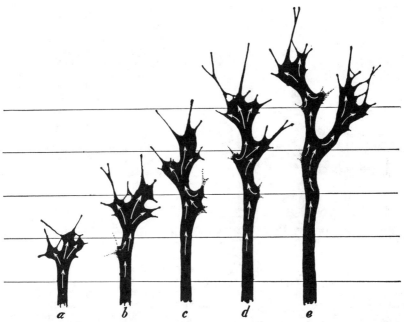

Fig. 127. Five consecutive phases in the advance of an axon tip (semidiagrammatic). Arrows indicate directions of flow, thrust and drain of neuroplasm. In *e*, dichotomous branching of fiber has been initiated. Dotted portions represent the location of earlier protrusions that have been sucked back by the draining force of the axial stream.

distorted. This explains why ontogenetic shifts, hence phylogenetic relations, of individual muscles can often be traced through their nerve supply, as in the pelvic fins of fishes that have migrated far forward until they have come to lie ahead of the pectoral fins.

During its period of free advance, the orientation of the nerve fiber is of course determined by the course which its roving tip takes. The early "pioneer" or pathfinder fibers thus lay down the primary nerve connections to the nerveless tissues which they invade. Since later fibers simply follow the course of the earlier ones, the problem of nerve orientation concerns primarily the pioneers. Much experimental work, and even more speculation, has been devoted to this

Mechanism of Orientation. Without recounting the trials and errors of the past, it is yet instructive to point to one basic fallacy of earlier concepts, namely, the tacit assumption that nerve fibers can penetrate structureless space in the manner in which plants can grow into air or water—an impression strengthened by the selective nerve stains, which impregnate nerve fibers to the exclusion of their surroundings. The suggestiveness of plant growth as a model of nerve growth is clearly reflected in the widespread use of botanical similes in neurological terminology; e.g., "dendrites," "rami," "roots," "arborization," "sprouts." Actually, however, according to the best available experimental evidence, nerve processes, like most animal tissue cells, are unable to push freely into a liquid, but can only proceed along interfaces, either between a solid and a liquid, or between two immiscible liquids, or between a liquid and a gas. The nearest analogon among plants would be the clinging vine. A nerve tip can traverse not even a small liquid gap without an interfacial bridge.

Interfaces capable of serving as the requisite substrata are furnished in the body by

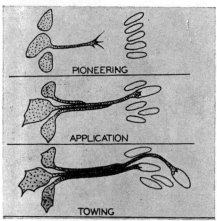

Fig. 128. Three phases in development of nerves (diagrammatic). *Top:* Pioneering phase (free fiber tip advances into surroundings). *Middle:* Application phase (pioneering tip has become attached to peripheral cell, younger tips apply themselves to course of older ones). *Bottom:* Towing phase (shift of peripheral cell produces corresponding displacement of attached nerve fiber).

all the fibrous units (fibrils, fibers, filaments) that pervade the liquid spaces in and between cells and tissues and constitute the solid framework of the "ground substances" (see Section III, Chapter 1, by Schmitt). They consist mostly of chains of filamentous protein molecules combined into bundles and networks of submicroscopic and microscopic dimensions. Along such filaments the terminal filopodia of the nerve fiber are drawn out by interfacial forces of still unresolved nature which cause protoplasm to spread out along the interface, grossly comparable to a "wetting" process. The linearity of the fibrous units along which they extend is a major factor in guiding the extending nerve fibers. In a planar interface, they would fuse to a sort of "terminal web." However, the linear guide structures are the ones of greatest practical importance, since even planar surfaces commonly contain inhomogeneities that describe linear tracts within the common plane (e.g., the fibrous constitu-

ents of coats or membranes). The principle according to which nerve fiber tips are guided in their course by contact with surrounding structures has been designated as *"contact guidance"* (Weiss, '41c).

In an irregular network, fibrils intersect at countless places and angles. Nerve tips advancing on such a trellis will be split at each intersection, but, as was explained above, competition will usually obliterate all but one of these terminal branches, and only this one will proceed. The decision of which one of the multiple projections will endure in any given instance may be essentially a matter of the accidents of the local situation. If so, the resulting nerve course will be irregular and tortuous (Fig. 129b, e), as is the case in the neuropil of the nerve centers, in scar tissue (e.g., between severed nerve stumps), and in the plasma clots of ordinary tissue cultures. On the other hand, the more the meshes of the fibrillar network are oriented in a given prevailing direction, the more the resulting nerve fiber course, tracing the common directional component, will likewise become definitely oriented (Fig. 129a). The extreme of this condition is attained when the fibrous matrix consists of parallel guide rails which leave the single-tracked nerve fibers no alternative course (Fig. 129c,d). In this case, nerve orientation resolves itself completely into a matter of the orientation of the underlying substratum and can therefore be controlled by way of the latter, as has been proved by a variety of observations and experiments both in the living animal and in vitro. The following examples may serve as illustrations.

When tension is applied in tissue culture to a blood plasma clot, either during or after coagulation, the meshes of the random network of fibrin threads are drawn out in the general direction of the lines of stress. Nerve fibers allowed to grow out in such a medium then move in the same prevailing direction (Weiss, '34a). Thus, by orienting the colloidal matrix, tension can indirectly orient nerve growth. The immediate factor is the orientation of the matrix, irrespective of how it has been obtained. Fibrous tissue exudates spreading along surfaces and being drawn out in the direction of flow, for instance, act in like manner (Weiss, '45). That this principle of contact guidance is equally valid within the living body has been substantiated in numerous instances, most strikingly by the directional control of nerve regeneration. Without intervention, regenerating nerve fibers commonly take random courses. But it has been possible to direct them into a straight oriented course by forcing the underlying matrix into parallel alignment. This has been achieved both in the gelatinous fin tissue of larval amphibians (Weiss, '50a) and in the blood clots binding severed nerve stumps of adult mammals (Weiss, '44; Weiss and Taylor, '43). In the latter case

tion. If the nerve course depends on preneural guide structures in the colloidal matrices, our attention must therefore turn to the factors producing structural orientation. Tension being presumably the commonest orienting agent, let us examine first the potential sources of tensional stresses in the body. Oriented tensions arise from external stretch-

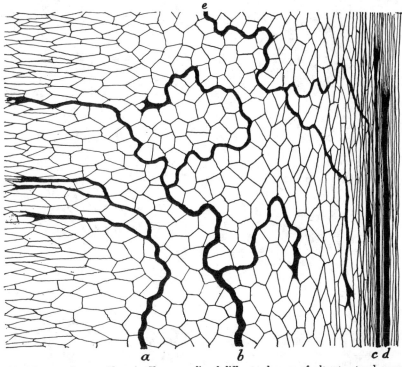

Fig. 129. Advance of nerve fibers in fibrous media of different degrees of ultrastructural organization (randomness in center turning into prevailing horizontal orientation in left part, and strict vertical orientation in right part of diagram). Along random meshes of center strip, the course of fibers *a, b* and *e* is tortuous, with frequent branching; in the more orderly parts of the medium, fiber courses become correspondingly aligned; in a rigorously oriented medium, fibers (*c, d*) run straight and remain undivided.

there is a primary phase, during which longitudinal tensions orient the fibrin of the blood clot in a prevailing direction from stump to stump, followed by a secondary phase, during which fibrinolytic agents discharged in the wound dissolve all remaining disoriented crosslinks between the longitudinal fibrin strands. This gives a good illustration of the multiplicity of factors involved in orientation.

In view of the ubiquitous presence of fibrous elements in the tissue spaces, these examples may be considered to be fair models of the normal mechanism of nerve orienta-

ing or internal shrinkage of a cohesive system. Differential growth, resulting in extensive displacement of body parts relative to one another, is an ample source of stretch effects. Nerve growth may thus be expected to trail actively advancing organs even prior to being taken in tow by them. Localized shrinkage is perhaps even more important as a source of stress. Such shrinkage occurs, for instance, around any intensely proliferating area as a result of a peculiar dehydrating effect which proliferating cells exert on surrounding colloids (Weiss, '29, '34a; Grossfeld, '34). The resulting local contraction of the fibrillar network automatically distorts the meshes into a radial pattern converging upon the proliferating center (Fig. 130, top). Subsequent nerve growth, being guided over these radial pathways toward the center, naturally will give the illusion of having been "attracted" by it. We may call this the

structures, cogently explicable in terms of demonstrable chains of physico-chemical events. This may appropriately be called the "two-center effect."

Although tension has been revealed as the most common effector mechanism in the production of guide structures, it is conceiv-

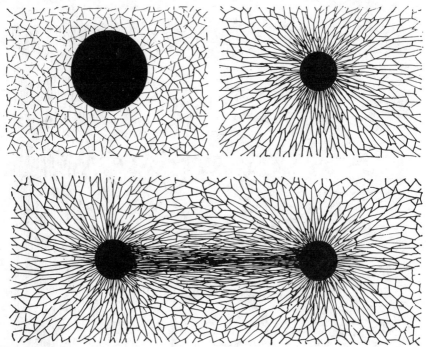

Fig. 130. Effect of local contraction on ultrastructure of a fibrous medium. *Top:* "One-center effect." Shrinkage of area indicated by black circle from the dimensions of the left panel to those of the right panel produces radial distortion of contiguous network. *Bottom:* "Two-center effect." Two "one-center effects" in a common network yield resultant preferential orientation along connecting line between the two centers.

"one-center effect." It is a concrete example of one way in which localized chemical activity can translate itself into structural patterns.

In the presence of two separate centers of proliferation (hence, two contracting foci), the intermediate fibrous matrix is being stretched, hence becomes aligned, along the connecting line. There is thus established a fibrillar bridge which any nerve fibers in that area are bound to follow (Fig. 130, bottom). Figure 131, top, shows, for example, the straight tract of nerve fibers grown reciprocally between two proliferating spinal ganglia in a thin plasma lamella, guided not by spurious "attractions" from the distance, but by contact with tangible guide

able that other vectorial agents besides tension, such as hydrodynamic currents, high electrostatic potentials, electrophoresis, or perhaps still wholly unsuspected processes, could effect fibrillar orientation of the requisite kind.

On a strictly oriented substratum, nerve fiber growth is thus fully determined by contact guidance. On a substratum of random configuration, that is, one not previously subjected to orienting factors, nerve growth would remain correspondingly random unless additional factors became operative. Since each one of the countless intersections of an irregular pathway system presents the nerve tip with alternative directions, any factor that systematically favors one general

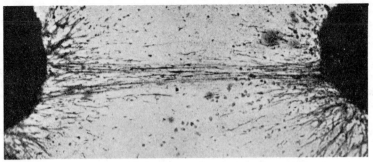

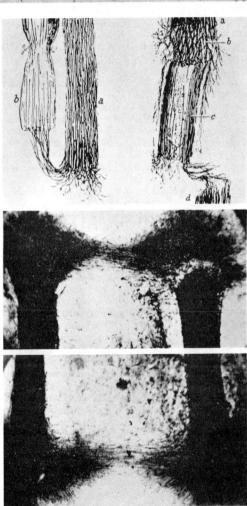

Fig. 131. Two-center effect. *Top:* "Bridge" of cells and nerve fibers that has formed between two embryonic spinal ganglia of chick (dark areas) cultured in vitro in thin blood plasma membrane. $\times$ 48. (From Weiss, '34.) *Middle:* Regenerated nerve fibers forming "bridges" between "proximal" stumps (*a, c*) and dislocated "peripheral" stumps (recurrent, *b;* laterally displaced, *d*) (from Cajal, '28). *Bottom:* "Bridges" of Schwann cells that have grown out between the open ends of two fragments of adult rat nerve explanted in a thin blood plasma clot (from Weiss, '52b).

355

direction over another would entail a statistical deviation of the fibers in the favored direction—an over-all trend rather than a common course. Many dendritic fields, for instance, show such a trend. The gradual deflection, rather than definite orientation, toward the cathodal site of neurons in tissue cultures exposed to electric fields of proper density (Marsh and Beams, '46) presents all the aspects of this picture, indicating simply relative inhibition of filopodial protrusion on the anodal side with no cathodal "stimulation" or "attraction," a view confirmed by direct observations on slime moulds (Anderson, '51). These electric effects evidently operate not by laying down pathways, but by prohibiting some of the existing ones (see Fig. 48 in Weiss, '50a).

It must be further postulated that the chemical characteristics of the pathway systems endow contact guidance with an element of selectivity. It would seem impossible otherwise to explain the fact reported below that different kinds of nerve fibers tend to choose different pathway systems when faced with a choice. Only a faint trace of such selectivity has thus far been observed in tissue culture in the preference of nerve tips for interfaces of tissue exudate rather than of fibrin (Weiss, '45). At any rate, such discriminatory ability is based on affinity for the chemical constitution of the contact surface rather than on the perception of concentration gradients of diffusing substances as surmised in the theory of chemotropism. A singularly strong affinity of this kind seems to exist between axoplasm and the protoplasm of the sheath cells of Schwann (see p. 367).

The described mode of advance of the nerve tip makes it clear that the "rate of free outgrowth" is a function of both the neuron itself and the configuration of the pathway system. The rates are of similar magnitude whether determined in the embryo, in nerve regeneration or in tissue culture (Harrison, '35b). It must be borne in mind, however, that these are over-all values of length over time without implying uniform speed. Actually, the advance consists of alternating spurts and delays, the frequency of the latter mounting with increasing irregularity ("intersectedness") of the substratum (see Weiss and Garber, '52). Consequently, the total rate is fastest along straight oriented pathways (e.g., during nerve regeneration inside old Schwann tubes; Gutmann, Guttmann, Medawar and Young, '42) and slowest in the dense and confused fiber tangle of a scar. The maximum rate of advance under optimal conditions is of the order of a few millimeters per day (at 37° C.), which is close to the autonomous rate of proximodistal movement of axoplasm observed in the perpetual growth of neurons, as described below (p. 364). Any faster elongation of nerve fibers (e.g., Wislocki and Singer, '46) suggests passive elongation by towing.

Neurotropism. "Contact guidance," as here described, is but a modified and more detailed version of such concepts of nerve orientation as have been proposed by His (1887), Harrison ('14), and Dustin ('10). They all imply that the nerve fiber is conducted on its way by markings of its immediate contact surroundings, rather than directed from a distance by the tissue of destination issuing "attractive" forces or merely acting in the manner of a beacon Such "distance action," commonly referred to as "neurotropism" and assumed to be a form of either galvanotropism or chemotropism, has been invoked to explain oriented nerve growth in the embryo (e.g., Kappers, '17), as well as during later nerve regeneration (foremost: Cajal, '28; Forssman, 1900). This concept dates from a period in which the mechanism of nerve growth was still poorly understood; before it was realized, for instance, that nerve fibers cannot penetrate into the interior of a structureless fluid in the manner of plants. It was assumed that remote tissues, by virtue of their electric charges or of specific chemical emanations, could "attract" nerve growth from a distance. This assumption implies (1) that the supposed gradients be steady and durable, and undisturbed by any activities within the intervening distance, and (2) that the nerve tip has means not only for perceiving the required minute differentials of potential or concentration, but also for translating them into corresponding steering actions. Neither these premises nor the basic thesis of distance attraction has ever been critically demonstrated. On the contrary, overwhelming evidence has accumulated over the years to disprove them.

Repeated attempts to obtain directed nerve growth along the stream lines of an electric field have remained unsuccessful. Indeed the very possibility of an electric guidance is ruled out by the fact that nerve growth often proceeds simultaneously in diametrically opposite directions (e.g., the ascending and descending branches of dorsal root fibers; recurrent fibers in nerve regeneration: re-

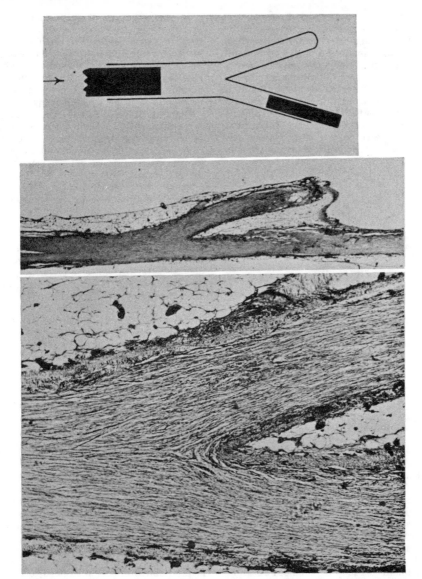

Fig. 132. Nerve growth in "alternate-choice" experiment (from Weiss and Taylor, '44). *Top:* Diagram of operation. Proximal nerve stump (left) is introduced into stem of Y-shaped artery; one branch of artery is sealed off distally, the other branch contains degenerating nerve as supposed "lure." *Middle:* Experimental case, 20 weeks after operation, showing both the blind and the connected branches filled with regenerated nerve fibers. *Bottom:* Detail from same case at bifurcation at higher magnification.

ciprocal fiber tracts in the brain, etc.). Thus, the only known electric effects are the inhibitory ones mentioned above (p. 356).

Chemical "attractions" have been postulated largely on the strength of Cajal's ('28) varied experiments demonstrating a tendency of regenerating nerve fibers to converge upon the open end of any degenerated nerve stump (Fig. 131, middle), as if the latter were a source of "neurotropically" active substances. While the observations were correct, the interpretation was not. The nerve fibers are guided toward the peripheral stump, not by a chemical concentration gradient, but by a structural bridge of Schwann cells which has previously spanned the gap as a result of the orienting "two-center effect" (see p. 354) which the two proliferating cut surfaces exert upon the intervening blood clot. It is easy to demonstrate this effect directly in tissue culture (Fig. 131, bottom) by placing two fragments of degenerated (axon-free) peripheral nerve into a thin plasma clot (Weiss, '52b). Evidently, if axons were to

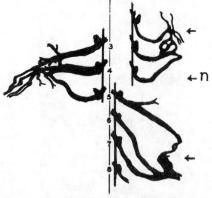

Fig. 133. Deflection of peripheral limb nerve plexus toward transplanted limb buds (combined from Detwiler, '36b). The left half shows the plexus of a normal forelimb (contribution from segments 3, 4, 5), the right half nerve supply in two experimental cases in which limb buds had been transplanted from their normal site (n) to anterior or posterior levels, respectively, as indicated by arrows.

grow from one of the stumps, the connecting strand of Schwann cells would automatically lead them over into the other stump. The chemical activity of the degenerated stump thus plays no part other than that of an accessory aid to structural orientation. In confirmation of this fact, degenerated nerve in a liquid medium leaves nerve growth wholly unaffected despite enhanced diffusion (Weiss and Taylor, '44), and conversely, oriented structural pathways are followed by nerve fibers regardless of whether or not they lead to supposedly "attractive" destinations. For instance, when a proximal nerve stump as fiber source is introduced into the stem of a bifurcated blood-filled tube, one branch of which contains degenerated nerve while the other ends blindly (Fig. 132), regenerating nerve fibers fill both branches equally well and abundantly (Weiss and Taylor, '44).

In conclusion, the idea that remote tissues of destination can attract nerve fibers directly may be safely discounted; such tissues do, however, contribute to the formation of nerve patterns indirectly by the creation of pathways, as here outlined, as well as by various secondary effects on later neuron development to be detailed below.

Ontogeny of Nerve Patterns. Our task is now to explore whether what we have outlined in the foregoing pages for nerve orientation in general is sufficient to account adequately for the specific nerve patterns observed in the organism.

Nerve Deflection Toward Growing Organs. Evidence that embryonic nerve growth is often actively routed toward rapidly growing peripheral organs rests largely on the experimental work of Detwiler (summarized in Detwiler, '36b). Transplanting urodele limb buds, prior to the outgrowth of segmental nerves, to farther anterior or posterior sites entailed a certain shift of their nerve supply, as is illustrated in Figure 133, which is a composite of two typical cases. It can be seen that there is a tendency for the limb plexus to originate in more anterior or more posterior segments than normally. Yet, since this shift of the nerve source is less extensive than the displacement of the limb, the nerve trunks appear to slant forward or backward, as if "attracted" by the actual limb site (see also Lovell, '31). Such deflection toward the actively growing limb can readily be understood as an instance of the "two-center effect" outlined above. That the effect is quite unspecific is demonstrated by the fact that the limb nerves are similarly deflected toward transplanted eyes and nasal placodes (Detwiler and Van Dyke, '34), although in the latter case it has not been made clear how much of the observed cord-nasal connection originated in the cord and how much in the olfactory epithelium. Brain grafts on the other hand exert no such effect (Detwiler, '36a), perhaps because the proliferating cell layer is shut in and not exposed to the surrounding matrix.

Frog limb buds deprived of their ipsilateral nerve source often secure vicarious supply from the opposite side (Hamburger, '29). It must be considered, however, that this is initiated during an early stage, when both hind limbs are still close together, and that subsequent dislocations of the plexus and fasciculation of the successful branches (see below, p. 366) tend to create an exaggerated idea of the power of nerves to reach their destination by detours.

Despite this qualification, it seems fairly obvious that pioneer fibers often do take directive courses toward growing organs, which by their very growth activity have become hubs of pathway systems. It is in line with this view that nerves can be made to converge upon a transplanted limb bud only if the operation is performed prior to their first outgrowth; once established, their course can no longer be redirected (Detwiler, '24b).

Intracentral Connections. There are hardly any systematic investigations on the manner in which the different intracentral nerve tracts are laid down, the routing of which is of such paramount importance to orderly function. In attempting a causal analysis, it is well to keep in mind two basic factors. First, there is no microprecision, in the sense of rigidly determined connection patterns, on the level of the individual neuron. Only the gross group characters of the various tracts are determined, while the details are merely statistically defined, the individual elements conforming to some "norm" but being otherwise indeterminate. This considerably reduces the number of relevant patterns to be accounted for. Second, the incredibly complex structure of the adult brain owes its intricacy to the fact that it is the compound result of innumerable elementary patterns laid down one after another in a long succession of separate ontogenetic steps, each one in itself rather simple. If we assume that intracentral fibers, like peripheral fibers, trace oriented pathways in their colloidal surroundings, then each pathway system that temporarily dominates a given embryonic period will leave a permanent record behind in those neuron systems which happen to grow out during that period. As conditions change, the colloidal matrix will adapt to the change, assume new orientation and thus establish new nerve courses, often unrelated geometrically to the earlier ones. However, actually to resolve central nerve patterns into such simple constituent steps is still largely a task for the future.

That it promises success is indicated, for instance, by the observation that fiber tracts tend to develop between central neuron groups that develop contemporaneously (Coghill, '29). This looks like the "two-center effect" at work again. Reasonable guesses are also possible regarding the pathway structures underlying the longitudinal fiber tracts, the commissural fiber systems and the early internuncial connections of the cord. The longitudinal tracts appear to be determined by the longitudinal stretch to which the neural tube is subjected by the growth in length of the surrounding body (see below). This assumption finds support in the early appearance of axial birefringence in the neural tube (Hobson, '41), indicating polar orientation of the substratum. The arched transverse pattern of the ventral commissures might be attributable to transverse stresses which the median strip of the medullary plate suffers during the bending of the plate into the tube. The early internuncial fibers travel along an interface clearly demarcated

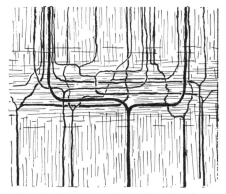

Fig. 134. Deflection and recombination of nerve fibers (plexus formation) along intersecting systems of ultrastructural pathways.

between the dense neural epithelium surrounding the central canal and the more loosely packed mantle zone.

All these preneural guide structures, however, can only account for the initial orientation of nerve patterns. Other sets of factors determine their further elaboration with regard to numbers, size, and connections (see below).

Deflection and Plexus Formation. Many nerve courses show a sudden angular deflection from one direction into another. This may be the result of a passive distortion— for instance, by sudden change of course of a towing organ or by wedging in of another organ—or it may be a sign of actual angular outgrowth. The latter condition is realized whenever pioneering fiber tips proceeding along one pathway system come upon another one running crosswise (Fig. 134). Depending on how completely the intersecting system obliterates the original system, fewer or more of the tips will be diverted into the new direction; a tight barrier (e.g., membrane) will produce total deflection. Intersecting structures of this kind arise, for instance, in the border zone between fibrous colloids of different concentrations, and model experiments in tissue culture have verified the tangential deflection of radial nerve fiber growth along such borders (Weiss, '34a). Similar cross patterns may arise in the body at the boundary between masses or layers of cells of different kinds which exert different effects on the surrounding colloids. Many other processes that would lead to the same end are imaginable, all of them thus far untested.

Striking examples of angular deflection in the embryo are the dorsal roots of the cord, the various central and peripheral plexuses, and the partially decussating systems in the brain. Dorsal root fibers, after entering the cord laterally, turn abruptly into a longitudinal course (with or without branching), forming thus the dorsal funiculi. Evidently the switch is produced by the encounter with longitudinal pathways in the marginal veil oriented lengthwise by the passive elongation of the tube mentioned before (p. 359). Plexus formation is to be expected wherever layers with predominantly radial structure alternate with tangentially oriented ones, as in the retina or in the various strata of the cortex (see Fig. 134). Thus the horizontal interconnections among the vertical projection systems, which are such an important functional feature, are presumably anticipated by lamination in the texture of the ground substance, which in turn might be due either to the differential growth expansion of the various cell strata or to differential impregnation of the ground substance from different concentric cell layers (see Weiss, '39, p. 509). Peripheral nerve plexuses are probably likewise caused by "crossroads"; the brachial and pelvic plexuses, for instance, by the tangentially disposed girdle mesenchyme which lies across the nerve paths radiating toward the limb base. A cross structure in the optic chiasma, whose angle of intersection changes with the relative shifts between eyes and brain, could account for the ipsilateral deflection of optic fibers in forms with partial decussation, with the probability of diversion, hence the proportion of uncrossed fibers (important in binocular vision) being perhaps a function of the chiasmatic angle during the growth phase.

Hypothetical though many of these detailed applications of the principle of contact guidance to concrete embryological problems may be, they at least formulate the problems involved for practical experimental attack. For final judgment, the results of the latter must be awaited. At any rate, it appears clear that plexus formation as such, with fibers turning off their former course at a sharp angle and intermingling in a common plane, often to emerge again later as independent bundles, defeats any but a structural concept of guidance.

Branching. Individual neurons may remain essentially unbranched, as in many sensory types, or they may branch more or less profusely, as do the motor neurons. Since, according to the all-or-none principle, the neuron can only act as a unit, the extent of branching has great functional significance and must be either preadapted to, or actively regulated by, functional needs. Extensive branching, economical in the motor field where it enables a single neuron to engage several hundred muscle fibers at a time, would be undesirable in the sensory field, where it would blur discrimination. Despite its biological importance, however, the problem of branching has not yet been systematically studied (Sunderland and Lavarack, '53).

Branching occurs either at the tip of a growing fiber by dichotomy (terminal branching) or along the stem some distance behind the tip which is either still free or already connected (collateral branching). Terminal branching results whenever two simultaneous terminal pseudopods (see Fig. 127e) are of equal strength so that they can divide the inflow of protoplasm between themselves and continue to advance with independent tips (see Speidel, '33). The frequency of this occurrence depends on the structure of the pathway system; the more intersected the latter, the higher the incidence of branching (Fig. 129). Accordingly, terminal branching is profuse in the maze of central neuropil, as well as in peripheral scar tissue (e.g., after nerve severance), but is infrequent along well-oriented pathways.

Collateral branches arise as side sprouts from already consolidated fiber stems, presumably in response to local irritations, mechanical, chemical or electrical (Peterfi and Kapel, '28; Speidel, '33; Edds, '53). The repeated branching of motor fibers, for instance, could be ascribed to a seriation of such irritations as would attend consecutive divisions of young muscle fibers. The size of a "motor unit" (number of muscle fibers attached to a single neuron) would then simply reflect the degree of ulterior growth of that muscle after receiving its primary quota of fibers. The systematic occurrence of similar irritations near certain layers or nuclei of the brain and spinal cord could account for the regular emergence of collaterals at those sites. Possibly different fiber types might even react in different degrees to the same irritant so that one type would give off a branch while another type would not. These are merely some pointers to future work. Concrete information is scanty.

In view of the labile state of the neuron (see later), we must expect it to spring minor leaks in its surface all the time, especially in its unsheathed terminal branches and at the nodes of Ranvier. Whether such weak spots will be repaired or become the source of a collateral branch will presumably depend on the vigor and rate of growth of the neuron and the competitive strength of the main stem of the fiber, which counteracts accessory outgrowths. Agents capable of either loosening the axonal surface or invigorating neuronal growth or merely reducing the drain into the main axis of the fiber (as after amputation) should, therefore, automatically increase the frequency of collateral branching. The compensatory sprouting of peripheral collaterals after partial denervation of muscles or after injection of substances from degenerated muscles (Hoffman, '50; Edds, '53), as well as the "parasitic" branches forming from severed or otherwise truncated neurons (Nageotte, '22), seem to bear out this expectation.

Nerve Patterns Within Peripheral Organs. Usually, the factors that guide nerves to a given organ are not the same that will determine the distribution pattern within the organ (Hamburger, '29). For instance, when limb buds are transplanted to the head region and innervated by foreign cranial nerves, the latter assume a distribution pattern which is essentially a typical limb pattern. It is from this very observation that Harrison ('07b) first deduced the structural guidance of nerve fibers, a conclusion which was soon also adopted by Braus ('11), who had previously interpreted his own similar observations as evidence of a peripheral (autonomous) origin of nerves. Evidently, the growing limb can impose a limb-specific arrangement upon nerve fibers coming from whatever source (see also Hamburger, '29; Piatt, '41; Weiss, '37a). This plainly contradicts the gratuitous contention (Ruud, '29) that nerves from a given source contain the geometry of their future distribution in themselves. Rather, the "limb pattern" of distribution is determined by a complex, multifactorial chain of events, roughly divisible into two phases—a primary one governed by the structural and chemical properties of the preneural pathways in the limb blastema, and a secondary one of elaboration of the primary pattern by towing, fasciculation (see below, p. 366), and the differential survival, growth, and resorption of fibers, depending on the physiological adequacy of their terminal connections. The decisive patterning effect of the primary phase is revealed by the observation that virtually all nerve branches of the mature limb (in the frog) are already recognizable as such in the early limb bud at a very primitive stage of morphogenesis (Taylor, '43). The principal nerve paths are thus laid down by factors in the early limb blastema.

If, on the other hand, a limb is kept nerveless ("aneurogenic") during its differentiation and is then grafted to a normal host body from which it can derive belated innervation, the invading nerves follow quite irregular and aberrant courses (Piatt, '52). A certain predilection for some major invasion routes at times creates some gross resemblance to a limb pattern (Piatt, '42), but this could be due simply to trivial anatomical features, offering only limited spaces between skin, muscles and skeleton for the massive advance of nerve fibers. In this instance, major blood vessels may also play a leading role (Hamburger, '29), although in normal development the noted parallelism between vascular and nerve trunks is more likely to be a sign of common guidance of both systems by the same ultrastructural pattern in the common matrix. Whether the nerve distribution pattern within the limb follows normal or aberrant lines is of no consequence, however, as far as the later functional activity is concerned. As will be described below (p. 384), functional coordination between the central nervous system and receptor and effector organs remains orderly even if the anatomical nerve connections are utterly confused. The relative stereotypism of peripheral nerves is presumably significant only as a means of insuring ubiquitous innervation of adequate quantity.

PERIPHERAL CONNECTIONS

Specificity of Preneural Pathways. Nerve fibers of a given kind can penetrate foreign organs with ease. After heterotopic transplantations or other deviations, cranial nerves have been followed into limbs (see above; Harrison, '07b; Braus, '11; Nicholas, '33; Piatt, '41), midbrain fibers into trunk muscles (Hoadley, '25) in the chick (not observed in comparable experiments in urodeles: Detwiler, '36a), spinal fiber tracts into limbs (Nicholas, '29; Weiss, '50a), limb nerves into tumors (Bueker, '48; Levi-Montalcini and Hamburger, '51), optic nerves into the nose (Weiss, '41c) or the pharynx (Ferreira-Berutti, '51).

Yet, the peripheral nervous system of normal individuals is relatively stereotyped, not only in the mode of its arborization but also in its terminal connections. By and large, ventral root fibers end in skeletal muscles, spinal ganglion fibers in sensory end organs, sympathetic fibers in glands or smooth muscles. Since the attempts to refer this specificity of connections to selective neurotropic attractions have proved untenable, other explanations must be sought.

Mindful of the fact that the first outgrowth of motor fibers antedates that of sensory fibers (Coghill, '29), it has been suggested (Harrison, '35b; Weiss, '39) that a systematic change in the peripheral pathway structure, with the earlier pathways leading to muscles, the later ones to skin, would automatically account for the correct routing. However, this time-lag explanation is ruled out by the observation that motor and sensory fibers take each their typical courses even when both grow out simultaneously, as for instance, in the innervation of the hind limb of the anuran tadpole. When the bud makes its late appearance, both motor and sensory nerve masses are already waiting at its base ready to invade it (Taylor, '43). As they penetrate the limb bud, they assort themselves according to kinds into specifically muscular and cutaneous branches, respectively, coursing sometimes jointly, but often also independently. This has been revealed by withholding either the sensory or the motor nerve quota from the limb (Hamburger, '29), and most conclusively by extirpating the appropriate spinal ganglia or spinal cord segments (Taylor, '44); the developed limbs then lacked the corresponding kind of nerve branches.

It seems difficult to account for these facts otherwise than by the assumption of selective contact affinities of given nerve fiber types for matching types of preneural pathways. This view is strengthened by the predilection which nerves with aberrant origins or courses show for their typical sites or channels, as has been described for the lateral line nerve (Harrison, '03), the dorsal roots (Detwiler and Maclean, '40; Holtzer, '52b), and Mauthner's fibers (Oppenheimer, '41; Piatt, '44; Stefanelli, '50; Holtzer, '52b). Such selective application of one tissue to another is not uncommon in development (see, for instance, the guided growth of the pronephric duct; Holtfreter, '44); but, save for a hypothetical reference to its possible stereochemical basis (Weiss, '47), the underlying mechanism is still obscure.

Specificity in Regeneration. The ability of given kinds of nerve fibers to select conforming pathways seems to last beyond the pioneering phase. After transection of the mixed nerves to a young differentiating limb, the regenerating motor fibers retrace essentially the original muscular branches, and the regenerating sensory fibers the cutaneous branches (Taylor, '44). Similarly, regenerating lateral line nerves have been reported to give preference to an old lateral line branch over a nearby cutaneous branch (Speidel, '48), which even suggests finer subspecificities within the sensory class. Yet, with the progress of maturation, this selectivity of outgrowth is lost. Adult nerves of different qualities, when cross-connected, regenerate into each other's channels indiscriminately and without difficulty. For example, sensory fibers regenerate into motor stumps (Boeke, '17; Gutmann, '45; Weiss and Edds, '45) and vice versa (Weiss and Cummings, '43), somatic nerves into sympathetic stumps and vice versa (Simpson and Young, '45; Hammond and Hinsey, '45), etc. Apparently, the residual Schwann cords of degenerated stumps, which serve as pathways to the regenerating fibers, are of the same quality in motor, sensory, somatic and autonomic nerves, hence are indistinguishable to the regenerating fibers, which, as will be shown below, have not lost their constitutional differentials.

Terminal Connections. Nerve fibers may reach the peripheral tissues either preassorted over proper pathways or intermingled over aberrant routes (see above), but neither mode of approach is decisive for whether or not they will make transmissive connections, that is, connections which will permit impulses to pass between nerve fiber and end organ. A clear distinction must be made between (a) penetration of a tissue by nerve fibers ("neurotization"), (b) microscopic contiguity between nerve ending and effector or receptor cell, and (c) physiologically effective junction. No absolute specificity prevails in (a) and (b), but (c) occurs only if end-organ and nerve fiber are generally related.

For example, when sensory nerve fibers are led into muscles, they terminate on the muscle fibers in what histologically appear to be intimate motor connections (Boeke, '17); yet electric stimulation of such nerves never yields muscular contraction (Gutmann, '45; Weiss and Edds, '45). Cross unions between somatic, sympathetic and parasympathetic nerves that have been tried in various combinations likewise are physiologically sterile. Cholinergic and adrenergic nerves fail to achieve physiological innervation of each other's peripheries (Langley and Anderson, '04; Dale, '35), not because of lack of regenerative penetration, but because of transmissive failure of the terminal junction.

The fact of neuro-terminal selectivity is proof of the existence of specific protoplasmic differences both among the major classes of neurons (sensory, motor, etc.) and among the corresponding terminal tissues. Within each class, however, transmissive junctions can be made indiscriminately. Any motor nerve shows functional affinity to any skeletal muscle (Weiss, '37a; Weiss and Hoag, '46); cross connections of different kinds of sensory nerves have likewise been effected successfully (Anokhin, '35), and the paradoxical sensations noted after irregular sensory nerve regeneration in man (Stopford, '30) also indicate interchangeability within the sensory field. There are additional finer functional selectivities, beyond those controlling junction, but these are imposed upon the connected neurons from their endings and will be discussed later (see p. 384).

Synaptic Connections. Naturally, the question arises whether specificities similar to those observed in peripheral connections govern the establishment of central synaptic junctions. In the few instances thus far examined, intracentral neurons have shown a remarkable lack of discrimination in making terminal connections. Limb buds inserted into gaps of the embryonic neural tube receive effective motor innervation from central fiber tracts (Nicholas, '33), and the central gray matter of isolated fragments of larval spinal cord or medulla oblongata establishes fully functional connections with both muscles and skin in the complete absence of primary motor and sensory neurons (Weiss, '50a). The promiscuity of junctional relations manifested in these cases contrasts sharply with the acute selectivity of functional response relations (see below, p. 384), which throws doubt upon any theory explaining the latter purely in terms of specific anatomical connections. The fact that a junction capable of transmitting an impulse has been established does not explain when and how it will be actuated in the coordinated group activities of the centers, nor indeed whether or not it will be used at all. Whether disuse entails eventual rupture of junctions has not yet been clearly decided.

AXON GROWTH

Growth of Axon Caliber. While the elongation of the nerve fiber is essentially a phenomenon of protoplasmic convection, it proceeds pari passu with real growth, that is, increase of the total protoplasmic mass of the neuron, and is actually sustained by the latter. This growth process continues after the fiber has reached its final length and can, in fact, best be studied during that later period, when all further protoplasmic gain accrues solely to the width of the fiber. Since the eventual caliber of the axon, usually referred to as "fiber size," is of considerable functional significance, as it determines velocity of impulse conduction, thresholds of excitability and susceptibility to noxious agents, etc. (Erlanger and Gasser, '37), a study of axonal growth offers both physiological and developmental interest. Nerve fiber caliber increases as animals grow to mature size (Hursh, '39).

Analytical information on axon growth is mostly derived from recent experiments dealing with the restoration of fiber diameter in regenerated nerve fibers (Weiss and Hiscoe, '48). These experiments are schematically summarized in Figure 135, which shows a series of mature neurons in various stages of normal (*A-E*) and modified (*F-I*) regeneration. The nucleated cell body is at the left, the peripheral end-organ at the right, both connected by the neurilemmal tube that envelops the fiber. From the proximal stump of the severed fiber (*B*), a thin axonal sprout advances toward the periphery (*C*), effects peripheral connection (*D*) and gradually grows in width until it approximates its old caliber and the width of the tube (*E*). This recovery, however, can be significantly impeded if one constricts the distal stump and thereby reduces the diameter of all tubes at a given spot. At first, regeneration proceeds normally (compare *D* and *F*), but as soon as the axon has reached the girth at which it fills the narrow (constricted) part of the tube, the portion lying distally to the constriction ceases to gain in width, while at the proximal side of the constriction excess axoplasm begins to pile up in configurations such as are ordinarily assumed by a steadily propelled column of plastic material suddenly faced with an obstruction (*G, H*). If, later, the constriction is released allowing the tube to re-expand, the dammed-up material moves on peripherad, thus widening the formerly stunted distal portion (*I*). The rate of this movement was estimated to be of the order of a few millimeters per day, which corresponds closely to the optimal rate of free advance in regenerating fibers (see p. 356).

These results have led to the conclusions that (1) axoplasm is synthesized solely in the terminal swellings of blocked regenerating nerve fibers (see Cajal, '28; Nageotte, '22). Although we know nothing about the nature of the axonal pumping mechanism,* it is reasonable to assume that it is the same for first outgrowth (see p. 350) and regeneration. While the fiber tip advances, the material is used for elongation; after the fiber has ceased to elongate, the continuing sup-

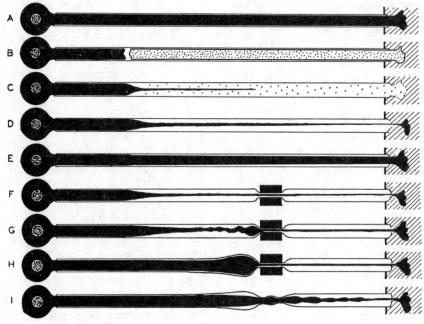

Fig. 135. Damming of axoplasm in constricted nerve fibers. *A–E*, consecutive stages of unimpeded regeneration; *F–H*, consecutive stages of regeneration with "bottleneck"; *I*, following *H* after release of constriction. (From Weiss and Hiscoe, '48.)

central cell body near the nucleus; (2) axoplasm is conveyed peripherad in a steady movement accommodated to the width of the tube which serves as channel; (3) axoplasm is subject to continuous catabolic degradation all along the fiber. Accordingly, any local reduction of the width of the channel throttles downward flow, hence reduces the rate of replacement of the "downstream" portion, while excess material accumulates on the "upstream" side. Thus is visualized directly what used to be postulated by earlier students of nerve growth as "vis a tergo" (Held, '09) or "formative turgor" (Cajal, '28).

Damming of axoplasm can now be taken as a direct sign of obstructed axonal transport. As such it is seen, for instance, in the

ply adds to its width until a steady state is reached between rate of supply and rate of catabolic consumption. Since there is evidence (Weiss and Hiscoe, '48) that this centrifugal supply stream continues throughout the life of the mature neuron, nerve regeneration turns out to be but a special manifestation of a perpetual growth process. This explains why nerves can regenerate repeatedly in succession with undiminished vigor (Duncan and Jarvis, '43).

* If the rhythmic pulsations demonstrated for central glia cells (Pomerat, '51) were also a property of peripheral Schwann cells and if these were coordinated in the manner of heart muscle contractions or ciliary beats, this might offer a mechanism for the massaging of axoplasm downward within its sheath.

The caliber of a nerve fiber is thus determined essentially by three factors: (1) the amount of synthesis of new axoplasm in the cell body; (2) the rate of its centrifugal movement; and (3) the rate of its peripheral breakdown. Since the rate of movement is limited by the width of the channel in which it occurs, large nerve fibers regenerating into narrower tubes fail to gain full normal width (Holmes and Young, '42; Sanders and Young, '44; Simpson and Young, '45; Hammond and Hinsey, '45). However, no such limitation is to be expected during embryonic growth, before firm neurilemmal tubes have formed. Assuming, furthermore, rather uniform rates of catabolism, we are left with the rate of central synthesis as the main variable in the determination of fiber caliber, which, in turn, is rather closely correlated with the size of the nerve cell body.

Factors Controlling Neuron Growth. Early in development different neuron groups seem to acquire constitutional growth differentials which place them in different size classes. Within each class itself, however, growth rate and size are subject to further modifications which are due to extraneous conditions, as illustrated in the following.

When a nerve fiber is severed, hence disconnected from its terminal organ, the whole neuron begins to atrophy (Weiss, Edds and Cavanaugh, '45; Sanders and Young, '46; Aitken, Sharman and Young, '47). If we disregard certain acute traumatic changes ("ascending degeneration," "axon reaction") referable to the injury as such, the main long-range effect of the loss consists of a progressive reduction of the dimensions of the neuron, beginning with the nucleolus and spreading to the nucleus, the cell body, and finally the diameter of the axon (Cavanaugh, '51). Conversely, upon reconnection with a peripheral organ, the dimensions enlarge again. Moreover, when a neuron is "overloaded," that is, made to innervate a larger volume of peripheral tissue than originally (e.g., by collateral branching into a denervated field), nucleus and cell body enlarge above their normal dimensions (Terni, '20; Edds, '49; Cavanaugh, '51). The production center of neuronal synthesis thus adapts itself sensitively to the demands of the peripheral innervation volume.

Variations of functional activity have similar effects. Not only do neurons tend to atrophy, when they are chronically deprived of excitation (e.g., Edds, '51), but they hypertrophy, again starting from the nucleus, in response to intensified physiological demands (Hamberger and Hydén, '49). Enlargement of the nuclei and nucleoli of the cells in certain brain centers following induced hyperfunction of these centers (e.g., antidiuretic center in the hypothalamus) has also been recorded (Ortmann, '51). The interpretation of all these facts requires caution, because nuclear enlargement may signify either true protoplasmic growth generally associated with increase in desoxyribonucleic acids (Hydén, '50), or merely water uptake, accumulation of functional products and other transitory changes subserving functional activity rather than true growth (see Leuchtenberger and Schrader, '52).

At any rate, the realization that the size of a neuron is subject to continual upward or downward regulations in accordance with extraneous influences received from both its afferent and (ascendingly) efferent ends, certainly controverts the classic view which has endowed the central nervous system, at least in morphological regards, with a nimbus of static and rigid fixity.

The significance of this demonstrated plasticity for our concepts of central activity is evident. The backward projection of peripheral conditions into the centers, which we encounter here for the first time in our discussion and which will be amplified below, is particularly noteworthy. This makes it all the more important to stress the fact that the reported influences do not "determine" activity, growth, or size, of a neuron in any absolute sense, but simply enhance or depress its inherent activities, and within relatively narrow limits at that (for instance, even the chronically disconnected ganglion cell still retains about 60 per cent of its normal mass).

Biochemistry of Neuron Growth. The morphological evidence for the localized growth of the neuron from the nuclear territory (Weiss and Hiscoe, '48) is supported by the cytochemical demonstration of abundance of desoxyribonucleic acids and a high rate of protein synthesis in the nuclear territory (Caspersson, '50; Hydén, '50), with fluctuations that closely parallel the growth activity of the neuron. Thus, the intensity of these syntheses increases during the regenerative phase following nerve section (Bodian, '47), during the growth reaction resulting from hyperactivity (Hamberger and Hydén, '45) and, embryonically, during the phase of the functional alerting of brain cells (Flexner, '50).

In agreement with this monopoly of the nuclear territory as the growth center of the neuron, the well-known impairment of nerve growth in thiamine deficiency (beriberi) is observed only if the cell bodies are bathed by the deficient medium (in vitro), even though the rest of the nerve, including the growing tips, lies in normal medium (Burt, '43a).

The correlation of cytological, biochemical and physiological data for normal and deficiency states of the nervous system is making encouraging progress (see p. 376). One of the major tasks in these studies which remains is to distinguish clearly between the relative contributions of the metabolic machinery of the neuron to its growth (i.e., protoplasmic reproduction) on the one hand, and to its functional activity on the other; a task rendered more difficult by the fact just outlined, that having reached a stationary size, a neuron keeps "growing" without change of total mass.

DEVELOPMENT OF GROUP RELATIONS

Fasciculation. Outside the gray matter and the terminal arborizations, nerve fibers

of pioneering fibers, the routing is achieved not by "attraction" but by a form of contact guidance. When a nerve source and a peripheral organ, e.g., a limb, are implanted at some distance from each other in a loose connective tissue bed (e.g., the dorsal fin of an amphibian larva), a strong nerve cable soon develops between them (Fig. 136) in the following manner (Weiss, '50a). Pioneering fibers from the nerve center invade the surroundings. Those that happen upon the limb and succeed in connecting with its tissues thereby become somehow adhesive for other nerve fibers growing out subsequently; older fibers thus become guides to the limb for younger ones, endowing them, in turn, with adhesiveness, and so forth, in a sort of chain reaction. It is not known what eventually terminates the agglomeration; perhaps fasciculation ceases automatically as soon as peripheral saturation (see p. 368) has been reached, that is, when further newcomer fibers no longer find functional attachments, hence, do not become adhesive.

The lessons of nerve anatomy which show that nerve fibers of identical functional

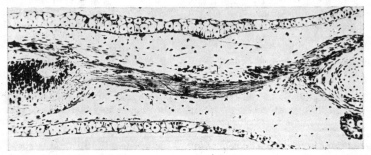

Fig. 136. Fasciculation. Nerve cable that has formed between a fragment of spinal cord (left) and a limb (right), both deplanted to the dorsal fin of a urodele larva (frontal section, showing the loose connective tissue of the fin between the two borders of epidermis). (From Weiss, '50a.)

rarely appear solitary. They commonly associate with other nerve fibers to form bundles, as well as with the Schwann cells and connective tissue cells. The grouping of fibers into bundles seems to come about in two ways: (a) by a primary tendency of younger fibers to follow the course of older fibers in close application of one to the other ("fasciculation"); and (b) by the secondary gathering of small groups into larger assemblies through the formation of common connective tissue sheaths.

Primary fasciculation is not a chance event but a systematic device to route a sufficient number of nerve connections toward a destination in need of them. As in the outgrowth

properties (e.g., fibers subserving pain or special sensations) often course together, both in peripheral nerve trunks and central funiculi, indicate an element of selectivity in the process of fasciculation. Young fibers of a given kind would apply themselves preferentially to older fibers belonging to the same, rather than to another, category. Some experimental proof for "selective fasciculation" by contact affinities may be seen in the observation that supernumerary Mauthner's fibers of the amphibian brain run alongside the normal Mauthner's fibers of that side much more frequently than could be expected on mere chance; and in the further observation that transected longitudinal fiber tracts of the spinal cord, when regenerating through a connective tissue gap, even over great distances, tend to retain their fascicular identity (Hooker, '30; Holtzer, '52b). Evidently, such selectivity of association implies two things: first, that nerve fibers of different functional designations are constitutionally (i.e., substantially) different, and second, that they can recognize and distinguish one another according to kind.

Fasciculation occurs by non-detachment among fibers that have made contact, rather than by active association. It therefore is promoted by conditions furthering the chances of contact. These chances are low in compact tissues containing innumerable separate fibrous guide lines, but high in tissues with large liquid spaces, where the nerve pathways are crowded into the relatively few land bridges. Judging from tissue cultures, established nerve fibers may themselves bring about the latter condition by liquefying surrounding colloids (Weiss, '34a) and thus facilitate bundling. Moreover, liquefaction around attached nerve fibers will cause their floating stems to cling together, according to the same principle that makes wet threads stick together in air, thus assembling them secondarily into trunks. These considerations furnish a ready explanation of the fact that fibers tend to remain separate in the gray matter, in the peripheral tissues and in nerve scars, whereas they are aggregated into bundles in the more liquid-filled interstices, particularly along the blood vessels. However, much remains still to be found out about the mechanisms of fasciculation; particularly the factors effecting the sorting and collecting of fascicles into still larger assemblies by wrappings of connective tissue are still wholly unexplored.

Association with Sheath Cells; Myelinization. The specific affinity between Schwann cells and axons appears to be mutual. Sheath cells attach themselves to nerve sprouts (Speidel '32). The tips of nerve fibers, conversely, show a definite predilection for strands of Schwann cells (Nageotte, '22; Dustin, '17), and it is doubtful whether naked sprouts, not enveloped by sheath cells, can persist over appreciable distances. The two cell types, when in contact, thus seem to form firm unions, which actively resist separation (Abercrombie, Johnson and Thomas, '49). Sheath cells have been seen to shuttle freely between nerve fibers of different kinds (Speidel, '33), with a certain preference for transfer from unmyelinated to myelinated ones (Speidel, '50). Sheath cells,

however, do not share the specificity of the nerve fibers which they coat; this can be inferred from the fact that regenerating sensory or motor nerve sprouts penetrate Schwann cords of either nerve type with equal ease (see p. 362).

Myelin is presumably formed in the surface of the axon, with the sheath cells (or, in the central nervous system, the glia cells) furnishing some essential stimulus or complement (Speidel, '33, '35), but the details of the process are not known. Since the same sheath cell has been observed either to induce, or fail to induce, myelin formation, depending on whether it joined the branch of a potentially myelinated or a potentially unmedullated fiber (Speidel, '33), the differential faculty for myelinization must be a property of the nerve fiber itself. The laminated structure of the myelin sheath (see p. 347) and the proportionality between its thickness and the caliber of the axon suggest that successive layers are shed by the surface as the axon grows in width (see Geren and Raskind, '53).

As Schwann cells line up in tandem along the axons, myelin formation progresses in a general proximodistal sequence, starting in each cell from the region of the nucleus. The length of the cell defines a myelin segment, and the junction of two cells, the node of Ranvier. The standard length of individual segments (internodes) amounts to about 300 micra, which agrees with the average length of an extended Schwann cell in tissue culture. The same average length is found in regenerated nerve fibers regardless of diameter (Hiscoe, '47; Vizoso and Young, '48). The greater internodal length in primary (non-regenerated) fibers, which varies directly with fiber diameter attaining up to about 1500 micra, is presumably to be ascribed to passive elongation by the stretching of the nerves in tow of growing organs (Hiscoe, '47; Young, '50). The longest fibers having undergone the greatest extension would also end up with the longest segments, and since the longest fibers (within the same class) have the largest caliber (Kölliker, 1896), a general proportionality between fiber diameter and internodal length would result (Thomas and Young, '49), which fact has recently assumed added significance in connection with the saltatory theory of nerve conduction.

Saturation Factors. Volume and density of peripheral innervation vary relevantly from organ to organ and from region to region within the same systems (skin, intestine, connective tissue). This characteristic distribution is grossly anticipated in the relative allocations of neurons to different peripheral sectors (see below, p. 374), in the frequency of preterminal branching and in the peripheral control of fasciculation. Since this rough preallocation would still leave a wide margin of variability in the number of fibers actually arriving in a tissue in a given individual, there are additional screening factors in operation in the terminal tissues themselves which adjust the final quota of terminals to a stable norm. Each tissue would thus maintain a characteristic "saturation" density of innervation. While not much is known about the means by which this control is exerted, it is already becoming obvious that they are different for different tissues, and that the mechanisms for upward regulation from a deficient source are of a different kind than those involved in the downward regulation from an excessive source. They will therefore be considered separately.

When supernumerary (Detwiler, '36b) or excessively large (Harrison, '35a) limbs are transplanted to the limb region of urodele embryos, the enlarged periphery, while causing no adaptive increase in the central nerve source (see below, p. 382), yet derives from that undersized source the full contingent of nerve fiber branches appropriate to its larger mass. Similarly, limbs transplanted in later larval stages, and provided with only a small branch for regenerative innervation, contain eventually the full contingent of fibers normal for a limb (Weiss, '37a). In nerve regeneration in the adult, likewise, the number of regenerated fibers in the distal stumps approximates the normal quota, even if the proximal source of fiber stems has been drastically reduced (Dogliotti, '35; Litwiller, '38a; Weiss and Campbell, '44; Billig, van Harreveld and Wiersma, '46).

This compensatory increase of the volume of innervation is due to more extensive peripheral branching of the individual neurons. Being the rule in the regeneration of transected nerves (see above, p. 350), such branching is satisfactorily accounted for in the cases just mentioned in which nerves have been severed. However, compensatory branches may also arise, as if in response to peripheral needs, from nerves that have not been deliberately traumatized. When musculature is partially denervated by the experimental elimination of part of its tributary ventral roots, the residual healthy intra-

muscular fibers develop "spontaneously" collateral branches that take over the innervation of the neighboring denervated muscle elements (see Edds, '53). The fact that such collateral branching can be artificially induced by intramuscular injection of extracts from degenerating muscle (Hoffman, '52) suggests an active participation of the denervated muscle fibers in tapping the locally available nerve sources for extra branches. As indicated in our discussion of branching mechanisms (p. 361), this need imply nothing more than the weakening of the axonal surface, particularly at the nodes, to permit ever-present abortive axonal leaks to yield durable offshoots. Perhaps substances reported to enhance nerve regeneration (von Muralt, '46) should be viewed in the same light, as facilitating the protrusion of branches or diminishing the resistance of tissues to penetration by them.

Compensatory collateral innervation, comparable to that observed in muscle, has also been described to occur in denervated sectors of skin, whose infiltration by side branches from nerves of the surrounding intact area has been either observed directly in experimental cases (Weddell, Guttmann and Gutmann, '41) or deduced from clinical results (Livingston, '43). Again, the explanation may lie either in a true activation of branching by emanations from the denervated tissue or, conversely, in the removal of an active suppressing principle that could be assumed to emanate from nerve-saturated tissue as a bar to its invasion by nerve branches continually forming as a result of intra-axonal growth pressure and surface instability. The latter alternative seems plausible since the assumed abortive branching has actually been observed in living preparations (Speidel, '42). Negative microscopic evidence, on the other hand, would be meaningless in view of the electronmicroscopic demonstration of fiber collaterals far below the range of microscopic visibility (Fernández-Morán, '52).

In conclusion, if overproduction of branches is a regular occurrence, it would account for a reservoir of fibers sufficiently large to supply the needs of even a considerably enlarged periphery; on the other hand, it may be necessary in addition to assume peripheral factors that facilitate, if not the production, at least the further outgrowth and consolidation, of branches in accordance with the size of the periphery to be innervated. Either mechanism insures to the peripheral tissue a full quota of innervation even from an undersized nerve fiber source.

Equally important, however, is the upper limitation set to nerve density, referred to above as "saturation." Even in the face of a superabundant supply of nerve fibers, the tissue restricts the admission of terminals to its normal quota. The best-studied examples are muscle, peripheral nerve, and regenerating limbs. Individual muscle fibers rarely contain more than one ending of nerve fibers of the same kind. That this embodies an active self-protection of the muscle fiber against multiple innervation ("hyper-

Of different causation, but of comparable effect, is the peripheral control of nerve fiber numbers in nerve regeneration. Irrespective of the size of the nerve fiber source and even in the presence of an excessive amount of branches produced, the number contained in the regenerated distal stumps approximates the normal number closely enough to intimate active regulation (e.g., Davenport, Chor and Dolkart, '37; Weiss, '37a; Weiss and Campbell, '44; Litwiller, '38a; Weiss and Cummings, '43). Since new fibers course both inside and between old nerve tubes (Holmes and Young, '42), the

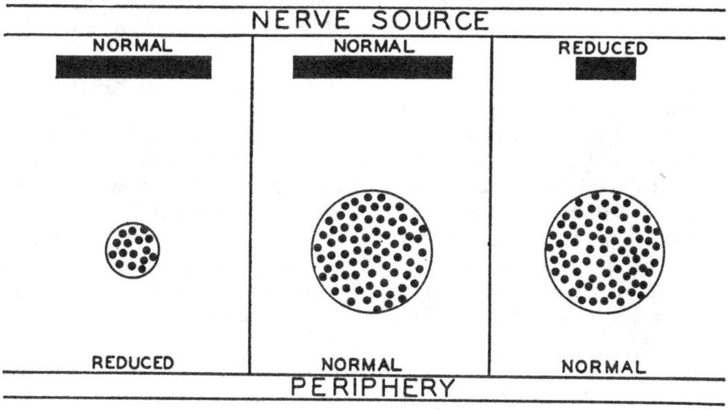

Fig. 137. Diagram summarizing the regulation of density of peripheral innervation in instances of abnormal ratios of nerve source to peripheral field.

neurotization"), comparable to the self-protection of fertilized eggs against multiple insemination (Harrison, '10), is evidenced by the fact that it is impossible to force appreciable surplus innervation upon a muscle even by inserting an excessive supply of nerve fibers right into it (Elsberg, '17; Fort, '40; Weiss and Hoag, '46). Only uninnervated muscle fibers seem to be ready to accept nerve endings, but once a connection has been effected, the muscle fiber shields itself somehow from further impregnation. Since this physiological insulation requires some time to develop, there exists, of course, an open interim during which additional endings can take. This explains why there is always a certain percentage of muscle fibers found with multiple endings, and why the incidence of "hyperneurotization" is higher when superabundant nerve masses are allowed to pervade the muscle simultaneously (Hoffmann, '51). The nature of the protective reaction is unknown, but may be looked for in a change of surface properties.

capacity of the latter cannot be the limiting factor. Indeed, the numerical restriction is observed even if the peripheral nerve stumps have been evulsed (Litwiller, '38a). Even more instructive is the similarly restrictive influence exerted by regenerating limbs on the quota of nerve branches they admit to their territory. When a urodele limb is amputated, the cut nerves promptly sprout branches in numbers superabundant for the supply of a full-sized limb. Nevertheless, only a small fraction enters the young regeneration blastema, and this fraction increases only gradually, in direct proportion to the growth of the blastema (Weiss and Walker, '34; Litwiller, 38b), with a saturation constant of ca. 40 nerve terminals per cubic millimeter of tissue. It is difficult to escape the conclusion that each innervated tissue fragment establishes an inhibitory field around it which prevents the penetration of competing fiber branches (analogous to territorial dominance observed in other tissue complexes; see Wigglesworth, '48; Willier, '52; Weiss, '53). Similar factors may be responsible for the great local differences in the density of the central neuropil (see Herrick, '48, pp. 29-39).

It is interesting to note, in this connection, that topical application of carcinogens entails a marked rise in the density of the local cutaneous nerve net (Julius, '30), and that the presence of mouse sarcomata in chick embryos similarly opens certain visceral organs, e.g., the mesonephros, which normally would have remained uninnervated, to profuse invasion by sympathetic fibers (Levi-Montalcini and Hamburger, '53). These observations seem to indicate that the mechanisms controlling saturation density can be suspended by certain agents, among which tumor agents seem to be prominent.

The peripheral density control (Fig. 137), whatever its nature may be, serves to insure, in combination with the other numerical controls outlined earlier, the attainment and maintenance of an adequate functional state despite wide fluctuations of the individual developmental histories. It should have become clear from our discussion that such purportedly goal-directed performances, when properly analyzed, are resolvable into chains of causal mechanisms.

DEVELOPMENT OF THE CENTRAL NERVOUS SYSTEM (CNS)

DETERMINATION OF THE CNS

The foregoing chapters, devoted to nerve fibers, have taken the existence of nerve cells for granted. To consider the origin of the nerve cells themselves, we must now turn back to an earlier phase of the embryonic history. As for the manner in which neural differentiation is initiated and the primordia of the neural system are mapped out in the early embryo, we may simply refer to the article in this book by Holtfreter and Hamburger. We shall take up the story from the time when the anterodorsal sector of the ectoderm has become irrevocably earmarked for the formation of the neural organs and endowed with the capacity to produce parts with the morphological, histological and chemical characteristics of central nervous system even when isolated from the rest of the germ. At that stage, by virtue of anteceding interactions of induction and segregation, the neural plate has become constituted as a system of fields, the median ones directing the transformation to central nervous structures—anteriorly, brain and its derivatives;

posteriorly, spinal cord—while the marginal ones give rise to neural crest. That this area already has biochemical properties that are distinctly neural is indicated by its selective immune response to antibodies prepared against adult neural antigens (Ebert, '50). At least in anteroposterior direction, it constitutes a definite mosaic of fields (Dalcq, '47; Nieuwkoop, '52), the individual regions of which already contain differential conditions guiding the subsequent steps of morphogenesis toward the formation of specific localized parts of the CNS. It is these steps, involving mainly folding, cell movements, proliferation, cell growth, cytodifferentiation, secretion, and cell degeneration, that we shall now consider in greater detail.

EARLY MORPHOGENESIS

Neurulation. Transformation of the neural plate into the neural tube occurs by means of forces residing within the plate itself, for as was shown by Roux (1895), the folding takes place even in excised and isolated plates. The expansive pressure of the surrounding epidermis in the germ plays merely an adjuvant role (Giersberg, '24). The dynamics of the folding process, as those of similar invaginations (e.g., gastrulation; see article by Costello in this book) are still not fully understood. They are based on the development of differences in surface expanse between the outer and inner sides of the plate. An earlier suggestion, attributing this difference to differential water uptake (Glaser, '14), has now been discounted (Glaser, '16; Brown, Hamburger and Schmitt, '41). Differential cell growth or cell multiplication has likewise been ruled out (Burt, '43b; Gillette, '44; Hutchinson, '44). The most likely assumption is that of an active contraction of the outer surface of the plate, the contractile elements, presumably fiber proteins, being either in the cells (Lewis, '47) or in their outer coating (Holtfreter, '43), or perhaps in the intercellular fiber cement under the outer cell poles seen under the microscope as "terminal web" (Sauer, '35). Active elongation of the medullary cells may normally assist this process (Brown, Hamburger and Schmitt, '41; Holtfreter, '46); ultraviolet irradiation of the germ with wave lengths near the absorption maximum of sterols inhibits it (Davis, '44).

When the raised folds meet from the two sides, epidermis fuses with epidermis, and neural layer with neural layer. Since this occurs even in asymmetrically mutilated embryos under mechanically wholly aberrant conditions (Holtzer, '51), it cannot be simply a mechanical accident, but must be viewed as a case of selective fusion of tissues according to their respective affinities (see Holtfreter, '39; Chiakulas, '52). Similarly, the extrusion at this stage of the neural crest cells from the confines of the neural plate might be an expression of a

cylindrical lumen. This actually occurs in isolated pieces of plate in homogeneous surroundings (Holtfreter, '34). The slit-shape of the normal tube has been shown to depend on the presence of notochord (Lehmann, '35) (Fig. 138C, E). The effect may be credited to a vertical system of fibers, spanning the thickness of the plate along a median strip coextensive with the notochord and apparently attached to it, which

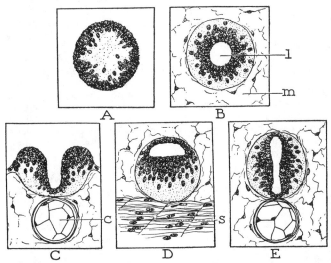

Fig. 138. Shape of neural tube under different conditions (from Holtfreter, '34). A, Solid neural mass developed in explantation: nuclei of gray matter crowded near the surface; white matter in the interior. B, Neural tube surrounded by mesenchyme: shape cylindrical with central lumen; nuclei massed at the inner (free) surface. C, Asyntaxia dorsalis (failure of the tube to close); thinning of the floor of the tube in contact with the notochord; gray matter along the free surface. D, Neural tube underlain by musculature; lumen eccentric at far side; white matter at near side. E, Neural tube underlain by notochord; normal appearance; slit-shaped lumen, oriented towards notochord. l, Lumen; m, mesenchyme; c, notochord; s, segmented musculature.

transient incompatibility (or disaffinity) between the two groups. Thus, visible movements and shaping processes appear as the observable results of more intimate physicochemical distinctions within the prospective neural system.

Early Morphogenesis of Brain and Cord. The gross shapes of the early brain and cord, respectively, are anticipated in the proportions of the neural plate, whose wide anterior part, upon folding upward, forms the large vault of a brain ventricle, while the narrower posterior part encloses the narrow lumen of the central canal of the spinal cord.

The shape of the canal varies with the details of the folding process (Fig. 138). Uniform curling of the plate would leave a

holds the midline firmly anchored as a hinge about which the flanks of the plate fold up (Weiss, '50c). A similar fibrous plane seems to define the border between the alar and basal plate cell masses; as the latter grow and bulge, it gives rise to the lateral sulcus. Because of their importance for the later regular distribution and grouping of cell columns, such tangible traces of early subdivisions would merit more intensive study; at present, we have no more than vague hints as to their presumable role.

After the closure of the groove, the turgor of the fluid in the lumen assumes the morphogenetic role of firm support for the limp walls, which otherwise would collapse. The source of this turgor has been found in the secretion of fluid from the cells of the inner lining of the early ventricles (Weiss, '34b; Holtzer, '51). Furthermore, the ciliary beat of the lining may propel the fluid anteriorly, which in the normal embryo would help to maintain the distention of the brain cavity. In cyclostomes and teleosts, in which the CNS is laid down initially as a solid cell cord, this same secretion process seems to be the method by which the central lumen is secondarily established in the interior. The shrinkage of the central canal by partial fusion of its walls (see Hamburger, '48), paralleled by the decline of mitotic activity, may reflect a reduction of turgor in the spinal portion.

With hydrostatic pressure on the inside and the confining skull capsule on the outside, continued enlargement of the brain wall by growth, cell migrations and the deposition of white matter must be expected to lead to deformations, which, depending on the local conditions, manifest themselves as cave-ins, outpocketings, fissures or folds. Practically nothing is known about the mechanics of these elementary shaping processes, although there are at least some indications that the fissures between major divisions of the cortex actually arise as cave-ins along lines of least resistance in the wall which tends to expand in confined space (Clark, '45; Källén, '51). It must be emphasized, however, that the systematic pattern, according to which such mechanical events take place, is intrinsically prepared by the inequalities established previously by the locally differing processes of proliferation, migration, aggregation and differentiation (see Bergquist and Källén, '53a); the gross mechanical factors do not create these differentials, but merely translate them into more conspicuous spatial configurations.

Accordingly, the attainment of normal brain configuration depends not only on the typical development of the brain wall, but also on the proper harmony between the latter and the growth of the skull capsule (or in the case of the cord, the spine) on the outside, and the turgor of the cerebrospinal liquor on the inside. If this harmony is disturbed, either by a genetically determined imbalance between the component tissues or by later trauma or nutritional deficiencies, serious aberrations of the CNS will ensue. Genetically conditioned hypersecretion of central fluid, for instance, leads to hydrocephalus and brain herniation (Little and Bagg, '24; Bonnevie, '34; see Section XIV, Teratogenesis, by Zwilling); delayed closure of the folds past the onset of secretion, to various grades of spina bifida with draining fistulae (for an example of mechanical production of spina bifida, see Fowler, '53); and retardation of skull growth in vitamin A deficiency, with unimpeded growth of the CNS, to brain compression and herniation (Wolbach and Bessey, '42). The early cartilaginous capsule, at least in the spinal region, can accommodate its size to the actual dimensions of the enclosed CNS (Holtzer, '52a), but this adaptability is certainly greatly reduced in later stages.

Morphogenesis of the Neural Crest. The neural crest, which contains precursor cells for spinal ganglia, sympathetic ganglia, Schwann cells, pigment cells, and, in lower vertebrates, also branchial skeleton and ordinary mesenchyme, is regionally specialized even before its cells start on their migrations away from the dorsal midline (Hörstadius, '50; Niu, '47). The bilateral cell masses first move down in rather coherent sheets (Detwiler, '37b); the parts of prime interest here, those giving rise to the ganglia, then settle down in two major columns, one between spinal cord and myotomes, the other alongside the aorta, with further outposts moving into the viscera. The localization of the ganglionic columns is hardly a simple matter of filling open grooves between the tissues, but rather an expression of specific contact affinities between the crest cells and the surrounding cell systems. We find a model of this process in the formation of pigment bands by neural crest–derived melanophores (Twitty, '49), where the migrating cells likewise aggregate along certain tracts preformed in the surrounding tissues.

Later the continuous columns break up into segmental clusters. The tendency to separate into smaller groups seems to be intrinsic to the cells, but the segmental localization of these groups is determined by the segmental arrangement of the myotomes, for the experimental removal (or disarrangement) of the latter abolishes (or correspondingly disarranges) the segmental array of the ganglia (Lehmann, '27; Detwiler, '34, '35). The segmental arrangement of the nerve roots and neural arches is likewise dependent on the presence of axial mesoderm (Detwiler, '37b), but just how these processes are causally interrelated is not yet clear.

GROWTH PATTERNS

Proliferative Sources. In the ganglia, cell division is rather ubiquitous. In the CNS, on the other hand, mitoses are, in post-neurulation stages, confined to the inner surface, lining central canal and brain ventricles (Fig. 139). More peripheral layers are essentially devoid of mitotic figures; the cells there continue to grow in size, but without ensuing divisions. Whether the inner "germinal" layer is subject to some active mitogenic stimulation by its exposure to the lumen, or rather division in the outer layers is actively inhibited by local conditions in the mantle, is uncertain. However, upon injury to the early CNS (Hooker, '25), as well as after unilateral ablation (cord: Detwiler, '44; Holtzer, '51; not observed in midbrain: Detwiler, '46b), mitotic cells may appear throughout the mantle, which seems to disprove an early loss of divisory faculty. There is a remote possibility that the confinement of mitotic figures to the inner surface might not truly express the position of the germinal cells in the resting stage, but that the latter might merely rise to the surface during mitosis (Sauer, '35). The observation that x-irradiation of embryos destroys a cell layer somewhat deeper than the inner lining (Hicks, '52) could be interpreted in two ways: either these deeper cells are the true germinal ones, but are impaired in their normal premitotic centripetal movement, or else they are postmitotic cells defying the general supposition that germinal cells are the most sensitive to radiation (Hicks, '53). At any rate, once neuronal differentiation has become marked, none of the resulting nerve cells would ever divide again under ordinary circumstances. We therefore can confine our consideration of proliferative patterns to the inner, "germinal," layer, whatever its precise delineation may be. In this layer, mitotic density and rate vary characteristically both along the longitudinal and in the dorsoventral direction, as will be described more fully below.

Growth and Shape. Daughter cells of a germinal mitosis may either remain in the germinal layer or move off into the deeper layers. In the former event, they can continue to proliferate, while in the latter event, they merely add to the bulk of the mantle without further reproduction. Since the relative frequency of the two events will depend on the spatial arrangement, the configuration of

early brain and cord assumes significance for their over-all growth rate. According to Hertwig's rule, the plane of division of a radially elongate medullary cell should lie parallel to the surface; hence, of the two daughter cells only one would remain a germinal cell. We know neither what rearrangements take place after division, nor what actuates and guides the movement of the proliferated cells. However, it seems that, at least in the earlier stages, they glide along other medullary cells stretching across the

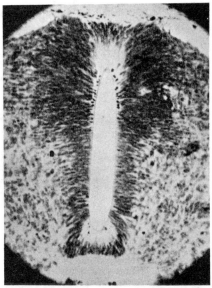

Fig. 139. Cross section of spinal cord (15th segment) of 6½-day chick embryo showing mitotic activity of germinal layer, predominantly in dorsal half (from Hamburger, '48).

neural tube and brain wall, or along radial fibers deposited by the medullary cells. If all new cells kept on being thus displaced in the radial direction, the neural tube would gain only in width, but not in length.

The factor counteracting this trend seems to be the longitudinal stretch to which the tube is passively subjected by the lengthwise extension of the surrounding tissues, especially the notochord (Hörstadius, '44; Kitchin, '49). This would divert a certain fraction of the new cells in the longitudinal, rather than radial, direction, and by extending the germinal surface area, also lead to a progressive expansion of the proliferative source. While still hypothetical, this view is supported by the observation that isolated sections of the spinal cord, transplanted to the flank, where they are deprived of axial stretch, do become much thicker and shorter than if they had developed in continuity with the rest of the cord (Zacharias, '38). The ease with which lateral halves of the cord are regenerated with the participation of transverse cell shifts from the intact half (Detwiler, '47b; Harrison, '47; Holtzer, '51), contrasted with the failure to repair major gaps in the longitudinal direction, likewise indicates the

tivity declines at some levels and flares up at others. Moreover, the centers of proliferation often form a quiltlike pattern with foci at the intersections of four longitudinal columns with transverse bands (neuromeres) (Bergquist and Källén, '54). Some of the segmental peaks coincide with the appearance of prominent peripheral organs in the corresponding sector, for instance, in the limb segments. As will be shown later (p. 381), part of this correspondence is due to an active control exerted upon the centers by their respective

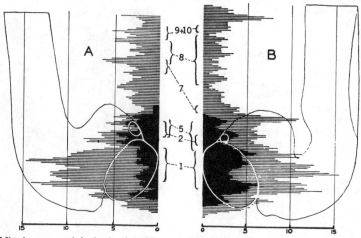

Fig. 140. Mitotic pattern of the brain of Amblystoma (after Burr, '32). *A*, Earlier stage (31, after Harrison). *B*, Later stage. (35, after Harrison).

To facilitate comparison, the two stages are represented side by side in symmetrical arrangement. The outline of the brain is indicated. Horizontal lines express the number of mitotic figures contained in serial brain slices of 30μ each. Abscissa: Number of mitoses. Full black: Mitoses in forebrain and hypothalamus. Individual bars: Mitoses in the rest of the brain. Brackets indicate position and extent of sensory placodes. Note the change in the distribution of peaks from *A* to *B*.

need of extraneous stretch for elongation. In the brain, the hydrostatic turgor deserves similar attention as a potential regulator of the expanse of the proliferative surface, hence of the over-all growth rate. These considerations would not apply, of course, to those parts of the CNS which arise, not as transformations of the original neural plate, but by secondary budding processes (e.g., the posterior parts of midbrain and spinal cord in amphibians).

Regional Patterns of Proliferation. Regional variations of mitotic activity within the germinal layer have been mapped out for several species and stages (urodele spinal cord: Coghill, '24, '36; urodele brain: Burr, '32; chick cord: Hamburger, '48; comparative studies: Bergquist and Källén, 53b). Each stage has its own characteristic pattern (Fig. 140); that is, as development proceeds, ac-

peripheries. But there are also some basic intrinsic growth differentials among different regions of the CNS (Coghill, '36; Detwiler, '24a, '36b; Hamburger, '48), the origin of which remains in need of explanation.

It has been proposed that local proliferation is regulated by the number of intracentral tract fibers ending in a given locality (Detwiler, '36b). This has been inferred from experiments in which posterior cord pieces of potentially smaller end size (of urodele tail-bud stages) and anterior ones of potentially larger size had been mutually exchanged and found to develop in accordance with their new sites, the former growing beyond, the latter remaining below, the sizes they would have attained in their original positions (Detwiler, '23, '24a). Since more descending brain fibers terminate at more anterior than at more posterior levels, these fibers were thought to have determined the site-specific growth rates. Confirmatory evidence was seen in the fact that when the anterior cord segments were replaced by a supernumerary medulla as extra fiber source, the spinal host segments lying immediately posterior to the graft became abnormally large (Detwiler, '25c).

In the light of later work, however, this view has become untenable. For instance, when the normal medulla as the supplier of supposedly stimulating fiber tracts was replaced by a spinal fragment of much lower fiber productivity, the host spinal cord behind developed quite normally, without the expected diminution (Detwiler, '37c). Similarly, suppression of forebrain development entails no deficienies in the medulla (Detwiler, '45). In the chick, cord segments which have been transected and prevented from receiving down-growing fiber tracts still gain normal dimensions (Levi-Montalcini, '45; Hamburger, '46). Also, the assumption that descending fibers would have an intrinsic preassigned length at which they would stop is gratuitous; free nerve fibers do not stop spontaneously, but are stopped by their surroundings, usually a recipient cell. Hence, fiber tracts cannot be the major determinants of axial growth patterns, although they can exert some modifying effects (see p. 383).

All evidence thus leads to the conclusion that the closed neural tube represents a longitudinal mosaic of specifically different local fields, each guiding the further fate of the area under its control; differential proliferation is but one expression of these different fates, with which we shall deal more fully below in the proper context (p. 376).

Besides the longitudinal pattern, there is also a notable dorsoventral differential of mitotic activity, both in regard to intensity and time course. Proliferation is more abundant and lasts longer in the dorsal than in the ventral half of the cord, with a rather sharp demarcation between the two zones (see Fig. 139). Generally noted in amphibians (Detwiler, '25a; Maclean, '32; Coghill, '33), this fact has been most conclusively demonstrated in the chick (Hamburger, '48). It may be related to the general precocity of the ventral, as compared to the dorsal, portions, including the precession of motor over sensory function (Coghill, '29). Dorsal and ventral halves also differ in other respects, the ventral one being far richer in alkaline phosphatase (Moog, '43), and at the same time being the first to receive vascularization (Feeney and Watterson, '46).

Growth Rate. Conventionally, the term "growth rate" refers to average increment of an organic object per unit of time. It is determined by measuring the object at the beginning and end of given intervals and dividing by the times elapsed. The resulting values are useful for rough orientation, but are often meaningless for analytical and comparative purposes, except for homogeneous systems. If the dimensions of one part of the CNS increase faster than those of another part, this need not mean that the intrinsic growth activity of the former has been greater or that its mitotic rate has been higher. If we consider, for example, a given subdivision of the CNS bounded by certain landmarks by which it can be identified at successive stages, its volume increase is the resultant of the following tributary processes: cell growth, accompanied by division in the germinal layer; cell growth without division in the mantle; immigration of nerve cells and other cell types (glia) from neighboring regions; emigration of cells; outgrowth of axons and deposition of myelin (with that portion of the axons which meanwhile has moved beyond our landmarks being unaccountably lost); passage of axons from other areas; invasion of blood vessels; accumulation of interstitial fluid; and cell disintegration. Large-scale destruction and resorption of cells is a common, if neglected, feature of embryonic development (Glücksmann, '51), and as we shall see presently, is quite prominent in the embryonic nervous system.

From this listing, it should be plain that comparisons of the "growth" of different parts of the CNS on the basis of mere measurements of volume or mass cannot be very revealing and must be interpreted with due caution. There is an even wider margin for error when, instead of volume determinations, only one, supposedly representative, dimension is sampled; e.g., cord diameter. The case is illustrated by the fact that the increase in area observed in cross sections of isolated cord segments (Severinghaus, '30) often was interpreted as hyperplasia until more complete determinations disclosed that there had been a corresponding reduction in length (Zacharias, '38) (see p. 374).

This comment should not detract from the value of the summary quantitative treatment usually accorded to CNS growth, which has been a true advance over earlier, purely verbal, descriptions; rather is it to stress the need for going even further and identifying precisely and quantitatively the various component processes of unequal kind and weight, whose disparate contributions are indistinguishably lumped in any bulk determination.

REGIONAL AND CYTOLOGICAL DIFFERENTIATION

Histochemistry of Differentiation. Superimposed upon the growth processes just discussed appear the cytological specializations usually designated as "differentiations." It is an axiom of development, however, that the morphological (i.e., microscopically discernible) "differentiation" of a cell (other than trivial geometrical changes) is but the visible expression of intimate changes in the composition and distribution of at least part of the molecular population which constitutes that cell (cf. Weiss, '49, '53). Any fundamental distinction between physicochemical (sometimes called "physiological") and morphological differentiation is thus purely artificial, for it refers not to any dichotomy in the properties of a cell but merely to two different techniques of observation, both with definite limitations, hence, supplementing each other. Accordingly, marked differences in morphology point to antecedent physicochemical changes, even though the latter may not yet be detectable by our relatively crude analytical tools, and conversely, demonstrable differences of physicochemical constitution (including differential staining in histological preparations) signify basic differences of protoplasmic properties (cytodifferentiation) even if these have failed to express themselves in corresponding differences of structural detail. It is with these qualifications in mind that the results of correlated studies between morphological and chemical ontogeny of the nervous system should be viewed (see also Section III, Chapter 1, by Schmitt).

A mental separation must be made between those chemical systems that are common to all cells (e.g., the ones engaged in respiration, energy transfer, protein reproduction, etc.) and those that are peculiar to the nervous system. In practice, this is not feasible because of the fragmentary state of our present knowledge and because there are undoubtedly quantitative variations of the former class which are as distinctive of nerve cells as are qualitatively specific compounds. Cytochemical studies of neuron growth have already been referred to above (p. 365). Even less is known about the specific biochemistry of neural differentiation.

Among the most profitable contributions to this field have been studies on the development of the cerebral cortex in which cytological, chemical, metabolic and functional observations were correlated for a series of sample stages. They have led to the recognition of certain critical phases during which differentiation advances in spurts. Within the same brief interval, the nucleus reaches mature dimensions, Nissl bodies appear in quantity, dendrites become more numerous, neurofibrils more prominent, the activities of cytochrome c, adenylpyrophosphatase, and succinic dehydrogenase rise sharply, and electric brain potentials are recordable for the first time (Flexner, '50). In amphibians, motility develops in close parallelism with the production of acetylcholinesterase (Youngstrom, '38; Sawyer, '43; Boell and Shen, '50), which is instrumental in nerve conduction, and experimental modifications of the size of the brain (see p. 383) are reflected in corresponding changes in its content of these products (Boell and Shen, '51).

These examples may suffice to discourage the practice of divorcing morphological from underlying physicochemical considerations. At the same time, much of this work must still be counted in the descriptive class, furnishing important data of information but not yet much causal understanding.

Appearance of Regional Differences. As mentioned above, different levels along the longitudinal axis of the early CNS enter different developmental courses, which subsequently express themselves in the overt mosaic of morphological, histological, and eventually, functional specializations. Although some gross mosaic features may be conceded to the neural plate from its very first appearance (e.g., Nieuwkoop, '52; see above, p. 370), its finer parcellation is a continuing process the progress of which can be tested by appropriate experiments (see Section VI, Chapter 1, by Holtfreter and Hamburger). The standard test consists of displacing the part in question (by explantation, inversion, or heterotopic transplantation) in a graded series of stages and establishing precisely from what stage it can carry on a course of development typical of its original site even under aberrant environmental conditions.

This test presupposes that features attained under the original and under the aberrant conditions are sufficiently distinct to be used as criteria. Individual blood cells, muscle cells and pigment cells, for instance, can be easily distinguished by their inclusions, different gland cells by their secretions; but individual nerve cells, judged by their shapes, whose normally great variability is further exaggerated under experimental conditions,

within each class, which must be postulated on functional evidence (see below, p. 384), for instance, between motor cells innervating different muscles or between neurons subserving different sensory modalities. The

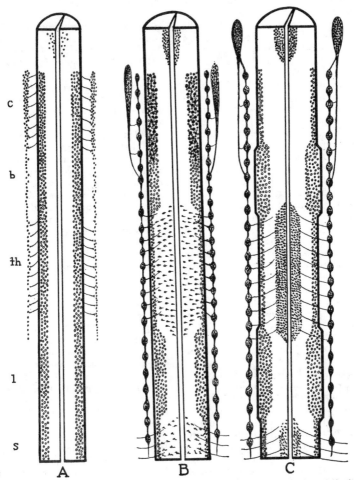

Fig. 141. Diagrammatic frontal sections of the spinal cord of chick embryos of 4 days (*A*), 5 days (*B*) and 8 days (*C*), showing the regionally differing formation of the motor columns from a morphologically rather uniform condition. In *B*, degeneration of cells in the cervical region (*c*, black circles), and centripetal emigration of cells in the thoracic and sacral regions (*th*) have set in, resulting in the distribution shown in *C*. (From Hamburger and Levi-Montalcini, '50.)

cannot always be so readily identified as to the precise type to which they belong. Large motor cells, Rohon-Beard cells, spinal ganglion cells, commissural cells, and a very few others are sufficiently distinctive to be used as cytological indicators for the respective neuron types. But there are no corresponding microscopic signs for the finer distinctions

only individual cell that can be strictly identified as such is Mauthner's neuron, of which there is in many species only a single pair, situated at the otic level of the hindbrain of lower vertebrates, and which can be recognized by its giant size. For the rest, one must rely on general morphological group criteria, such as cross-sectional configuration, characteristic location and distribution of cell columns within the unit, and the like.

Applying these tests, it has been found that the consolidation of regional properties follows a definite time sequence: in general, more anterior parts have a head start over more posterior ones, and fixation along the longitudinal axis seems to precede fixation in the mediolateral direction. Presumptive medulla oblongata of a urodele tail-bud embryo transplanted in the place of the first cord segments of another embryo develops into a supernumerary medulla oblongata (Detwiler, '25c). Even an isolated lateral half of presumptive medulla grafted into a lateral gap of spinal cord develops according to its origin, quite incongruously for the location, into half a medulla (Detwiler, '43a). Yet, while anterior spinal levels at the same stage show similar capacity for self-differentiation (Maclean, '32), more posterior segments are still able in some measure to conform to site-specific determinative influences (p. 387).

All existing evidence leads to the conclusion that, in the later neurula stage, allocation of differential developmental properties within the CNS has already made notable progress. The cord seems to lag slightly behind the brain, but by the time different cord segments have first become externally distinguishable (in birds), each one after transfer to another region develops essentially as if it were still in the original place, mosaic-fashion (B. Wenger, '51). The regionally specific "developmental properties" contain the whole ground plan for all subsequent transformations, that is, they determine pattern and basic rate of proliferation, specific differentiation of cell types, migration, establishment of specific mutual group relations, patterns of cell destruction, and the physiological mechanisms underlying functional activity and coordination. Thus segmental organization in the chick embryo, for instance, which begins to emerge on the fifth day of incubation, shows up (Fig. 141) in abundant cell degeneration in the cervical segments, segregation of a large lateral motor column in the brachial segments, absence of a lateral column and presence of a characteristic column of preganglionic autonomic cells (nucleus of Terni) at the thoracic and sacral levels (Levi-Montalcini, '50; Hamburger and Levi-Montalcini, '50). In the amphibians, where functional tests have been carried further, it includes such properties as the ability of the limb seg-

ments to engender coordinated limb movements, in contrast to the lack of this faculty in the trunk and head regions (see below, p. 387).

Similar early differences of properties at different levels of the main axis have been demonstrated for the spinal ganglia in regard to cell proliferation and regulatory ability (amphibians: Lehman and Youngs, '52) and incidence of cell degeneration (chick: Hamburger and Levi-Montalcini, '49).

It must be stressed that even as the mosaic of diverse parts of the CNS emerges, each area at first seems to operate "field"-fashion, that is, while its general fate is fixed, the detailed course of its component elements would still be variable. This is indicated by such observations as the following. At a time when the development of the medulla oblongata has already become irrevocably identified with the part of the tube lying at the presumptive hindbrain level (see above), one can still turn that piece around, reversing its anteroposterior axis, and yet see it yield a medulla of normal (unreversed) configuration (Detwiler, '43b). Cord regions of the same stage after anteroposterior reversal regulate similarly (Detwiler, '24a).

However, the interpretation of these regulatory effects calls for some caution. While shape and proliferation rates, which served as criteria, may indeed be as adaptable as indicated, this need not apply equally to the segregation of the various qualitatively specialized cell strains, which might follow a totally different time pattern and whose determination might be either precocious or delayed relative to those other features. Experiments with Mauthner's cell (M-cell) seem to be pertinent to this problem. Unilateral extirpation in a post–tail-bud stage of the hindbrain at the prospective M-cell level leads to permanent absence of an M-cell on the operated side (Detwiler, '33). Since heterotopic grafts of the same area from a neurula yield supernumerary M-cells (Piatt, '44; Stefanelli, '50)—and assuming that the history of the M-cell is representative of that of other, less conspicuous, cell types—we must conclude that even at this early stage a rather detailed fixation of type characteristics has occurred in the various precursor cells of the later cerebral neuron strains. Repetition of the experiments in earlier stages using the M-cell as marker has narrowed the critical period of determination to the late gastrula (in frogs). At that stage, while an explant or transplant from the presumptive M-cell region can already give rise to an M-cell independently, another M-cell may develop at the normal site from amidst the residual neural cells that have closed the gap from adjacent levels (Stefanelli, '50). This proves that the factors localizing M-cell development in the hindbrain had already been in operation but were still enough active to turn out a second set; furthermore, that there were still cells in the surrounding brain regions sufficiently labile in character to respond to redirection. These results suggest that the character of cell strains is fixed much earlier than are the numbers, distribution and arrangement of their descendent cells.

Determination in the transverse direction, that is, along the mediolateral axis of the neural plate, is likewise a gradual process. This can be concluded from the fact that at stages at which transverse strips of neural plate manifest definite "self-differentiation" of regional character after displacement, they still are capable of extensive regulation in the lateral direction (Roach, '45). However, at the stage of the closure of the neural folds, some further mosaic subdivision has also developed in the mesiolateral direction (which after folding appears as ventro-dorsal direction); for in birds, localized defects placed in the neural epithelium at that stage result in cords in which the whole radial sector that would normally arise from and cover the destroyed patch is completely missing (E. Wenger, '50).

It is to be noted that these results prove only the loss of capacity for regulative redistribution of tasks within the residual fragment of nervous system itself; no regeneration of the missing sectors had been initiated. If regeneration, i.e., mobilization of new cell material to replace missing parts, can be activated, as has been possible in amphibians, the regulative faculty extends into considerably later stages; again, it is far wider in the lateral than in the longitudinal direction. After the excision of a lateral half of presumptive midbrain, medulla or spinal cord segments from the neural tube, increased proliferation and migration of cell masses across the midline from the residual intact half restore the missing portion with remarkable morphological and, in earlier stages, also histological, perfection (Detwiler, '44, '46b, '47b; Harrison, '47; Holtzer, '51).

A comparative view of all these results leads us to distinguish rather sharply between determination of individual cell fate, strictly cell-wise, on the one hand, and "determination" of a cell complex, on the other, the latter connoting the imparting of some frame of conditions to the cell group which only in further consequence would gradually fix the characters of the individual component cells. In the case of the CNS, this presents us with the alternative that either (a) the diverse cell types of the later mantle are already preformed as such in a corresponding variety of precursor cells in the neural epithelium, or (b) the cells of the neural epithelium are still equipotential and acquire their differential type characteristics only through local influences of the different mantle portions in which they come to lie.

There is not enough evidence on hand to decide this alternative crucially one way or the other. Except for some indirect morphological and pathological indications (Globus and Kuhlenbeck, '44), it has not even been definitely settled whether the dichotomy between glia (spongioblasts) and nerve cells (neuroblasts) is already effected in the germinal epithelium or whether both are derived from common stem cells. In the case of Mauthner's cell described above one could assume, according to (a), that during neurulation a particular cell of the plate is endowed with the ability either to turn into an M-cell itself or to undergo an orderly sequence of unequal divisions eventuating in the segregation of one of the descendents as an M-cell. A model for such a process is known, for instance, in the production of the mother cells of scales in certain insects (Henke, '53). The occasional occurrence of twin M-cells in haploid embryos (Fankhauser, '52) could be taken as a sign of the disturbance of the regular cell lineage because of the undersized mass of the haploid cells. According to (b), one would assume that a particular cell block in the presumptive hindbrain would be endowed with "inductive" activities that would reach a rather sharp peak at a given focus, and that the cell that happened to be thus pin-pointed would thereby be singled out to grow up into an M-cell.

There is some suggestive, but meager, evidence pointing to early cell type divergence according to (a). In the experiments on the repair of excised halves of spinal cord from cell sources of the opposite half (see above, this page), it was noted that when the operation was performed in successively older embryos, definite cell types would begin to be missing in otherwise morphologically well restituted halves, with the large motor cells dropping out first, commissural neurons next and general internuncials last (Holtzer, '51). This indicates that the regenerated cell types stem each from the homologous cell type of the intact half; that the various types lose their mobility or become otherwise unavailable as sources of replacement, one by one, in the observed time sequence; and that the descendent cells of different strains can no longer substitute for one another.

If this be the case, the term "indifferent," commonly given to cells of no particular morphological distinctiveness, is misleading. Actually, these cells would constitute a heterogeneous population, each with definite differential type characteristics, which may or may never come to the fully mature expression amenable to morphological classification; they would not be a common pool of truly equivalent elements, which could still be switched into the various types of specific neurons by determinative local influences. It is by no means unlikely that eventually both assumptions (a) and (b) will turn out to be partly correct in the sense that some distinctive type specificity is already inherent in the cells leaving the germinal layer for the mantle, but that additional diversity is imposed upon them by conditions along their path and at their final locations.

The appearance of qualitative diversity among sensory neurons has also been demonstrated for the spinal ganglia. Aside from indirect deductions from the fact of selective fasciculation (see above, p. 366), tangible microscopic, topographical and behavioral differences between cell groups subserving different functions have been revealed under the microscope (Levi-Montalcini and Levi, '43); as will be shown below, they likewise represent qualitatively different segments of a heterogeneous neuron population.

In conclusion, there is ample evidence for the early emergence in the CNS of qualitatively diverse cell strains, the number of recognized varieties being severely limited by the inadequacy of our means of discrimination; there is some evidence that the diversity of strains can at least partly be projected right back to a corresponding diversity within their production source, the neural epithelium; and that this mode of development of qualitative regional diversity leaves an adequate margin for quantitative adjustments of numbers within each type— the adjustments which will form the subject of the following pages.

PERIPHERAL EFFECTS ON CENTRAL DEVELOPMENT

Historical Remarks. A quantitative correspondence between nerve centers and their peripheral area of innervation has long been inferred from comparative and pathological studies. Congenital absence of an extremity, for instance, was found to be reflected in unilateral underdevelopment of the corresponding spinal segments (e.g., Edinger, '21). However, whether the missing parts had failed to develop from the start or had been formed but secondarily degenerated from lack of peripheral outlets could not be decided by such static observations. The first attempt to reproduce the results experimentally by removing limb buds in chick embryos (Shorey, '09) led essentially to a confirmation of the fact that centers faced with a reduced periphery became (or remained) undersized; they also proved that the relation was a causal one, without, however, elucidating its nature. In further corroboration, removal of an eye in early amphibian larvae was found to entail reduced size of the optic centers in the corresponding (i.e., contralateral) midbrain hemisphere (Steinitz, '06; Dürken, '13). Yet, not until these defect experiments were supplemented by overloading experiments could the actively stimulating nature of the peripheral influence be regarded as firmly established. The first well attested case was the excessive development of spinal ganglia in trunk segments whose peripheral mass had been increased by the addition of a grafted limb (Detwiler, '20). Continued experimentation in amphibians (chiefly by Detwiler and his school), and later even more penetratingly in birds (by Hamburger and coworkers), has reiterated an old lesson of biological research: a relation that on first acquaintance appears simple and transparent, when subject to more minute analysis more often than not turns out to be much more complex, if not more obscure, than originally suspected. Significant differences were discovered in the response of different species, of spinal ganglia vs. spinal cord, between brain parts, and among different regions of the cord. Meanwhile, other types of peripheral influences upon central development have been discovered, such as the control of neuronal size reported above

(p. 365) and the functional specialization of centers by their end-organs discussed below (p. 384), all of which add to our conviction that the potent role of the periphery is exerted not by a single unitary mechanism, but by a multiplicity of interlocking ones.

In the earlier studies of peripheral rebound on central development, attention was focussed almost solely on the final size (number of cells and total mass) of the affected central part. Depending on whether it was above or below the expected normal size (mostly calculated from the asymmetry between the experimental and opposite control halves of normally symmetrical systems), the difference was described as "hyperplasia" or "hypoplasia," signifying an overproduction or underproduction of cells. However, since final size is determined not only by proliferation rate but also by cell migration, cell growth, cell destruction, etc (see above, p. 375), these terms are apt to be misleading and will not be used in the following discussion (see also Hamburger and Levi-Montalcini, '49). When speaking of "periphery," we shall mean tissues to be innervated, not just any extra-neural environment.

Peripheral Rebound on Primary Neurons.
Ganglia. No conspicuous excess of brachial over trunk ganglia can be detected after the respective peripheries have been roughly equalized by the suppression of the development of the limb (Detwiler, '24c; Hamburger and Levi-Montalcini, '49). The intrinsic development in the absence of a limb may therefore be taken as the baseline over which effects of peripheral increase build up. Suppression of trunk muscles by myotomectomy results in still smaller ganglia (Detwiler, '27), but in view of the relative uniformity of myotomes in the normal animal, this fact can have no influence on the shape of our "baseline." When a single limb develops (i.e., in the normal case) there results then a rise of this base value to the (normal) magnitude typical of intact limb levels. Adding a limb to a trunk segment raises the base value of the latter so that the spinal ganglia turn out larger than those of normal trunk segments (Detwiler, '20; Hamburger, '39b). In amphibians, the effect can be obtained throughout the larval stages until after metamorphosis (Carpenter, '32, '33). Cranial ganglia likewise enlarge when they are made to innervate a supernumerary organ grafted to the head (Detwiler, '30b). These increases are only partly due to increased proliferation; for the most part they

result from the fact that more of the "indifferent" neuroblasts (see above, p. 380) in the ganglion are caused to mature into large typical dorsal root neurons (Hamburger and Levi-Montalcini, '49), which thus add not only to the tally of identifiable sensory cells, but being larger, also to the mass of the ganglion. Besides, there occurs normally in various ganglia a certain amount of cell degeneration, which in the presence of a larger periphery, e.g., a limb, is held in check (Hamburger and Levi-Montalcini, '49). Thus, the final count of cells is regulated through at least three devices: proliferation, maturation and elimination.

Whether the effect is of a generalized kind, involving all neurons of the overloaded region, or a selective response of specifically matching types is still an open question. That there is some selectivity is definitely indicated by the ganglionic response to tumor transplantation. Ganglia at the level of a transplanted mouse sarcoma (in chick embryos) show the typical increase commonly observed under conditions of peripheral overload (Bueker, '48). The effect is selective in that it exempts the motoneurons of the cord, remains confined to the mediodorsal neurons in the spinal ganglia, and reaches its greatest intensity in the purely sympathetic para- and prevertebral ganglia (Levi-Montalcini and Hamburger, '51, '53).

This whole problem has recently been complicated by the discovery that the sympathetic ganglia of the chick embryo develop excessively even when the inducing sarcoma graft has been placed on the allantoic membrane, beyond the reach of actual fiber connections, evidently exerting its effect by some humoral agent (Levi-Montalcini, '52; Levi-Montalcini and Hamburger, '53). One could tentatively assume that the primary effect of the tumor agent consists of a general unstabilization of cell surfaces. The nerve cell bodies would thereby be enabled to issue more sprouts, and the nerve fibers more branches (see above, p. 361); this effect has actually been observed in tissue culture (Levi-Montalcini et al., '54). The visceral organs, on the other hand, would lose their surface protection against fiber invasion and could absorb the outgrowing branches (see p. 370). But the relation, if any, between these events and the ganglionic hyperplasia is by no means clear, and the factual analysis will have to be driven much further before any definitive explanation can be adopted.

Spinal Cord. As in the spinal ganglia, the

peripheral rebound on the development of the spinal cord is superimposed upon an intrinsic pattern of regional differences (see p. 374), which may again serve as "baseline." Even without limbs, this baseline is higher in limb segments than in cervical and thoracic segments (Bueker, '43; Hamburger, '46). As for its potential alteration by changes in peripheral area, the results seemed at first to vary according to species. In urodeles, the presence of a limb caused no increase in the number of cells in the "motor" half of the respective cord region (Detwiler, '24c), although in accordance with the conclusions reported under *Factors Controlling Neuron Growth*, p. 365, the individual neurons, hence the cross sections of the motor roots, were larger (Detwiler and Lewis, '25). In anurans (May, '33) and birds (Hamburger, '34), on the other hand, the presence of a limb entailed a considerable enlargement of the "motor" cell columns of the cord. This apparent discrepancy turned out to be one of terminology. Whereas in the latter group the large cell bodies of motoneurons are compactly assembled in separate cell columns ("motor horns") and therefore can be tallied separately, in urodeles they lie intermingled with other cell types so that for practical reasons the total number of cells in the ventral half of the cord was counted as "motor." Subsequent cell counts in the chick (Hamburger and Keefe, '44) showed that in this form likewise the total cell numbers in the ventral cord were not appreciably different whether or not a limb was there, but that in the presence of one, the ratio of "indifferent" to fully matured motor horn cells was shifted in favor of the latter, and only the latter had been counted in the earlier studies.

It is clear from these facts that one of the effects of the actual presence of a limb in the limb segments is a recruitment process by which neuroblasts that would otherwise have remained less distinctive are induced to mature into large motoneurons. However, this is only part of the story. First, there seems to be also a certain, though minor, stimulation of (mitotic) cell proliferation (Hamburger and Keefe, '44); why this does not lead to an increased cell number in cases with overloaded peripheries has not been resolved. Second, the ways in which the "baseline" values are attained in different regions vary markedly and the ways of the peripheral influences vary accordingly. As outlined before (p. 378), in the chick the

various levels of the spinal cord, initially of comparable cell content, gradually assume unequal sizes owing to increased cell degeneration in the cervical region, increased maturation of ventral horn cells in the brachial region, and characteristic migrations of the cell bodies (or just the nuclei?) of preganglionic sympathetic and parasympathetic neurons in the thoracic and sacral regions, respectively (Levi-Montalcini, '50) (see Fig. 141). A limb added to any of these regions will then cause segmental enlargement by either reducing degeneration, or promoting maturation, or checking emigration, respectively.

This diversity of ways in which the final cell tally can be altered complicates the search for the underlying mechanisms and raises doubts in the assumption of a single common mechanism. As in the case of the spinal ganglia, one could maintain that it takes a primary connection between a center and its peripheral district by some pioneering fibers in order to furnish that center with an estimate of its peripheral domain. But how does the pioneering neuron convey its information to others still in immature state? We have already commented on those changes in metabolic activity and other properties of a successfully connected neuron that express themselves in its size (p. 365) and fasciculation (p. 366). One need only assume that certain effects of these changes spread to neighboring cells (Hamburger, '39b; Hamburger and Keefe, '44). Observations in sheep embryos, showing coincidence between the arrival of motoneurons at the periphery and the development of their dendritic fields, have led to the contention that spreading dendrites might be the transmitters of the inducing stimulus (Barron, '43, '46). But this explains little. For one thing, it could not apply to spinal ganglion cells, which lack dendritic interconnections, and moreover, the unknown influence becomes no better known by being transferred from the perikaryon to the dendrites.

The numerical increase of peripherally overloaded centers is limited by the output capacity of the respective centers. Thus, whereas the addition of a limb produces a marked increase over the limbless state, the further addition of one, two or even three extra limbs to the plexus fails to produce an appreciable further augmentation (Verzár and Weiss, '30; Weiss, '37a; Bueker, '45). It is perhaps for this reason that large limbs transplanted orthotopically to a small body fail to evoke a corresponding cellular increase in the spinal limb centers (Schwind, '31; Harrison, '35a). On the other hand, genetically hyperdactylous mice have been reported to have larger limb cord segments (Tsang, '39; Baumann and Landauer, '43). Whether this increase of central cell number as a result of the presence of extra toes is as limited as that observed in urodeles or whether the limb centers of rodents have perhaps retained a higher output capacity from their phylogenetic past, when they possessed more toes, is an open question.

Rebound on Secondary Units. Modifications of the size of spinal ganglia due to alterations of the periphery are also reflected in corresponding variations of the sensory columns of the spinal cord with which the former connect (Hamburger, '34; Barron, '45). This demonstrates the existence of transneuronal effects "in series" similar to the transneuronal effects "in parallel" just discussed. Instead of a non-neural periphery affecting its correlated neurons, one neuronal group now influences the quantitative development of another to which it bears an effector relation. No numerical increase of the internuncial cells discharging into the motor columns has as yet been seen to follow an induced increase of the latter, although the reverse, secondary degeneration of more proximal neurons in consequence of destruction of central fiber tracts, has been observed (see Bodian, '42).

Results comparable to those in the spinal segments have also been obtained with cranial nerves. Elimination of the labyrinth including the acoustic ganglion entails underdevelopment of some associated cell groups of the medulla (Levi-Montalcini, '49). After the early removal of one eye in larval amphibians, the midbrain roof of the opposite side, end station of the crossed optic nerve fibers, develops defectively. Its size remains subnormal (Steinitz, '06; Dürken, '13; Larsell, '31), mitotic activity being reduced and the segregation of typical cell strata being impaired (Kollros, '53). As in the spinal centers, the effect is complex in nature, involving proliferation, migration and cell enlargement, although in the present case it is transmitted not directly but through intermediary neurons.

It is not surprising to find that the morphological underdevelopment of an eyeless midbrain hemisphere is reflected in a deficit of its chemical products. Thus, the activity of acetylcholinesterase, an obligatory constituent of neural tissue, is reduced in pro-

portion to the reduced number of nerve cells (Boell and Shen, '51).

Midbrain centers connected with eyes of subnormal size (transplantation from small to large animals) are intermediate between those of normal and anophthalmic specimens (Twitty, '32). Genetically determined reduction or suppression of eye development (microphthalmia, anophthalmia) has the same effect on the size of the optic brain centers as has the corresponding experimental interference (Chase, '45). It is noteworthy that in insects, too, eye reduction, either experimentally produced (Kopeć, '22) or genetically caused (Power, '43), is correlated with reduction of optic ganglia. Cephalopods react similarly (Ranzi, '28).

An artificial increase in the volume of optic nerve fibers reaching the brain yields the expected central enlargement. This has been obtained in the midbrain after replacement of the normal eye by one of excessive size (Harrison, '29; Twitty, '32), or after adding a supernumerary eye (Pasquini, '27); and in the medulla, in response to the entry of an aberrant optic nerve from an eye grafted in the place of an ear (May and Detwiler, '25).

In conclusion, there is widespread evidence of quantitative regulation of the maturation of nerve centers from both the effector and receptor ends. Although the modes of action may differ, the principle is the same whether the "receptors" and "effectors" concerned are sensory organs and muscles or other neuron groups. Presumably some of the intracentral regulations outlined below (p. 386) are manifestations of this same principle. Its operation provides the nerve centers with the necessary latitude of adjustment to insure adequate central control despite the wide individual variability and unpredictability of the detailed patterns of innervation illustrated throughout this article. It is important, however, to remember that the degree of adaptive latitude is limited by intrinsic properties of the responding centers which date back to their earlier prefunctional and even preneural stages.

Specific Modulation and Resonance. The peripheral encroachment upon central development reaches its climax of refinement in the process of qualitative adaptation ("modulation") of neurons in conformance with the type of effector or receptor organ with which they connect. Let us explain this phenomenon in the case of muscle innervation where it was first discovered (Weiss, '24).

In discussing nerve outgrowth, we have referred to several provisions for the over-all guidance of masses of motoneurons to muscle masses as their appropriate destinations (selective contact guidance, selective fasciculation, etc.), as well as for the preclusion of peripheral connections with inappropriate kinds of tissues. It must be remembered, however, that orderly motor function presupposes that the whole muscle mass of a region be not thrown into contraction indiscriminately or all at once, but that at any one moment, only definite selections of individual muscles be made to contract in combinations yielding a "coordinated" movement. Physiological concepts of coordination are still rather controversial but they all agree on one point, namely, that the coordination of muscle contraction is the result of the selective excitation of the motor ganglion cells connected with the muscle fibers to be actuated. Thus, in order to effect an orderly movement, the motor centers must "know" precisely which ganglion cells are hitched to what muscles.

Theoretically, the way in which this knowledge is acquired could be conceived of about as follows: Either (a) there is a predestined motor cell group for each individual muscle and some detailed mechanism exists by which the axons of that cell group are routed precisely to the matching muscle to the exclusion of all other muscles, so that the pattern of connections would be stereotyped for all individuals; or (b) lacking such stereotyped connections, the centers would "learn" about their specific relations to the periphery by "trial-and-error," actuating muscles at first in random combinations and then fixing somehow those central linkages that had incidentally yielded useful movements. Most past and current thinking about coordination implies either one or the other of these assumptions. Yet, both are contradicted by the facts. As for (a), predestination of motor fibers for particular muscles (rather than just muscles in general) is ruled out not only by the normal variability in plexus formation, but above all by the experimental proof that any motor fiber will innervate equally readily any individual muscle (see above, p. 363) and that, as will be described presently, coordinated function can be obtained even after deliberate randomization of the peripheral pathways. And as regards (b), not only has the "trial-and-error" period supposed to produce basic coordination by gradual learning never been

observed (see later, p. 391), but, as we shall show below, the very crux of this thesis, that the degree of utility to the individual of an achieved movement is at all critical for the development of coordination, has been experimentally invalidated. Neither alternative being tenable, the solution came from a third and unexpected direction.

In condensed version, it is as follows: (1) Each individual muscle has some constitutional specificity by which it is distinguished (presumably in its finer protoplasmic chemistry) from all other muscles (except homologous ones); (2) it imparts its specificity to the motor nerve fiber to which it has become attached, and through the axon, to the ganglion cell; this progressive specification of motoneurons by, and in conformance with, their individual terminations has been termed "nerve modulation." It is through this direct epigenetic backward projection of the mosaic of muscular specificities upon the population of motor ganglion cells that the centers are informed as to just where their communication lines terminate. For fuller information, the reader may be referred to earlier reviews (Weiss, '36, '50b, '52a). Only the basic experiment will be briefly summarized here.

When a limb muscle of a larval amphibian is transplanted near a normal limb and provided with innervation from a nerve branch diverted from the normal limb plexus—any limb nerve branch—the transplanted muscle is always found to contract simultaneously with the muscle of the same name in the normal limb (principle of "myotypic" function). With several supernumerary muscles, the rule applies to each of them separately, so that if a whole limb with a full extra set of muscles is added, their total activity duplicates the overt actions of the normal limb; or if transplant and normal limb are of reverse asymmetry, their movements mirror each other (Fig. 142). Thus, ganglion cells of the limb level of the cord that happen to innervate muscles of the same name (i.e., of identical constitutional specificity) become functionally linked, even though the functional effects of supernumerary muscles or limbs are useless, or outright detrimental, to the animals. Since in these experiments the choice of ganglion cells for the test muscle was entirely a matter of chance or assignment by the experimenter, it is evident that the muscle must have conveyed its name to the central cell, and since this happens even in the complete absence of sensory innervation (Weiss, '41a), it must have occurred by way of the motor axon itself.

While the earlier experiments were carried out in functional larval stages, requiring the remodulation of neurons that had already been modulated once before, the results are the same after embryonic transplantations (Detwiler, '25b, '42). On the other hand, modulation has thus far been proven experimentally only in larval amphibians. After the locality of origin of the transplanted patch, rather than bearing the "local sign" (Miner, '51). Similar results have been described for vestibular neurons (Sperry, '45). The retina likewise consists of a mosaic of sectors of different constitutional specificities which are projected into the optic nerve fibers, thereby enabling the latter to establish selective discharge relations with a corresponding central mosaic of specific receptor units in the midbrain roof (Sperry, '43,

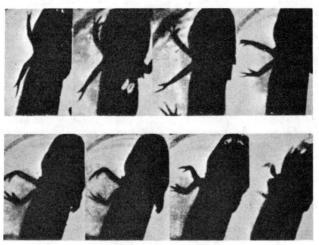

Fig. 142. Myotypic function of supernumerary muscles. A transplanted limb with reversed symmetry (right limb) near a normal left limb mirrors the movements of the latter. (From motion picture, Weiss, '52a.)

metamorphosis, neurons lose their plasticity and retain the specificity acquired previously. Rat nerves transposed to other muscles postnatally likewise failed to undergo remodulation (Sperry, '41). At the same time, there is strong evidence that modulation takes place in prenatal stages in all mammals, including man (Weiss, '35).

Sensory neurons are subject to the same qualitative modulation by their respective end-organs as are motoneurons. Proprioceptive fibers connected with any kind of muscle signal to the cord the correct name of the particular muscle (Verzár and Weiss, '30). Trigeminal neurons of the skin newly made to innervate transplanted cornea thereby acquire corneal character and corresponding reflex relations (Weiss, '42; Kollros, '43b). A transplanted larval skin patch from a foreign sector imparts its foreign specificity to the local cutaneous fibers that innervate it; thereafter when these fibers are stimulated they evoke reflexes characteristic of '44). In urodele embryos this qualitative mosaic condition is attained about the neurula stage (Stone, '44).

While the rather general validity of the principle of specific neuron modulation by effector and receptor organs seems thus well established, the nature of the processes involved is still undefined. To judge from its slow rate, as well as its qualitative diversity, modulation belongs to quite a different class of processes than nerve conduction. Its specificity sets it apart from more general "trophic" effects. Perhaps it resembles most closely phenomena of induction, infection and immunological sensitization.

Modulation, it must be stressed, clarifies only one aspect of what really is a two-sided phenomenon. By labelling, as it were, the ganglion cells according to their terminations, it produces a qualitative point-for-point replica in the centers of the peripheral receptor and effector units. Possibly the "labelled" neurons can, in turn, transfer their specificities to other, more proximal neurons (Weiss, '41a; Sperry, '51). None of this, however, touches on the problem of coordination and its origin as such; that is, on the mechanisms by which the individual units are actuated in such orderly groupings and sequences that their total effect yields an integrated movement, such as walking, swimming, feeding, etc. As the physiological study of the neural elements has far outdistanced the understanding of their group behavior, we are still without a concept of coordination that could claim cogency or general applicability. This matter would be of no particular concern to us in the present context but for two reasons: first, no consideration of neurogenesis would be complete unless it included some account of the development of the "integrated activity" of behavior; with this we shall deal briefly later. And second, much light can be shed on the nature of coordination from a study of its ontogeny; for this, the experiments just reported offer a relevant example.

The experiments have shown that not only does an extra set of muscles operate in the correct combinations and time sequences required for normal coordination (as expressed by the near-by normal limb), but a single original set of muscles, when scrambled or otherwise abnormally arranged and innervated, also operates in the same stereotyped order; that is, each muscle as an individual contracts at such time and in such strength as would be called for in the particular movement of a normal limb (Weiss, '41a), regardless of the fact that, owing to the anatomical disarrangement, this blind execution of sequences designed for normal arrangement results in a wholly senseless performance. Thus, an amphibian provided with limbs of reverse symmetry (by exchanging right and left limbs) executes all movements in reverse, e.g., walks backwards whenever it is due to advance, and vice versa, all its life (Weiss, '37b). Since this occurs likewise in animals in which the limbs had been reversed as buds and which therefore had never experienced the use of normal limbs, it is plain that the basic coordinating mechanisms, which call the different muscles for a given movement into operation in the proper selection and sequence, are intrinsic and stereotyped products of CNS development and operate blindly regardless of the effectiveness or inefficacy of the resulting movements. These central mechanisms in which the various coordination patterns are preformed might be called,

with a non-committal term, "central action systems." They deal not with the muscles as such, but with the ganglion cells modulated by the latter. Modulation merely sets the muscles into the proper response relations with the central action systems, but it does not govern their construction. Formally, the relation between central action systems and the modulated receptor and effector neurons resembles communication by "resonance."

In conclusion, the response relations within the CNS are now recognized to be ruled by qualitative specificities of great subtlety, far beyond morphological detection, and not simply by geometrical relations of otherwise equivalent units.

DEVELOPMENT OF CENTRAL ACTION SYSTEMS

The realization that in order to call forth, for instance, a coordinated elbow movement, the CNS must have developed the specific means to excite ganglion cells modulated by elbow muscles, presents us with a practical test of the presence or absence of specific action systems in a given central sector: a muscle group transplanted to the sector will not operate unless the center contains the matching set of specific activators. Applying this test, it was found that coordinated limb activities are engendered only within the normal limb segments of the cord (Detwiler and Carpenter, '29). Even a completely isolated brachial cord section can yield coordinated activities in a limb innervated by it, whereas an isolated piece of trunk cord in otherwise identical circumstances cannot (Rogers, '34). The function of limbs innervated by trunk nerves alone remains abortive. Similarly, limbs transplanted to the head and innervated by cranial nerves, while twitching in association with head muscles, never exhibit orderly independent movements (Detwiler, '30b); moreover, such movements as are observed are attributable chiefly to local eye, gill or gular muscles that have attached themselves to the skeleton of the grafted limb, with the limb muscles themselves being essentially uninvolved (Weiss, '36; Piatt, '41). We learn from these results that the regional differences within the cord, some of whose quantitative expressions we have previously encountered (under *Regional and Cytological Differentiation*, p. 376), are really much more profound, pertaining not only to numbers and configurations of cells but to all those other properties on which coordinated function depends. Since the mere attachment of a limb to a foreign spinal or cerebral region does not induce there the differentiation of effective limb control, the experiments also confirm our conclusion that modulation plays no constructive part in the design of central coordination patterns.

The prevalent tendency to base orderly central function on precise patterns of neuronal connections gains little support from the experimental work in embryonic and larval stages. Any sufficiently large fraction of the limb level of the cord contains the full coordinative machinery for a limb; in amphibians one-third of the normal segments is sufficient (Detwiler and Carpenter, '29; Detwiler and McKennon, '30; Weiss, '36). Not only reduction but considerable morphological disarrangement may be inflicted upon the spinal limb centers without abolishing the essentially coordinated development of their typical action systems. For instance, lateral halves of the limb cord restituted after ablation by regeneration from the opposite half (Detwiler, '47b; Holtzer, '51), as well as limb segments grafted in dorso-ventral inversion (Holtzer, '50), still yield the typical limb coordination patterns. Antero-posterior reversal of the early tail-bud medulla (Detwiler, '51) or midbrain (Detwiler, '48) likewise fail to impair functional activity appreciably (Detwiler, '52).

The existence of serial functional localization in the spinal cord raises the question of the time sequence and manner of its origin. Is it already inherent in the early neural plate organization, or is it acquired only in the course of subsequent morphogenesis as a result of intracentral segregations and inductive interactions? The appropriate test is the standard one of heterotopic transplantation or isolation. Overt morphological criteria, such as architecture, growth rates, cell numbers, and the like, indicate that some of the regional differences are rather firmly laid down as early as the neural fold stage (see above, p. 376). However, we do not know to what extent these morphological features signify distinctive functional properties. Only a combination of morphological and functional tests can tell. Of the few thus far made, the following are pertinent.

When the prospective limb segments of the cord of a urodele embryo in the neurula stage are replaced by a corresponding length of trunk cord, which would normally have remained smaller and incapable of control-ling a limb, the grafted piece acquires the approximate size, as well as the functional qualifications, of true limb segments (Detwiler, '23). Conversely, prospective limb segments shifted to the trunk region remain undersized and fail to develop the action systems for limb control (Moyer, '43). Since this positional adaptation appears prior to the development of the limb, it must be ascribed to intracentral regulatory interactions, rather than to peripheral influences. If trunk segments are grafted in the brachial region in the later tail-bud stage, however, the adjustment is incomplete and limb function remains defective (Table 6 in Detwiler, '36b). Evidently, the spinal action systems become fixed during that period.

The spinal region anterior to the limb centers, when tested at the comparable stage as before, shows less plasticity and tends to "self-differentiate" in disharmony with its new site (Detwiler, '25a). In its turn, however, it causes certain conforming modifications in the adjacent posterior host segments (judged by their enlargement, as functional tests have not been carried out). This tendency toward self-differentiation followed by some "inductive" influence spreading caudad is even more marked when brain parts are transplanted to more posterior sites, e.g., a supernumerary medulla oblongata in the place of anterior spinal cord (Detwiler, '25c).

It thus appears that functional localization along the spinal axis continues into postneurulation stages, proceeding in antero-posterior sequence. Whether the determination of regional cell number, the "baseline" of our earlier discussion, is effected by a separate agency from that determining functional pattern is uncertain. If it were, some sort of transneuronal stimulation such as that noted above (p. 383) at the junction of optic fibers and midbrain centers might be invoked (Detwiler, '36b; see, however, the objections raised on p. 375 regarding this hypothesis). There are so few facts to go by that speculation has free rein. What is needed is more critical analytical research.

Parenthetically, we may point to the potential usefulness of heteroplastic transplantation in the further exploration of this field. Since exchange of parts between different species is feasible during the younger stages of lower vertebrates, unique test combinations could readily be produced. Exchange of parts of essentially similar function would, of course, be less instructive than exchange of those with regard to which the two species differ crucially. So far, heteroplastic work has dealt largely with the former. The limbs of a given species of salamander are readily controlled by limb spinal cord of another species, no matter whether the strange combination is effected by transplanting the limb to the foreign host (Detwiler, '30a; Twitty and Schwind, '31; Harrison, '35a) or by substituting foreign limb cord segments for those of the host (Wieman, '26; Detwiler, '31); even newt cord can coordinate salamander leg function (Hertwig, '26). But then, activities do not differ markedly between these species. The exchange of limbs between anurans and urodeles should be more rewarding, since the combination is feasible (Guyénot, '27), and one could test whether or not a urodele center can make a frog leg jump. Recent studies on the behavior of animals with hybrid vestibular organs show clearly the great potentialities of such research (Andres, '45).

Taking all these sketchy fragments of information together, the conclusion emerges that spinal cord and brain develop early a gross topographic mosaic of functionally specialized areas, each with specific physicochemical and structural peculiarities not fully shared by the others, whereas each sector of this mosaic within itself manifests wide powers of regulation and substitution; so much so that any theory of coordination that would rely on a rigidly predetermined order of microconnections among neurons (rather than merely statistical regularities) seems clearly controverted by the facts of experimental embryology. It is highly instructive that these embryological data parallel closely the results of work on functional localization in the cortex, which have likewise revealed macrolocalization of functional districts without microlocalization on the cellular level (Lashley, '42). It is in problems of this kind that embryology, physiology and psychology become confluent so that a conjoint approach promises to lead to much deeper insight than we now possess.* The techniques of experimental morphology, able to manufacture crucial test situations in young animals never attainable in the adult, have hardly yet been called upon to contribute their share to this teamwork. Their exploitation seems to hold rich prizes, but space restrictions do not permit us to elaborate the matter in this place.

* See the Survey of Neurobiology; Publication No. 237 by the National Academy of Sciences–National Research Council, Washington, D. C., 1952.

THE HUMORAL MILIEU IN NEURAL DEVELOPMENT

It is beyond the scope of this article to review the specific nutrient requirements of the various components of neurogenesis. As in other organ development, the internal milieu must provide not only all factors requisite for general cell life, growth and differentiation, but must in addition satisfy the more specialized needs of the countless steps of which "the development of the nervous system" is composed. Even in its early formative stage, the CNS is already distinguished from other organ rudiments by its different metabolic requirements (Spratt, '52). Neuropathology, on the other hand, has been able to trace many neural defects of the adult to deficiencies in the availability or utilization of nutrients, thus identifying the role of the latter in neurogenesis. Nerve degeneration in thiamine deficiency (beriberi) is a familiar example. Yet, the still obscure "demyelinization" diseases prove that we do not even yet know the requirements of such a common process as myelin formation. Mental derangements have been related to the lack of certain metabolic enzymes (Hoagland, '47), but the effects of metabolic disturbances on the earlier phases of neural development have not yet been adequately explored. There is need for much more systematic investigation.

The condensed outline of neurogenesis presented in this article ought to have given some idea of the almost endless array of peculiar conditions of chemical and physical nature called for at every turn of this complicated course. To satisfy these ever-changing needs, the milieu presumably undergoes phase-specific changes of composition. In this, non-neural parts or even some other parts of the nervous system may act as providers of the required supplements—in a sense, as sources of specific nutriment. Yet this "symbiotic" interdependence among the tissues is practically unexplored.

It can readily be seen that the role of hormones, the circularized products of endocrine glands, is but a special case in this general category of relations. Just a few cursory remarks can be made here on this topic. For convenience, one may distinguish functional from developmental hormone effects, the former modifying the performance of nervous systems that already possess their full complement of neurons, the latter influencing the growth and differentiation of still incomplete nervous systems; although in view of our concept of the continuous growth of neurons (see p. 364) and the instability of their connections (see p. 363), particularly in the submicroscopic realm, the distinction between the two groups is apt to fade. The former group is best illustrated by the hormonal effects on sexual behavior (see Beach, '47), the latter by the hormone dependence of the transformation of neural structures and functions from the larval to the adult state in metamorphosing species.

thyroxine carrier) near the abducens nucleus, which effects the central linkage (Kollros, '43a). Similarly, the morphological signs of brain metamorphosis, such as increased proliferation, cell increase and histogenetic changes, can be locally evoked (Kollros et al., '50; Weiss and Rossetti, '51). Particularly instructive in the latter sense is the response of Mauthner's neuron, which normally regresses during metamorphosis; if metamorphosis of the hindbrain is enforced by the local application of a thyroxine source, the nerve cell bodies enlarge

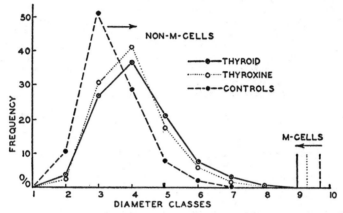

Fig. 143. Metamorphic size changes of opposite sign in Mauthner's cells (M-cells) and their surrounding neuron population (non-M-cells) in urodele larvae with thyroid or thyroxine-agar implants near brain. Histograms of nuclear diameters in 1000 non-M-cells each of control, thyroid and thyroxine cases, as well as mean diameters of M-cells for the corresponding groups of animals. (From Weiss and Rossetti, '51.)

As outlined in Section XII, amphibian metamorphosis is under the direct control of the thyroid hormone; insect metamorphosis similarly depends upon the hormones of certain head glands. The directness of the control is proven by the fact that upon localized topical application of hormone, only the surrounding local region of the tissue undergoes transformation. The same has now been demonstrated for the "adaptive" changes in the nervous control mechanism which must necessarily accompany the other bodily transformations if the metamorphosed animal is to function properly. That these neural changes are likewise under the primary control of the hormone is revealed by the following experiment. The "wink" reflex of the frog, which is normally not executed by the larva although sensory and motor elements are present and individually capable of functioning (Kollros, '42), can be made to mature precociously by the implantation of thyroid gland (or an artificial

markedly (Fig. 143) save for Mauthner's cell, which shrinks (Weiss and Rossetti, '51). This result proves that the various neuron types respond to the hormone each in its own distinctive fashion, determined by preformed metabolic patterns, which further substantiates the qualitative diversity within the neuronal population emphasized throughout our discussion.

Again these experiments are only modest openings into a rich field of future investigation, for in no other event of neurogenesis do we find such a favorable constellation of circumstances as in metamorphosis, where dramatic changes in neural composition, architecture and function, crowded into a relatively brief span of time, supervene in a nervous system that had already attained an advanced state of functional perfection, whose parts are distinct, relatively large and easily accessible to manipulation, and whose transformations can be set off by a controllable agent.

DEVELOPMENT OF BEHAVIOR

No account of neurogenesis can be complete without relating itself to the problems of behavior. After all, behavior is not only another overt sign of the molecular, cytological, morphological and functional organization of the nervous system, but is its dominant manifestation to the accomplishment of which all other features have been made subservient by phylogenetic and ontogenetic adaptation. Unfortunately, space restrictions do not permit me to give the topic its due treatment. However, in order to indicate at least some major aspects, I repeat here, with slight modifications, a summary published on an earlier occasion (Weiss, '50c).

It is a healthy sign that the sharp separation once advocated between a purely phenomenological study of behavior, on the one hand, and the physiological study of its possible neurological foundations, on the other, has not been generally adopted. The pursuit of any one scientific field under an injunction against trespassing into another is neither rational nor productive, especially if both have common objects. It simply is not true that nothing can be learned about the "organism as a whole" by studying its constituent parts and their interrelations. On the other hand, it would, of course, be equally erroneous to assume that mere preoccupation with the elements will tell the full story of their collective behavior. In the light of developments, it would seem unwarranted to subscribe to either a purely holistic or a purely elementarian theory of neural functions and behavior to the exclusion of the other, or to pursue studies on behavior alone or on its neurological foundations alone without the benefits that each field can derive from the advances of the other. Regardless of the pertinence of his detailed propositions, it certainly has been the historical merit of Coghill to have built a strong case for the conjoint attack on the problems of behavior and against the separatist trends of technical disciplines.

The realization that much can be learned about behavior by the study of its development is of relatively recent date. But, as frequently happens in the history of science, the formation of theory outraced the acquisition of factual knowledge, and soon students of the development of behavior were found to be rallied around two opposite doctrines, one stressing the primacy of the holistic, the other the elementarian, viewpoint. Each centered its arguments on certain objects, observations, and techniques different from those of the other, and evidently each party felt justified in considering its particular niche as a fair sample of the behavioral universe. Thus what in sober evaluation would have become a fruitful stimulus to further clarification of the issues assumed the dogmatic aspect of an irreconcilable antithesis. Again, as often happens in the course of scientific history, the conflict is turning out to be a matter of one-sided viewpoints and undue generalizations rather than of facts. Contrasting views on whether neural functions emerge as mass actions (Coghill, '29; Hooker, '52) or in localized fragments (Windle, '50) can be reconciled if the diversity of sample species and techniques is duly considered and if one refrains from raising observations gathered from a limited field to the dignity of doctrines of universal and unqualified validity.

PHENOMENOLOGY OF THE DEVELOPMENT OF BEHAVIOR

The phenomenology of behavioral development is actually an old discipline. It started with the recognition of the fact that behavior does have a stepwise ontogenetic history, and it went on to describe the steps involved. Only in the second instance did it proceed to test the significance of the steps as instruments or causal links in the development of the whole sequence. However, ever since the demonstration that embryos raised in narcosis would develop behavioral patterns of normal organization (Carmichael, '26; Matthews and Detwiler, '26), even though the overt expression of the whole series of precursor steps had been suppressed, it has been clear that the behavioral steps are merely external manifestations of underlying intrinsic developments rather than practice steps. The complex performances of later stages cannot possibly be founded upon the tested success of their simpler precursors, since they seem none the worse for the omission of the intermediate functional tests due to narcosis. Again, undue generalizations must be avoided, and what is said here for the early and fundamental steps of behavioral development does not apply equally to the terminal phases, in which the inherent developmental patterns are polished and perfected by actual practice and adjustment.

The phenomenological study of the development of behavior has revealed that, like all development, it follows a trend from the general to the specific and from more widespread involvement of elements to more restricted and differential activation. Coghill's principle of "individuation" from a background of mass reaction is based on this realization. It still holds true as designating a trend of events, even if the initial performance under consideration has never been a total activity of the whole body. In some cases and for some functions the primordial activity undoubtedly involves all the neural apparatuses capable of functioning at the same time (Hooker, '52; Barron, '50), while in other cases and for some other functions, it seems equally clear that activity is territorially localized from the beginning (Windle, '50).

To give a clear-cut example of the latter type, we need only refer to the appearance of the lid-closure reflex in amphibians (Kollros, '42, '43b). This reflex appears only at metamorphosis after having been completely absent in the otherwise fully functional larva (p. 389). But from its very onset it constitutes a strictly localized and circumscribed act, which has never been part of a "total pattern" of central functions. Evidently, individuation from mass action does not apply to this type of response, but this, in turn, does not invalidate the principle for other performances. The sobering lesson from all this work has been that we cannot find a key formula for the development of behavior which will save us the trouble of investigating each component of behavioral development in its own right.

THE NEURAL BASIS OF INDIVIDUATION

The development of behavior shows clearly two phases—an early expansive and a later restrictive one (Carmichael, '33). During the expansive phase, wider and wider areas of the body come under neural control. This sequence has been clearly correlated with the gradual expansion of intracentral nerve connections and pathways (Coghill, '29). In a sense this correlation is obvious, as it merely expresses the fact that where there is no neural pathway, there can be no neural function. Reactions during this early phase are remarkably stereotyped, indicating absence of discriminative response mechanisms. However, the more the nervous system approaches structural completion, the more prominent becomes its ability to activate restricted portions and patterns of the existing network independently in selected and coordinated combinations. It is this restrictive "individuation" for which the proper neural correlate is still to be revealed.

It had been thought that the development of limb innervation in amphibians could serve as an exquisite model of "individuation" in strictly anatomical terms (Coghill, '29; Youngstrom, '40). The limbs move at first only in association with trunk movements, which was explained by the fact that their early innervation consists of collaterals from the motor neurons of trunk muscles. Later "dissociation" from the trunk appeared linked to the development of a secondary separate fiber system from the limb segments of the cord (Youngstrom, '40). Other studies (Taylor, '43), however, suggest that the so-called "primary" associated limb movements are, in reality, passive movements effected through the trunk muscles of the shoulder, while the intrinsic true limb movements do not appear until after the limb muscles have received the independent set of segmental "secondary" neurons. Hence the intrinsic limb function arises as a separate and individualized activity from the very first rather than as an "individuated" offshoot of an earlier mass response. Although some aspects of the situation are still in doubt (Herrick, '48, p. 128), it is quite evident that this singular instance cannot possibly serve as the key model for "individuation" in general, as originally proposed. The neural correlate of individuation thus remains as obscure as ever, nor is it very likely to reveal itself in gross microscopic features. Moreover, the progressive refinement and localization of coordinated function are only in part attributable to improvements in the central action systems, as the progressive muscle-specific modulation of effector neurons (see p. 384), establishing more discriminatory relations with the central action systems, undoubtedly has a share in the process (Weiss, '36; Barron, '50).

CENTRAL ORIGIN OF COORDINATION

Many modern concepts of neurophysiology attempt to derive the properties of the output of the nervous system directly from the pattern of the sensory input. Such a concept is clearly contradicted by the studies on development. The fact that the appearance of motor performance antedates sensory control has often been stressed (see Coghill, '29; Herrick, '48). Even more striking is the evidence of animals in which the development of the sensory nervous system had been experimentally suppressed. The basic patterns of motor coordination in such anesthetic areas develop without major impairment, and limbs lacking sensory innervation from the beginning function coordinately without sensory control having ever had a chance to play a constructive part in the development of the motor patterns (Weiss, '41a; Yntema, '43; Detwiler, '47a). Since neither learning nor patterns of sensory stimuli have any basic part in the development of orderly central functions, we must look to the autonomous processes of central development itself, outlined earlier in this chapter (pp. 376–388), as the main source of coordination patterns. The one fact that has been conclusively established by experimental results is that the central nervous system develops a finite repertory of behavioral performances which are pre-functional in origin and ready to be exhibited as soon as a proper effector apparatus becomes available (Weiss, '41a).

A clear distinction must be made between the mere generation of a central discharge and the pattern of its distribution (coordination). Contrary to a widespread belief, a central discharge does not depend for its generation upon afferent influx but can originate within the centers. Many instances of rhythmic automatisms of nerve centers have been reported (see Bremer, '53) and referred to underlying fluctuations in the metabolic and electric state of the neurons in interaction with the humoral milieu. The observation that any isolated and deranged fragment of medulla or spinal cord will permanently exhibit trains of spontaneous rhythmic discharges (Weiss, '41b) suggests that such activity is a basic property of pools of neurons rather than a specialty of certain centers only. The different rates of "spontaneity" in urodeles with removed or variously exchanged brain parts (Detwiler, '48) may be indicative of differential pacemaker loci in the central generator network.

The sole purpose of these very sketchy comments on behavioral development has been to illustrate the crucial role the methods of experimental embryology and morphology are destined to play in arriving at objective and exact information, and in dispelling misinformation, concerning the principles of behavior.

CONCLUSIONS

The only valid summary of this chapter on neurogenesis is to say that, by the very nature of the developmental process, it does not lend itself to verbal summarization. Any attempt to embrace such intricately complicated events as those dealt with in this chapter in a simple and glibly summarizing formula would end up with either meaningless platitudes or fictitious oversimplifica-

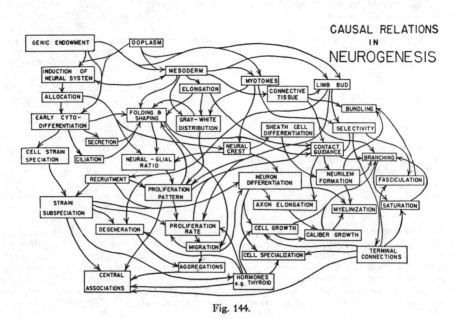

Fig. 144.

tions, undoing all the gains achieved by laborious factual analysis. If it were more generally realized that the subject matter of biology is really more nearly cognate to that of engineering than that of plain physics—that in biology we not only have to establish and reconfirm the validity of general laws and principles, but also have to clarify the complex mechanisms of their operation—then the demand for sweeping generalizations would rapidly subside. The deeper we have penetrated into the analysis of neurogenesis, the more component processes we have been able to identify and single out for methodical analysis. From this analysis, and only after it, have we gained certainty that the component processes are really of many diverse kinds—that the complexity which we encounter is not due to our dearth of knowledge or lack of comprehension but is inherent in our subject, much as it is in a machine. Simplicity, and not complexity, is the illusion.

But faced with this reality, the task of disentangling the complexity and reducing it to an irreducible minimum of elementary events and their interactions becomes all the more challenging. The picture that emerges is a most intricate web of interrelations, each thread definable and either known or amenable to further experimental or conceptual resolution. It seems fitting, therefore, to conclude our discussion with a pictorial representation of this web, constructed according to the analytical results detailed in the text (Fig. 144). The single- and double-headed arrows express causal relations and interrelations, respectively. Most of these can be found documented in our discussion. This diagram, however crude and incomplete, is still the most pertinent summary of neurogenesis that there could be; as such it gives a fair portrayal in miniature of the developmental process in general.

REFERENCES

Abercrombie, M., Johnson, M. L., and Thomas, G. A. 1949 The influence of nerve fibers on Schwann cell migration investigated in tissue culture. Proc. Roy. Soc., B, *136*:448–460.

Aitken, J. T., Sharman, M., and Young, J. Z. 1947 Maturation of regenerating nerve fibers with various peripheral connections. J. Anat., *81*:1–22.

Anderson, J. D. 1951 Galvanotaxis of slime mold. J. Gen. Physiol., *35*:1–16.

Andres, G. 1945 Über die Entwicklung des Anurenlabyrinths in Urodelen (Xenoplastischer Austausch zwischen Bombinator und *Triton alpestris*). Rev. suisse Zool., *52*:400–406.

Anokhin, P. 1935 Reports on the Problem of Center and Periphery in the Physiology of Nervous Activity. State Publishing House, Gorky.

Barron, D. H. 1943 The early development of the motor cells and columns in the spinal cord of the sheep. J. Comp. Neur., *78*:1–27.

———— 1945 The role of the sensory fibers in the differentiation of the spinal cord in sheep. J. Exp. Zool., *100*:431–443.

———— 1946 Observations on the early differentiation of the motor neuroblasts in the spinal cord of the chick. J. Comp. Neur., *85*:149–169.

———— 1950 Genetic neurology and the behavior problem; in Genetic Neurology, edited by P. Weiss, pp. 223–231. University of Chicago Press, Chicago.

Baumann, L., and Landauer, W. 1943 Polydactyly and anterior horn cells in fowl. J. Comp. Neur., *79*:153–163.

Beach, F. A. 1947 Hormones and mating behavior in vertebrates. Recent Prog. Hormone Res. (Proc. Laurentian Conf.), *1*:27–63.

Bergquist, H., and Källén, B. 1953a On the development of neuromeres to migration areas in the vertebrate cerebral tube. Acta Anat., *18*:65–73.

———— 1953b Studies on the topography of the migration areas in the vertebrate brain. Acta Anat., *17*:353–369.

———— 1954 Notes on the early histogenesis and morphogenesis of the central nervous system in vertebrates. J. Embryol. Exp. Morph., *2*: in press.

Billig, H. E., Harreveld, A. van, and Wiersma, C. A. G. 1946 On re-innervation of paretic muscles by the use of their residual nerve supply. J. Neuropath. & Exp. Neur., *5*:1–23.

Bodian, D. 1942 Cytological aspects of synaptic function. Physiol. Rev., *22*:146–169.

———— 1947 Nucleic acid in nerve-cell regeneration. Symp. Soc. Exp. Biol., *1*:163–178.

Boeke, J. 1917 Studien zur Nervenregeneration II. Die Regeneration nach Vereinigung ungleichartiger Nervenstücke (heterogene Regeneration), und die Funktion der Augenmuskelund Zungennerven. Die allgemeinen Gesetze der Nervenregeneration. Verh. Akad. Wet., Amst., *19*:1–71.

———— 1935 Nervenregeneration; in Bumke-Foerster, Handbuch der Neurologie, vol. 1, pp. 996–1122. Springer, Berlin.

Boell, E. J., and Shen, S. C. 1950 Development of cholinesterase in the central nervous system of *Amblystoma punctatum*. J. Exp. Zool., *113*:583–600.

————, and Shen, S. C. 1951 Appearance and development of cholinesterase in the amphibian midbrain. Science, *114*:477.

Bonnevie, K. 1934 Embryological analysis of gene manifestation in Little and Bagg's abnormal mouse tribe. J. Exp. Zool., *67*:443–520.

Braus, H. 1911 Die Entstehung der Nervenbahnen. Vhdlg. Ges. deutsch. Natf. u. Ärzte, *83*:114–148.

Bremer, F. 1953 Some Problems in Neurophysiology. Athlone Press, London.

Brown, M. G., Hamburger, V., and Schmitt, F. O. 1941 Density studies on amphibian embryos with special reference to the mechanism of organizer action. J. Exp. Zool., *88:*353–372.

Bueker, E. D. 1943 Intracentral and peripheral factors in the differentiation of motor neurons in transplanted lumbo-sacral spinal cords of chick embryos. J. Exp. Zool., *93:*99–129.

——— 1945 Hyperplastic changes in the nervous system of a frog (Rana) as associated with multiple functional limbs. Anat. Rec., *93:*323–331.

——— 1948 Implantation of tumors in the hind limb field of the embryonic chick and the developmental response of the lumbo-sacral nervous system. Anat. Rec., *102:*369–390.

Burr, H. S. 1932 An electro-dynamic theory of development suggested by studies of proliferation rates in the brain of Amblystoma. J. Comp. Neur., *56:*347–371.

Burt, A. S. 1943a Growth of spinal ganglia in plasma from vitamin B$_1$ deficient chickens. J. Cell. & Comp. Physiol., *22:*205–222.

——— 1943b Neurulation in mechanically and chemically inhibited Amblystoma. Biol. Bull., *85:*103–115.

Cajal, S. Ramon y 1928 Degeneration and Regeneration of the Nervous System, translated and edited by Raoul M. May. Oxford University Press, Humphrey Milford, London.

Carmichael, L. 1926 The development of behavior in vertebrates experimentally removed from the influence of external stimulation. Psychol. Rev., *33:*51–58.

——— 1933 Original and prenatal growth of behavior; in A Handbook of Child Psychology, 2d ed., edited by C. A. Murchison, pp. 31–159. Clark University Press, Worcester, Massachusetts.

Carpenter, R. L. 1932 Spinal-ganglion responses to the transplantation of differentiated limbs in Amblystoma larvae. J. Exp. Zool., *61:*149–173.

——— 1933 Spinal-ganglion responses to the transplantation of limbs after metamorphosis in *Amblystoma punctatum.* J. Exp. Zool., *64:*287–301.

Caspersson, T. O. 1950 Cell Growth and Cell Function. Norton and Company, New York.

Cavanaugh, M. W. 1951 Quantitative effects of the peripheral innervation area on nerves and spinal ganglion cells. J. Comp. Neur., *94:*181–220.

Chase, H. B. 1945 Studies on an anophthalmic strain of mice. V. Associated cranial nerves and brain centers. J. Comp. Neur., *83:*121–139.

Chiakulas, J. J. 1952 The role of tissue specificity in the healing of epithelial wounds. J. Exp. Zool., *121:*383–417.

Clark, W. E. Le G. 1945 Deformation patterns in the cerebral cortex; in Essays on Growth and Form, edited by W. E. Le Gros Clark and P. B. Medawar, pp. 1–22. Clarendon Press, Oxford, England.

Coghill, G. E. 1924 Correlated anatomical and physiological studies of the growth of the nervous system of Amphibia. IV. Rates of proliferation and differentiation in the central nervous system of Amblystoma. J. Comp. Neur., *37:*71–120.

——— 1929 Anatomy and the Problem of Behavior. Cambridge University Press, Cambridge, England.

——— 1933 Correlated anatomical and physiological studies of the growth of the nervous system of Amphibia. XI. The proliferation of cells in the spinal cord as a factor in the individuation of reflexes of the hind leg of *Amblystoma punctatum,* Cope. J. Comp. Neur., *57:*327–345.

——— 1936 Correlated anatomical and physiological studies of the growth of the nervous system of Amphibia. XII. Quantitative relations of the spinal cord and ganglia correlated with the development of reflexes of the leg in *Amblystoma punctatum,* Cope. J. Comp. Neur., *64:*135–167.

Dalcq, A. 1947 Recent experimental contributions to brain morphogenesis in amphibians. 6th Growth Symp., pp. 85–119.

Dale, H. 1935 Pharmacology and nerve endings. Proc. Roy. Soc. Med., *28:*15–28.

Davenport, H. A., Chor, H., and Dolkart, R. E. 1937 The ratio of myelinated to unmyelinated fibers in regenerated sciatic nerves of *Macacus rhesus.* J. Comp. Neur., *67:*483–491.

Davis, J. O. 1944 Photochemical spectral analysis of neural tube formation. Biol. Bull., *87:*73–95.

Detwiler, S. R. 1920 On the hyperplasia of nerve centers resulting from excessive peripheral loading. Proc. Nat. Acad. Sci. (USA), *6:*96–101.

——— 1922 Experiments on the transplantation of limbs in Amblystoma. Further observations on peripheral nerve connections. J. Exp. Zool., *35:*115–161.

——— 1923 Experiments on the transplantation of the spinal cord in Amblystoma, and their bearing upon the stimuli involved in the differentiation of nerve cells. J. Exp. Zool., *37:*339–393.

——— 1924a Further observations on proliferation of nerve cells in grafted units of spinal cord. Anat. Rec. *27:*87–94.

——— 1924b Experiments on the transplantation of limbs in Amblystoma. The innervation and function of limbs transplanted after the outgrowth of peripheral nerves. Am. J. Anat., *33:*407–419.

——— 1924c The effects of bilateral extirpation of the anterior limb rudiments in Amblystoma embryos. J. Comp. Neur., *37:*1–14.

——— 1925a An experimental study of cellular proliferation in the anterior portion of the spinal cord of Amblystoma. J. Exp. Zool., 42:333.

——— 1925b Coordinated movements in supernumerary transplanted limbs. J. Comp. Neur., *38:*461–493.

——— 1925c The results of substituting an extraneous medulla for the cephalic end of the embryonic spinal cord in Amblystoma. J. Exp. Zool., *41:*293–347.

——— 1927 The effects of extensive muscle loss upon the development of spinal ganglia in Amblystoma. J. Exp. Zool., *48:*1–26.

——— 1928 Experiments on the reversal of the anterior end of the spinal cord in Amblystoma embryos. J. Comp. Neur., *45:*191–209.

——— 1930a Some observations upon the

growth, innervation and function of heteroplastic limbs. J. Exp. Zool., 57:183–203.

Detwiler, S. R. 1930b Observations upon the growth, function, and nerve supply of limbs when grafted to the head of salamander embryos. J. Exp. Zool., 55:319–379.

—— 1931 Heteroplastic transplantations of embryonic spinal-cord segments in Amblystoma. J. Exp. Zool., 60:141–171.

—— 1933 Further experiments upon the extirpation of Mauthner's neurones in amphibian embryos (Amblystoma mexicanum). J. Exp. Zool., 64:415–431.

—— 1934 An experimental study of spinal nerve segmentation in Amblystoma with reference to the plurisegmental contribution to the brachial plexus. J. Exp. Zool., 67:395–441.

—— 1935 The development of spinal ganglia following transplantation of the spinal cord with or without somites. Anat. Rec., 61:441–455.

—— 1936a Growth responses of spinal nerves to grafted brain tissue. J. Exp. Zool., 74:477–495.

—— 1936b Neuroembryology: An Experimental Study. The Macmillan Co., New York.

—— 1937a Substitution of lateral for axial mesoderm in relation to the development and segmentation of spinal ganglia. J. Exp. Zool., 76: 36–45.

—— 1937b Observations upon the migration of neural crest cells, and upon the development of the spinal ganglia and vertebral arches in Amblystoma. Am. J. Anat., 61:63–94.

—— 1937c Does the developing medulla influence cellular proliferation within the spinal cord? J. Exp. Zool., 77:109–122.

—— 1942 Thirteen years of homologous function in normal and supernumerary grafted limbs. Proc. Soc. Exp. Biol. & Med., 51:176–177.

—— 1943a Unilateral substitution of the brachial region of the spinal cord by the corresponding half of the medulla in Amblystoma. J. Exp. Zool., 92:247–261.

—— 1943b Reversal of the medulla in Amblystoma embryos. J. Exp. Zool., 94:169–179.

—— 1944 Restitution of the medulla following unilateral excision in the embryo. J. Exp. Zool,. 96:129–142.

—— 1945 The results of unilateral and bilateral extirpation of the forebrain of Amblystoma. J. Exp. Zool., 100:103–117.

—— 1946a Experiments upon the midbrain of Amblystoma embryos. Am. J. Anat., 78:115–138.

—— 1946b Midbrain regeneration in Amblystoma. Anat. Rec., 94:229–238.

—— 1947a Further observations on the function and posture of limbs following removal of the trunk neural crest in Amblystoma. J. Exp. Zool., 106:299–312.

—— 1947b Restitution of the brachial region of the cord following unilateral excision in the embryo. J. Exp. Zool., 104:53–68.

—— 1948 Further quantitative studies on locomotor capacity of larval Amblystoma following surgical procedures upon the embryonic brain. J. Exp. Zool., 108:45–74.

—— 1951 Structural and functional adjustments following reversal of the embryonic medulla in Amblystoma. J. Exp. Zool., 116:431–446.

—— 1952 Further observations on motor responses of Amblystoma larvae following transplantation of primary brain segments. J. Exp. Zool., 119:189–204.

——, and Carpenter, R. L. 1929 An experimental study of the mechanism of coordinated movements in heterotopic limbs. J. Comp. Neur., 47:427–447.

——, and Lewis, R. W. 1925 Size changes in primary brachial motor neurons following limb excision in Amblystoma embryos. J. Comp. Neur., 39:291.

——, and Maclean, B. 1940 Substitution of limbs for brachial somites. J. Exp. Zool., 83:445–456.

——, and McKennon, G. E. 1930 Further studies upon the nerve supply and function of supernumerary grafted limbs. Biol. Bull., 59:353–363.

——, and Van Dyke, R. H. 1934 Further observations upon abnormal growth responses of spinal nerves in Amblystoma embryos. J. Exp. Zool., 69:137–164.

Dogliotti, A. M. 1935 Etudes expérimentales et première application clinique d'une nouvelle opération destinée à augmenter et à équilibrer la fonction neuromusculaire dans la paralysie partielle des nerfs. J. Chir. (Paris), 45:30–48.

Dürken, B. 1913 Über einseitige Augenexstirpation bei jungen Froschlarven. Zeitschr. wiss. Zool., 105:192.

Duncan, Donald, and Jarvis, W. H. 1943 Observations on repeated regeneration of the facial nerve in cats. J. Comp. Neur., 79:315–327.

Dustin, A. P. 1910 Le rôle des tropismes et de l'odogénèse dans la régénération du système nerveux. Arch. Biol., 25:269–388.

—— 1917 Les lésions posttraumatiques des nerfs. Contribution à l'histopathologie du système nerveux periphérique chez l'homme. Ambulance de "L'Ocean," Paris, 1:71–161.

Ebert, J. D. 1950 An analysis of the effects of anti-organ sera on the development, in vitro, of the early chick blastoderm. J. Exp. Zool., 115:351–378.

Edds, M. V., Jr. 1949 Experiments on partially deneurotized nerves. II. Hypertrophy of residual fibers. J. Exp. Zool., 112:29–47.

—— 1951 Atrophy of motor root fibers following destruction of sensory roots in the rat. Anat. Rec., 109:369–370.

—— 1953 Collateral nerve regeneration. Quart. Rev. Biol., 28:260–276.

Edinger, L. 1921 Einführung in die Lehre vom Bau und den Verrichtungen des Nervensystems, 3d ed., revised by Goldstein and Wallenberg. Vogel, Leipzig.

Elsberg, C. A. 1917 Experiments on motor nerve regeneration and the direct neurotization of paralyzed muscles by their own and by foreign nerves. Science, 45:318–320.

Erlanger, J., and Gasser, H. S. 1937 Electrical signs of nervous activity. Johnson Foundation

Lectures, University of Pennsylvania Press, Philadelphia.

Fankhauser, G. 1952 Nucleo-cytoplasmic relations in amphibian development. Internat. Rev. Cytology, *1*:165–193.

Feeney, J. F., and Watterson, R. L. 1946 The development of the vascular pattern within the walls of the central nervous system of the chick embryo. J. Morph., *78*:231–304.

Fernández-Morán, H. 1952 The submicroscopic organization of vertebrate nerve fibers. Exp. Cell Res., *3*:282–359.

Ferreira-Berutti, P. 1951 Experimental deflection of the course of the optic nerve in the chick embryo. Proc. Soc. Exp. Biol. & Med., *76*:302–303.

Flexner, L. B. 1950 The cytological, biochemical, and physiological differentiation of the neuroblast; in Genetic Neurology, edited by P. Weiss, pp. 194–198. University of Chicago Press, Chicago.

Forssman, J. 1900 Zur Kenntnis des Neurotropismus. Weitere Beiträge. Beitr. path. Anat., *27*:407–430.

Fort, W. B. 1940 An experimental study of the factors involved in the establishment of neuromuscular connections. Dissertation, University of Chicago.

Fowler, I. 1953 Responses of the chick neural tube in mechanically produced spina bifida. J. Exp. Zool., *123*:115–152.

Geren, B. B., and Raskind, J. 1953 Development of the fine structure of the myelin sheath in sciatic nerves of chick embryos. Proc. Nat. Acad. Sci. (USA), *39*:880–884.

Giersberg, H. 1924 Beiträge zur Entwicklungsphysiologie der Amphibien. II. Neurulation bei Rana und Triton. Roux' Arch. Entw.-mech., *103*:387–424.

Gillette, R. 1944 Cell number and cell size in the ectoderm during neurulation (*Amblystoma maculatum*). J. Exp. Zool., *96*:201–222.

Glaser, O. C. 1914 On the mechanism of the morphological differentiation in the nervous system. Anat. Rec., *8*:525–551.

―――― 1916 The theory of autonomous folding in embryogenesis. Science, *44*:505–509.

Globus, J. H., and Kuhlenbeck, H. 1944 The subependymal cell plate (matrix) and its relationship to brain tumors of the ependymal type. J. Neuropath. & Exp. Neur., *3*:1–35.

Glücksmann, A. 1951 Cell deaths in normal vertebrate ontogeny. Biol. Rev., *26*:59–86.

Grossfeld, H. 1934 Zellstreckung und Kohäsionskräfte im gallertigen Wachstumsmedium. Roux' Arch. Entw.-mech., *131*:324–332.

Gutmann, E. 1945 The reinnervation of muscle by sensory nerve fibres. J. Anat., *79*:1–8.

Gutmann, E., Guttmann, L., Medawar, P. B., and Young, J. Z. 1942 The rate of regeneration of nerve. J. Exp. Biol., *19*:14–44.

Guyénot, E. 1927 La perte du pouvoir régénérateur des Anoures, étudiée par la méthode des hétérogreffes. Rev. suisse Zool., *34*:1–53.

Hamberger, C.-A., and Hydén, H. 1945 Cytochemical changes in the cochlear ganglion caused by acoustic stimulation and trauma. Acta Oto-laryngol., *61* (suppl.):5–89.

―――― 1949 Production of nucleoproteins in the vestibular ganglion. Acta Oto-laryngol., *75*:53–81.

Hamburger, V. 1929 Experimentelle Beiträge zur Entwicklungsphysiologie der Nervenbahnen in der Froschextremität. Roux' Arch. Entw.-mech., *119*:47–99.

―――― 1934 The effects of wing bud extirpation on the development of the central nervous system in chick embryos. J. Exp. Zool., *68*:449–494.

―――― 1939a The development and innervation of transplanted limb primordia of chick embryos. J. Exp. Zool., *80*:347–389.

―――― 1939b Motor and sensory hyperplasia following limb-bud transplantations in chick embryos. Physiol. Zool., *12*:268–284.

―――― 1946 Isolation of the brachial segments of the spinal cord of the chick embryo by means of tantalum foil blocks. J. Exp. Zool., *103*:113–142.

―――― 1948 The mitotic patterns in the spinal cord of the chick embryo and their relation to histogenetic processes. J. Comp. Neur., *88*:221–284.

――――, and Keefe, E. L. 1944 The effects of peripheral factors on the proliferation and differentiation in the spinal cord of chick embryos. J. Exp. Zool., *96*:223–242.

――――, and Levi-Montalcini, R. 1949 Proliferation, differentiation and degeneration in the spinal ganglia of the chick embryo under normal and experimental conditions. J. Exp. Zool., *111*:457–502.

――――, and Levi-Montalcini, R. 1950 Some aspects of neuroembryology; in Genetic Neurology, edited by P. Weiss, pp. 128–160. University of Chicago Press, Chicago.

Hammond, W. S., and Hinsey, J. C. 1945 The diameters of nerve fibers in normal and regenerating nerves. J. Comp. Neur., *83*:79–92.

Harrison, R. G. 1903 Experimentelle Untersuchungen über die Entwicklung der Sinnesorgane der Seitenlinie bei den Amphibien. Arch. f. mikr. Anat. u. Entw.-gesch., *63*:35–149.

―――― 1907a Observations on the living developing nerve fiber. Anat. Rec., *1*:116–118.

―――― 1907b Experiments in transplanting limbs and their bearing upon the problems of the development of nerves. J. Exp. Zool., *4*:239–281.

―――― 1910 The outgrowth of the nerve fiber as a mode of protoplasmic movement. J. Exp. Zool., *9*:787–848.

―――― 1914 The reaction of embryonic cells to solid structures. J. Exp. Zool., *17*:521–544.

―――― 1929 Correlation in the development and growth of the eye studied by means of heteroplastic transplantation. Roux' Arch. Entw.-mech., *120*:1–55.

―――― 1935a Heteroplastic grafting in embryology. Harvey Lectures, 1933–34, p. 116–157.

―――― 1935b The Croonian lecture on the origin and development of the nervous system studied by the methods of experimental embryology. Proc. Roy. Soc., London, B, *118*:155–196.

Harrison, R. G. 1947 Wound healing and reconstitution of the central nervous system of the amphibian embryo after removal of parts of the neural plate. J. Exp. Zool., 106:27–84.

Held, Hans 1909 Die Entwicklung des Nervengewebes bei den Wirbeltieren. J. A. Barth, Leipzig.

Henke, K. 1953 Über Zelldifferenzierung im Integument der Insekten und ihre Bedingungen. J. Embryol. exp. Morph., 1:217–226.

Herrick, C. J. 1948 The Brain of the Tiger Salamander. University of Chicago Press, Chicago.

Hertwig, G. 1926 Die Funktions- und Regenerationsfähigkeit artgleicher und artfremder Extremitätentransplantate. Sitzber. u. Abh. naturf. Ges. Rostock, series III, 1:62–65.

Hicks, S. P. 1952 Some effects of ionizing radiation and metabolic inhibition on the developing mammalian nervous system. J. Pediat., 40:489–513.

———— 1953 Developmental malformations produced by radiation. Am. J. Roentgenol., Radium Therapy & Nuclear Med., 69:272–293.

His, W. 1887 Die Entwicklung der ersten Nervenbahnen beim menschlichen Embryo. Uebersichtliche Darstellung. Arch. Anat. Physiol. (Anat. Abt.), Jg. 1887:368–378.

Hiscoe, H. B. 1947 Distribution of nodes and incisures in normal and regenerated nerve fibers. Anat. Rec., 99:447–476.

Hoadley, L. 1925 The differentiation of isolated chick primordia in chorio-allantoic grafts. III. On the specificity of nerve processes arising from the mesencephalon in grafts. J. Exp. Zool., 42:163–182.

Hoagland, H. 1947 Enzyme kinetics and the dynamics of behavior. J. Comp. & Physiol. Psych., 40:107–127.

Hobson, L. B. 1941 On the ultrastructure of the neural plate and tube of the early chick embryo, with notes on the effects of dehydration. J. Exp. Zool., 88:107–134.

Hörstadius, S. 1944 Über die Folgen von Chordaexstirpation an späten Gastrulae und Neurulae von Amblystoma punctatum. Acta Zool., 25:75–87.

———— 1950 The Neural Crest. Oxford University Press, Oxford, England.

Hoffman, H. 1950 Local re-innervation in partially denervated muscle: A histophysiological study. Australian J. Exp. Biol. & Med. Sci., 28:383–397.

———— 1951 Fate of interrupted nerve-fibres regenerating into partially denervated muscles. Australian J. Exp. Biol. & Med. Sci., 29:211–219.

———— 1952 Acceleration and retardation of the process of axon-sprouting in partially denervated muscles. Australian J. Exp. Biol. & Med. Sci., 30:541–566.

Holmes, W., and Young, J. Z. 1942 Nerve regeneration after immediate and delayed suture. J. Anat., 77:63–96.

Holtfreter, J. 1934 Formative Reize in der Embryonalentwicklung der Amphibien dargestellt an Explantationsversuchen. Arch. exp. Zellforsch, 15:281–301.

———— 1939 Gewebeaffinität, ein Mittel der embryonalen Formbildung. Arch. exp. Zellforsch., 23:169–209.

———— 1943 Properties and functions of the surface coat in amphibian embryos. J. Exp. Zool., 93:251–323.

———— 1944 Experimental studies on the development of the pronephros. Rev. Can. de Biol., 3:220–250.

———— 1946 Structure, motility and locomotion in isolated embryonic amphibian cells. J. Morph., 79:27–62.

Holtzer, H. 1950 Differentiation of the regional action systems in the urodele spinal cord. Anat. Rec., 108:127–128.

———— 1951 Reconstitution of the urodele spinal cord following unilateral ablation. I. Chronology of neuron regulation. J. Exp. Zool., 117:523–558.

———— 1952a An experimental analysis of the development of the spinal column. I. Response of pre-cartilage cells to size variation of the spinal cord. J. Exp. Zool., 121:121–148.

———— 1952b Reconstitution of the urodele spinal cord following unilateral ablation. II. Regeneration of the longitudinal tracts and ectopic synaptic unions of the Mauthner's fiber. J. Exp. Zool., 119:263–302.

Hooker, D. 1925 Studies on regeneration in the spinal cord. III. Reestablishment of anatomical and physiological continuity after transection in frog tadpoles. J. Comp. Neur., 38:315–347.

———— 1930 Studies on regeneration in the spinal cord. IV. Rotation about its longitudinal axis of a portion of the cord in Amblystoma punctatum embryos. J. Exp. Zool., 55:23–38.

———— 1952 The Prenatal Origin of Behavior. University of Kansas Press, Lawrence, Kansas.

Hursh, J. B. 1939 The properties of growing nerve fibers. Am. J. Physiol., 127:140–153.

Hutchinson, C. 1944 Cell number-volume relationship in the medullary plate of Amblystoma punctatum. Anat. Rec., 88:439.

Hydén, H. 1950 Spectroscopic studies on nerve cells in development, growth, and function; in Genetic Neurology, edited by P. Weiss, pp. 177–193. University of Chicago Press, Chicago.

Julius, H. W. 1930 Nervenreaktionen in der Mäusehaut bei Teerpinselungen und anderen chronischen Schädigungen. Virchows Arch. f. path. Anat., 278:518–528.

Källén, B. 1951 On the ontogeny of the reptilian forebrain. Nuclear structures and ventricular sulci. J. Comp. Neur., 95:307–348.

Kappers, C. U. A. 1917 Further contributions on neurobiotaxis. IX. An attempt to compare the phenomena of neurobiotaxis with other phenomena of taxis and tropism. J. Comp. Neur., 27:261–298.

Kitchin, I. C. 1949 The effects of notochordectomy in Amblystoma mexicanum. J. Exp. Zool., 112:393–416.

Kölliker, A. 1896 Handbuch der Gewebelehre des Menschen. II. Nervensystem. Engelmann, Leipzig.

Kollros, J. J. 1942 Experimental studies on the development of the corneal reflex in Amphibia.

I. The onset of the reflex and its relationship to metamorphosis. J. Exp. Zool., 89:37–67.

Kollros, J. J. 1943a Experimental studies on the development of the corneal reflex in Amphibia. II. Localized maturation of the reflex mechanism effected by thyroxin-agar implants into the hindbrain. Physiol. Zool., 16:269–279.

——— 1943b Experimental studies on the development of the corneal reflex in Amphibia. III. The influence of the periphery upon the reflex center. J. Exp. Zool., 92:121–142.

——— 1953 The development of the optic lobes in the frog. I. The effects of unilateral enucleation in embryonic stages. J. Exp. Zool., 123:153–188.

———, Pepernik, V., Hill, R., and Kaltenbach, J. C. 1950 The growth of mesencephalic V nucleus cells as a metamorphic event in anurans. Anat. Rec., 108:565.

Kopeć, S. 1922 Mutual relationship in the development of the brain and eyes of Lepidoptera. J. Exp. Zool., 36:459–467.

Langley, J. N., and Anderson, H. K. 1904 The union of different kinds of nerve fibers. J. Physiol., 31:365–391.

Larsell, O. 1931 The effect of experimental excision of one eye on the development of the optic lobe and opticus layer in larvae of the tree-toad (Hyla regilla). J. Exp. Zool., 58:1–20.

Lashley, K. S. 1942 The problem of cerebral organization in vision. Biol. Symposia, 7:301–322.

Lehman, H. E., and Youngs, L. M. 1952 An analysis of regulation in the amphibian neural crest. J. Exp. Zool., 121:419–447.

Lehmann, F. E. 1927 Further studies on the morphogenetic role of the somites in the development of the nervous system of amphibians. The differentiation and arrangement of the spinal ganglia in Pleurodeles waltli. J. Exp. Zool., 49:93–129.

——— 1935 Die Entwicklung von Rückenmark, Spinalganglien und Wirbelanlagen in chordalosen Körperregionen von Tritonlarven. Rev. suisse Zool., 42:405–415.

Leuchtenberger, C., and Schrader, F. 1952 Variation in the amounts of desoxyribose nucleic acid (DNA) in cells of the same tissue and its correlation with secretory function. Proc. Nat. Acad. Sci. (USA), 38:99–105.

Levi, G. 1934 Explantation, besonders die Struktur und die biologischen Eigenschaften der in vitro gezüchteten Zellen und Gewebe. Ergebn. Anat. Entw. Gesch., 31:125–707.

Levi-Montalcini, R. 1945 Corrélations dans le développement des différentes parties du système nerveux. II. Corrélations entre le développement de l'encephale et celui de la moelle épinière dans l'embryon de poulet. Arch. Biol., 56:71–81.

——— 1949 The development of the acoustico-vestibular centers in the chick embryo in the absence of the afferent root fibers and of descending fiber tracts. J. Comp. Neur., 91:209–242.

——— 1950 The origin and development of the visceral system in the spinal cord of the chick embryo. J. Morph., 86:253–284.

——— 1952 Effect of mouse tumor transplanta-tion on the nervous system. Ann. N. Y. Acad. Sci., 55:330–343.

———, and Hamburger, V. 1951 Selective growth stimulating effects of mouse sarcoma on the sensory and sympathetic nervous system of the chick embryo. J. Exp. Zool., 116:321–362.

———, and Hamburger, V. 1953 A diffusible agent of mouse sarcoma, producing hyperplasia of sympathetic ganglia and hyperneurotization of viscera in the chick embryo. J. Exp. Zool., 123:233–288.

———, and Levi, G. 1943 Recherches quantitatives sur la marche du processus de différenciation des neurones dans les ganglions spinaux de l'embryon de poulet. Arch. Biol., 54:198–206.

———, Meyer, H., and Hamburger, V. 1954 In vitro experiments on the effects of mouse sarcomas 180 and 37 on the spinal and sympathetic ganglia of the chick embryo. Cancer Res., 14:49–57.

Lewis, W. H. 1947 Mechanics of invagination. Anat. Rec., 97:139–156.

——— 1950 Motion picture of neurons and neuroglia in tissue culture; in Genetic Neurology, edited by P. Weiss, pp. 53–65. University of Chicago Press, Chicago.

———, and Lewis, M. R. 1912 The cultivation of sympathetic nerves from the intestine of chick embryos in saline solutions. Anat. Rec. 6:7–31.

Little, C. C., and Bagg, H. J. 1924 The occurrence of four inheritable morphological variations in mice and their possible relations to treatment with x-rays. J. Exp. Zool., 41:45–91.

Litwiller, R. 1938a Quantitative studies on nerve regeneration in Amphibia. I. Factors controlling nerve regeneration in adult limbs. J. Comp. Neur., 69:427–447.

——— 1938b Quantitative studies on nerve regeneration in Amphibia. II. Factors controlling nerve regeneration in regenerating limbs. J. Exp. Zool., 79:377–397.

Livingston, W. K. 1943 Pain Mechanisms. The Macmillan Co., New York.

Lovell, H. B. 1931 Innervation and function of grafted hind limbs in Amblystoma punctatum. Proc. Soc. Exp. Biol. & Med., 29:180–182.

Maclean, B. L. 1932 Growth responses in caudally grafted brachial segments of the embryonic spinal cord of Amblystoma. J. Exp. Zool., 64:71–108.

Marsh, G., and Beams, H. W. 1946 In vitro control of growing chick nerve fibers by applied electric currents. J. Cell. & Comp. Physiol., 27:139–157.

Matthews, S. A., and Detwiler, S. R. 1926 The reactions of Amblystoma embryos following prolonged treatment with Chloretone. J. Exp. Zool., 45:279–292.

May, R. M. 1933 Réactions neurogéniques de la moelle à la greffe en surnombre, ou à l'ablation d'une ébauche de patte postérieure chez l'embryon de l'anoure, Discoglossus pictus, Otth. Biol. Bull., 67:327–349.

———, and Detwiler, S. R. 1925 The relation of transplanted eyes to developing nerve centers. J. Exp. Zool., 43:83–103.

Miner, N. 1951 Cutaneous localization following 180° rotation of skin grafts. Anat. Rec., *109:* 326–327.

Moog, F. 1943 The distribution of phosphatase in the spinal cord of chick embryos of one to eight days incubation. Proc. Nat. Acad. Sci. (USA), *29:* 176–183.

Moyer, E. K. 1943 The innervation of supernumerary limbs by heterotopically grafted brachial cords in *A.punctatum.* J. Exp. Zool., *94:* 97–114.

Muralt, A. v. 1946 Die Signalübermittlung im Nerven. Birkhäuser, Basel.

Nageotte, J. 1922 L'Organisation de la Matière dans ses Rapports avec la Vie. Felix Alcan, Paris.

Nicholas, J. S. 1929 An analysis of the responses of isolated portions of the amphibian nervous system. Roux' Arch. Entw-mech., *118:* 78–120.

——— 1933 The correlation of movement and nerve supply in transplanted limbs of Amblystoma. J. Comp. Neur., *57:*252–283.

Nieuwkoop, P. D. 1952 Activation and organization of the central nervous system in amphibians. J. Exp. Zool., *120:*1–108.

Niu, M. C. 1947 The axial organization of the neural crest, studied with particular reference to its pigmentary component. J. Exp. Zool., *105:*79–114.

Oppenheimer, J. M. 1941 The anatomical relationships of abnormally located Mauthner's cells in Fundulus embryos. J. Comp. Neur., *74:* 131–167.

Ortmann, R. 1951 Über experimentelle Veränderungen der Morphologie des Hypophysenzwischenhirnsystems und die Beziehung der sog. "Gomorisubstanz" zum Adiuretin. Z. Zellforsch., *36:*92–140.

Pasquini, P. 1927 Ricerche di embriologia sperimentale sui trapianti omeoplastici della vesicola ottica primaria in *Pleurodeles waltli.* Boll. dell'-Ist. Zool., Roma, *5:*1–83.

Peterfi, T., and Kapel, O. 1928 Die Wirkung des Anstechens auf das Protoplasma der in vitro gezüchteten Gewebezellen. III. Anstichversuche an den Nervenzellen. Arch. exp. Zellforsch., *5:*341–348.

Piatt, J. 1941 Grafting of limbs in place of the eye in Amblystoma. J. Exp. Zool., *86:*77–85.

——— 1942 Transplantation of aneurogenic forelimbs in *Amblystoma punctatum.* J. Exp. Zool., *91:*79–101.

——— 1944 Experiments on the decussation and course of Mauthner's fibers in *Amblystoma punctatum.* J. Comp. Neur., *80:*335–353.

——— 1952 Transplantation of aneurogenic forelimbs in place of the hindlimb in Amblystoma. J. Exp. Zool., *120:*247–285.

Pomerat, C. M. 1951 Pulsatile activity of cells from the human brain in tissue culture. J. Nerv. & Ment. Dis., *114:*430–440.

Power, M. E. 1943 The effect of reduction in numbers of ommatidia upon the brain of *Drosophila melanogaster.* J. Exp. Zool., *94:*33–71.

Ranzi, S. 1928 Correlazioni tra organi di senso

e centri nervosi in via di sviluppo. Roux' Arch. Entw.-mech., *114:*364–370.

Roach, F. C. 1945 Differentiation of the central nervous system after axial reversal of the medullary plate of Amblystoma. J. Exp. Zool., *99:*53–75.

Rogers, W. M. 1934 Heterotopic spinal cord grafts in salamander embryos. Proc. Nat. Acad. Sci. (USA), *20:*247–249.

Roux, W. 1895 Beiträge zur Entwicklungsmechanik des Embryo. I; in Roux' gesammelte Abhandlungen über Entwicklungsmechanik der Organismen, vol. 2, pp. 143–255. Engelmann, Leipzig.

Ruud, G. 1929 Heteronom-orthotopische Transplantationen von Extremitätenanlagen bei Axolotlembryonen. Roux' Arch. Entw-mech., *118:* 30`-351.

Sanders, F. K., and Young, J. Z. 1944 The role of the peripheral stump in the control of fibre diameter in regenerating nerves. J. Physiol., *103:* 119–136.

——— and Young, J. Z. 1946 The influence of peripheral connexion on the diameter of regenerating nerve fibers. J. Exp. Biol., *22:*203–212.

Sauer, F. C. 1935 The cellular structure of the neural tube. J. Comp. Neur., *63:*13–23.

Sawyer, C. H. 1943 Cholinesterase and the behavior problem in Amblystoma. J. Exp. Zool., *94:* 1–31.

Schwind, J. L. 1931 Heteroplastic experiments on the limb and shoulder girdle of Amblystoma. J. Exp. Zool., *59:*265–295.

Severinghaus, A. E. 1930 Cellular proliferation in heterotopic spinal cord grafts. J. Comp. Neur., *51:*237.

Shorey, M. L. 1909 The effect of the destruction of peripheral areas on the differentiation of the neuroblasts. J. Exp. Zool., *7:*25–63.

Simpson, S. A., and Young, J. Z. 1945 Regeneration of fibre diameter after cross-unions of visceral and somatic nerves. J. Anat., *79:*48–65.

Speidel, C. C. 1932 Studies of living nerves. I. The movements of individual sheath cells and nerve sprouts correlated with the process of myelin-sheath formation in amphibian larvae. J. Exp. Zool., *61:*279–331.

——— 1933 Studies of living nerves. II. Activities of ameboid growth cones, sheath cells, and myelin segments, as revealed by prolonged observation of individual nerve fibers in frog tadpoles. Am. J. Anat., *52:*1–79.

——— 1935 Studies of living nerves. IV. Growth, regeneration, and myelination of peripheral nerves in salamanders. Biol. Bull., *68:* 140–161.

——— 1942 Studies of living nerves. VII. Growth adjustments of cutaneous terminal arborizations. J. Comp. Neur., *76:*57–73.

——— 1948 Correlated studies of sense organs and nerves of the lateral line in living tadpoles. II. Am. J. Anat., *82:*277–320.

——— 1950 Adjustments of peripheral nerve fibers; in Genetic Neurology, edited by P. Weiss, pp. 66–77. University of Chicago Press, Chicago.

Sperry, R. W. 1941 The effect of crossing nerves

to antagonistic muscles in the hind limb of the rat. J. Comp. Neur., 75:1–19.

Sperry, R. W. 1943 Visuomotor coordination in the newt (*Triturus viridescens*) after regeneration of the optic nerve. J. Comp. Neur., 79:33–55.

——— 1944 Optic nerve regeneration with return of vision in anurans. J. Neurophysiol., 7:57–70.

——— 1945 Centripetal regeneration of the 8th cranial nerve root with systematic restoration of vestibular reflexes. Am. J. Physiol., 144:735–741.

——— 1951 Regulative factors in the orderly growth of neural circuits. Growth Symp., 10:63–87.

Spratt, N. T., Jr. 1952 Metabolism of the early embryo. Ann. N. Y. Acad. Sci., 55:40–49.

Stefanelli, A. 1950 Studies on the development of Mauthner's cell; in Genetic Neurology, edited by P. Weiss, pp. 210–211. University of Chicago Press, Chicago.

Steinitz, E. 1906 Über den Einfluss der Elimination der embryonalen Augenblasen auf die Entwicklung des Gesamtorganismus beim Frosche. Roux' Arch. Entw.-mech., 20:537–578.

Stone, L. S. 1944 Functional polarization in retinal development and its re-establishment in regenerating retinae of rotated grafted eyes. Proc. Soc. Exp. Biol. & Med., 57:13–14.

Stopford, J. S. B. 1930 Sensation and the Sensory Pathway. Longmans, Green & Co., New York.

Sunderland, S., and Lavarack, J. O. 1953 The branching of nerve fibres. Acta Anat., 17:46–61.

Taylor, A. C. 1943 Development of the innervation pattern in the limb bud of the frog. Anat. Rec., 87:379–413.

——— 1944 Selectivity of nerve fibers from the dorsal and ventral roots in the development of the frog limb. J. Exp. Zool., 96:159–185.

Terni, T. 1920 Sulla correlazione fra ampiezza del territorio di innervazione e grandezza delle cellule ganglionari. II. Arch. ital. di Anat. e di Embryol., 17:235–278.

Thomas, P. K., and Young, J. Z. 1949 Internode lengths in the nerves of fishes. J. Anat., 83:336–350.

Tsang, Y. C. 1939 Ventral horn cells and polydactyly in mice. J. Comp. Neur., 70:1–8.

Twitty, V. C. 1932 Influence of the eye on the growth of its associated structures, studied by means of heteroplastic transplantation. J. Exp. Zool., 61:333–374.

——— 1949 Developmental analysis of amphibian pigmentation. Growth (suppl.), 9:133–161.

———, and Schwind, J. L. 1931 The growth of eyes and limbs transplanted heteroplastically between two species of Amblystoma. J. Exp. Zool., 59:61–86.

Verzár, F., and Weiss, P. 1930 Untersuchungen über das Phänomen der identischen Bewegungsfunktion mehrfacher benachbarter Extremitäten. Zugleich: Direkte Vorführung von Eigenreflexen. Pflügers Arch., 223:671–684.

Vizoso, A. D., and Young, J. Z. 1948 Internode length and fibre diameter in developing and regenerating nerves. J. Anat., 82:110–134.

Weddell, G., Guttmann, L., and Gutmann, E. 1941

The local extension of nerve fibers into denervated areas of skin. J. Neurol. Psychiat., 4:206–225.

Weiss, P. 1924 Die Funktion transplantierter Amphibienextremitäten. Aufstellung einer Resonanztheorie der motorischen Nerventätigkeit auf Grund abgestimmter Endorgane. Roux' Arch. Entw.-mech., 102:635–672.

——— 1929 Erzwingung elementarer Strukturverschiedenheiten am in vitro wachsenden Gewebe. Die Wirkung mechanischer Spannung auf Richtung und Intensität des Gewebewachstums und ihre Analyse. Roux' Arch. Entw.-mech., 116:438–554.

——— 1934a In vitro experiments on the factors determining the course of the outgrowing nerve fiber. J. Exp. Zool., 68:393–448.

——— 1934b Secretory activity of the inner layer of the embryonic midbrain of the chick, as revealed by tissue culture. Anat. Rec., 58:299–302.

——— 1935 Homologous (resonance-like) function in supernumerary fingers in a human case. Proc. Soc. Exp. Biol. & Med., 33:426–430.

——— 1936 Selectivity controlling the central-peripheral relations in the nervous system. Biol. Rev., 11:494–531.

——— 1937a Further experimental investigations on the phenomenon of homologous response in transplanted amphibian limbs. II. Nerve regeneration and the innervation of transplanted limbs. J. Comp. Neur., 66:481–535.

——— 1937b Further experimental investigations on the phenomenon of homologous response in transplanted amphibian limbs. IV. Reverse locomotion after the interchange of right and left limbs. J. Comp. Neur., 67:269–315.

——— 1939 Principles of Development. Henry Holt & Co., New York.

——— 1941a Self-differentiation of the basic patterns of coordination. Comp. Psychol. Monographs, 17:1–96.

——— 1941b Further experiments with deplanted and deranged nerve centers in amphibians. Proc. Soc. Exp. Biol. & Med., 46:14–15.

——— 1941c Nerve patterns: The mechanics of nerve growth. Growth (suppl.), 5:163–203.

——— 1942 Lid-closure reflex from eyes transplanted to atypical locations in *Triturus torosus*: Evidence of a peripheral origin of sensory specificity. J. Comp. Neur., 77:131–169.

——— 1944 The technology of nerve regeneration: A review. Sutureless tubulation and related methods of nerve repair. J. Neurosurg., 1:400–450.

——— 1945 Experiments on cell and axon orientation in vitro: The role of colloidal exudates in tissue organization. J. Exp. Zool., 100:353–386.

——— 1947 The problem of specificity in growth and development. Yale J. Biol. & Med., 19:235–278.

——— 1949 Differential growth; in Chemistry and Physiology of Growth, edited by A. K. Parpart, pp. 135–186. Princeton University Press, Princeton, New Jersey.

——— 1950a The deplantation of fragments of nervous system in amphibians. I. Central reorganization and the formation of nerves. J. Exp. Zool., *113:*397–461.

Weiss, P.   1950b   Experimental analysis of co-ordination by the disarrangement of central-peripheral relations. Symposia Soc. Exp. Biol., *4:* 92–111.

———— 1950c   Introduction to genetic neurology; in Genetic Neurology, edited by P. Weiss, pp. 1–39. University of Chicago Press, Chicago.

———— 1952a   Central versus peripheral factors in the development of coordination. Res. Publ. Ass. Nerv. Ment. Dis., *30:*3–23.

———— 1952b   "Attraction fields" between growing tissue cultures. Science, *115:*293–295.

———— 1953   Some introductory remarks on the cellular basis of differentiation. J. Embryol. exp. Morph., *1:*181–211.

————, and Campbell, C. J.   1944   Nerve fiber counts and muscle tension after nerve regeneration in the rat. Am. J. Physiol., *140:*616–626.

————, and Cummings, J. B.   1943   Regeneration of the lateral line nerve of Amblystoma from different nerve fiber sources. Anat. Rec., *87:*119–125.

————, and Edds, Jr.   1945   Sensory-motor nerve crosses in the rat. J. Neurophysiol., *8:*173–193.

————, Edds, M. V., Jr., and Cavanaugh, M. W.   1945   The effect of terminal connections on the caliber of nerve fibers. Anat. Rec., *92:*215–233.

————, and Garber, B.   1952   Shape and movement of mesenchyme cells as functions of the physical structure of the medium. Contributions to a quantitative cell morphology. Proc. Nat. Acad. Sci. (USA) *38:*264–280.

————, and Hiscoe, H. B.   1948   Experiments on the mechanism of nerve growth. J. Exp. Zool., *107:*315–396.

————, and Hoag, A.   1946   Competitive reinnervation of rat muscles by their own and foreign nerves. J. Neurophysiol., *9:*413–418.

————, and Rossetti, F.   1951   Growth responses of opposite sign among different neuron types exposed to thyroid hormone. Proc. Nat. Acad. Sci. (USA) *37:*540–556.

————, and Taylor, A. C.   1943   Histomechanical analysis of nerve reunion in the rat after tubular splicing. Arch. Surg., *47:*419–447.

———— 1944   Further experimental evidence against "neurotropism" in nerve regeneration. J. Exp. Zool., *95:*233–257.

————, and Walker, R.   1934   Nerve pattern in regenerated urodele limbs. Proc. Soc. Exp. Biol. & Med., *31:*810–812.

Wenger, B. S.   1951   Determination of structural patterns in the spinal cord of the chick embryo studied by transplantation between brachial and adjacent levels. J. Exp. Zool., *116:*123–164.

Wenger, E. L.   1950   An experimental analysis of relations between parts of the brachial spinal cord of the embryonic chick. J. Exp. Zool., *114:*51–86.

Whitaker, D. M.   1940   Physical factors of growth. Growth, 2nd Symp. (suppl.), pp. 75–90.

Wieman, H. L.   1926   The effect of heteroplastic grafts of the spinal cord on the development of the limb in Amblystoma. J. Exp. Zool., *45:*335–348.

Wigglesworth, V. B.   1948   The role of the cell in determination; in Growth in Relation to Differentiation and Morphogenesis. Symp. Soc. Exp. Biol., *2:*1–16.

Willier, B. H.   1952   Cells, feathers and colors. Bios, *23:*109–125.

Windle, W. F.   1950   Reflexes of mammalian embryos and fetuses; in Genetic Neurology, edited by P. Weiss, pp. 214–222. University of Chicago Press, Chicago.

Wislocki, G. B., and Singer, M.   1946   The occurrence and function of nerves in the growing antlers of deer. J. Comp. Neur., *85:*1–20.

Wolbach, S. B., and Bessey, O. A.   1942   Tissue changes in vitamin deficiencies. Physiol. Rev., *22:*233–289.

Yntema, C. L.   1943   Deficient efferent innervation of the extremities following removal of neural crest in Amblystoma. J. Exp. Zool., *94:*319–349.

Young, J. Z.   1950   The determination of the specific characteristics of nerve fibers; in Genetic Neurology, edited by P. Weiss, pp. 92–104. University of Chicago Press, Chicago.

Youngstrom, K. A.   1938   On the relationship between choline esterase and the development of behavior in amphibia. J. Neurophysiol., *1:*357–363.

———— 1940   A primary and a secondary somatic motor innervation in Amblystoma. J. Comp. Neur., *73:*139–151.

Zacharias, L. R.   1938   An analysis of cellular proliferation in grafted segments of embryonic spinal cord. J. Exp. Zool., *78:*135–157.

The very sketchy reference in the past article to the fact that neurons grow perpetually *throughout life is more broadly elaborated and documented in the following two articles—in general terms in the first, and in a more specialized version in the second.*

Reprinted from
AMERICAN SCIENTIST, 57, 3, pp. 287–305, 1969

"PANTA' RHEI"—AND SO FLOW
OUR NERVES*,

By PAUL A. WEISS

MORE THAN two millennia ago, Heraklites, the Greek philosopher, epitomized his dynamic concept of the Universe in the thesis, ‘"παντα ρἐι"—"everything flows; all is in flux," marking, by emphasizing "all," one extreme excursion of the philosophical and cultural pendulum which, throughout history, has been swinging back and forth between conservative staticism and progressive dynamism—between stress on that which rigidly endures and that which churns and changes. Yet to the scientist, constancy and change in nature are not antithetical. Both are there. Accent on one or the other merely reflects which partial aspects of nature one cares to single out and spotlight—stability or flux. For science as a whole, the predilection for one over the other seems to have fluctuated with the temper of the times, with the tides of culture oscillating between security-minded status-quo mentality and venturesome propagation of change for its own sake. Now, could it be that a recent shift of emphasis from static to more dynamic concepts of the nervous system has thus been prompted by the stepped-up general agitation of our age?

The conventional comparison between the nervous system and a telephone network will indicate what I mean by "the static concept." A switchboard and the lines from sender to receiver consist of wires—static fixtures. A similar fixity has been imputed to the nerve centers and the nerve fibers connecting them with sense organs and muscles. Telephone wires carry electric pulses; nerve fibers, electric impulses. Tele-

* This paper is reproduced by permission of the author and the Society from the *Proceedings* of The American Philosophical Society, April 1969 [1].

287

phone lines are laid by the telephone company; nerve fibers, spun out by the growing embryo. Both are then turned over for use as message transmitters, the former to the subscriber, the latter to the finished body. Thus one does not seem to have conceded much more life to a finished nerve fiber than to a "live" electric wire. This notion was strengthened by the fact that, unlike most other cell types, nerve cells no longer multiply after birth. The baby is born with a dowry of some ten billion brain cells, and this will have to do for the rest of his life.

Thus, the whole post natal history of the nerve elements looked like a record of stagnation. True, one did concede to the nerve cell and its fiber the enzyme activity needed to sustain energy metabolism and conductivity, but, by and large, even those enzymes were taken for granted, with little concern for their origin and fate.

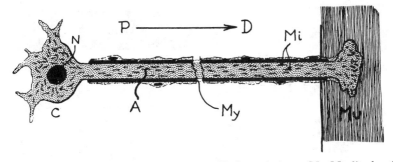

Fig. 1.   Diagram of Neuron. C, Cell body; N, Nucleus; A, Axon; My, Myelin sheath; Mi, Mitochondria; Mu, Muscle fiber; $P \to D$, Proximo-distal direction.

Then, just twenty-five years ago [2] I stumbled on an observation, quite by chance, which thoroughly upset that placid picture of our nerves. What had been viewed as a static fixture, all of a sudden revealed itself to me as a structure in constant flux, engaged in ceaseless, life-long growth, and indeed, growing at a rate which matched the fastest proliferating cells of the adult body. Nerve cells do grow, even though, as I said before, they do not multiply after birth, for just as economics, an increment in mass, i.e., growth, of cells, as of capital, can be spent either on making more new cells as enterprises or on the manufacture of products by the old ones. The latter is the way of nerve cells: their continued production is taking care of their own internal household.

This fact, known now for a quarter of a century, has attracted just within the last few years intense research effort. It therefore seems timely to bring an account of such "useful knowledge" before the American Philosophical Society for Promoting Useful Knowledge. In a thumbnail sketch, I shall briefly outline the history and current state of this new dimension in our knowledge and thinking about the nervous system and our cerebral activity.

Here is how it came about. It happened during the Second World War, when I was entrusted by the Office of Scientific Research and Development with the task of developing improved methods for the healing of shattered nerves, for which my past research on nerve growth offered some promise. Let me just briefly give a glossary of fundamentals. The universal cellular unit of the nervous system is a singularly unorthodox cell, the *neuron* (Fig. 1). This is a highly asymmetrical structure, in which the cell nucleus (N), with its chromosomes and working genes, surrounded by a large mass of cytoplasm (C), lies close to one end of an

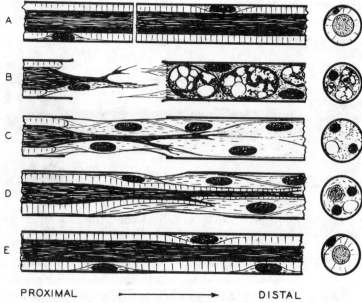

FIG. 2.   Diagram of the regeneration of a transected nerve fiber. Explanation in text.

extremely elongated protoplasmic process, called the *axon* (A), the other end of which connects with another cell in brain, spinal cord, muscle (Mu), skin, or gland. (Shorter extensions from the massive bulk of the eccentric cell center, called dendrites, link the neuronal unit with the vast network of nerve centers.) The axons are lined by accessory sheath cells and often an intermediate layer of myelin (My). The whole complex is commonly referred to as the "nerve fiber," although it is not really a fiber, but a tube, the lumen of which is occupied by the cylindrical axonal column. Let us from here on focus solely on that protoplasmic core, which is as continuous and integral a part of the central cell body as a river is of the lake from which it springs. All illustrations in the following are so oriented that the proximo-distal direction from cell to peripheral termination of the axon is from left to right.

When a nerve fiber is cut (Fig. 2), the severed distal stump of its axon degenerates (Fig. 2B), whereas the proximal stump remains not only essentially intact, but sprouts a new distal extension (Fig. 2B, C), which can eventually reach and reconnect with the deserted terminal (Fig. 2D, E). This is the basis of the regenerative capacity of severed nerves in animals and man. Its practical success, however, is seriously handicapped by the formation of scar tissue in the gap between the

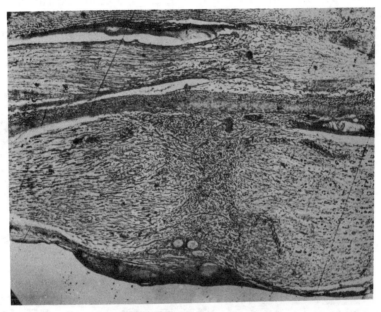

FIG. 3.   Early stages of nerve regeneration in transected rat nerves after simple apposition (below) and splicing with arterial sleeve (S, above).

separated stumps; this scar consists of a pathless fiber jungle, in which most of the outgrowing new nerve sprouts get stuck and lost. Now, in applying some of my earlier results on how to guide nerve sprouts into chosen directions, I succeeded in preventing that hurdle from forming by splicing the severed ends together by a snugly fitting segment of artery as cuff. Figure 3 shows, for example, two neighboring nerve trunks in the rat, transected five days previously. In the lower one, the stumps had been simply apposed and left alone; in the upper one, they had been joined by an arterial sleeve (S). Note the striking contrast. In the lower one, the gap between the stumps has become filled with a messy tangle of cells and fibers, while in the upper one, the stumps have already become linked by perfectly straight fiber bridges as pathways to guide the nerve fibers across the gap.

In elaborating this method, from rats through cats and monkeys and finally to man, some of the arterial sleeves have been too tight, partially strangling the enclosed nerve fibers. I shall call that constricted stretch the "bottleneck." In cases of this kind, I noticed that, centrally to the "bottleneck," the nerve fibers were greatly enlarged and contorted, while on the far side they were extremely thin and remained so for life. Figure 4 shows the central entrance to such a bottleneck, sectioned lengthwise, many months after the operation. Note the dark-stained axons approaching the squeeze from the left, piling up in weird contortions, and then suddenly turning straight and thin. Their various deformations, prior to entry, are summarized in Figure 5—a composite of some one hundred thousand such fibers studied. From there on down to their endings, the fibers remain permanently as undersized as they are in the bottleneck itself.

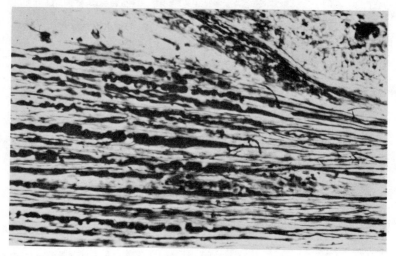

Fig. 4. Damming of axoplasm at proximal entrance to "bottleneck" (4 weeks p. op.)—Magnification 188×.

There was never an exception to this spectacular disparity of size between the stretches of nerve fibers on the side of the cell and those at the far side of the bottleneck. The plausible interpretation of this asymmetry was, of course, that something crucial for the growth of the nerve fiber was coming down from the cell body, but was throttled in its downward passage by the local narrowing of its traffic channel. Was it perhaps some stimulant for the local growth of regenerating fibers? Definitely, not. The fact that these first observations were made on regenerating, that is, actively outgrowing, nerve fibers, proved wholly coincidental and immaterial. For if one places constrictions on normal intact uninterrupted nerves, one obtains exactly the same picture (Fig. 6).

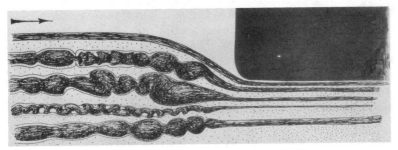

FIG. 5.   Diagram of major forms of damming figures.

The same asymmetry of size and configuration with regard to the level of constriction develops: inflations and convolutions on the proximal side of the constriction, coupled now, instead of with a failure to grow up, with an active shrinkage of the distal fiber caliber (Fig. 6, B–C). Evidently, *the mere local narrowing of a nerve fiber has the effect of throttling the traffic of something that is moving down from the cell body continuously, even in the intact functional neuron.*

It did not take much acumen to realize what that something was. It had to be, of course, a stream, a traffic stream, and Figure 7 shows its prototype, familiar to any driver. Constricting a nerve is like putting a barrier across part of a highway. It leads to a traffic jam, from which only a trickle can escape through the squeeze. In short, the substance of our

FIG. 6.   Diagram of effects of constriction of mature nerve fibers.

nerves flows steadily down from their cell bodies, and when it finds itself confronted with bottlenecks in its flow channels, it becomes dammed up in front of them.

This analogy of traffic flow at once prompted an experimental test: would the removal of the barrier restore the rate and volume of normal, unimpeded flow, as in the lower half of the picture? Indeed, it does (see Fig. 6D). As soon as one takes off the tight sleeve after many months of throttled traffic, even as late as one year, the dammed up nerve plasma flows down and fills out the formerly attenuated distal portions of the fibers. Figure 8 shows sample fibers from two nerves of the same animal, which had been kept constricted for one month; the lower one was left constricted to serve as control, while the upper one had been deconstricted four days prior to preservation. Note how in the latter the axoplasm, released from its straightjacket, has forced its way down in a proximo-distal tidal wave, draining the dammed up bulges, while widening the former bottleneck in lumps, like a boa constrictor gorging down a pig. And just as the progress of the bulge in the snake's body gives us a measure of the rate of transport in the alimentary tract, so the advancing front of the flood wave of released axoplasm has served me as an indicator

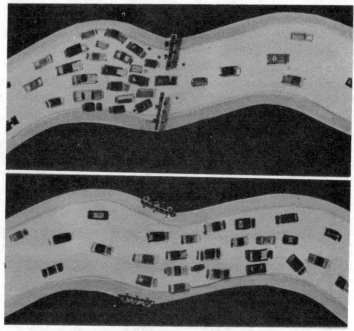

FIG. 7.   Highway traffic jam. Top: 3-lane flow restricted to single lane. Bottom: resumption of free flow upon removal of barrier. (Picture by Vera Teleki)

of the mean rate of axoplasmic flow. It turned out to be of the order of *one millimeter per day*. This rate has in the meantime been corroborated by several laboratories using various methods and it begins to look like a fundamental constant, at least by order of magnitude.

Let us now examine the nature of this flow more closely by focusing on a few selected highlights. One conclusion emerged early, namely, that the one-millimeter flow is not a stream of substance *inside* a stationary axon, but that it is *the whole axon itself* which is on the move, advancing as a semisolid column of a consistency somewhere between that of molten lava and toothpaste squeezed from a tube. Its semisolid condition was ascertained from the characteristic deformities it assumed during damming; these were analyzed by electronmicroscopy and by a quantitative comparison with technological models simulating the damming effect. Figure 9 is the electronmicrogram of a longitudinal section of a chronically constricted axon in the region of damming; one sees that all the fine-structural elements (neurotubules and filaments) of the axonal

FIG. 8. Downflow of dammed axoplasm after deconstriction. Samples of nerve fibers from the zone of constriction (*C*) and the adjacent proximal (*P*) and distal (*D*) portions of nerve fibers with constrictions removed (upper) and maintained (lower).

content, which normally would run in straight lines from left to right, have been folded into a uniform set of identical convolutions. This fact alone attests to the cohesiveness of the whole column, as it advances in a translatory motion, but even more conclusive were the results of the quantitative studies, which proved that the deforming force declined, as had been predicted from physical considerations, as a linear function of the distance from the bottleneck.

Now, what does this whole commotion in and of the neuron mean; what is its drive, its purpose, and its fate? If we had known in the early forties what we have in the meantime come to know about the molecular biology of cells, some answers to these questions could have been anticipated. Yet, at the time, I had to fall back on conjecture and experimental probing. My first contentions were rather plausible. I proposed the following inferences from the phenomenon of axonal flow: (1) the macromolecules in the neuron, particularly enzymes and other proteins, do not persist indefinitely, but on the contrary, their population undergoes continuous degradation and dissipation; (2) their renewal through the manufacture of new macromolecules, especially protein, does not occur ubiquitously, but is strictly a preserve of the eccentric cell body around the nucleus; (3) accordingly, the enzyme and structural protein requirements of the axon, depleted by steady dwindling along the line, must be steadily replenished from that localized central source if the whole unit is to be kept alive; and (4) since the mass of a long axon can be more than one hundred times as great as that of its cell body, the rate of that steady supply stream must bear a direct relation to the rate of consumption in the axon.

This concept gave the whole phenomenon an aspect of market economy. There is the manufacturing center in the cell body, the consumer population in the long nerve fibers, and the feeder line of traffic from source to user. To test the correctness of the concept, I searched the literature for

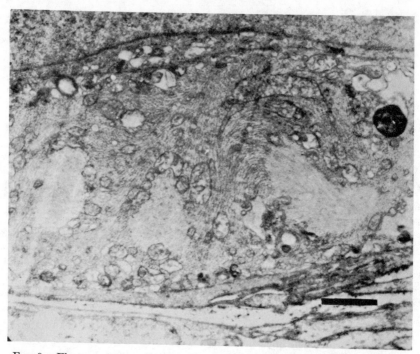

Fig. 9. Electronmicrograph of longitudinal section of dammed portion of axon with convoluted microstructure. Neurotubular masses in mantle, neurofibrillar bundles in the axial core, mitochondria "beached" along surface and interfaces. Scale unit: 1 micron.

data that would substantiate the fact that nerve fibers actually lose protein along their course. Reports that nerves give off a singularly high amount of ammonia seemed pertinent in that this compound could be interpreted as the terminal product of complete protein deamination. By calculating then on this assumption the daily loss of nerve protein from the reported data, I could determine the rate of replenishment of protein stock from the central cell body that would be required to balance the depletion and keep the axonal protein in a steady state. It turned out that to satisfy the requirement would take a protein supply column traveling about one millimeter a day. Since this postulated figure jibed with the actually observed rate of the axonal flow, I felt, of course, encouraged to keep on treating protein as a fair marker for the whole axonal column and to pursue that particular line further. That was in 1947.

It was during this time that radioactive isotopes came into widespread use for tracing metabolic processes. The presence of such molecules is readily detected by a radiation counter, and their position, by letting the emitted rays blacken the silver grains of a photographic emulsion. To track isotope-labeled protein molecules from their cell source down the axon, thus seemed a straightforward task. Using first isotopes of phosphorus and carbon, my own and other laboratories brought confirmations of the proximo-distal axonal flow, and even of its rate, but little else. A major forward step came only with the labeling of protein by tritium—a beta-ray emitting hydrogen—which was applied to the track-

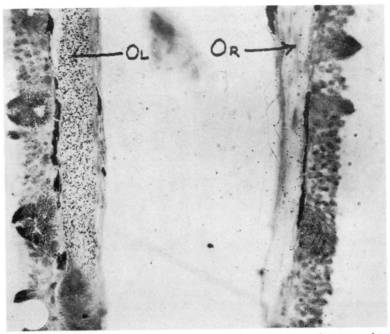

FIG. 10. Autoradiogram of frontal (longitudinal) section of nasal septum of toad two weeks after labeling proteins in left nostril by tritiated leucine, showing strongly radioactive left (O_L) and blank right (O_R) olfactory nerves.

ing of axonal flow first by Droz and Leblond. Our own efforts aimed at and succeeded in applying this radioactive marker directly and in strict localization to nerve cells without contamination of the surrounding tissues. This proved feasible in both the nose and the eye.

We insert, for instance, a little gelatine, soaked in a tritiated amino acid—a building stone of protein—into one nostril, where it is promptly incorporated into the proteins of the cells of origin of the olfactory nerve, which lie in the nasal membrane (Fig. 10). A few days later, tissue sections are made, coated with photographic emulsion, left in the dark for some weeks, and then developed. The density of silver grains, blackened by radiating protein molecules, gives us then a direct quantitative measure of the shifts which the underlying proteins have undergone since their local tagging in the cell bodies. The serial study of these shifts is like looking at successive stages of a horse race. Figure 10 shows an *olfactory* nerve on the treated left side heavily radioactive (O_L), which reveals that the race of labeled neuroplasm has already passed beyond this level. In fact, it has already reached the brain (Fig. 11), where one can see the terminal branches of the nerve splay out. The absence of radioactivity in the right olfactory nerve (O_R), originating in the right, untreated, nostril (Figs. 10 and 11), demonstrates how sharply the label remains confined to the selected neuron systems. Incidentally, this technical by-product of our studies obviously offers a new and superior method for the anatomical tracing of nerve-fiber systems to their terminals in the maze of neuronal connections.

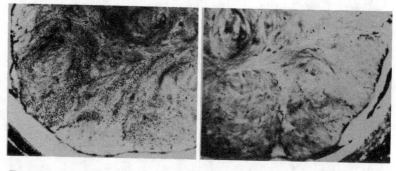

Fig. 11. Autoradiogram of symmetrical left and right sectors of forebrain of toad, 11 days after labeling of left nostril as in figure 10, showing in the left half the localization of the strongly radioactive axon bundles of the left olfactory nerve, in sharp contrast to the lack of radioactivity (lack of silver grains) in the right half.

Figure 12 gives a graphic record of the daily progress of flow in the axons of the *optic* nerve after labeling their cells of origin in the retina. It shows that the wave has advanced again at an approximate daily rate of one millimeter, but also that the crest of the wave has spread out with time, which indicates, like the dispersal of a field of racing horses, that not all axons move at the same speed.

The success of these experiments in the intact animal led to the bolder effort of carrying the further analysis outside the animal, *in vitro*. So we excised spinal ganglia, which contain the cell bodies of sensory skin nerves (Fig. 13) with their nerves left attached, and dipped the ganglionic ends for a few hours into radioactive amino acid (Fig. 13, 1). We then transferred them to nutrient solution pair-wise, one member with its ganglion left on, the other decapitated (Fig. 13, 2–3). After several days of joint subsistence *in vitro*, the remaining ganglion was also cut off (Fig. 13, 4), and the radioactivities of the two nerves were measured (Fig. 13, 5). Without exception, the nerve which had been in possession of its ganglionic protein source during the stay in culture was significantly more strongly radioactive than its sourceless mate (compare the diagrammatic summary block graphs of radioactivity in the two respective sets of nerves in Figure 13, 5). Obviously, axonal inflow from the ganglion had continued even in isolation. This made it possible to determine the proportion of cell protein moving out daily from the cell body; it amounted to 6–11 percent. This enormously high production rate would correspond roughly to an average renewal rate of the whole solid content of each central nerve cell body almost once a day, or about 10,000 times in a life span.

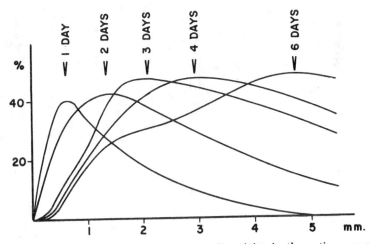

FIG. 12. Tracing of intra-axonal protein radioactivity in the optic nerve after localized application of tritiated leucine to the retinal cells. The ordinates represent the percentage change of fresh protein in the slow axonal flow along the nerve from the eye bulb towards the brain in daily intervals.

After all these mutually concordant results, further supported by confirmations from other laboratories, the fact that *the mature neuron is in perpetual rapid growth and grows forth as axon, consuming its substance on the way*, had thus been firmly established—a dramatic turn from the old notion of a stable unit.

The isolation method has expedited deeper probing into this extraordinary rush of neuronal growth activity, particularly its dependence upon functional activity and on the variables of the neuronal environment, such as oxygen, metabolites, hormones, or drugs. These studies are just in their beginnings. Here are a few examples. Thus far, excitations of short duration did not seem to raise the rate of central synthesis appreciably, if any, although from the classical observations of Hydén long-lasting stimulation could be predicted to enhance it. On the other hand, it was startling to find that a brief exposure to narcotics has a conspicuous and most unusual effect. When isolated ganglia were placed in the usual media with an admixture of a narcotic, for instance a barbiturate, within one hour a significant amount of their freshly synthetized protein leaked out. This precipitous loss of protein was so alarmingly consistent that one begins to wonder how truly innocuous a sleeping pill is. Further experiments, of course, are being carried on.

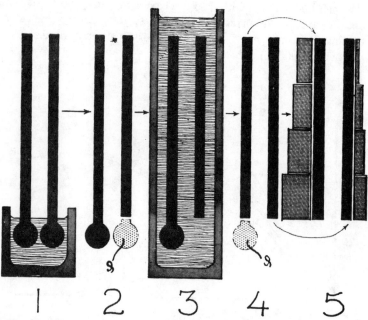

Fig. 13. Experimental design for the testing of cellulifugal shift of radioactive protein *in vitro*. Explanation in text.

Whereas these last examples have illustrated the usefulness of the isotope techniques in the study of the central neuroplasmic production process, the traffic aspects of axonal flow continue likewise to receive further elucidation through the labeling procedure. There is a gratifying upsurge of research along this line. For example, several investigators have observed, besides the one-millimeter flow rate, a second faster rate of cellulifugal traffic in nerve fibers, from ten to a hundred times as fast. It evidently signifies that there is in the axon "flow within flow," coursing in intra-axonal channels. Present indications are that the axon contains special rapid transport lines for carrying centrally synthesized transmitter substances to their peripheral working stations at neuro-muscular or neuro-neural junctions. Candidates for such pipe lines inside the axon

(Fig. 14) are the neurotubules (t), about 200 Angström units ($= 2 \times 10^{-5}$ mm) in diameter, and a wider, less well defined, canal system (c), which I discovered in the interstices between the tubules. But the substratum and, above all, the hydrodynamic driving mechanism in these miniature channels, in which macromolecules and even particles can race down in one second a distance one hundred times the width of the lumen, are still in deep obscurity.

One clue is beginning to emerge. It goes back to the original damming experiment. Friede had noted that certain respiratory enzymes accumulate at the proximal side of a ligature placed around a nerve. This ob-

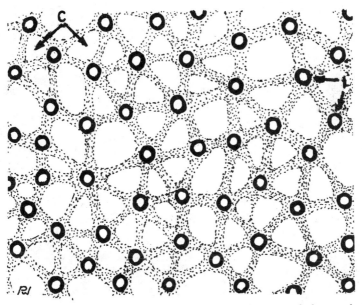

FIG. 14.   Diagram of arrangement of neurotubules (t) and intertubular canals (c) in an electronmicrogram of axonal cross section. Magnification $\sim$150,000$\times$.

servation found a logical explanation when we discovered (Fig. 15) that the vehicles of those enzymes, the mitochondria (Fig. 1, Mi), float down with the slow axonal stream, and therefore, like the rest of axoplasm, pile up when meeting an obstruction, as is illustrated in this picture. But later similar accumulations at constrictions were also reported for the rapid transport of non-mitochondrial enzymes, such as cholinesterase, and of transmitter substances, like noradrenalin storage granules, as in this picture by Dahlström (Fig. 16). Such rapid traffic must be assumed to travel in intra-axonal tubes. Since neurotubules resemble the tubular fibers ("microtubules") of the mitotic spindles, which pull the chromosomes apart in cell division, and since this mitotic movement can be blocked by colchicine, Dr. Kreutzberg in my laboratory tested whether this drug might also interfere with intra-axonal traffic. And indeed, by a local injection of a minute dose of colchicine into a nerve, he could stall the passage of the test enzyme, cholinesterase, across the drugged stretch. Dahlström demonstrated similarly the blockage by colchicine of down-

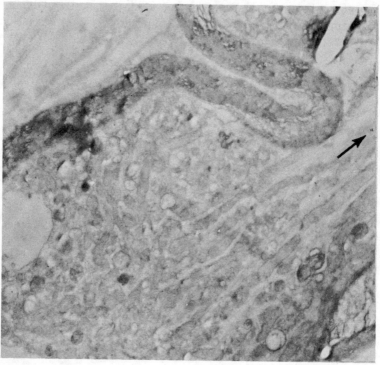

FIG. 15. Accumulation of dammed mitochondria in front of obstructing kink of constricted nerve fiber. Electron micrograph; magnification about 12,000. (A section of equal size in a normal unconstricted fiber would contain no more than about 4 mitochondria, while the illustrated jam consists of several hundreds.)

ward transport of noradrenalin storage granules. This result seems to point, however indirectly, to the intra-axonal pipelines as the fast traffic systems, but this is, at present, the only meager clue we have.

The slow axonal flow, that is, the propulsion of the axonal column as a whole, is closer to our comprehension. You will remember that unlike the fast transport in the liquid channels, the axon advances as a cohesive semisolid mass. The mechanism of this advance has been reasonably well identified by deduction, models, and experiments. It consists (Fig. 17) of a roller-belt-like conveyor drive: a succession of peristaltic waves traveling over the axonal surface in the cellulifugal direction. As the cell body manufactures new neuroplasm, adds new lengths to the neurotubules and fibrils at their roots, and spawns new mitochondria, this whole growing complex is then continuously massaged forth inside the more stationary wrappings of its sheaths. The power for the drive is presumably supplied from the surrounding sheath cells.

We have been able to record this process in motion pictures. The essence of the rather involved technique is illustrated in Figure 18. Spinal ganglia (S) and their sensory nerves, excised from mature mice, were kept alive for more than a week in special chambers perfused by nutrient solutions. Some of the nerve fiber bundles were teased apart for better visibility, and time-lapse motion pictures were taken of them under a phase-contrast microscope. The films, which were projected in the course

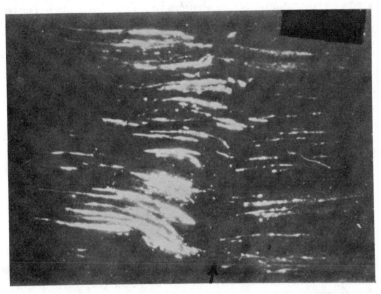

Fig. 16. Accumulation of masses of catecholamine storage granules, visible by their bright fluorescence, in front of a crush (at arrow) of a sympathetic nerve (A. Dahlström).

of this lecture, reeled off at speeds in which one minute on the screen corresponded to one day of actual life, were samples from a large collection taken over a period of years. Although it is impossible to reproduce in a verbal account the vividness of the direct visual impression, the major lessons of the film study can at least be summarized here as follows.

The postulated peristaltic waves are of spectacular and consistent regularity. They sweep over the surface of the axons, with the participation of the myelin sheath, in the cellulifugal direction at a rather constant frequency of three to four cycles per hour, regardless of whether a fiber is still continuous or already in a state of fragmentation. This is in full accord with my earlier deduction of a roller-belt-type mechanism, in which every element of the track generates and contributes to the driving force (see Fig. 17). In favorable cases, one observes in the fiber surface a local "pacemaker" center in regular pulsation, like a beating heart, from which then, every once in a while, a propagated wave of surface contraction originates which travels on over the rest of the fiber. While the contractile surface waves move smoothly, the axonal content, propelled by them, proceeds more spasmodically and intermittently, due to its stalling by local inhomogeneities of the flow channel, such as kinks. Meandering fiber stretches are especially demonstrative. But truly, no description can match the visual experience of "seeing is believing."

There has been no evidence ever of a reversed flow, nor do any of our other results encourage such an assumption. Yet, there have been sporadic voices raised to suggest the possibility of "bidirectional flow." Some of them can be discounted as being based on gratuitous extrapolations on

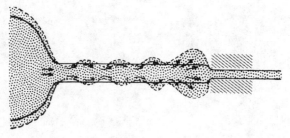

Fig. 17. Diagram of microperistaltic surface wave driving the axonal flow downward from the cell body.

questionable interpretations, but this does not invalidate the claim that some sort of reverse communication from periphery to center via nerve exists. For instance, the central cell "knows" promptly when its nerve fiber has been cut, and I myself have produced evidence a long time ago for a specifying effect proceeding from a muscle centrally over its motor nerve. But to ascribe this to reverse axonal flow is just as unwarranted as if one would infer from the observation of upstream navigation of a riverboat that the river is flowing backwards. One can conceive of many physical ways of moving against the tide, for instance by electrically promoted transfer of charged bodies along interfaces ("phase boundaries"), but it is not even certain that centripetal "messages" running over the axon involve the transfer of substance at all.

With these comments about uncertainties, which could be generously augmented from our store of documents of ignorance, we have approached the border where the safe track of solid knowledge is apt to get lost in the quicksand of fantasy. So, I conclude this presentation.

The squirming and writhing of the nerve fibers, that I illustrated in the films have given a faithful, albeit accelerated, portrayal of the agitation going on perpetually in our nerves beside and beneath the race of functional excitations. "Panta' rhei—all is in flux"; and so flow our nerves. A new dimension of vitality has been inserted into our thinking about the nervous system and ourselves. Small wonder that it is attracting in growing numbers investigators of a generation in search of dynamism and escape from staidness and rigidity. Let us hope that their enthusiasm will not outrun the measured pace of arduous disciplined labor and critical evaluation that are now called for.

Clearly, the realization that our brain cells will not be the same next week that they are today confronts us with many unsuspected and per-

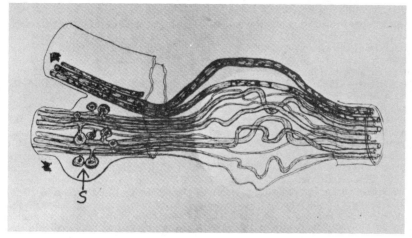

Fig. 18.   Diagram of nerve preparations used for cinemicrography of axonal flow. S, spinal ganglion. (The light circle indicates schematically the microscopic field.)

plexing problems. How is it possible, for instance, amidst all this flux, for our mind to preserve our sense of personal identity? To what extent, on the other hand, does that very flux add to our understanding of the adaptive, as well as maladaptive, plasticity of our nervous system, which is displayed in memory, habituation, acquired hypersensitivities, idiosyncrasies, and drug addiction? And will perhaps the phenomena of maintenance of tissue integrity by nerves, known by the name of "trophic," but wholly unknown as to their modes of action, now find an explanation? Is it conceivable that ways will now be found to invigorate our steady neural growth, or at least obviate its decline with disuse and age? In sum, will further "useful knowledge" flow from this new trend, kindled by a fortunate, but, let me repeat, wholly fortuitous, observation? More work, not idle speculation, holds the answers. There may be many more surprises coming our way.

I trust you will pardon me if I close this brief life history of a chance discovery with a jingle I once wrote in a similar spirit:

"Something we find with intention
Commonly is called invention.
If the goal was practical,
Then, of course, it's tactical
To exploit its fruits for money,
Much as bees milk plants for honey.
But when I, of mind more humble
Just observing nature, stumble
Upon a discovery,
What it holds as prize for me
Is the thrill to have detected
Something wholly unexpected."

REFERENCES

1. A paper presented at the November 1968 meeting of The American Philosophical Society, Philadelphia, Pa. Research referred to in the paper has been aided by grants from the National Institutes of Health of the U.S. Public Health Service (recently Grant NB-07348-02) and from the Faith Foundation. Over the years, many collaborators have contributed to its progress, most notably A. Cecil Taylor, Helen Hiscoe, Heinrich Waelsch, Abel Lajtha, Aiyappan Pillai, Yvonne Holland, and Albert Bock.

2. The first three preliminary reports appeared in 1943, followed in 1948 by a comprehensive account (Paul Weiss and Helen B. Hiscoe, "Experiments on the mechanism of nerve growth," *Jour. Exp. Zool.*, *107* (1948): 315–395). The most recent review of the current status of this research, with extensive bibliography, will be found in Samuel H. Barondes, "Axoplasmic Transport," *Neurosciences Research Program Bulletin.* *5*, No. 4 (1967): 307–419; and particularly the essay by Paul Weiss, "Neuronal Dynamics," *ibid.*, pp. 371–400. See also the article "Neuroplasmic Flow as Mechanism and Indicator of Neuronal Dynamics" by Paul A. Weiss, in "Cellular Dynamics of the Neuron" (in press in: *Annual Symposia of the International Society for Cell Biology, 8,* 1969; Academic Press, New York & London), which contains bibliographic references to the work of authors not specifically cited in this lecture.

Reprinted from Cellular Dynamics of the Neuron (Ed. Samuel H. Barondes),
Symposium of International Society for Cell Biology, Vol. 8. Copyright 1969 by
Academic Press

NEURONAL DYNAMICS AND NEUROPLASMIC ("AXONAL") FLOW

PAUL A. WEISS

Rockefeller University, New York, New York

From the very first observations of axonal flow [67–70, 78, 83], it has
been clear that that phenomenon must be studied and evaluated in the
broader context of the whole dynamics of the neuron, for which it serves
as an indicator and measure. The present symposium on the biology of
the neuron as a *cell* offers a unique opportunity to present the *phenomenon* of axonal flow in this broader perspective, with the aim of combining
aspects gained by various specialized techniques into a unified picture.
I am stressing that this is to be the presentation of a "phenomenon,"
rather than of a "theory," for even though a unified picture is beginning
to emerge, so many features are still either wholly obscure or, at best,
conjectural that it seems far more important to set in clear focus the
facts that have been established firmly than to indulge in ambitious
generalizations.

The usage of the simple term "axonal flow" itself carries a risk—the
risk of oversimplification, unrealistic interpretations, and premature over-
extension. The intricacies of the phenomenon are barely realized, let
alone resolved. The real situation must not be allowed to be lost sight
of by letting the term "flow" conjure up simplistic, primitive, and unrealistic connotations. Some signs of such a trend are already noticeable
in the literature, for instance, when one reads innocent references to
"migratory" proteins, as though proteins had organs of locomotion. To
stem such trends, let me, as one who, through his diversified experience
with the processes lumped under the term "axonal flow," has become
fully cognizant of the glaring deficiencies in our knowledge and understanding of them, state at the outset that I shall try to hold this report
to a description of recorded facts, and such conclusions as can be cogently—or, at times, tentatively—derived from them, without pretending
to formulate a "theory." Moreover, the lopsided proportion that I have
allocated in my presentation to the investigations of my own laboratory
is simply an expression of my confidence that most of the work of others
on neuronal phenomena relevant to axonal flow will be summarized
much more competently by its authors in the course of this symposium.

Axonal flow is essentially a cell-biological phenomenon characteristic

3

of a cell of peculiar constitution, the neuron. The peculiarity of that cell lies in its usual possession of enormous elongations and in the resulting extreme eccentricity of the site of the nucleus and its surrounding cytoplasmic mass—the "perikaryon." In the molecular communities of most other cells, the processes of synthesis, macromolecular assemblage, internal transport, catabolic breakdown, and elimination of metabolites and cell products are so grossly intermingled that they are difficult to separate. Likewise, the neuron used to be taken for granted as a cell in which anabolic and catabolic processes go on ubiquitously. Axonal flow has radically changed that notion by demonstrating that in the neuron the major production site of cellular constituents and the area of their consumption are not intermingled and coextensive but are rather neatly segregated, which necessarily requires an organized traffic system from source to consumers—and this is exactly what axonal flow provides. In that sense, the neuron constitutes a uniquely favorable object for basic studies in cell biology in general. In turn, what has been learned through these studies about the dynamics of that specialized cell has introduced a new dimension into our thinking about the nervous system; for the shift of our image of the nerve cell, from that of a rather static fixture to that of a rapidly and continuously growing system, widens considerably the range of possibilities for explaining the great adaptability of nervous functions throughout life.

HISTORY

The concept of continuous axonal flow has emerged from the observation that surplus axoplasm piles up at the proximal side of a chronic nerve constriction, coupled with a corresponding reduction of the fiber diameter at the distal side [for an account of the history, see Weiss, 76a]. The early investigations were concerned with (a) the acute effects of a constriction; (b) physiological effects (reversible pressure block of conductivity) [78]; (c) the development of edema between the nerve fibers at the proximal side [67]; (d) the proximodistal flow of endoneurial fluid [79]; (e) the demyelinization within the constricted zone [83]; and (f) above all, the permanent changes in the constricted fibers [80] to be detailed below.

The conclusion from those experiments was inescapably that something in the neuron was constantly moving in a proximodistal direction and that any local throttling of the progress of that "something" resulted in the piling up of neuronal content. The "something" emanating from the perikaryon might have been construed to be some "growth factor" indispensable for local growth and maintenance of the axon all along its length. This supposition would have been in line with hypothetical deductions put forth by Waller [66] in 1852 and reiterated by G. H. Parker [53] and Gerard [20] in 1932. It soon, however, became evident [78] that this interpretation was incorrect and that the damming actually signified that one is dealing with a movement *of* the axon rather than *in* the axon, the axon growing forth continuously from its root in the cell body. It was only relatively recently that the disclosure of additional axonal transport processes at rates considerably faster than the axonal flow itself made it necessary to postulate also flow channels within the moving axonal matrix (see below).

In contrast to its identified central source, the fate of the incessant axonal growth in a nerve fiber, which, after all, retains stationary dimensions, remained conjectural. The most plausible assumption was that the axon, incapable of synthesizing its major protein constituents, must be supplied with them from its central cell body and that the axonal column, as it moves along, replaces the catabolically degrading elements of its molecular population by fresh ones in a statistical equilibrium between degradation and replenishment.

These assumptions dictated the further steps in our experimental program of exploring some of the major aspects of axonal flow in greater detail, essentially in three directions: (1) extension of the morphological evidence for the phenomenon from the microscopic to the electron microscopic level; (2) a search for direct chemical markers, preferably isotopic labels, for the finer resolution of the molecular traffic involved; (3) a cinemicrographic recording, if possible, of the mode of movement as a clue to the underlying motile mechanism.

In order to serve the purpose of this symposium, I shall present the several diverse studies of this complex phenomenon separately according to methodological points of view. But first, a few terminological comments are called for. In the first place, "axonal flow" is but the most conspicuous aspect of the general "neuroplasmic renewal," which keeps advancing from the near-nuclear cell center into all the more peripheral regions of the neuron, the dendrites being dependent as the axon upon the soma of the cell for their macromolecular replacements. However, since the difference in geometry between axon and dendrites makes the traffic in the latter appear more in the nature of seepage than of flow, the usage of the term "axonal flow," now widely adopted, seems innocuous as long as one bears in mind that it is only one manifestation and indicator of the growth dynamics of the neuron. A second point to stress is the need for a clear distinction between "axonal flow" and "intraaxonal transport." Although one might tentatively consider the latter as "flow within a flowing system," that is, as convection within intraaxonal conduits, there is as yet no conclusive evidence that it is actually a process

of non-Newtonian fluid mechanics in the technological sense of "flow."
I shall speak of "intraaxonal flow" with this reservation in mind.

THE BASIC TEST: DAMMING

The crucial test, as well as most common assay method, of axonal
flow is provided by any sudden narrowing of the flow channel within
which the axon is constrained in its extracellular course. The manner in
which this diminution of the flow channel is produced is of no consequence. Local constriction by an artificial ligature (Fig. 1, A–C) has the
same effect as the natural entrance of a nerve fiber from a looser packing
into a fibrotic zone, such as a scar. Conversely, a very thin regenerating
axon, advancing in an old oversized, though partly ligated, tube (see

FIG. 1.   Schematic representation of single nerve fibers subject to chronic constrictions. A, normal mature fiber; B, same fiber as A, immediately after application
of constricting cuff; C, same fiber as B after assuming new stationary asymmetry:
damming of neuroplasm on the proximal side of the "bottleneck," coupled with reduction of caliber distally; D, same fiber as C after removal of chronic constriction:
downflow of dammed-up neuroplasm.

Fig. 3, F–H, in Weiss and Hiscoe [80]) continues unimpeded without
deformation until it has enlarged up to the width of the lumen left open
in the pinched portion; only during its further growth in width does
excess material begin to dam up at the entrance to the narrow stretch.
While the distal portion of such *regenerating* fibers simply stops widening, the parts distal to the constriction of a *mature* full-sized fiber actually
lose size (Fig. 1, C). Since in both cases the results are principally the
same, I shall deal from here on only with *mature, uninterrupted fibers*
in a steady-state condition, so as to dispel any notion that axonal flow
and damming might be features peculiar to "growing" embryonic or
regenerating fibers with free mobile tips, in which the need for being
fed by influx from the cell body is self-evident.

In contrast to our technique of *partial* constriction by placing an
elastic cuff of contractile artery around the nerve trunk, thus only narrowing the lumen of the nerve fiber locally, but not occluding it, subsequent investigators have often applied the more extreme procedure of

tightly ligating or crushing the nerve so that a major fraction of the axons was completely severed. Any one of these interventions gives rise to transitory local changes in the nerve, varying with the severity of the trauma, but generally subsiding within days. These acute changes find expression in a flanging of the nerve at both ends of a stricture [67, 78] associated with histochemical manifestations, such as accumulation of mitochondria and mitochondrial enzymes [38, 38a, 43], of acetylcholinesterase [43], and of transmitter substances [7, 45]. The extrusion of nerve substance from within the constricted zone into the adjacent free zones is hardly large enough to explain the reported increases of material on both sides of a lesion. However, the well-known strong electronegativity arising at a nerve injury [e.g., Heilbrunn, 26] could perhaps explain the effect in terms of cathodal galvanotaxis of mitochondria and electrophoretic displacement toward the lesion of molecules and particulates with a net positive charge [see also Friede, 17].

At any rate, these acute sequelae of the operation, being of short duration, do not concern us here. The following account deals solely with nerves that have been kept under moderate local constriction chronically, for at least several months up to more than a year. Such specimens displayed no gross functional impairment in impulse transmission or muscle function. Monkeys kept in this condition (histologically verified) for about 10 months, while showing a mild muscular atrophy (15% on the average), showed perfect motor coordination in the use of their legs [1, 44].

To characterize properly the permanent axonal changes at the proximal side of a constriction (hereafter referred to as "bottleneck"), the term "damming," used for brevity, is not sufficiently descriptive, as it suggests a mere *quantitative* piling up of surplus material. The morphological expression of such a simple congestion would be a massive bulbous swelling, tapering off in the proximal direction (see the schematic version in Fig. 1B). The actual changes, however, consist of complicated structural deformations, illustrated in Fig. 2.

In a technological interpretation, these deformations denote resistance met by a semisolid cohesive cylindrical column propelled smoothly in a channel of matching size when entering a narrower portion of the channel. The sudden throttling of entry into the channel jams up the traffic column proximally, a situation comparable to the traffic jam on a partially obstructed road (Fig. 3). Concurrently with these proximal alterations, the parts of the nerve fiber lying distal to the bottleneck become emaciated in proportion to the throttling of inflow through the bottleneck and retain this attenuated size as long as the constriction is maintained.

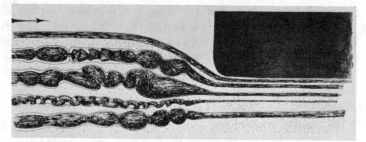

FIG. 2. Tracings of characteristic axonal deformations at the proximal entrance to a constricted zone.

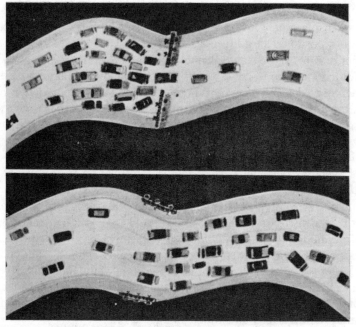

FIG. 3. Traffic analogue of axonal flow. *Top*: Barrier reducing lanes for automobile traffic causes jam. *Bottom*: Resumption of free flow upon removal of barrier.

After a moderate constriction, the distal fiber portions, though reduced in size, are still wide enough to register the effects of a second constriction applied in tandem farther down. In such cases, individual fibers can be shown to have become dammed up at the proximal entrances to both the upper and lower bottlenecks [80]. The marked proximodistal structural asymmetry in the stretch of fiber lying between two bottlenecks, also confirmed by chemical tests [8, 45], proves clearly that the driving mechanism of axonal flow operates unidirectionally and is operative actively at every point along a nerve fiber (see below).

The engorgement proximal to a constriction, concomitant with distal emaciation, is not a static, structurally fixed condition, but the expression of a stationary dynamic configuration of the flow pattern of a highly viscous and relatively form-consistent material, comparable vaguely to the flow of lava with internal reinforcement by semirigid fibers. To test the flow properties directly, constricted nerves were deconstricted many months after attainment of stationary asymmetry [77]. The dammed up material could then be seen (Fig. 1, D) to be gorged down through the formerly constricted region into the distal portion in the form of a tidal wave (cf. Fig. 3, lower panel), eventually restoring the emaciated distal stretch to near-normal dimensions. This wave front advanced roughly one to several millimeters per day. From this we reached the reasonable, but unsubstantiated, conclusion that the observed rate was a fair measure of the order of magnitude of the normal progress of axonal flow.

It was risky to generalize this conclusion; yet, convection rates in nerve of the order of millimeters per day have in the meantime been confirmed in such a variety of forms and conditions, as documented below, that the value is beginning to assume an aspect of universality. It refers only to the advance of the axonal column as a whole, not to other traffic within the axon. Moreover, the simplification of expressing volume flow rates in the linear dimension of millimeters is permissible only in comparisons between axons or parts of axons of nearly the same diameter; otherwise, unit volume displacement per unit of time would have to be recorded.

We have also studied axonal consistency and flow properties by direct cinemicrography of enforced flow. Myelinated nerve fibers of mature animals (mice, rats, etc.) were filmed while mild compression was applied to the nerve at a point outside the visual field. The axonal column was seen to yield to the local compression by translatory displacement: it moved like a semisolid body with frictional delay along the wall, yet with considerable resilience, as evidenced by its recoil to the original position after decompression. There was evidence, corroborated by electron microscopic criteria, that the axonal mass moves with a radial velocity gradient grading off from the central axis to the sheath. Consequently, any summary values for axonal flow rates must be taken as statistical averages across the axonal cross section. The films have also revealed signs of lability in the local physical state of axoplasm in fresh mature nerve fibers even in the absence of microsurgical interventions such as were observed by de Rényi [58] and Péterfi [55] in 1929. The entry into "Brownian motion" of formerly absolutely stationary granular inclusions signaled the formation of small local pools of lique-faction in the otherwise gelated axoplasmic column. Enforced flow of the axon either bypassed those blisters or swept them along.

In this connection one point must be stressed rather forcefully. Extensive first-hand experience with living nerve fibers in both the embryonic and consolidated mature state leaves no doubt that their differences in physical consistency and in structural and hydrodynamic properties are so profound that unverified extrapolations of observations and conclusions from one to the other are as misleading as if one were to equate the nucleated and highly mobile mammalian erythroblast cell with the mature, anucleate, encysted red blood corpuscle into which it becomes converted. Even more gratuitous are comparisons between the polarized axonal flow and the cyclic "fountain currents" of cytoplasmic streaming in protistan cells [Allen, see ref. 2] although the possibility of common elementary molecular mechanisms of all cell motility need not be questioned.

ELECTRON MICROSCOPY

Because the structural deformities in the damming process are decisive for the issue of axonal flow, we have carried on extensive studies on the ultrastructural details of constricted nerves under the electron microscope [for preliminary notes, see Weiss et al., 82, 84; a comprehensive account is being prepared for publication]. In general, our electron optical data on normal axons are in accord with the observations reported by others in the current literature. The matrix contains the commonly acknowledged longitudinal structures—rectilinear neurotubules, about 220 Å wide, more wavy neurofilaments, about 80 Å thick, and sparse stretches of vacuolated strands that could pass for endoplasmic reticulum. The neurotubules unquestionably are serious candidates for the role of conduits for intraaxonal transport. One additional feature, rather common in overosmicated preparations, deserves special mention as a possible channel for a special transport system within the interior of the axon. As is illustrated in Fig. 4 and diagrammatically in Fig. 5, cross sections often show the rather regularly distributed neurotubules at the intersections of a lattice of rather electron-dense strands, delineating spaces between them, which by their rounded contours intimate liquid turgidity. Those meshes, ranging between 500 and 800 Å in width, could easily be the cross sections of a longitudinal canalicular system in the axonal matrix. Both in position and size, these "intertubular spaces" correspond closely to the far more regular "honeycomb" arrays of tube-like structures discovered recently in a wide variety of neurons, both

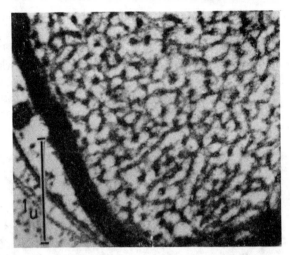

Fig. 4. Electron micrograph of cross section through rat axon showing the regular lattice arrangement of neurotubules and intertubular canals.

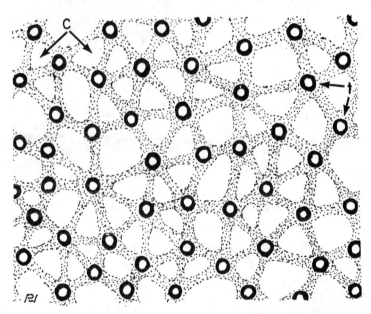

Fig. 5. Schematic representation of lattice arrangement of Fig. 4. Neurotubules (dark rings, *t*) lie in a spongy matrix permeated by cavities (*C*), which by the shape of their contours indicate turgidity of enclosed liquid (possibly exaggerated as a result of fixation).

central and peripheral, and under both "normal" and "pathological" conditions [27, 48]. The very haphazard way in which this structure has cropped out in the literature, as well as in our own records, seems to suggest that it represents a common feature of neurons, which, under the conventional treatments for electron microscopic study, remains indistinct, but can emerge into the range of visibility as a result of either pathological changes in the local axoplasmic state or of modified treatment, as after overosmication.

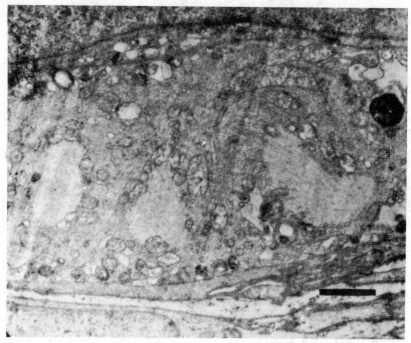

Fig. 6.   Electron micrograph of longitudinal section through the "dammed" portion of a constricted axon, showing the windings and foldings in the fine structural elements. Scale = 1 micron.

The electron microscopic pictures of the dammed portions of constricted nerve fibers were in full accord with our earlier microscopic observations. In cross sections of axons at this level, the bundles of neurofilaments and neurotubules showed confused, contorted courses with intersections of whorls and loops. In longitudinal sections, the convoluted course of both neurotubules and neurofilaments conformed exactly to the contour folds and twists of the whole axon (Fig. 6). This seals the proof that the deformities, pictured in Fig. 2, reflect the interior structure of the axon faithfully. The neurotubules were found more crowded toward the surface, while the filaments occupied mainly the axial core. In many cases, the outline between these two regions was quite sharp, indicating an interface of laminar flow between the frictionally retarded flow along the axonal wall and the swifter flow in the middle. Microstructures thus serve as flow gauges.

The occurrence of strings of vesicles proximal to constrictions, as well as at the blind ends of completely severed axons, first described by van Breemen *et al.* [5], has been observed routinely in our preparations of both partially and totally occluded nerves. Their possible bearing on the

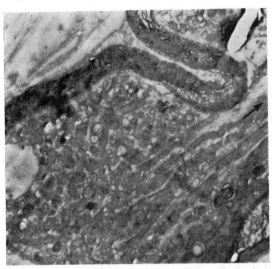

FIG. 7. Electron micrograph of the dammed portion of a partially constricted axon, showing the accumulation of mitochondria at a cross fold. Note the marked difference between the normal straight mitochondria in the middle region, where flow is unobstructed (arrow), and the pile of stranded mitochondria in all stages of degeneration nearer the surface, especially behind the fold.

origin of "synaptic vesicles" calls for more systematic investigations into the pinched-off bulbous swellings at the blind ends of the various canal systems in the axon [11, 54].

The most conspicuous electron microscopic disclosure was the shift in the mitochondrial distribution [32, 82]. A 50-mμ-thick cross section through a normal axon contains, on an average, two mitochondrial cross sections. A similar section through an axon at a chronic bottleneck shows within a few days, and thereafter continuously, a hundred or more mitochondrial sections (Fig. 7). Like the neurotubules, and interspersed with them, they are concentrated in the superficial layers of the axon, in various stages of degeneration. In the axial part, the mitochondria are numerous, but elongated and of normal appearance. Taken together, cinemicrography of enforced flow and electron microscopy of partially obstructed flow patterns lead to the following conclusions. The damming of flow within each individual axon permits the unimpeded passing of only the axial center of the stream, while the more superficial layers are increasingly retarded. As a result, the mitochondria traveling near the surface are arrested and accumulate like floats washed ashore at the banks of a river. Conceivably, the breakdown products of the stagnated mitochondria lead to the coagulation of an axonal crust. The fact that the mitochondria are being carried down continuously with the axonal stream in no way precludes the possibility of their carrying out additional active local excursions on their own within a narrow range, particularly also in the liquid pools mentioned above, much as a swimmer can swim upstream or downstream in a current. The active motility of mitochondria has, after all, been well known since the classical motion pictures of cultured tissue cells by Fréderic and Chèvremont [15].

Since the density of the sparse mitochondrial population of the axon does not seem to vary along its course, the main and presumably exclusive source of mitochondrial reproduction must lie in the perikaryon. Thus the rate of reproduction can then be estimated. If mitochondria of a length of a few microns are carried down by axonal flow a few millimeters per day, the distance of their daily travel is about 500 to 1000 times their own length. Accordingly, in order to maintain this standard rate of export of mitochondria, the cell body would have to reproduce up to 1000 mitochondria per day, and this number then passes daily any given level of a nerve fiber. Applied to the level of the entrance to a bottleneck and assuming a case in which only about 80% could move through freely in the axial part of the stream, this would calculate to a local retention and accumulation of the order of 100 mitochondria in front of the entrance, a value which agrees roughly with our actual observations. As this arrested population represents the equilibrium ratio of new arrivals over disintegrated earlier arrivals, breakdown of arrested neural mitochondria would seem to be very rapid. As far as the axon is concerned, the mitochondrion serves mainly as a useful marker and index of the axonal stream. One wonders, however, about the fate and possible recycling of the breakdown products of mitochondria that have reached the end of the line at nerve terminations, particularly nucleic acids, amino acids, and nucleotides set free.

Having dealt with the phenomenon of axonal flow in descriptive terms, we can now turn our attention to the meaning of this chemical transport system.

CHEMICAL INTERPRETATION AND ISOTOPE STUDIES

The observations on axonal flow led to the hypothesis that it represented a feeder column carrying materials produced in the cell body for the needs of both the internal household of the nerve fiber and the periphery innervated by it. As I stated in 1944, "mature axons thus seem to grow perpetually from their cells, undergoing commensurate peripheral dissipation" [68]. I also indicated at that time that the dissipation might include "the discharge of substances (e.g., acetylcholine and other neurohumors) from peripheral nerve." I then made the fairly broad jump to postulate that the primacy of the perikaryon for macromolecular synthesis pertained particularly to the *proteins* destined for the axon as replacements for its catabolically degrading enzyme systems. This antedated our knowledge of Hydén's work [28], which clearly anticipated and corroborated our presumptions by far more direct means. All of this, of course, also preceded by a considerable period the identification of the pathway of synthesis from DNA through transcription to RNA, to eventual translation into primary protein assembly.

My rationale at that time was derived from scattered data in the literature about the high level of ammonia liberation from peripheral nerves. The argument ran about as follows [80]: If protein is manufactured exclusively in the perikaryon and shipped from there into the peripheral nerve fiber, then its progressive catabolic degradation there, with no opportunity for local reutilization of the breakdown products, should end in complete deamination, the end product being eliminated as ammonia. By calculating, on that highly tenuous assumption, the average rate of catabolism of proteins in nerve, we arrived at a figure for their half-life time of the order of a month. This rough estimate permitted us to make a tentative calculation of what the rate of replenishment of protein in nerve fibers would have to be if the whole supply were to come from a central source in step with its peripheral degradation. It turned out that this would require a steady supply stream from the cell advancing at a rate of the order of millimeters per day. The correspondence between this figure and the actually observed rate of advance of dammed axoplasm in deconstricted fibers, suggestive though it was, might also have been sheer coincidence.

It did, however, encourage more direct tests, such as the tracing of the purported transport from its site of origin with radioactive markers. Our first experiments were confined to tracking endoneurial flow [85], which is about 25 times faster than the axonal flow in the same direction. Attempts to mark the latter started in 1949 with radioactive phosphorus, both in my laboratory [61] and that of Gerard [59], the latter demonstrating a general shift of radioactivity in ^{35}P-labeled nerves, corroborated later by others [51] and finding a temporary climax when Waelsch [65], using ^{14}C-amino acids as labels, demonstrated the progressive proximodistal shift of protein in nerve by chemical identification [also H. Koenig, 37]. There followed from many laboratories a large volume of investigations on the problem with a rich yield. Since they have been summarized in this symposium, as well as in three preceding ones [2, 24, 34], the reader may be referred to those sources for further information. A major advance came through the development of radio-autography, expedited by the introduction of tritium as isotopic marker by Droz and Leblond [12], which we then adopted and further adapted to our aims.

Our main object has remained to use the cellulifugal shift of proteins as recorder of axonal flow, and tritiated amino acid as a marker for the proteins in which it had become incorporated. It is evident, however, that the incorporation process itself in the cell body forms as much an integral part of the study program as does the transport and further fate of the labeled mass. Axonal flow thus turns into an important indicator of the biosynthetic growth dynamics of the neuronal cell body. In the following, I shall concentrate mainly on results obtained in my laboratory since the last comprehensive review [76a].

By selecting nerves singularly suited for the purpose by their anatomy, we succeeded in keeping the labeling of the protein source more rigorously localized to the nerve cells themselves without the radiocontamination of the rest of the animal, which is unavoidable in most pulse injection methods. Moreover, the resulting increase of the signal-to-noise ratio of "hot" axons over a "cold" background permits the performance of large-scale experiments with scintillation counter recording. The first experiments, the administering of microinjections of tritiated leucine into the vitreous body of the eye in the mouse, fully met the requirement [62]. The amino acid was promptly incorporated and remained strictly confined to the cells of the retina, which contains the cells of origin of the optic nerve, leaving the rest of the animal unmarked. The radioautographic records of the optic nerves (Fig. 8) revealed that some of the labeling solution had seeped into the extraaxonal spaces between the optic nerve fibers during the first 3 hours after injection and had become fixed in the proteins of the glial cells of the nerve near its exit from the orbit (shaded area in Fig. 8), while the intraaxonal advance of the label from the retina to the brain had proceeded in the form of a traveling wave, again at the rate of about 1 mm per day. Its crest shows a progressive flattening, which proves that different points along the wave front advance at different rates as predicted by the core-to-surface velocity gradient with the individual axon, as described above. Presumably this is further accentuated by rate differentials between axons of different kinds and sizes. Further experiments with the same technique in fish [46] identified two waves of proteins advancing from retina toward brain at different speeds, one of the usual axonal flow rate of the order of 1 mm per day, the other faster by one order of magnitude, each different from the other chemically and in its terminal localization in the brain. We shall return below to the problem of such fast transport.

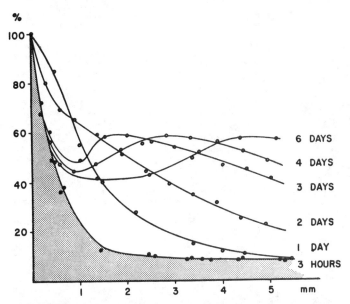

FIG. 8. Counts of silver grains over radioautographs of optic nerves from eyes injected with tritiated leucine, normalized by setting each highest count (at exit from bulb) as 100%.

The nerve most conveniently to be labeled at its source is the olfactory, whose cell bodies lie in the nasal lining and therefore can be readily marked from the outside. In tracing radioautographically the advance of the labeled proteins toward the brain (Fig. 9) [81], no transsynaptic transfer of labeled material beyond the primary neuron was seen, at least for the first 3 weeks. However, this experimental design has not yet been further exploited, largely because it has been superseded by our success in altogether eliminating, for short-range tests of neuronal growth dynamics, the living animal. As it turned out, *in vitro* experiments are not only simpler and less laborious, but can yield fully conclusive answers to many urgent questions faster and on a much larger scale than do experiments with whole animals.

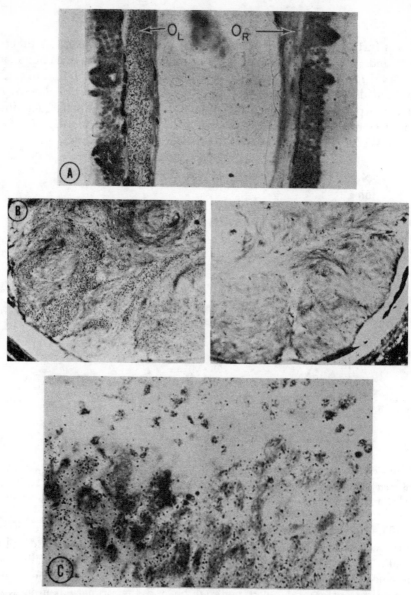

Fɪɢ. 9. Radioautographs of olfactory nerves of toads which had received tritiated leucine in their left nostrils (A and C, 14 days; B, 11 days, previously). (A) Frontal section through nasal septum, showing the bilateral nerves, the left (O_L) heavily radioactive, the right (O_R) blank. (B) Flaring of olfactory nerve bundles at entrance into fore brain (symmetrical sectors of same brain cross section), the streaks of silver grains indicating fascicles from labeled regions of the nasal epithelium. (C) Longitudinal section through synaptic zone of labeled fibers (from A) in the olfactory bulb, showing no passage of labeled protein beyond the boundaries of the primary neuron.

The basic technique (Fig. 10) is as follows [76]. Spinal ganglia, with their sensory nerves left attached, are excised, and the ganglionic ends are immersed in tritiated leucine for 2 hours. In order to test for contamination of the initial segment of peripheral nerves by labeling solution, the labeled ganglia of half of them are then cut off, while the other half retain theirs as protein source. After a few days in nutrient

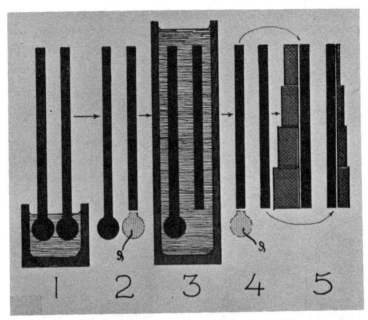

Fig. 10. Experimental design for testing transfer of labeled protein from spinal ganglion to peripheral nerve *in vitro* or in subcutaneous transplants. *1*, Immersion of ganglia of two sensory nerves into solution containing radioactive amino acid; *2*, amputation of ganglion from one of the nerves; *3*, immersion of both nerves in nutrient (or transplanted subcutaneously); *4*, postculturing ablation of second ganglion; *5*, determination of radioactivity in the pair of nerve stumps (shaded areas representing respective activity counts in corresponding quarter sections of the two nerves).

medium, radioactivity was then invariably found to be about twice as high in the axons of the ganglionated specimens as in the control sets (Fig. 11), the difference corresponding to a minimum daily influx from the ganglion cells into the axons of 6–11% protein, varying with the length and conditions of culture. Assuming a commensurate traffic rate for the nonprotein compounds, one can roughly calculate that the whole macromolecular population of the nerve cell is renewed about once every day, which, translated into axonal dimensions, again gives an average centrifugal outflow from the cell of the order of 1 mm of axonal length per day. Allowance must be made, however, for the fact that nerve cell bodies whose axons have been cut show an early rise of their synthetic (regenerative) activity [50].

Incidentally, in view of the recurrent question about possible relations between nerve excitation and axonal flow, it is worth stressing that in

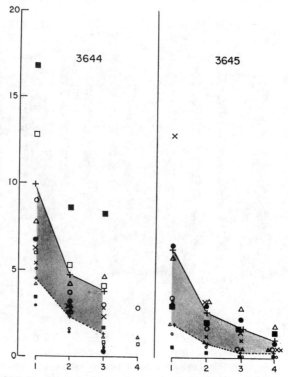

Fig. 11. Activity counts in 2 experiments with 6 and 5 nerve pairs, respectively, treated as in Fig. 10 (subcutaneous for 4 days). Counts of the ganglionated and de-ganglionated members of each pair are represented by identical symbols of larger and smaller sizes, respectively. Means for each set are marked by large and small plus (+) signs and are connected by lines, the shaded area between them representing the 4-day radioactive influx from the ganglion.

these tests with sensory ganglia, the protein-marked flow was strictly *cellulifugal*, that is, in the direction *opposite* to afferent impulse conduction from sensory receptors. We can also corroborate the finding [40] that the flow of and in the dorsal root branches of the ganglionic neurons is toward the spinal cord, that is, parallel to impulse propagation, as in all motor fibers.

Even though the *in vitro* experiments include several hundreds of nerves, they must be treated as no more than bulk determinations, on several accounts. The cells of any given ganglion differ widely in their degree of amino acid incorporation, reflecting either constitutional disparity or physiological fluctuations. Lumping all proteins under a single measure is likewise not very informative, particularly in view of the presumable difference in rates of advance of such constituents as solid structures (e.g., filaments and tubules), free enzymes, protein cores or shells of granules). In that sense, the high resolution attained by the combination of radioautography and electron microscopy in the studies of Droz [13], also reviewed in this symposium, promises to bring far more penetrating insights into the dynamics of perpetual neuronal growth.

On the other hand, the rapidity and ease of the direct immersion method for labeling neural protein synthesis, especially in connection with the elegant microincineration techniques of Gupta [22] for scintillation counter measurements of microamounts of radioactivity, has induced me to start a rough assay, survey-fashion, of factors of potentially enhancing, inhibitory, or otherwise modifying, influence on the mature neuron—revealed now as one of the fastest growing cells of the adult body. Most of these tests are still incomplete and are listed here simply as signs of the wide applicability of the method. The ones sampled in the following paragraph are no longer concerned primarily with "axonal flow" as index of the neuronal production plant, but with the latter itself. The assays consisted of comparing radioactive protein values of (a) isolated control spinal ganglia soaked for 2 hours in standard medium with leucine-^{3}H, with those of (b) ganglia that had been exposed to various test treatments (in order for such measurements of radioactivity to be assigned to protein alone, the radioactive leucine bath must be followed by a chase of at least one hour with ordinary leucine).

As for the medium itself, there was no noticeable difference over the few hours of duration of our experiments between different balanced salt solutions commonly in use for explants (T.C. 199; Earle's; Eagles' solution). Differences in pH, surprisingly, did not materially affect incorporation rates, either. Stimulation (electrical for ganglia and cord; light for retina) did seem to have some effect, but not consistent enough to be reported even tentatively. This was unexpected in view of the well-established increase of protein synthesis in functionally exercised nerve cells in the intact animal [29, 30]. Of course, allowance must be made for the relative brevity of our test periods. One striking effect deserving to be followed up in more detail has been the greatly reduced incorporation of leucine in protein of nerve tissue immersed for a few hours in isotope solution to which anesthetics (e.g., sodium barbital) have been added. Addition of such agents leads to a loss of protein from the tissue, as evidenced by both the drastic reduction of radioactivity in the tissue and the retrieval of the lost protein in the solution. The rapidity of such changes recommends the technique of labeling by direct immersion as an adjunct to the more analytical techniques of higher chemical resolving power, to be reviewed by others in this symposium.

SUPPORTING DATA

The evidence gathered thus far strongly supports the conclusion that the perikaryon is by far the *major* source of macromolecular synthesis and further assembly of cell products for the whole neuron. On the other hand, whether it is the exclusive source of *all* protein, is still debated. The requirement of RNA for the patterning of amino acid sequences in proteins, together with the high concentration of ribonucleoprotein (Nissl substance) in the perikaryon, definitely marks the territory around the nucleus as the site of protein synthesis. Moreover, cytochemically, virtually all RNA in the neuron has been found concentrated in the perikaryon. Axons have been described as either devoid of it or containing minimal amounts [35] with some noteworthy exceptions, such as the Mauthner's fiber in lower vertebrates [31] (see also the report by A. Edström in this symposium). *In vitro* tests with tritiated uridine have shown RNA turnover to be sharply confined to the perikaryon with no incorporation beyond the axon hillock [63]. However, since some protein synthesis has been claimed to occur peripherally [36, 49], particularly that of cholinesterase, it would be unsafe at the present stage to take a definite position. The question is a purely empirical one. In this connection, the possible role of DNA and RNA liberated from the disintegrating mitochondria arriving daily at nerve endings in large numbers deserves to be examined.

Far more definite than its connection with the internal metabolic household of the neuron is the role of axonal flow as a vehicle for the transport of specialized cell products from the central site of manufacture to peripheral destinations. The whole field of neurosecretion is full of illustrative examples [19]. In fact, as one now recognizes, the cases in which traveling neuroendocrine products of the cell body can be tracked visually by their particulate or vacuolar form are merely special manifestations of the general principle of axonal flow. Originally derived from microscopic observations, the list of pertinent examples has been greatly enlarged with the advent of the electron microscope, many of the formed globules being of submicroscopic dimensions. Whenever rates of movement of microscopically visible inclusions were recorded, they fell predominantly again in the millimeter-per-day range. But this rule applies no longer uniformly for the convection of either submicroscopic particles or substances in molecular form, as outlined in the following paragraphs.

There has been increasingly conclusive evidence for the fact that substances instrumental in impulse transmission are manufactured in the perikaryon and conducted from there down the axon to their peripheral destinations. The most comprehensive demonstration has been furnished for the catecholamines in sympathetic nerves [64], the container granules of which prove their cellulifugal convection by piling up progressively in front of nerve constrictions [9, 10, 33]; (see also the report by Dahlström in this symposium). However, rate determinations of this transport yielded velocity values far in excess of the millimeter-per-day class. Similar rapid dispatch of labeled materials in proximodistal direction has been recorded for phospholipids [47], and furthermore for the fast component of the bimodal rate curve of protein shift in nerve [41, 46], in which the slow component is consistently of the millimeter rate of the axonal flow proper. The fact that the observed slow and fast rates do not form a graded scale, but cluster about distinctly separate modes, strongly suggests a multiplicity of pathways in the system of the nerve, to which we shall return below.

Additional experiments on more diffuse labeling of nerve sources in brain and spinal cord have confirmed the proximodistal convection [52, 57], but are of lower resolving power than those reported in the preceding sections. One further observation, presumably related to the internal catabolic degradation of the axonal column on its way, is the proximodistal decline of the axonal content of cholinesterase and choline acetylase [25, 43].

A special place in the modes of cellulifugal traffic must be assigned to those respiratory enzyme systems that are physically incorporated in mitochondria. Such enzymes have been demonstrated histochemically to accumulate at the level of obstruction in constricted or crushed nerves (succinic acid dehydrogenase [16], diphosphopyridine nucleotide dehydrogenase [38a]). This fact is obviously fully explained by the proximodistal movement of their carriers, the mitochondria, which in turn are conveyed downward by the axonal flow, as described earlier in this paper.

TRANSPORT MECHANISMS

Axonal Flow

The technological analysis of axonal flow had led to certain minimum presuppositions about the driving mechanism involved. *Static* pressure from an expanding cell body with increasing turgor [86] can definitely be ruled out, for in any tubular system with some degree of elasticity and plasticity, such as a nerve fiber, inflation from the end could only result in a dilation of the base, tapering off toward the tip, which is exactly the reverse of the polarity of the observed deformations of dammed axons. The actual mechanism had to be sought in a *dynamic* drive operating all along the length of the nerve fiber, roughly comparable to the roller belt of an assembly conveyor. This fact is demonstrated most convincingly by the double damming of axoplasm in front of both of two partial constrictions placed on the same fibers in tandem [8, 45, 80]. The most plausible assumption was a microperistaltic wave in the surface of the fiber propelling the enclosed content away from the cell (Fig. 12).

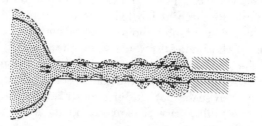

Fig. 12. Diagram showing the deforming effects of peristaltic hydrodynamic propulsion.

In mechanical devices of this kind, the rate of the traveling wave of the drive need not be directly related to the rate of the advance of the driven core. Observations on rhythmic contraction-relaxation pulses sweeping over the surfaces of certain eggs and tissue cells [72] and the fact that such circling waves, when constrained linearly into a cylindrical path, assume the aspect and properties of a peristaltic wave, encouraged the attempt to obtain direct visual signs of the axonal drive by cinemicrography [73, 84].

Spinal ganglia of the trunk region of young mice, excised with their intercostal nerves attached, were placed into specially designed chambers continuously perfused by a carefully balanced nutrient medium, in which they stayed alive for a week or longer. In a given region of the nerve, stripped of its perineurium, the nerve fibers were teased apart so as to expose individual fibers to high-power phase-contrast microscopy. Time-lapse cinemicrographs were then taken continuously for days. The major features can be summarized as follows.

Both intact fibers and fibers in the early stages of Wallerian degeneration, already segmented into ovoids, show continuous peristaltic motions, polarized, as far as can be discerned, proximodistally with regard to the position of the ganglion. Once started, these waves go on without interruption at a relatively constant rhythm of about 16 minutes per single contraction-relaxation cycle. This rhythm was about the same regardless of the fiber diameter. It was found both when the fiber was still continuous or when it had segmented as a result of degeneration. This fact evidently confirms the inference drawn from the sum of our experiments that the motive mechanism for the axonal propulsion must be present at every point along the whole length of the fiber. The wave appears as a conspicuous traveling deformation of both the myelin sheath and the enclosed axon, involving either the whole circumference or rippling only a part of it. The axonal content often moves more slowly than the surface wave. In the presence of obstructions by kinks or convolutions, the former may be completely arrested until its continuing longitudinal compression has built up a sufficient pressure head to ram the front across the block.

Sheath cells glide up and down along the fiber within the endoneurial tube with great agility, but so erratically that it is doubtful that the axonal beat in its polarization could be correlated with their motility. At the same time, the observation of rhythmic pulsation in explanted glia cells [56], extended now to many other cell types [72], as well as the general symbiotic relation between Schwann cell and axon, call for a far more systematic investigation of their respective roles in the axonal drive. Considering the paucity of mitochondria within the axon, it would seem logical to ascribe the energy supply for the perpetual axonal drive to the mitochondria-laden Schwann cell. The actual motile mechanism, however, must be located somewhere in the myelin sheath, or the axolemma, or perhaps in the cooperative process between the lipid layers and the spiral windings of sheath cell protoplasm sandwiched between them. I have presented a hypothetical model of how such a combined lipid-protein array, surrounding an incompressible content, could act as mechanism for a peristaltic drive in cells in general [74], but factual data to support the model are still missing. One reason why the Schwann cell, though perhaps energizing the axonal drive, is unlikely to contain also the effectuating machinery is that the frequency range observed in the pulsation of glia cells [56] is about twice as high as that of nerve fibers [73].

A lucky incident in one of the films has furnished a significant clue to the understanding of the peristaltic process. A rather quiescent nerve fiber had one local spot on its surface at which the myelin sheath bulged into the axon in the form of a dimple, and this local pit contracted rhythmically and continuously at the usual frequency of about 4 pulses per hour. The rest of the myelin sheath and of the axon remained mostly inactive and smooth. Every once in a while, however, a polarized traveling wave would start from the beating center and run off as a peristaltic movement down the whole stretch of fiber in the visual field. Formally, the picture is similar, except for the time parameters involved, to that of a local rhythmic excitatory process of subliminal intensity building up gradually to threshold level and actuating then a propagated disturbance. Any more specific contentions about the process would seem unwarranted. In all of this, the conspicuous activities of the myelin sheath must be regarded only as amplified indicators of underlying motility in the axolemma-sheath cell-membrane, for one must remember that there is axonal flow in unmyelinated fibers.

Despite our extensive cinemicrographic studies over many years, more questions have remained open than have been answered. For instance, our attempts to demonstrate axonal flow in small subcutaneous nerve bundles in anesthetized living animals have remained inconclusive. It is possible that the spectacular surface deformations that mark the peristaltic wave in our teased fibers, which are unconstrained, could not occur in intact nerves *in situ*, whose fibers are tightly packed within an indistensible perineurial sheath. Therefore, the conspicuous waves of *isotonic* contractions seen in our unsheated fibers *in vitro* could, in the intact nerves of the animal, be represented by *isometric* waves of pressure differences, which do not register optically and for which adequate engineering models are still lacking. We are now in the process of designing and testing models of non-Newtonian flow in narrow channels to simulate axonal flow. One encouraging development has been the theoretical confirmation [18] that traveling surface waves of amplitudes that are small in proportion to the lumen of a channel can effectively propel the content of the channel; and that the resulting flow proceeds with a paraboloid velocity profile, in good correspondence with the evidence of an axis-to-surface velocity gradient which we have found in our electron micrographs and in the motion pictures of enforced flow.

Intraaxonal Transport

As stated above, the discovery of cellulifugal transmission of materials down the axon at speeds that are at least one order of magnitude faster than the average rate of the axonal flow proper make it imperative to search for a separate intraaxonal transport system. This search is severely handicapped by the lack of specific data and theory in matters of transport mechanisms at high velocities for macromolecules and particles in systems in which free mobility is rigorously restricted by microstructural constraints.

If we assume that at least the transport of substance in molecular dispersion is carried out in solution, and further suppose, as indicated earlier, that the neurotubules with a lumen of the order of 10^2 Å serve as liquid conduits, then at the reported speeds of up to 500 mm (5×10^9 Å) per day [39], each unit would move a distance of the order of 100 times the width of the channel per second. Considering, in addition, that in those small dimensions the inner surface of a tube, which exerts frictional drag on flow, is relatively immense—the ratio of channel circumference to channel cross section for a microtubule being 100,000 times as large, for instance, as that for a 1-mm wide tube—the gravity of the problem of the hydrodynamics of rapid flow in those minute dimensions can be appreciated. The pumping force for such a convection would have to be inordinately high, which obviously presupposes continuity and great structural strength of the pipeline; this fact, in turn, sets up limiting conditions for the permeability of the wall—all being factors on which we have no data. The scale models we are designing to simulate fluid mechanics in ultramicrodimensions are intended to shed some light on whether or not a *liquid* column can at all be propelled in such minute conduits at the requisite speeds.

Crucial to the answer to this question is the nature of the propulsive drive, at present equally unknown. The driving mechanism could again be visualized as some sort of submicroperistalsis, comparable in principle to the drive of axonal flow, scaled down in its dimensions by two orders of magnitude. One could, for instance, conceive of the following possibility. Suppose the purportedly globular protein subunits of the dozen or so spiral filaments that compose the wall of a neurotubule [60] change their conformation in response to an input of electrical or chemical energy at their central end. Suppose further that the resulting volume shrinkage or closer packing of the constituent molecules occurs in synchrony around the circumference of a tubule. This would then amount to a transitory local constriction of the lumen. Now, if the conformational change were self-propagating along the axis of the tube in the manner of a molecular "bucket brigade," comparable to a fuse, such a chain reaction would constitute the element of a peristaltic pump.

A similar mechanism could be assumed to operate in the propulsion of macromolecular clusters, micelles, and particulates of diameters approximately equal to the width of the lumen of a contractile tube. The correspondence in size between the intertubular spaces of 600–800 Å diameters, referred to above, and catecholamine granules suggests that the former might be the conduits for the latter, the granules being massaged downward by the aggregate effect of the peristalsis of the several neurotubules spaced around the circumference of each channel. An alternative mechanism, invoking a sort of direct molecular cogwheel traction exerted by matching subunits at the sites of contact between granule and tubular wall, has been suggested by Schmitt [60]. However, none of these hypotheses about rapid transfer of solid particulates otherwise than by passive flushing down in a liquid stream, have taken due account of the tremendous resistance that must be overcome in transit through a stagnant medium, whether of high or low viscosity. "Frictional" resistance to movement in cylinders with narrow diameters would be expected to be enormous. Even allowing for empirical corrections for the difference between straight translatory motion and rolling, there are powerful obstacles to rapid transport.

In conclusion, a realistic look at possible mechanisms of both liquid and solid transfer systems confronts us with problems which in our present state of knowledge still seem insoluble. Evidently, we miss some basic key to the general understanding of how subcellular units in the macromolecular size range and above are dispatched from source to destination. Pending detection, and perhaps as a step to it, we must make do with the kind of tentative conjectures exemplified in the preceding paragraphs.

In contrast to the uncertainties regarding the mechanism of fast transfer, the supposition that the neurotubules are instrumental in it rests on firmer ground. Their bulbous widening at obstructions, often accompanied by the pinching off of the widened ends as vesicles, as observed electron microscopically [see above; also 5, 54] indicates that their fluid content is under steady hydrodynamic pressure in the centrifugal direction. But aside from this proof of distensibility of the tubular wall, no further information about intratubular flow has come from these observations.

A possible role of neurotubules in fast axoplasmic transport is supported by recent experiments of Kreutzberg [38]. He found that injection of colchicine under the epineurial sheath blocks the transport of acetylcholinesterase down the axon across the blocked stretch, resulting in a piling up of enzyme at the proximal margin. Since colchicine has been known to destroy the motility of microtubules, which are the constituents and contractile elements of the mitotic spindles of tissue cells, and since ordinary microtubules and neurotubules appear to be closely related, if not indeed identical, it seems reasonable to ascribe with Kreutzberg the colchicine effect on nerve to a direct action on the neurotubular apparatus, thus assigning to the latter the function not only of conduit, but also of motile agent for fast intraaxonal flow [see also Schmitt, 60].

Questions raised about the essentiality of neurotubules for fast transport on grounds of their erratic appearance in electron micrographs can be countered by pointing at uncontrolled variables, such as fluctuations in the local physiological state of a given nerve, capricious variations in the histological technique, and constitutional differences between different types of nerves, all of which result in erratic image formation.

Significantly, the same submaximal doses of colchicine that stalled the transit of *fast* traffic, however, left the *slow* advance of the axonal flow, as gauged by a mitochondrion-associated enzyme (diphosphopyridine nucleotide diaphorase) unaffected [38], thus further substantiating the distinction between the two systems and their respective drives.

COMMENTS

Both the axonal and intraaxonal traffic considered in the preceding sections have been in the proximodistal direction with regard to the perikaryon (cellulifugal). Nothing in our observations on either type of flow has given any indication that a reversal in the direction of streaming ever takes place. Nor can I find any evidence in the pertinent literature that would make it necessary to postulate such a reversal. Claims to the contrary have been presented, but pending more conclusive substantiation, all of them lend themselves to alternative interpretations, fully compatible with unidirectionality of axonal and intraaxonal flow. As I have already pointed out above, observations on embryonic or regenerating nerve sprouts in tissue culture, in which bidirectional movements have been noted, cannot be applied by extrapolation to the mature and fully differentiated neuron. The fact that after the ligation or crushing of a nerve, there appears besides the progressively increasing and *lasting* accumulation of mitochondria, enzymes and transmitter substances at the proximal side of the obstruction, also a minor transitory accumulation of *short* duration on the distal side [42], has likewise been interpreted as a sign of centripetal flow. It has never been made clear by the proponents of such an interpretation whether they ascribe the effect to the presence in the nerve of a mixed population of fibers with opposite traffic directions or to bidirectionality of flow channels within a given axon. There is no *a priori* reason why such temporary antiperistalsis could not exist, but as long as the presumption remains based exclusively on observations near a *nerve lesion*, it would seem more reasonable to view those fleeting accumulations on the distal side as local disturbances resulting from the lesion, rather than as a sign of reversed flow. The observation reported above of small intraaxonal liquid pools, extending sometimes over a length of a few microns, likewise admits of free mobility of content, but these are sporadic, local inclusions in the moving axonal column.

Yet, even though the direction of axonal flow, according to the best evidence available at present, is unidirectionally *cellulifugal*, there are incontrovertible facts to make us postulate the existence of some sort of direct communication in the *centripetal* direction, i.e., from the periphery toward the cell body, mediated by a method other than impulse conduction. For example, there is evidence that neurotropic viruses (e.g., poliomyelitis) and some toxins (e.g., tetanus), when applied peripherally, reach the nerve centers by way of nerves. Even though in most cases the exact pathway, whether intraaxonal or interaxonal, has not been identified, at least the route of poliovirus has been described as being centripetal inside the axon [3, 4].

The most compelling case for postulating ascending communication between periphery and centers, not mediated through impulse conduction, rests on the chromatolytic reaction of the cell body upon severance of its axon. The peripheral disturbance in the state of the nerve evidently registers in the cell body within a matter of hours and initiates profound changes in the metabolic activity of the perikaryon. These changes consist of two overlapping phases, an upgrading and a regressive one, often wrongly treated as a single syndrome. While the former is clearly related to the restoration of neuronal integrity by regenerative outgrowth, the latter process is a direct result of the loss by the cell body of a functional connection with the peripheral tissues; for if regeneration of the axon is permanently suppressed, there ensues a lasting atrophy of the neuron [79], progressing sequentially from nucleolus to nucleus to cell body to axon [6].

There is thus clear evidence of a "trophic" influence continuously exerted by the intact peripheral connection of a neuron upon the metabolic state of the cell body. This afferent influence operates in the opposite direction from the better known efferent "trophic" maintenance effects of nerves upon the innervated tissues, both together establishing a "feedback" loop of reciprocal mutualism. The whole field of so-called "trophic" effects, however, is still so obscure [23] that it would be unwarranted to speculate about whether or not both branches of this circuit employ the same mechanism. We are equally in the dark in regard to the mechanisms by which effectors and receptors "modulate" their innervating neurons [75] or a similar, reciprocal, process with which nerves can modify their muscles [14]. All these reciprocal interrelations between neurons and peripheral tissues have in common that while the efferent, cellulifugal, component could readily be conceived of as another hypothetical function of axonal flow, the inverse afferent communication must be regarded, in the light of all currently available evidence, as a matter of "upstream navigation," rather than as a true reversal of the direction of flow.

Even though pleading ignorance of the nature of ascending traffic in nerve, I wish to come back to a suggestion I made earlier [73], which might offer a clue to a future solution of the problem. This is *interfacial transport*, or "creep," in multiphasic systems. In studying the spread of macromolecules in tendons, composed of collagen fibers in a continuous mucopolysaccharide matrix, we found test substances to concentrate heavily along the fiber surfaces and to spread there much faster in the direction of the fiber axes than in other directions [21, 72]. Since this was observed only for molecules and particles that carried an electric charge, and since clusters formed at the periodically spaced polar bands of the collagen fibers, one is led to conclude that this might represent a general model of fast saltatory transfer along a structured interface with periodically arranged sites of electric charges. It would seem conceivable to ascribe a similar guiding function to the interfaces between neurofilaments and their surrounding axonal matrix. But since it seems that such a possibility could be readily tested by appropriate isotope-marking experiments, we need not indulge in further guesswork.

It is self-evident, however, that having established the unsuspectedly high reproductive renewal rate of the molecular population of the neuron, combined with the correspondingly rapid and continuous communication from unit to unit, of which the "trophic" and neuroendocrine interactions are merely prominent examples, has opened a wholly new parameter for our thinking about the mechanism of *plastic and adaptive modifications* of the nervous system. These manifest themselves in such diverse phenomena as memory, acquired hypersensitivities, idiosyncrasies, drug addiction, and functional reconstitution after brain lesions.

The ability to account for adaptive plasticity is one of the severest tests any theory of the functioning of the central nervous sytsem must meet. Let me, in closing, translate it sketchily into concrete terms. The brain alone is reported to contain 10^{11} neurons, each with about 10^4 synaptic connections with other neurons, and every neuron, moreover, as I indicated earlier, is subject to about 10^4 internal self-renewals in a lifetime. This adds up to the astronomical figure of at least 10^{19} different constellations of neuronal states, which the integrative activity of the nervous system must deal with in such a coordinated manner that the *continuity and integrity of the overall patterns of performance* will be preserved in spite of that perpetual, inordinately rapid flux within and among the component units. This feature of conservatism becomes even more impressive if one bears in mind the extent of actual *loss* of neuronal units which a behavioral pattern can survive, not only after surgical deletions, but as a result of the steady reduction of the population of neurons due to wear and tear, amounting to about 10^3 neurons per day. As if these considerations were not enough to illustrate the difficulty of conceiving a theory that would satisfactorily explain the *conservation* of pattern amidst all that flux, the added feature of the *modifiability* of some of those patterns compounds the difficulty immeasurably.

In this sense, the demonstration of the inconstancy and continuous rapid renewal of the individual neuron may serve as a stimulus for an intensified search for the *integrative principles of the group dynamics* of neuronal collectives, which cannot be reconstructed from the knowledge of the cell biology of the individual neuronal elements with their vagaries and fluctuations. Yet, this is a matter that transcends the task of this symposium, which has been to focus on the neuron as a cellular unit. As far as that task is concerned, I hope to have demonstrated that the mature working neuron has emerged from its auxiliary status as only an inert conductor and distributor of impulses into the ranks of full-fledged growing cells, thus offering itself as a prime test object for the study of basic *cell biological* problems

ACKNOWLEDGMENTS

Original work reported in this article was partially supported by grants from the National Institutes of Health of the United States Public Health Service (current Grant No. NB-07348 to Paul Weiss as Principal Investigator) and from the Faith Foundation of Houston. None of this program could have been carried forth without the extraordinarily resourceful collaboration of members of my staff, particularly Dr. A. Cecil Taylor, Dr. Aiyappan Pillai, Dr. Bernice Grafstein, Dr. Katherine Lyser, Mrs. Yvonne Holland, and Mr. Albert Bock, as well as the invaluable help of friends from other institutions, especially Dr. Heinrich Waelsch and Dr. Abel Lajtha.

REFERENCES

1. Alexander, E., Jr., Woods, R. P., and Weiss, P., *Proc. Soc. Exptl. Biol. Med.* **68**, p. 380 (1948).
2. Barondes, S. H. and Samson, F. E., *Neurosci. Res. Program Bull.* **5**, 307 (1967).
3. Bodian, D., and Howe, H. A., *Bull. Johns Hopkins Hosp.* **68**, 248 (1941).
4. Bodian, D., and Howe, H. A., *Bull. Johns Hopkins Hosp.* **69**, 79 (1941).
5. Breemen, V. L. van, Anderson, E., and Reger, J. F., *Exptl. Cell Res.* **5**, Suppl., 153 (1958).
6. Cavanaugh, M. W., *J. Comp. Neurol.* **94**, 181 (1951).
7. Dahlström, A., *J. Anat.* **99**, 667 (1965).
8. Dahlström, A., *Acta Physiol. Scand.* **69**, 158 (1967).
9. Dahlström, A., and Häggendal, J., *Acta Physiol. Scand.* **67**, 271 (1966).
10. Dahlström, A., and Häggendal, J., *Acta Physiol. Scand.* **67**, 278 (1966)
11. De Robertis, E., *Science* **156**, 907 (1967).
12. Droz, B., and Leblond, C. P., *J. Comp. Neurol.* **121**, 325 (1963).
13. Droz, B., *J. Microscopie* **6**, 201 (1967).
14. Eccles, J. C., *in* "Exploratory Concepts in Muscular Dystrophy and Related Disorders" (A.T. Milhorat, ed.), p. 151. Excerpta Med. Found., Amsterdam, 1967.
15. Fréderic, J., and Chèvremont, M., *Arch. Biol.* (*Liege*) **63**, 109 (1952).
16. Friede, R. L., *Exptl. Neurol.* **1**, 441 (1959).

17. Friede, R. L., *Acta Neuropathol.* 3, 217 (1964).
18. Fung, Y. C., and Yih, C. S., *Trans. ASME (Am. Soc. Mech. Engrs.)* Paper No. 68-WA/APM-11 (1968).
19. Gabe, M., "Neurosecretion." Pergamon Press, Oxford, 1966.
20. Gerard, R. W., *Physiol. Rev.* 12, 469 (1932).
21. Grover, N., *Biophys. J.* 6, 71 (1966).
22. Gupta, G. N., *Anal. Chem.* 38, 1356 (1966).
23. Guth, L., *Physiol. Rev.* 48, 645 (1968).
24. Gutmann, E., and Hník, P., eds., "The Effect of Use and Disuse on Neuromuscular Functions." Publ. House Czech. Acad. Sci., Prague, 1963.
25. Hebb, C. O., and Silver, A., *Nature* 189, 123 (1961).
26. Heilbrunn, L. V., "An Outline of General Physiology," 2nd ed. Saunders, Philadelphia, Pennsylvania, 1943.
27. Hirano, A., Rubin, B., Sutton, C. H., and Zimmerman, H. M., *Acta Neuropathol.* 10, 17 (1968).
28. Hydén, H., *Acta Physiol. Scand.* 6, Suppl. 17, 5 (1943).
29. Hydén, H., *in* "Brain Function: RNA and Brain Function, Memory and Learning" (M.A.B. Brazier, ed.), p. 29. Univ. of California Press, Berkeley, California, 1965.
30. Hydén, H., *in* "The Neurosciences: A Study Program" (G. C. Quarton, T. Melnechuk, and F. O. Schmitt, eds.), p. 765. Rockefeller Univ. Press, New York, 1967
31. Jakoubek, B., and Edström, J. E., *J. Neurochem.* 12, 845 (1965).
32. Kapeller, K., and Mayor, D., *J. Physiol. (London)*, 191, 70 (1967).
33. Kapeller, K., and Mayor, D., *Proc. Roy. Soc.* B167, 282 (1967).
34. Kety, S. S., and Elkes, J., eds., "Regional Neurochemistry." Pergamon Press, Oxford, 1961.
35. Koenig, E., *J. Neurochem.* 12, 357 (1965).
36. Koenig, E., *J. Neurochem.* 14, 437 (1967).
37. Koenig, H., *Trans. Am. Neurol. Assoc.* 1958, 162 (1958).
38. Kreutzberg, G. W., *Proc. Natl. Acad. Sci. U.S.* 62, 722 (1969).
38a. Kreutzberg, G. W., and Wechsler, W., *Acta Neuropathol.* 2, 349 (1963).
39. Lasek, R. *J. Neurosci. Res. Program Bull.* 5, 314 (1967).
40. Lasek, R. J., *Brain Res.* 7, 360 (1968).
41. Lasek, R. J., *Exptl. Neurol.* 21, 41 (1968).
42. Lubínska, L., Niemierko, S., Oderfeld, B., Szwarc, L., and Zelená, J., *Acta Biol. Exptl. (Varsovie)* 23, 239 (1963).
43. Lubínska, L., *in* "Mechanisms of Neural Regeneration" (M. Singer and J. P. Schadé, eds.), Vol. 13, p. 1. Elsevier, Amsterdam, 1964.
44. Matson, D. D., Alexander, E., Jr., and Weiss, P., *J. Neurosurg.* 5, 230 (1948).
45. Mayor, D., and Kapeller, K., *J. Roy. Microscop. Soc.* [3] 87, 277 (1967).
46. McEwen, B. S., and Grafstein, B., *J. Cell Biol.* 38, 494 (1968).
47. Miani, N., *in* "Mechanisms of Neural Regeneration" (M. Singer and J. P. Schadé, eds.), Vol. 13, p. 115. Elsevier, Amsterdam, 1964.
48. Morales, R., and Duncan, D., *J. Ultrastruct. Res.* 15, 480 (1966).
49. Morgan, I. G., and Austin, L., *J. Neurochem.* 15, 41 (1968).
50. Murray, M., and Grafstein, B., *Exptl. Neurol.* 23, 544 (1969).
51. Ochs, S., and Burger, E., *Am. J. Physiol.* 194, 499 (1958).
52. Ochs, S., Dalrymple, D., and Richards, G., *Exptl. Neurol.* 5, 349 (1962).
53. Parker, G. H., *Am. Naturalist* 67, 147 (1932).

54. Pellegrino de Iraldi, A., and De Robertis, E., *Z. Zellforsch. Mikroskop. Anat.* **87**, 330 (1968).
55. Péterfi, J., *in* "Handbuch der normalen und pathologischen Physiologie" (A. Bethe *et al.*, eds.), Vol. 9, p. 79. Springer, Berlin, 1925–1932.
56. Pomerat, C. M., *Intern. Rev. Cytol.* **11**, 307 (1961).
57. Rahmann, H., *Z. Zellforsch. Mikroskop. Anat.* **86**, 214 (1968).
58. Rényi, G. J. de, *J. Comp. Neurol.* **47**, 405 (1929).
59. Samuels, A. J., Boyarsky, L. L., Gerard, R. W., Libet, B., and Brust, M., *Am. J. Physiol.* **164**, 1 (1951).
60. Schmitt, F. O., *Neurosci. Res. Program Bull.* **6**, 38 (1968).
61. Shepherd, E. H., Ph.D. Dissertation, University of Chicago (1951).
62. Taylor, A. C., and Weiss, P., *Proc. Natl. Acad. Sci. U. S.* **54**, 1521 (1965).
63. Utakoji, T., and Hsu, T. C., *J. Exptl. Zool.* **158**, 181 (1965).
64. von Euler, U. S., *Acta Physiol. Scand.* **43**, 155 (1958).
65. Waelsch, H., *J. Nervous Mental Disease* **126**, 33 (1958).
66. Waller, A., *Arch. Anat. Physiol. (Leipzig)* (1852).
67. Weiss, P., *Anat. Record* **86**, 491 (1943).
68. Weiss, P., *Anat. Record* **88**, Suppl., 464 (1944).
69. Weiss, P., *Biol. Bull.* **87**, 160 (1944).
70. Weiss, P., *J. Neurosurg.* **1**, 400 (1944).
71. Weiss, P., *in* "Regional Neurochemistry" (S. S. Kety and J. Elkes, eds.), p. 220. Pergamon Press, Oxford, 1961.
72. Weiss, P., *Proc. Robert A. Welch Found. Conf. Chem. Res.* **5**, 5 (1961).
73. Weiss, P., *in* "The Effect of Use and Disuse of Neuromuscular Functions" (E. Gutmann and P. Hnik, eds.), p. 171. Publ. House Czech. Acad. Sci., Prague, 1963.
74. Weiss, P., *Proc. Natl. Acad. Sci. U.S.* **52**, 1024 (1964).
75. Weiss, P., *Neurosci. Res. Program Bull.* **3**, No. 5, 1 (1965).
76. Weiss, P., *Proc. Natl. Acad. Sci. U. S.* **57**, 1239 (1967).
76a. Weiss, P., "Dynamics of Development: Experiments and Inferences," Chapter 23. Academic Press, New York, 1968.
77. Weiss, P., and Cavanaugh, M. W., *J. Exptl. Zool.* **142**, 461 (1959).
78. Weiss, P., and Davis, H., *J. Neurophysiol.* **6**, 269 (1943).
79. Weiss, P., Edds, M. V., Jr., and Cavanaugh, M. W., *Anat. Record* **92**, 215 (1945)
80. Weiss, P., and Hiscoe, H. B., *J. Exptl. Zool.* **107**, 315 (1948).
81. Weiss, P., and Holland, Y., *Proc. Natl. Acad. Sci. U.S.* **57**, 258 (1967).
82. Weiss, P., and Pillai, A., *Proc. Natl. Acad. Sci. U.S.* **54**, 48 (1965).
83. Weiss, P., and Taylor, A. C., *Proc. Soc. Exptl. Biol. Med.* **55**, 77 (1944).
84. Weiss, P., Taylor, A. C., and Pillai, P. A., *Science* **136**, 330 (1962).
85. Weiss, P., Wang, H., Taylor, A. C., and Edds, M. V., Jr., *Am. J. Physiol.* **143**, 521 (1945).
86. Young, J. Z., *in* "Essays on Growth and Form" (W. LeGros Clark and P. B. Medawar, eds.), p. 41. (Clarendon), Oxford Univ. Press, London and New York, 1945.

Several references scattered through the above surveys on neurogenesis (IV, 1 and 2) have pointed to the important role of specificity in neural growth, connections, and functional interrelations. *The following article gives now a more cohesive and integrated picture of the wide array of manifestations of specificity as a basic instrumentality in the establishment and maintenance of functional order in the nervous system.*

Neurosciences Res. Prog. Bull., Vol. 3, No. 5

Specificity in the Neurosciences

By Paul A. Weiss

The purpose of the Work Session "Specificity in the Neurosciences" has been to place on record the problem of <u>specificity</u> in the nervous system, so that it might attract more than casual attention, being one of the cardinal, yet least understood aspects of neural development, activity, coordination, and plasticity. This report will amount essentially to a listing of a variety of phenomena that reveal signs of specificity, so that any features they have in common may emerge as guides for more intensive investigation. The aim of this account is wholly provisional; it is not to resolve unsolved problems, adjudicate controversial issues, or labor pet theories, but rather to assemble under a common perspective a set of scattered observations and factual data which any future theory of the nervous system must take into account if it is to be consistent and useful as a guide to further analytical experimentation. The intent of this report, thus, is to call for attention rather than for acceptance.

In general, the term "specificity" has rather vague connotations. The present context demands greater precision, as follows: Specificity, in operational terms, refers invariably to a <u>relation</u> <u>between</u> <u>two</u> <u>systems</u> or events, x and y, of such kind that as the independent variable, x, goes through a continuously graded scale of values, the dependent effect, y, shows distinctive regional singularities in its response. The selective response of a tuned resonator to a continuous set of wave lengths may serve as illustration. The sharpness of the discrimination varies widely for different systems and indeed with the state of each system.

In general, in all cases where such <u>unique</u> relationship has been observed, it is based on time or space characteristics of the respective processes; for instance, frequencies or steric key-lock arrangements. The singularity of coupling between two such systems is sharpened if the independently variable process itself has a unique time or space configuration to which the dependent system is structurally matched. All reactions with signs of electivity and selectivity of response show evidence of such configurational matching. They represent universal mechanisms in the establishment and maintenance of order in biological systems, as exemplified by enzyme-substrate, antibody-antigen, hormone, and drug reactions, as well as cell affinities.

In the nervous system there are many instances of specificity, such as the following. Sensory receptors admit only
relatively narrow bands of the total spectrum of physical and
chemical events in the environment to be transduced into nerve
impulses. Nerve impulses, in turn, are recombined selectively
into coordinated effector actions. Hormones and drugs of given
chemical structure act differentially and discriminately on
different parts of the nervous system, although they are broadcast
and generally accessible throughout the body. Many more examples could be cited of this kind of matched interrelation on
which the orderly performance of the nervous system depends.
They form the substance of the following report.

There has been a general tendency to concede specificity
primarily to the peripheral transducers, and to treat the rest of
the nervous system as being composed of units operating mono-
tonically, that is, as all of one single kind. The receptors
are represented as translating and reducing the environmental
diversity of colors, smells and sounds to patterns of properly
timed and "dosed" electrochemical processes, which then are routed
over a geometrically ordered network of pathways of definite
orientations, lengths, branching densities, and destination
points. These patterns, in turn, have been conceived of variously as either rigidly and micro-precisely pre-established in
a prefunctional embryonic stage, or merely statistically determined, to be completed with the aid of actual function, with
latitude for some remodelling throughout life. It is inherent
in any such concept that specificity undergoes a definite amount
of degradation on the way from the afferent to the efferent
branch.

This point of view induced Johannes Müller to confine
what he called "specific energies" to the sensory side only,
and made DuBois-Reymond propose that if acoustic and optic
nerves could be cross-connected, we would hear lightning as
thunder and see a thunderbolt as a flash. In order to forego
such arbitrary confinement, our subsequent discussion will roam
widely beyond the sensory sector into the efferent field, beyond the consideration of the mature body back into the period
of neural development, and beyond the evidence of neurophysiological instrumentation into the indirect tests based on critical behavioral observations.

Keeping in mind our definition of selectivity as pertaining to two systems or processes mutually matched by singularly
corresponding properties, we can identify the following questions as foci for the discussion. How far into the nervous

system can specific relations of this kind be proven to extend? Are they based on constitutional differences among neurons, or merely simulated by less discriminative functional differences of degree? If the former, how do such constitutional differences arise? Granting constitutional diversity within the neuronal population, in what measure can and does it serve as an instrumentality for the establishment and maintenance of orderly relations? Within what range do these relations remain modifiable, and by what influences? To what extent can external patterns of stimuli truly specify neural activity as against merely modifying in characteristic ways an intrinsic, autonomously patterned, neural dynamics?

This chain of questions leads logically to starting our considerations from the point of entry of an external stimulus of characteristic configuration. Pattern perception in the visual and tactual fields is relatively easy to translate into patterned conduction in neuronal networks without recourse to postulates of chemical specificities. Hence, it does not confront us with the problem of molecular specificity as compellingly as do the chemical senses, in which receptor response is definitely selective for given molecular configurations of the stimulating agent. For this reason, the Work Session began with examples from tl.e field of chemo-reception and chemoperception. However, even in this area, the situation turned out to be by no means simple.

The following summary report contains first the gist of Zotterman's presentation on gustatory response. Recordings of the electric activity of single fibers of the gustatory system after various types of stimulation of the respective sensory areas revealed a great diversity of responses. In the lingual nerve, a drop of cold water to the tongue or a weak puff of air produced spikes of low amplitude in fibers of small diameters. Mild mechanical deformation of the tongue gave large spikes in the larger fibers, whereas stronger noxious deformation brought in additional small spikes from smaller fibers. The latter effect might be a common feature of noxious stimuli, since drops of burning-hot water also produced small spikes. In addition to these records from myelinated fibers, differential selective responses according to the kind of stimulus have been recorded from non-medullated C-fibers upon administration of mechanical and thermal stimuli. Some of the fibers responded only to temperature extremes, hence evidently signaling noxious properties. The selectivity for given stimulus situations seems actually to be more sharply defined in an unmyelinated than in a myelinated fiber, which latter may respond to more than one type of stimulation.

The strictly gustatory fibers similarly respond mostly
to a wide selection of gustatory stimuli, but a few have also
been demonstrated to be highly specialized. In the monkey, for
instance, sucrose may fire a large fiber and quinine a small
fiber; while both fibers react jointly to the application of
saccharine, glycerine and ethylene glycol, corresponding evidently to the bitter-sweet taste of them. In the dog, by contrast, saccharine, which still activates the same fibers as
quinine, leaves the sucrose units unaffected. In the monkey,
(but not in man), sucrose-responsive fibers can also be excited
by distilled water. In the carp, fibers were found that responded to human saliva, to milk and to fish-conditioned water.
The common active ingredient seems to be a phospholipid. Some
of these fibers responded exclusively to saliva or to milk, but
not to any of the other classes of gustatory stimuli tested.
Like the evocation of stimulus response, its suppression is also
discriminative. Thus, in man, for instance, gymnemic acid abolishes the response to sucrose and to saccharine, but leaves the
response to salts, acids, and quinine unaltered.

This series of experiments could serve as model for many
others to show that the population of sensory fibers consists
of a mosaic of units endowed with differential selectivity for
changes in the physico-chemical constitution or chemical composition of the outside medium. In some instances, the selectivity resides in a specific end organ; but in the case of the non-
medullated fibers with free intra-epithelial terminations, the
neuron itself will have to be conceded selective screening power.
Although the range and sharpness of responsiveness varies greatly
among the different units, the main conclusion is the positive
demonstration that wide qualitative differences among the sensory units do exist.

This qualitative mosaic of sensory neurons is even more
compellingly illustrated by the studies on insects reported by
Dethier. Blowflies have two groups of taste organs, one in the
form of hairs on oral protrusions, and the other in the form of
small papillae inside the mouth. Each hair is associated with
five bipolar neurons, the axons of which synapse directly with
the central nervous system. The dendrite of one of the five
neurons terminates at the base of the hair socket, while the
other four extend along the shaft of the hair, emerging through
a pore in the hair tip.

While structurally (electron microscopically) indistinguishable, these dendrites differ greatly in their chemical
sensitivities. One of them responds exclusively to certain

kinds of sugars including sucrose, fructose, maltose, d- and
l- arabinose, and, slightly, to galactose; while lactose and
mannose, as well as artificial sweeteners, glycerine and ethylene glycol are totally ineffective. Activity in a single
sugar-sensitive neuron is sufficient to elicit a typical feeding response, which involves the coordinated activation of five
sets of muscles which effect both the protrusion of parts of
the mouth, and suction in the pharynx. A second neuron of the
group, in response to the application of salt, evokes the withdrawal of an extended proboscis, hence activates a different
set of muscles than does the sugar neuron. Mixtures of sugar
and salt fire both neurons, with some depression of the sugar
response. The third neuron reacts to the administration of
distilled water. When salt is added to the water in low concentrations, the response of the water-sensitive unit declines
as that of the salt-sensitive one increases. The water-respon-
sive unit seems to be an osmo-receptor rather than a chemo-
receptor, as it is not affected by acids in the physiological
range. The fourth neuron is a mechano-receptor, responding to
bending of the hair even after amputation of the tip of the
hair, which eliminates most responses to chemical stimuli. The
role of the fifth unit has thus far remained undetermined.

The sensory organs inside the mouth of the fly are each
supplied with four neurons. One of them reacts strongly to
sucrose, glucose, and slightly to maltose, but not at all to
galactose. In marked contrast to the hair receptors, only the
d-form of arabinose activates the sugar unit, while the l-form
activates the salt unit and inhibits the sugar unit. The corresponding motor responses are likewise antagonistic: to the
d-form, sucking, and to the l-form, regurgitation. A more detailed investigation of the sugar-receptor mechanism dealt with
chemical substitutions in the glucose molecule, competition
between non-stimulating and stimulating sugars, and interactions
between glucose and fructose. An intimation of separate receptor sites for different sugars on the same dendrite was found
in the neural responses of flies which had been rendered less
glucose-receptive by high glucose diets; electric responses of
a given neuron to glucose were then markedly reduced, while
those to fructose mediated through the same neuron, were undiminished. It is evident that such qualitative discrimination
by different sites of the same cellular unit, if further substantiated, should be of most fundamental significance to our
concepts of central nervous activity. Constitutional differences between the hair and papilla receptor units are further
expressed in their differential response to calcium exposure:
all hair neurons are inhibited, whereas two of the four fibers

innervating each papilla are strongly stimulated by the same
exposure.

The discrimination of molecular structure is even more
conspicuously manifested in the reaction to organic substances
not involved in the metabolism of an animal. Such tests of the
olfactory sense, mostly in caterpillars, have largely relied on
the behavioral response as signal; but preliminary neurophysiological tests seem to validate the assumption that the olfactory
receptor cell is specifically organized to react highly selectively to a particular odor. This can be demonstrated in animals which feed exclusively on one type of plant and whose olfactory organs can be shown to respond electrically to specific
components of the plant extract. In view of the fact that food
habits of such animals can be changed, the case furnishes unique
opportunities for the exploration of mechanisms of specific
adaptation as models of memory in general. This is particularly
true since the adaptation in this case is clearly related to the
matching of specific molecular configurations, analogous to immunological specificity.

Experiments by Thorpe[1] have revealed that parasitic
wasps hatched from eggs artifically introduced into foreign
hosts, would, after metamorphosis, recognize the new host species and lay their eggs in them. A similar highly instructive
experiment by Hovanitz[2] reported by Dethier was the following.
Caterpillars hatched from eggs laid on cabbage, which is their
normal food (by virtue of genetic prefitting or of habituation?),
refused to feed on foreign plants. But if kept from starving
by sporadic offerings of native nutriment, although otherwise
reared on the foreign plant through successive instars, they
will eventually accept the foreign plant and feed on it preferentially. Significantly, this acquired chemical adaptation is
preserved and carried over through pupation into the imago.
This is evidenced by the fact that many of the females then
choose to deposit their eggs on the newly acquired habitat.

These observations raise the question of the degree of
specificity that might be conferred upon a neuron from its environment, be this an end-organ, the outside medium, or another
neuron. This question will be discussed more thoroughly below
in connection with animal experiments expressly designed for
that purpose. It is important, however, to keep in mind that
the problem presents itself continuously even for the normal
intact animal, in which, as a result of the major tissue changes
attending growth, proliferation, regeneration, ageing, metamorphosis, etc., the relations between neurons and their non-nervous

periphery are continually subject to disruptions and restoration.

In this connection, the taste buds of mammals can serve as illustrations. Each taste bud is a self-regenerative cell population of stationary mass, cells at its margin being reproduced, then moving toward the center, where they eventually are shed. The average lifetime of these sensory cells is of the order of a week. As a result of this, the gustatory fibers innervating these transitory cells evidently undergo disconnections and reconnections at a weekly cycle, although the details of this process are not yet clear. In view of the demonstrated specificity of these receptor units, discussed above, the question immediately arises whether a given neuron is predestined for connection with one type of peripheral cell only, or whether either the cell or the neuron owns primary specificity and imposes conforming specificity upon the other partner secondarily.

The past examples have furnished proof of the specific diversity of exteroceptive sensory neurons, as evidenced by their selective response to given chemical compounds or physicochemical constellations in their environment. There is further evidence of an analogous discriminative differentiation in the enteroceptive system, through which the central nervous system is informed about the status of the internal milieu, enabling it to mediate neurally a homeostatic response. The best investigated case is the response of the glomus of the carotid body, which assays the carbon dioxide concentration in the passing blood and regulates respiratory activity so as to maintain the steady-state condition. Similarly, the hypothalamus, which contains a center controlling the water balance of the body (diuresis and antidiuresis), registers blood dilution directly. This latter fact has been revealed by experiments demonstrating the ability of animals to give the appropriate behavioral responses (e.g., incessant drinking) following local infusion of the hypothalamus with anisosmotic solutions.

Behavioral responses have also proved to be critical indicators for far more refined chemical discrimination within the enteroceptive system. At the Work Session, Curt Richter presented the following samples of his crucial studies of this system. Rats whose sodium balance has been upset by adrenalectomy, within a few hours after the operation begin to drink sodium-containing solutions in distinct preference to pure water. Upon functionally successful reimplantation of adrenal glands, the animals return to normal water intake. Moreover,

if the adrenalectomized rats are presented simultaneously with
an array of solutions of different electrolytes, they tend to
take in the various constituents in proportions corresponding
to their normal serum ratios. Rats whose calcium metabolism
has been upset by extirpation of the parathyroid glands, promptly develop avidity for various compounds containing calcium,
but also for magnesium and strontium solutions. In nutrition-
ally produced vitamin deficiencies, the animals again select
promptly the missing vitamin from amongst an array of various
simultaneously offered compounds.

This technique of voluntary preferential food intake has
secondarily served as a convenient method for assaying taste
thresholds for various substances, as well as for the determination of internal levels of satiation signalled by the cessation
of the corresponding voluntary intake. The fact that animals
can still react appropriately after experimental exclusion of
the olfactory sense, assigns the primary role in the corrective
responses to the sense of taste. However, it remains to be determined whether or not the taste organs are also the recording
instruments for the specific deficiencies, that is, for the qualitative deviations of the metabolic state of the animal from
normal, as reflected presumably in the changed composition of
the circulating blood and lymph. At any rate, the reported
investigations definitely blur the line between constituents
of the external and internal milieu as activators of chemically
specialized neural selectors.

This fact links the series up with the vast store of
pharmacological data which show the selectivity with which different drugs circulated through the blood stream affect different sections of the nervous system or particular neuron groups.
While most of this field was intentionally bypassed at the
meeting, Elkes presented some examples of the way in which the
action of the so-called psychosomimetic drugs was related to
steric molecular configuration. In the case of lysergic acid
diethylamide (LSD-25) for example, changes in the ring system
lead to a striking change in the distribution of basic pharmacological properties, in terms of effects on peripheral autonomic and smooth muscle receptors. Yet many of the properties
of LSD-25 are also represented in the naturally occurring amide
of lysergic acid, ergonovine.[3] It would appear that ergot
derivatives (including LSD-25) may interfere with the storage
and release of a physiologically present indole (serotonin) in
some nodal areas of the brain, particularly the hypothalamus,
elements of the limbic system, and geniculate cell assemblies.
Elkes postulated the implication of these cell groups (and

physiologically present small molecules) in the play of a highly patterned inhibitory process concerned with the processes
of discriminate perception and focused attention. However,
he also pointed out the inordinate predilection of LSD-25 for
some primitive neural nets (e.g., the heart of Venus mercenaria
and molluscs) and the very low concentrations at which some of
these effects could be observed.[4] While the evidence for interaction between lysergic and serotonin storage sites is suggestive, it is equally significant, as shown some time ago by
Abood,[5] that certain anti-acetylcholine agents exert a powerful and specific effect on higher function in man.

    The main point in the present context is the incipient
demonstration of differentially discriminative reactions of
different neurons to molecules of characteristic steric configuration presented to them indiscriminately in a common pool.
Regardless of whether or not this selectivity has a bearing on
the physiological and pathological processes in the nervous system, its mere existence is a crucial test for the existence of
qualitative chemical differentials within the neuronal population, which have no detectable counterpart in microscopic or
submicroscopic morphology.

    Hormone response furnishes further examples of such chem-
ical selectivity. Elkes referred to experiments by Michael[6]
in which isotope-labelled stilbestrol pellets, implanted into
the brain of castrated animals, gave rise to characteristic
mating responses. Subsequent auto-radiography of brain sections
showed the accumulation of the labelled compound in quite localized cell groups, thus evidently implicating those neurons with
the behavioral response. Earlier similar experiments with thy-
roid-induced metamorphosis of amphibians had shown that behavioral changes from tadpole to frog can be produced locally by
local application of thyroid to the respective brain part.
Kollros,[7] for instance, induced metamorphic maturation of the
abducens center for the lid-closure reflex by implanting a
thyroid dispenser in the fourth ventricle. Even more pinpointed
is the thyroid action on the giant Mauthner's neuron, which is
related to swimming coordination in the larva and disappears
during metamorphosis. Exposing the hind-brain region housing
that neuron to a localized thyroxin source, Weiss and Rossetti[8]
observed that that particular nerve cell would regress, while
the surrounding cells grew rapidly in size, despite the fact
that both cell types were equally bathed by the metamorphotic
compound. The proof of such cell-specific effects notwithstanding, one should, however, bear in mind that chemicals need not
act on individual cell bodies, but can also become effective

by altering specific relations between neurons and their environment, including body fluids, glia cells, and other neurons.

Having established the case for the existence of chemical diversity among neural units, the next problem is whether
and to what extent these differential properties are also instrumental in establishing the requisite unequivocal correspondence between the nervous system and its non-nervous receptor
and effector organs, as well as establishing the orderly communication within the central system itself. The problem is
a general one for any system of intercommunication. The following possibilities must be considered whenever one is faced with
correspondences between two points in a communication network
or continuum: a) the two points are structurally connected by
an isolated private line whose unspecific activation from one
end is bound to reach the other end; b) in the absence of single-
track connections, the message emitted from the sending point,
and diffused more widely, must carry some characteristic code
specifically patterned for the recipient point, the latter being correspondingly specified so as to be able to recognize
and to respond selectivity to its proper signal. Proposition
(a) embraces a further alternative: the orderly single-track
connection might be the outcome of coincidental circumstances
unrelated to any interaction between the two points; or it
might have come about through a direct interaction between the
two stations, effective in the laying of the line, but not involved in its subsequent operation.

It can readily be seen that current concepts of the
nervous system are variously favoring one or the other of those
possibilities, depending on the preoccupation with one or another sector of neural phenomena or with one or another technical approach. Particularly, the latter limitation constitutes
a distinct handicap to progress toward an eventual comprehensive,
consistent, and unified theory. One should remember that the
fact that a photograph of a colorful landscape on an ordinary
black-white plate can only render light intensities, but not
color values, and therefore can never prove the absence of color
in the original. Similarly, explorations of the nervous system
with techniques unfit to detect chemical differentiations inev-
itably yield incomplete information. Due to our preoccupation
with single neurons in the mature nervous system, to the relative neglect of the operation of the system as a whole in its
continuous development from embryo to final maturation, the
problem of specificity as basic instrument in the establishment
of neural order has received only marginal attention. Thus, the
various alternatives of communicative correspondence just stated

above have to this date found no conclusive resolution.

It is evident that any communication and control system, such as the nervous system, can function properly only if there is a reasonable probability for the messages to arrive at their predetermined destinations. To appreciate the difficulty of the problem, one must bear in mind two complications. Organismic reactions, at least in higher animals, are not of the linear, push-button automaton kind, in which a given afferent input would always stereotypically produce identical efferent effects. Therefore, relay stations with multiple-choice distribution patterns are interpolated between the afferent and efferent branches. They screen, sort, integrate, and recombine the incoming messages into complexes that change from station to station. If, furthermore, one considers that the intermediate stations are not just transformers of input into output, but are themselves endowed with automatic activities, intrinsically patterned regardless of input, the problem of nervous coordination emerges in its true proportions, free from the distortion which has been produced by an exaggerated faith in the two- or three-neuron reflex arc as valid model for neural integration. That isolable simple reflex arc might more appropriately be viewed as a most refined terminal specialization, rather than as a basic and universal unit operation. It is no better suited to serve as prototype than a mammalian red cell without a nucleus could serve as a general model for a cell. However, the problem of automaticity of nerve centers is not a topic germane to this Work Session. It is sufficient for our purpose, though probably untrue, to assume that each neuron in the branched chain of relay stations lies silent until excited by an impulse from another station.

In this simplified version, which was dominant during the meeting, each neuron can therefore be visualized as simply the recipient of messages from other neurons. The whole system, then, can be seen as a network of point-to-point or point-to-points communication lines in the above sense. In such a network, the sheer presence of communication channels between the various points is, of course, an indispensable precondition for the successful transfer of messages. The alternatives (a) and (b) cited on page 14, however, differ crucially in regard to the relevance or irrelevance assigned to structural regularity of the channel pattern as the key to the orderly transmission of messages from source to destination.

A major part of the meeting revolved about this problem. No one could dispense with specificity of one kind or another,

but controversy persisted as to whether specificity was involved only in the orderly laying of the lines according to
(a), or actually extended into their operation, as in (b). In
anticipation of the conclusions, it can be stated that the controversy has not been resolved, nor could it possibly be resolved without far more factual information than we now possess.
Indeed, what has emerged from the discussions is that it is not
even warranted to expect categorical decisions in favor of one
or the other alternative. Even as arguments were advanced both
for the stereotypy of the line patterns and for the primacy of
specificity in neuronal coordination, it was stressed that experimental attempts at the reconciliation of both views were
either still underway or at least in prospect.

The following presentation of the major facets of the
problem will follow a logical pattern and disregard both historical precedents and the sequential order of the conference.
We start from the extreme end of conspicuous structural determinism.

The description of the crustacean nervous system by
Wiersma furnished a paradigm of a stereotyped, minutely predesigned reflex machine, the wiring diagram of which is faithfully reproduced in every single individual of the species.
This stereotypism, in combination with equally regular, almost
Morse code-like electric signals in its units, seems factually
adequate and intellectually satisfying in explaining the behavior of a crayfish; on the other hand, it leaves little latitude
for learning, memory, and adaptive behavior, of which there are
some overt indications. Some muscles have invariably three
motor fibers, some others are invariably equipped with five,
each one of the multiple fibers subserving a different function
correlated predictably with the frequency pattern of its firing.
Each proprioceptive receptor unit in muscles and joints likewise has its peculiar stereotyped impulse pattern which signals
stretch or joint position. The interneurons between the sensory and the motor sides also appear to be each narrowly earmarked for a particular definite form of reaction to the combined influx from peripheral neurons. For example, there are
interneurons receiving inputs from the visual field which record exclusively the rate of movement of an object in that field.

A nervous system of this kind seems to be built like
clockwork, its operation predesigned with microprecision during development, according to principles left to geneticists
and embryologists to explain, but taken for granted in their
orderliness by the student of the working machine. Unfortun-

ately, the question of how this rigid wiring system is restored
during the extensive regeneration of lost appendages of which
crustaceans are capable, has not yet been thoroughly investigated. It appears from preliminary experiments that the efferent axons induce in the regenerating areas their "own" muscles
with all their specific characteristics. Since the sense cells
have mostly lost their cell bodies which are peripherally located, they are presumably newly formed. It is clear that these
cells form all the appropriate connections, as the reflexes return to practically normal, but no information about how this
comes about is available.

Bullock's comparable correlated anatomical and physiological studies in a marine snail have substantiated essentially
for invertebrates a concept of the nervous system in which practically each individual neuron has a predesigned role, much as
a particular cog in an engine.

By extrapolation, one could, of course, postulate that
the nervous system of a higher vertebrate, which contains about
one hundred thousand to one million times as many neurons as
do the centers of a crayfish, is basically more of the same,
just a hundred thousand times more stencils superimposed upon
one another. For anyone familiar with the development of the
nervous system in higher animals and cognizant of the considerable degree of inter-individual variability from case to
case, such a postulate would seem quite unrealistic, even though
exceptional cases of rigidly predetermined numbers and connections of neurons have become known even in vertebrates (e. g.,
Mauthner's neuron in fishes and amphibians). Yet those less
familiar with the developmental process would obviously ask for
more crucial tests, either for or against the relevance of
stereotyped connection patterns for neural coordination. Such
crucial experimental tests have actually been performed. Their
basic design is as follows.

If the pattern of response of a given number of receiving
stations were simply the blind replica of the assortment of
separate individual pathways connecting the emitters and re-
ceivers (much as the harmonies issuing from the strings of a
piano are unequivocally determined by the keys that are being
struck), any arbitrary disarrangement of the traffic lines
ought to lead to neural noise rather than coordinated responses.
The matter comes up in the experience of neurosurgeons, who
often repair nerve lesions in man by switching healthy foreign
nerves from an intact central source into the denervated area.
However, the results of functional recovery have been ambiguous,

partly because of questionable standards of objectivity in
testing and describing "recovery" of sensation or coordination,
and partly because of man's considerable powers of adaptation,
compensation and substitution in neural functioning. This
latter capacity is so unique in man that it confounds the interpretation of what in lower animals can serve as a critical
test. We, therefore, turn to the less ambiguous experiments
in lower vertebrates.

Although the pertinent animal experiments by Weiss on
switching nerves arbitrarily among different muscle groups
have led to rather cogent conclusions for the motor field, their
presentation will be deferred in favor of our plan to progress
methodically from the afferent into the efferent sector. Considering first the afferent side, Sperry has conducted extensive
critical tests of the degree of relevance of the patterns of
innate point-to-point connections for the orderliness of point-
to-point communication.

The major experiments are here summarized. The visual
cells, upon photic excitation and some integrative interaction
of their impulses in intermediary retinal layers, produce excitation in the mosaic of retinal ganglion cells, whose nerve
fibers pass through the optic nerve into the brain, where they
then mediate the various visuo-motor responses. In amphibians,
the topography of the retinal mosaic seems rather faithfully
reproduced on the tectum of the mid-brain, so that in a normal
amphibian, stimulation of a given retinal area entails excitation of a correspondingly localized tectal sector. This correspondence has been mapped out by both negative and positive
tests. Negatively, the extinction of behavioral responses upon
localized tectal lesions has been correlated with corresponding
blind spots on the retina. Positively, electric signals have
been recorded in tectal sectors corresponding to given retinal
sectors. Behavioral responses to optic images falling on dorsal, ventral, medial, or lateral sectors of the retina are
sufficiently characteristic for each sector to serve as criteria
for the identification of the particular retinal sector from
which an optic signal has originated. Through observation of
these visuo-motor reactions, it was found that in amphibians
whose eyes had been surgically inverted in their orbits (without disruption of the optic nerve), the localization of a stimulus on the retina registered centrally in terms of the original
native axiation and intrinsic polarity of the eye, rather than
in terms of the orientation of the eye relative to the animal
and the outside world. That is to say, a constitutionally ventral part of the retina, which used to receive illumination

from above, yielded exactly the same motor response even after
having been turned upside down so that it then received illumination from below. Thus, the central nervous system records
retinal stimuli in terms of the congenital topography of the
retinal map, and automatically activates the corresponding
motor patterns, regardless of whether the resulting effect is
useful, irrelevant, or adverse for the animal as a whole. Both
in their functional significance and in their appearance to
an outside observer, the motor reactions of an animal with inverted eyes are disadvantageous to it. Yet in terms of a rigidly fixed congenital receptor–center–effector machine operation,
they are quite consequential.

The stereotypy of central-peripheral relations manifested
in these experiments is well established in both the sensory
and the motor sectors; the latter will be discussed more fully
below. In the lower vertebrates, it is rather unmodifiable,
even under the extreme exigencies which it imposes on the animals. By virtue of this inflexibility, however, it also furnishes a uniquely favorable technique for the exploration of
the specific mechanism that underlies such rigorous point-to-
point correspondence.

The tests applied in these explorations, and those to
be discussed below, make use of the capacity of peripheral nerve
fibers to regenerate. If a neuron is interrupted, the peripheral part degenerates, while the proximal stump, still connected
with the nerve cell body, sprouts new branches from its cut surface. The free tips of these sprouts advance into the surroundings and in the end may become reconnected with the denervated
peripheral receptor or effector structures. There is a vast
literature on peripheral nerve regeneration, some of which will
be summarized below. Regeneration of fibers in the central
nervous system is less well established, but in lower vertebrates it definitely does occur. At any rate, the optic nerve
fibers, whose cell bodies lie in the retina (a modified brain
part), can regenerate after transection. Sperry cut optic nerves
of inverted eyes and found, in line with earlier observers, return of vision as nerve regeneration proceeded. Interest centers on the manner of regeneration and the kind of restored
vision. His earlier reports indicated profuse branching and
straying of the regenerating optic nerve sprouts in the disar-
rayed region of the wound (the "scar" of classical neuropathology), hence, a morphological scrambling of the fibers in transit
to the denervated distal nerve stump, through which they were
then to be channeled back to the optic tectum. This would be
in accord with the established views on regeneration in periph-

eral nerve. Functional tests after the restoration of vision
proved unequivocally that visual stimulations of the dorsal,
ventral, medial, or lateral quadrants of the retina were selectively recorded in their correct corresponding central stations
in the optic tectum regardless of the actual position of the
eye and its retina in the animal. Inverted eyes, after the
regeneration of their optic nerves, elicited the same reversed
motor reactions that they had yielded before the section of the
nerve. This proved that the specific topographic correspondence between retina and tectum was not established only once
and for all in the embryonic phase, but was capable of being
typically restored throughout life.

One was thus faced with the following alternative possibilities: a) the fibers of each retinal area owned specific
properties critically distinguishing them from one another;
when transected, their outgrowing branches would retain that
specificity, and stray about until they found a deserted distal
channel of matching specificity which then would lead them back
to their original central destinations; b) same as (a) except
that there would be no selective entry into the distal nerve
stump, but all regenerated branches would arrive en masse at
the optic tectum and there spread out horizontally, searching
blindly for contact with a central cell of corresponding specificity; c) like (b), but with the establishment of matching connections not to be left to blind trial- and-error procedure,
but rather effected by the fiber terminals' being selectively
attracted each by its fitting partner cell; d) the regenerating fibers, specified according to their cells of origin, as
in (a), would regenerate into the tectum indiscriminately, and
there form wide ramifications, including perhaps indiscriminate
synaptic junctions; but the impulse patterns of each distinctive
neuron species would be of such configuration as to permit transmission into, and response of a "corresponding" midbrain cell
only if the latter is selectively responsive to that impulse
pattern. The possibility of electric impulse patterns being
carriers of such "coded" messages for selective reception was
sketched in the Work Session by Wall (see also a remark above
in Wiersma's account).

All four of these possible modes are compatible with the
fact that in the end, the excitation of each retinal sector,
like a homing pigeon, ends up in its proper corresponding midbrain locality. All four compellingly substantiate both the
thesis of the existence of specific differences among the retinal neurons, and the fact that these differentials are instrumental in establishing, as well as restoring, their orderly

projection and representation on the optic tectum. To that extent, the underlying principle is firmly established; the detailed mechanism of its operation, however, is still hypothetical, and, to some extent, controversial. Sperry in his presentation, for instance, seemed to veer from his earlier preference for mechanism (b) to a combination of (a) and (c), while Weiss contended that present knowledge was inadequate to resolve the problem decisively.

The case for selectivity in the establishment of synaptic connections between a given axon and a ganglion cell was partly strengthened, but partly also qualified, by experiments reported by Guth. Pre ganglionic fibers of the cat's thoracic sympathetic system, when stimulated, activate different post ganglionic pathways in their common relay station, the cervical ganglion; stimulation of T_1 producing dilation of the pupil; of T_4, dilation of aural blood vessels. Upon cutting the sympathetic trunkline containing all these thoracic preganglionic fibers, and allowing them to regenerate, correspondence between T_1 and the pupil, as well as between T_4 and the ear vessels, was found to be restored. This would indicate that the fibers issuing from these two segments must have had distinguishing characteristics by virtue of which they could each rejoin their correspondingly specified effector neuron in the cervical ganglion. In this sense, the experiments would seem to corroborate the thesis of strict specificity and selectivity in the establishment of morphological interneuronal connections. A further experiment, however, counsels caution. In it, preganglionic roots T_1 to T_3 were crushed, while the posterior ones, from T_4 down, including their connections to the cervical ganglion, were left intact. Under these circumstances, stimulation of any of the residual roots now yielded pupillary responses; that is, they activated ganglion cells originally belonging to T_1, which purportedly were of alien specificity. After some months, allowing for the regeneration of the crushed T_1 fibers, these resumed their control over the pupil, and the capacity to activate it from T_4 disappeared again, as if connections from T_1 had superseded the interim connections from T_4. Whatever the interpretation, the fact remains that T_4 cannot possibly have the sharp and exclusive specificity for vascular activation that the earlier experiment had suggested.

All of these cases have dealt with specified units of one kind which somehow manage to establish selective relations with other units of equally specified kind, without necessarily forcing one to postulate an active transfer or imposition of specificity from one upon the other. The next series of cases,

however, dealing with the efferent sector, does introduce this
further complication into the problem. The experiments concerned consist of the transposition and subsequent regeneration
of motor nerves in such a manner that motor ganglion cells,
having been severed from their original effector organs, are
allowed to find new connections either by accident or deliberate experimental design. The following basic experiments,
carried out by Weiss, may serve as one illustrative example
for an extensive series of similar experiments carried out by
him since 1922, and by others later.

The experiments were done in fully developed premetamor-
phic larvae of amphibians, whose limbs had been in fully coordinated operation for weeks or months. Anatomically, each limb
contains a few dozen muscles attached in characteristic ways
to the skeleton, and receiving innervation from a limited number of segments of the spinal cord and spinal ganglia. Physiologically, each limb displays a finite repertory of movement
patterns, such as in ambulatory progression, retreat, turning,
swimming, etc., each act in this repertory being executed by a
discrete "coordinated" pattern of activation of definite combinations of the available muscles in the appropriate timing,
"dosage" and sequential order. In terms of the simile of a
piano, the muscles which produce a harmonious movement would
represent the strings, and the innervating motor ganglion cells,
the keys. The mechanism responsible for the sequentially programmed activation of these keys could then perhaps be comparable to the coded stencil of a mechanical piano. Its counterpart
in the central nervous system can hardly be claimed to be known.
Some evidence as to what it cannot be, however, narrows the
scope for our speculation.

For instance, it cannot reside in a point-to-point connection between any one given receptor unit and any one given
motor unit, linearly and unequivocally interconnected, for the
following reasons. In the first place, stimulation of a given
sensory point can set into operation many different muscles,
and in varying combinations and, conversely, any given muscle
may participate in actions elicited from a great number of sensory points widely distributed over the body. Secondly, the
pattern of locomotor coordination of a limb is definitely independent of sensory instructions, including sensory messages
from that limb reaching the spinal cord. Contrary to a widespread misconception, completely deafferented limbs, that is,
limbs permanently deprived of all their sensory fibers, continue
to display rather perfect coordination during phases of motility. Furthermore, in normal embryonic development, many coor-

dinated motor functions of a high degree of perfection precede
the establishment of sensory connections between the motile
parts and the nerve centers. In addition, the experimental
suppression of sensory innervation does not preclude the appearance of the typical motor repertory. These basic facts rule
out the ingrained and cherished belief that limb coordination
can be explained as the assembled piecework of its own elementary reflex arcs. By contrast, however, attempts at formulat-
ing a positive theory of coordination have not made substantial
progress.

The experiments to be presented next have furnished some,
but only a few additional clues. A supernumerary limb, that
is, a duplicate set of muscles, was grafted in some arbitrary
orientation to the body wall of the larval amphibian near the
normal limb, and a small part of the nerve fibers of the nearby
limb plexus was transected, so as to permit the regenerated
branches to reconnect the transplant with the spinal cord. The
resulting double preparation thus consisted of the normal limb,
with most of its nerve supply still intact, serving as indicator
of what might be called the "motor intentions" of the spinal
cord at any given moment; and a test limb innervated from the
same spinal sector by regeneratively scrambled branches of motor
neurons. Despite this crucial difference in the structural orderliness of the fiber connections, however, the activity patterns in both the test and the control limb were always found
to be exactly identical. Whenever the spinal cord activated a
given selection of muscles in the normal limb, precisely the
same selection went into action in the transplant, activating
each muscle of the transplant at the same time, duration, and
relative strength as its namesake in the normal limb.

This phenomenon of "myotypic" response has been substantiated in numerous variations of the experimental design by
Weiss and others. Two of these variants are particularly pertinent to this discussion. If a right limb is grafted to the
left side and made to share in the innervation of the left limb,
then owing to the two limbs' being mirror images in their muscular anatomy, their resultant movements are likewise mirrored,
so that the transplant counteracts the graft in its mechanical
effects. As in the animals with inverted eyes, this phenomenol-
ogically "reversed" but muscularly correct function of the
grafts was retained indefinitely, despite its lack of utility
or its outright harm to the animal. The extreme test of this
was produced by removing the normal limbs altogether and replacing them by limbs of anatomically reversed muscle topography,
that is, by exchanging right and left limbs for each other.

In those cases, the animals throughout life kept on calling into operation the normally correct assortment of muscles required for a given act. The muscles called upon responded properly according to their names, translating, thus, correct central commands into absurd peripheral mechanical effects. When the animal tried to advance, its reversed legs shoved it backwards, and when it wanted to retreat from deleterious stimuli, its legs pushed it forward, toward the source of stimulation. Again, myotypic response was regularly obtained even in completely deafferented spinal sectors, so that we can confine its explanation to the relation between the motor part of the spinal cord and the muscles.

The fact that according to these experiments the spinal cord deals with each muscle discriminately in terms of its name signifies, of course, that the forty-odd muscles of the limb, as well as the other muscles of the body, must each possess some personal, hence presumably biochemical property which distinguishes it from all other non-homologous muscles. It further signifies that by virtue of this property, each muscle can establish a highly selective relation with a central agency in the spinal cord of exactly matching specificity. As in the case of the retina, we are thus confronted with a strict correspondence between two mosaics; in the present case, the muscles at one end and their central representatives among the motor spinal neurons at the other.

The qualitative diversity of specificities has thus been validly established as the basic principle instrumental in central-peripheral correspondences for both the sensory and motor sectors of the nervous system. However, the mechanism through which this correspondence between parts of matching specificity is attained, is largely still conjectural. One might advance the same four alternative possibilities as were suggested on page 20 for the restoration of vision. Yet in the motor field, these encounter further difficulties. One might suggest that the brachial spinal cord differentiates automatically forty-odd discrete and highly specific types of ganglion cells, a separate distinctive type for each particular muscle, and that their axons carrying the same specific tags would be admitted peripherally to functional connections exclusively with the muscles of the corresponding types. It could be further suggested that during the regeneration of the motor nerves, the peripheral nerve stumps would have retained their individual characteristics and would have selectively screened the arriving regenerating branches for exclusive admission to their matching distal pathways. In assessing the case, one must consider two sets of data, apparently contradictory, but both well established. In the first place, instances of selective differential preference by several types of nerve fibers for type-specific pathways evidently endowed with different specific chemical cues, have been demonstrated for the primary outgrowth of nerves (the "selective contact guidance" and "selective fasciculation" of Weiss). For instance, sensory fibers and motor fibers, as classes, follow special routes in their invasion of the embryonic limb buds. On the other hand, no residual path specificity has been found in the peripheral stumps of developed nerves after transection; those stumps admit regenerating motor and sensory fibers indiscriminately, regardless of their former contents. Secondly, no discrimination of any given muscle against motor fibers formerly belonging to another muscle has ever been demonstrated. On the contrary, there is plenty of evidence that motor fibers from whatever source establish transmissive connections with any type of cross-striated muscle.

Experiments reported by Székely bear out this point. Amphibian limbs grafted to the body wall in the thoracic region can be re-innervated by thoracic nerves. As will be mentioned later, such limbs fail, however, to show coordinated movements. Many experiments of similar kind have been reported in the literature. To clinch the argument, the most crucial case is perhaps the vigorous mass activity of limb muscles solely innervated by totally isolated fragments of cord or medulla oblongata, as studied in "deplantation" experiments by Weiss and Desmedt.[9] There is thus not only no support for, but ample experimental evidence against the supposition of such a minutely precise regenerative specificity as would be needed to explain myotypic function.

At the same time, the premise is inescapable of a faithful replica of the mosaic of specific muscles in the population of motor cells in the corresponding sector of the spinal cord. The original hypothesis proposed by Weiss[10] in the early 1920's soon proved untenable. That hypothesis had assumed that all motor fibers might conduct coded messages for all the muscles, with each motor end-plate then picking out its appropriate component according to its own specificity. This assumption was crucially disproved by the demonstration by Wiersma,[11] and many others later, that the peripheral motor nerves already carry excitations properly apportioned to the various muscles lying at the end. Selection, therefore, had to take place farther proximally, in the centers; and if, in view of the given indeterminacy of motor fiber outgrowth and regeneration, the ganglion cells could not know in advance precisely with which muscle they would eventually be connected, they evidently had

to learn it <u>after</u> they had become connected. Since, as mentioned earlier, the sensory system is absolutely dispensable
in this process, the necessary information evidently had to be
transmitted directly through the motor neuron itself. That is
to say, each muscle must somehow impart upon the nerve fibers
which have made connections with it those individual biochemical
characteristics that distinguish it from other muscles.

Weiss has called this process of retrograde specification
"modulation," and envisaged it as a more generalized case of
the antigen-antibody reaction principle. He assumed that the
molecular configuration of those compounds responsible for the
individual specificity of each muscle, might imprint a conforming configuration upon related compounds in the neuron, and that
the ascending specification might alter the selective relation
of the nerve cell body and its surface. This would of course
affect synaptic relations, as under proposition (d) above.

Proof has also been obtained of a similar modulation
process for those types of <u>afferent</u> neurons which, unlike those
of the retina, do not have their cell bodies in the receptor
periphery. <u>Proprioceptive</u> sensory fibers going to muscles of
supernumerary limbs signal centrally precisely the name of the
given muscle which an experimenter chooses to stretch. This
is revealed by the fact that the myotatic reflex response appears in precisely the corresponding muscle in both the stimulated transplant and the nearby normal indicator leg. Cutaneous
sensory fibers from the head have also been made to innervate
cornea and become modulated thereafter to function as corneal
receptors, eliciting now the corneal reflex instead of skin reflex.*   Sperry likewise has adduced additional clearcut examples
for other cranial nerves. Moreover, Miner,(12) in Sperry's
laboratory, demonstrated that stimulation of frog skin transplants exchanged between back and belly prior to metamorphosis
would yield wiping reflexes to the <u>native</u> rather than the <u>actual</u>
sites of the grafts. This likewise indicates the presence of
a mosaic of territorial skin specificities informing the cord
of their character, rather than of their relative positioning.

The series of results described in the foregoing section
have led to the postulate of some specific "information," unrelated to the transmission of impulse patterns, being imparted

---

* <u>Addition by Székely</u>: Recently Székely succeeded in showing
that the same effect could be obtained by producing a regeneration blastema at the end of a limb grafted into the salamander's
posterior head region. (March 17, 1965)

to neurons from the structures with which they have become connected. Modifying influences in the reverse direction, that is,
from nerves to peripheral tissues, are likewise a matter of record. Most of them have been lumped under the title of "trophic
influences." Their nature is still problematical. The prevalent
conjecture, that they are due to hypothetical "trophic" substances passing from nerve endings into muscle fibers and receptors, is plausible, particularly in view of the established fact
of cellulifugal "axonal flow" in peripheral nerve fibers. However a conclusive factual demonstration of such "trophic" substances is still lacking. At any rate, neurogenic hypertrophies
and atrophies in peripheral tissues have commonly been considered
as merely unspecific quantitative variations in the dosage of
the neural agent involved.

To these general "trophic" effects has now been added a
more determinative influence exerted by nerves on their muscles,
as follows. Eccles had found that after crossing the motor
nerves between mechanically "slow" and "fast" skeletal muscles
in the adult cat, the cross-innervated muscles would change from
their original speed characteristics to more nearly those of
their newly adopted nerves. Buller gave the conference a summary account of his continuation of those experiments, which
left little doubt as to the reality of the effect. The mode of
action, however, has again remained unresolved. Even though
muscles with rather marked speed differences were used (m. soleus
for slow, m. flexor hallucis longus for fast), the results were
not always sufficiently decisive. The inhomogeneity of the respective fiber populations, the lack of sequential studies during
the period of denervation and re-innervation, and the occurrence
of cases of incomplete reversal, precluded a final decision between two alternative explanations of the phenomenon. One possibility is that the constitutionally "slow" or "fast" nerve fibers
might impose conforming rate characteristics directly on the contractile (actomyosin) system of the particular muscle fibrils
which they happen to innervate. (Differential succinoxidase content in muscle fibers of different speeds, although without being
reflected in demonstrable differences among the respective mitochondrial populations carrying that enzyme system, was also reported.) An alternate possibility is that each muscle might contain a mixture of "slow" and "fast" contractile elements, with
one or the other predominant. The "slow" or "fast" neurons entering the muscle would selectively connect with muscle fibers
of the matching speed characteristics; the unmatched, permanently
disconnected ones would atrophy, while the reconnected units
would hypertrophy. Although no conclusive facts could be cited
to disprove either the former hypothesis, of truly adaptive

alteration, or the latter, of selective re-innervation, the weight of the discussion seemed to favor the former.

Even so, this class of efferent "developmental" influences still bears closer resemblance to the "trophic" types of neuron-tissue interactions than to the highly specific ascending "modulations." This multiplicity of modes of central-peripheral interactions is further underlined by the fact that in the ascending direction, too, plain "trophic" effects have been recorded in the varying rates of synthesis of central nerve cells. These rate variations are reflected in the varying sizes of their nucleoli, nuclei, and cell bodies, which fluctuate in proportion to the peripheral tissue load which they have to control. These latter effects appear to depend essentially on the amount, rather than on the distinctive specificity, of functionally innervated tissue.

Returning now from these more general reciprocal interactions between center and periphery to our main issue of specific inter-relations, three basic conclusions have emerged from the described phenomena. First, the group of non-nervous effectors and that of receptors represents each a highly diversified mosaic of units of distinctive and individually specific properties. Second, there exist in the centers two corresponding mosaics of entities whose equally distinctive specificities match these groups, item for item. Third, the orderly communication between the central and peripheral system is based on the strict selective relations between corresponding members of the respective mosaics. This summary seems to be the most general and non-committal formulation of the results. The rest is hypothetical, and as the Work Session discussions have made abundantly clear, the mechanism or mechanisms underlying the correspondence are still debatable. Both selective "affinity" in the establishment of morphological junctions and specific dynamic conformances of "coded" activity patterns ("resonance") have been considered; however, the data at hand are not only inconclusive for a decision between these propositions, but actually suggest that the eventual solution will come from a combination of both.

What has become quite evident is that the central and peripheral mosaics arise autonomously and independently of each other, "prematched" for later secondary linkage, but initially unrelated. This type of paired predetermination is a common developmental principle (e.g., the prematched differentiation of endocrine target cells for later selective response to the proper hormone from the independently developed incretory gland). The specific prematching between periphery and centers, discussed

at the meeting, belongs in the same class, developmentally, as
the "prematched" selective reactivity of taste buds or olfactory
receptors for particular molecules of matching configuration in
the external environment. Much as in the matching of sperm and
egg, or of parasite and host, we are confronted here with a universal biological principle, the incidence of which may be explained by evolutionary theory.

At the same time, it must be stressed that if the "prematching" of coordinated functional entities were carried to the
extreme of absolutely detailed and rigid point-to-point correspondence, a living system thus designed would be unable to cope
with the wide range of fluctuations in its outer, and secondarily
inner, environment. Evolution has therefore maintained a proper
measure of true adaptive latitude, within which grossly prematched units can be more minutely and precisely fitted, and if
necessary, refitted to each other in accordance with actual conditions met in the individual case. We readily recognize the
process of "modulation" as being an example of such adaptive
adjustments.

It is important to stress this point because of the recurrent attempts to attribute primacy either to rigid predetermination or to adaptive plasticity as the ruling principle in
the development and basic functioning of the nervous system, instead of acknowledging the relevance of both and determining
their relative roles and mechanisms. The discussions revealed,
for instance, that, four decades of assertions to the contrary
notwithstanding, the demonstration of diversified peripheral
specificities is still misinterpreted as implying a constructive
role in the shaping of the central patterns of coordinated function. Let it be repeated, therefore, that the myotypic "modulation" of the motor neuron, by which the individual muscle "in-
forms" the spinal motor cell of its name, is simply a device to
establish a representative replica of the muscle mosaic in the
neuronal population of "final common paths." It has no bearing
on the central command patterns which determine which muscles,
of what names and in what order, to call into action for any
given act of the motor repertory. It merely insures that every
excitation prescribed in those patterns for any muscle of a
given name actually gets to the correct addressee. It thereby
sets the effector system into unequivocal correspondence with
that still ill-defined, still farther central counterpart, in
which the stereotyped sequences of muscles needed for each motor
act are "encoded." However, the nature and mode of operation
of the latter system itself, the very problem of central coordination, is still at issue.

The analogous phenomenon on the afferent side, that is, the faithful replication of the peripheral sensory mosaic in the respective central sectors, is equally unrevealing as regards the machinery of intrinsic central coordination. No matter how the correct topographical representation of the retina on the midbrain roof is achieved, as in Sperry's experiments, and especially, if it is truly a detailed point-to-point projection, it seems illogical to try to derive from this fact a mechanism of central coordination in higher animals. For, in the first place, there is no point-to-point single-track connection between a given receptor unit and a given effector unit. Secondly, the set of differential specificities among the sensory neurons is definitely not identical with that of the motor neurons. Consequently, the principle of unequivocal linkage between receptors and their central representatives, on the one hand, and between muscles and their representative ganglion cells, on the other, cannot serve to explain the manner in which the two systems then deal with each other. (A possible qualification of this conclusion for the invertebrates was mentioned earlier in this report.) For vertebrates, however, the stronger the case becomes for differential specificity and selectivity of individual peripheral neurons, the less it can be applied directly to central activity. For, in the centers, the "grid" geometry of matching point-to-point connections dissolves into the network geometry of multiple-choice relations.

Even so, there are certain clues regarding the problem of internal coordination in the central nervous system itself, which the experiments on peripheral specificity have brought to light. Weiss' observations on the permanent reversed locomotion of amphibians with reversed limb musculature, Sperry's demonstration that animals with inverted eyes give permanantly reversed optokinetic responses, and other similar results, have given proof of the remarkable preformed rigidity in the central patterns of selection and sequential activation of muscle groups for basic coordinated acts. Metaphorically, if we compare the specific central representatives for the individual muscles to letters of the alphabet, the centers are endowed with a finite "vocabulary" for certain biologically significant "sentences." This basic vocabulary is innate, that is, it develops by central "maturation" without the benefit of informational feedback from experience. It also retains its stereotyped pattern rigidly, without corrective adaptations, even in the face of utterly adverse effects for the animal as a whole. Its autonomous development is well illustrated by an experiment by Anokhin.[13] He deprived salamander embryos of their prefunctional limb buds, and after the legless animals had grown up, transplanted test

limbs to their backs. Those transplants which had received
nerve connections from the regular limb region of the spinal
cord then exhibited, despite their abnormal and useless positioning, the typical coordinated limb movements that would have
been appropriate for normal limbs in swimming and ambulation.
Besides confirming, once more, the "myotypic" code which the
spinal coordination system employs, experiments of this type
also prove that the typical vocabulary of coordination not only
originates intracentrally but remains present in latent form
for indefinite periods of overt inactivity. Just what the matrix
of this coded central repertory is, should become a major topic
for unbiased exploration. Clearly, the cherished notion of sen-
sory-to-motor through-traffic, which tries to bypass the topic,
is no longer adequate.

The discussion brought out that in the higher vertebrates,
and progressively as one ascends to primates, the hierarchical
organization of the central nervous system has superimposed upon
the rigid basic mechanisms of the lower forms systems of greater
adaptive flexibility. These newer systems can, in the terms of
our simile, form new words from the letters of the innate vocabulary. Although this fact is significant for the distinction
among different forms of "learning," its relation to the problems of specificity is too remote for us to dwell on here.

Confining our consideration therefore to the more basic
types, it has been established that the specific sequences of
muscular activation required for coordinated limb movements are
generated and discharged exclusively in the spinal cord segments
which normally innervate limbs. In confirmation of earlier experiments by Detwiler,[14] Weiss,[15] and others, Székely reported that the muscles of amphibian limbs transplanted to trunk
segments, and innervated from them, never exhibit coordinated
sequences of contractions, but only indiscriminate twitches.
Thus, while motor nerve fibers from the alien region have by no
means failed to connect with the foreign muscles, and may in
part have become re-modulated accordingly, the typical central
mechanism for their coordinated sequential activation was evidently lacking in those segments.

In one respect, some of Székely's experiments, however,
went considerably beyond the earlier ones. He removed the prospective trunk sector of the embryonic spinal cord and replaced
it by a supernumerary prospective limb sector. An extra limb,
grafted to the flank and innervated from the grafted cord region,
then executed coordinated movements. Besides proving again the
intrinsic difference between trunk and limb cord regardless of

peripheral signals, these observations, however, revealed an additional important feature, namely, that the grafted limb functioned in unison with the original host limb in front of it. Since the nerve supply of the two limbs came from different sources, the results indicate that the normal and the grafted limb region of cord operated synchronously in tandem and duplicated each other's discharge patterns. Formally speaking, a grafted supernumerary central sector behaves just like a grafted supernumerary limb. To speculate beyond this formal conclusion would be precocious. The case does show, however, a feasible experimental approach to further factual elucidation of the segmental matrix of spinal integration.

Compared with these highly illuminating results, Székely's observations on movements in chick limbs, transplanted in the embryonic stage in the place of wings or to the flank, were less conclusive. The number of successful cases was small, and the movements obtained, as well as their cinematographic records, were too indistinct to permit determination of the actual sequences of muscle participation in them. The fact that leg muscles innervated from foreign segments contract at all, rules out again, if this were necessary, any notion of an exclusive preestablished affinity of given nerves for given muscles. But further interpretation of the movements will have to wait for a more penetrating description of the facts, such as: which muscles in the grafted leg react, and when? In how many distinctive combinations? How much of the external movements is to be attributed to tendons from local shoulder muscles that have invaded the leg? How many of the movements are massive, indicating failure of "modulation," as known from earlier experiments? One must also consider that fore and hind extremities of vertebrates have homologous muscles in common, which amphibian experiments have shown to possess identical specificity criteria.

What applies to these experiments, applies to the entire field on which the Work Session discussions revolved: the very principle of specificity in the constitution and operation of neural functions is firmly established as such, but the data presently at hand are too fragmentary to justify more detailed assertions about its nature. The gist of the principle lies in the employment by the nervous system of the extremely efficient "key-lock" mechanism of paired conformances, which insures high reliance of communication from source to destination despite a high degree of indeterminacy along the intervening course. This mechanism is based on the "recognition" of specific criteria of spatial or temporal configuration by a conformingly constituted receiver. In this general version, the mechanism is a universal feature of living nature, exemplified, as mentioned earlier, by the mutual recognition between host and parasite; egg and sperm; cell and virus; cell and matching cell; target cell and hormone; antigen and antibody; enzyme and substrate. The Work Session has augmented this list with further appropriate examples pertaining to the nervous system, such as the identification by selective receptors of given molecular species in the external as well as the internal milieu, whether foodstuffs, odors or drugs; and the accurate identification by a motor neuron of what, in the central pool, is intended for the particular muscle at its end.

Yet, nowhere in this broad spectrum of conformances do we as yet find any justification for presuming that they all reside in a single common mechanism, even though the antibody-antigen affinity certainly has appealing features to commend it as a model. Nor is there any evidence where we face alternative hypotheses, that the solution will have to be a categorical choice between one or the other, and not rather admission of both. In conclusion, pending a more decisive stock of relevant facts than we now possess, we would be shortsighted if we were to insist that the specific conformances in question are based solely on steric molecular fitting, or solely on matched kinetics, or solely on electric time patterns. It would be equally shortsighted to insist that selective morphological connections and selective functional activation are mutually exclusive; that there must be either microprecise determinism or else vast structural amorphousness; or that adaptive features are the privilege of one only of the levels of organization -- the molecular or the intracellular or the intercellular.

The Work Session has brought out into the open a number of such one-sided contentions. They bear, in general, the earmarks of confinement of viewpoint within a limited conceptual or technical framework, within which they have been found applicable and consistent. But, as the Work Session has also demonstrated, they lose their monopolistic claims as one expands the view to encompass and compare wider aspects of the nervous system, in which the inconsistencies and incompatibilities among the various sectional views come to notice.

In summary, the Work Session has essentially succeeded in: a) opening to view such a broader perspective, revealing the need for reconciliation of divergent views; b) proving the inadequacy of present factual knowledge to resolve the open problems thus brought to view; c) illustrating a few practical lines of experimentation on how to pursue some of that missing information; and foremost, d) setting the problem of specificity in proper focus for attention as a major, but largely neglected key to the understanding of the nervous system.

Works Cited

1. Thorpe, W. H. (1950): The concepts of learning and their relation to those of instinct. In: Symposia of the Society for Experimental Biology, No. 4. Physiological Mechanisms in Animal Behavior. Danielli, J. F. and Brown, R., eds. Cambridge: Academic.

2. Hovanitz, W. (unpublished), referred to by Hovanitz, W. and Chang, V. C. S. (1963): Change of food plant preference by larvae of Pieris rapae controlled by strain selection, and the inheritance of this trait. J. Res. Lepidoptera 1: 163-168.

3. Cerletti, A. (1959): Discussion on third symposium: Comparison of abnormal behaviorial states induced by psychotropic drugs in animals and man. In: Proceedings of the First International Congress of Neuro-psychopharmacology. Bradley, P. B., Deniker, P. and Radouco-Thomas, C., eds. Amsterdam: Elsevier. Pp. 117-123.

4. Mirolli, M. and Welsh, J. H. (1964): The effects of reserpine and LSD on molluscs. In: Comparative Neurochemistry. Richter, D., ed. Oxford: Pergamon. Pp. 433-443.

5. Abood, L. G., Biel, J. H. and Ostfield, A. M. (1959): The psychotogenic effects of some N-substituted piperidyl benzilates. In: Proceedings of the First International Congress of Neuro-psychopharmacology. Bradley, P. B., Deniker, P. and Radouco-Thomas, C., eds. Amsterdam: Elsevier. Pp. 433-437.

6. Michael, R. P. (1961): An investigation of the sensitivity of circumscribed neurological areas to hormonal stimulation by means of the application of oestrogens directly to the brain of the cat. In: Regional Neurochemistry. Kety, S. S. and Elkes, J., eds. Oxford: Pergamon. Pp. 465-480.

7. Kollros, J. J. (1942): Localized maturation of lid-closure
    reflex mechanism by thyroid implants into the tadpole
    hind brain. Proc. Soc. Exp. Biol. Med. 49: 204-206.

8. Weiss, P. A. and Rossetti, F. (1951): Growth responses
    of opposite sign among different neuron types exposed
    to thyroid hormones. Proc. Nat. Acad. Sci. 37: 540-556.

9. Desmedt, J. S. (1954): Paroxystic activity of deplanted
    nerve centers in Amphibia, as influenced by the ionic
    environment. Proc. Soc. Exp. Biol. Med. 85: 491-494.

10. Weiss, P. A. (1924): Die Funktion transplantierter Am-
    phibienextremitäten. Aufstellung einer Resonanztheorie
    der motorischen Nerventätigkeit auf Grund abgestimmter
    Endorgane. Roux' Arch. 102: 635-672.

11. Wiersma, C. A. G. (1931): An experiment on the "resonance
    theory" of muscular activity. Arch. Neerl. Physiol.
    16: 337-345.

12. Miner, N. (1951): Integumental specification of sensory
    neurons in the genesis of cutaneous local sign. Unpub-
    lished Ph.D. Thesis. University of Chicago.

13. Anokhin, P. (1941): Motor function of transplanted extrem-
    ities after secondary regeneration. Bull. Exp. Biol.
    Med. 11(1): 16-18. (In Russian)

14. Detwiler, R. S. (1936): Neuroembryology: An Experimental
    Study. New York: Macmillan.

15. Weiss, P. A. (1936): Selectivity controlling the central-
    peripheral relations in the nervous system. Biol. Rev.
    11: 494-531.

* * *

The next article is an epigram which epitomizes the principal lesson of the whole series in posing that the nervous system is of a far less rigid and machine-like, and far more dynamic, variable and adaptive *nature than it has conventionally been credited with, but at the same time, that the margin between fixity and plasticity, that is, the scope of opportunities within the set frame of biological organization is a matter to be determined empirically by disciplined scientific exploration rather than being left forever to ambiguities of personal opinion and poetic phantasy.*

Reprinted from the A. M. A. Archives of Neurology
June 1960, Vol. 2, pp. 595-599
Copyright 1960, by American Medical Association

Modifiability of the Neuron

For nearly a century neuroanatomists and neurophysiologists in concert have sought to understand the nervous *system* in terms of the properties of its elements. Yet, despite spectacular analytical advances, we are still far short of an explanation of its integrative, coordinative, regulatory, and adaptive features that would satisfy those who are mindful of the true problems of behavior and who find no comfort in fragmentary, unrepresentative, or even fictional models or purely verbal surrogates for knowledge. Does this impasse discredit the validity of the attempt to reconstruct the whole from the components? Or does it perhaps just signify that some deficiencies of discernment in dealing with the elements have made us overlook some relevant properties? The decision lies in the future. But resignation from the analytical course would seem premature so long as the elements have not been entered into the account with their full share of capacities, as thus far they have not.

Let us not forget that when we speak of "properties" and "faculties" of any natural object, we actually refer not to its full endowment but only to that empirical fraction which we have come to know from observations and measurements by suitable detector devices, each of which reveals but a limited absorption band from the total spectrum with which the object is endowed. A listening device registers acoustic signals; an electric instrument, electric information; an optical apparatus, pictures. This being so, it would be folly to concede to an object no wider a repertory of properties than that recorded by the limited choice of detection devices which we happen to have favored routinely; the limitations of the student and of his tools must not be projected into the object of his study. Rather, one must constantly be on the lookout for ever-new means of disclosing additional properties formerly undiscerned for lack of proper indicators. The time is ripe—and reasons are compelling—for giving the neuron the benefit of such more generous considerations and treatment.

Our customary treatment has concentrated on structural, electric, and metabolic features. Optical devices, microscopic and submicroscopic, have furnished structural data: numbers, dimensions, orientations, distributions, branchings, groupings, and connections, including their variations. Electric measurements have led to detailed information about potentials, conductances, resistances, capacitances, polarizations, thresholds, and the like, as well as about the time courses, periodic or aperiodic, of their changes during activity. Metabolic studies have given us the balance sheet of energy requirements and exchanges during rest, activity, and recovery, as well as insight into the underlying chemical processes. Furthermore, the discovery of chemical transmitters has upgraded neurochemistry to something above a mere supply source of metabolic energy.

Without in any way belittling the achievements of this tripartite methodology, still what it can tell us about the neuron is limited to the restricted vocabulary of the techniques employed. So, as a result of our confinement to these powerful, yet limited, techniques, a correspondingly constrained conception of the nervous system has crystallized in our minds, which unnecessarily and unnaturally denies to neurons a lot of properties that other living cells demonstrably possess. Frankly, in essence we credit neurons with "life" not much more fully than we do "live" wires in an electric circuit. They merely vegetate, subserving the monotonic— and monotonous—function of carrying and transmitting impulses, much as Atlas was thought to be no more than a "live" pillar to support the globe. Except for quantitative gradations of structural, electric, and metabolic parameters, plus a very few gross chemical distinctions, as between "cholinergic" and "adrenergic" units, the neuron population has been considered as all of one kind and character, and, for that matter, static throughout life. At best, the neurons were conceded some minor variations of size and threshold values, but decidedly none of the sharp and discriminatory character distinctions that mark the cells of other tissues; for instance, the cells of different glands which have radically different chemical production plants.

Another methodological self-confinement has helped to consolidate this picture. Neuroanatomy and neurophysiology have, in a sense, accepted delivery of the nervous system into their hands only after it was fully formed, ready-made, in working order. Just how it had gotten to be that way, was a matter for which they did not feel accountable. It was something that one labeled noncommitally as "maturation," plus "conditioning," and then left to other departments to crack. Yet, it was precisely in those other biological departments, where technical conventions were less restrictive, that the neuron was found to have some unsuspected new properties, which, on the one hand, tie it more closely to the rest of the family of truly living cell types, and, on the other, throw new light on its functional performances.

The two major new additions to the list of properties of neurons are the demonstration of (1) a wide range of "specific" type differences within the neuronal population as clue to the establishment and maintenance of supraelemental order; and (2) a state of flux and continuous self-renewal of the body of the neuron. The meaning of these points may here be briefly summarized.

"Specificity," which underlies our highly discriminative sensory perception, used to be relegated to the sense organs, which, as transducers, were thought to reduce diversity to a single code in common to all neurons. Yet the simple experiences of pharmacology, toxicology, and endocrinology, according to which agents of a given molecular structure have a selective action on certain groups of central neurons to the exclusion of others, prove clearly that specificity is not confined to the periphery. "Specificity," in this context, refers to that constitutional property which enables a given unit to respond discriminately to an outer agent, depending on whether or not the latter is of a properly matching configuration—much as a lock yields to a matching key. Such pairwise specific correspondences are among the most general attributes of living systems, as manifested, for instance, in hormone action, fertilization, parasitism, immunology, and enzymology.

Whatever the underlying mechanism may be—according to some, it lies in the steric conformance of complementary molecules—the only suitable detectors so far at our disposal are the specific biological responses themselves. Specific interactions between two systems, A and B, are of two kinds: Either A imposes its own specificity (or a complement to it) on a more plastic B ("modulation"); or, if both A and B are already fixed in their specificities, the degree of mutual correspondence or resonance ("affinity") will determine whether or not they will become linked, morphologically or functionally.

Ever since 1922, I have presented evidence to show that both individual muscles and individual receptor areas possess distinctive constitutional differentials, presumably biochemical in nature, which they confer upon the neurons to which they are attached ("modulation"), thus creating a corresponding number of distinctive subspecies among the peripheral neurons. The latter, in turn, would impose similar specificities upon penultimate neurons, and in this manner the centers would be briefed on just which central stations are connected in each case with precisely what muscle or receptor.[1] The receptor side of this principle, originally demonstrated for muscular proprioception[2] and corneal exteroception,[3] has since been widely confirmed for vision and other senses.[4] From all this, the conclusion became inescapable that neurons differ much more widely among one another in subtle biochemical characteristics than had previously been recognized, and that these highly specific differentials are instrumental in establishing the selective linkages requisite for the orderly functioning of the nervous system.

The nervous system thus is comparable to an integrated system of closed-circuit broadcasting networks. Whether the individual channels are controlled by a "resonance" system of communication,[5] or are joined by "wire connections,"[4] is debatable, but inconsequential for the general thesis, which is that "specifically matching properties" are a basic principle of neural intercommunication. The crucial points of this thesis are (1) that neuronal specificity can be modified ("modulated") by the terminal effectors and receptors, as well as by fellow neurons; and (2) that by virtue of the acquired "tunes," they can selectively enter into higher-order unions of concordant elements.

It is important to realize that neurons share both these properties with other living cells. Point 1 is illustrated by the various template analogues invoked in cell reproduction, differentiation, growth control, antibody production, induced enzyme formation, etc., in all of which cells undergo some specific adaptive reshaping of parts of their molecular populations.[6] Point 2 has recently been clinched by the following two discoveries: (a) Cells of a given kind, disseminated throughout the body by random routes, have been found "homing" at their specific sites of destination.[7] (b) Mixtures of cells of different types, scrambled at random, have been found to sort themselves out actively according to kinds and mutual "affinities"[8]: They recognize each other's kinds on contact and then react discriminately, remaining associated if they are alike, but separating again if they are unrelated.[9] There is thus now available definite proof that the "specific" faculties of neurons outlined above are quite in keeping with demonstrated properties of other living cells. Some more detailed suggestions have been set forth on how the interaction of specific complementary molecular end-groups facing each other across cell membranes at points of cell-to-cell contact (as at synaptic junctions) might force the carrier macromolecules from their "barrier" alignment in the cell surface into radial "open-gate" positions, thereby opening wide "pores" and "leaks" between them for the transcellular passage of substances and increased flow of current [9]; but such speculations indicate only the feasibility, rather than the attainment, of compatibility between the principle of specificity in cellular and neuronal interactions and the conventional, "nonspecific" concepts.

Once recognized, the property of specificity presents us with countless new questions: How many types are laid out as such in the mosaic of the embryonic nervous system, and how many additional subspecifications are later imposed upon them by modulating influences of somatic tissues, or even functional adaptation? How far do such secondary modifications become ingrained and indelible, and to what extent can they be superseded by new ones? And so forth. The answers to the What's and When's and How's will vary with the type of neuron. But it seems intriguing to contemplate that some degree of adaptive modifiability may be retained by almost any neuron, so that the plasticity of the nervous *system,* as manifested in behavior, might rest not only on latitude of *inter*neuronal relations, but on *intra*neuronal modifiability as well.

A tangible basis for such a lasting opportunity for specific adaptation is offered by the disclosure that the neuron is in a state of perpetual renewal of its substance, which proceeds from the nuclear territory of the cell. From this supply source, a continuous viscous stream of new cell substance is conveyed down the nerve fiber, where it evidently replenishes the stores of metabolically degraded macromolecules, besides serving as vehicle for neurohumors and other products to be discharged into the periphery.[10,11] The evidence, derived at first from the dynamic deformations of throttled supply streams, has recently been greatly strengthened by electron-microscopic, cytochemical, and isotope-tracer studies. The neuron, in this version, abandons its former aspect of a static fixture and assumes instead that of a stationary process in continuous flux. This obviously creates opportunities for specific adaptive changes in its molecular population, assuming that the reproductive source of cell-specific molecules can be refashioned, template-wise, as in cellular immune reactions, so as to adopt configurations of chemical structures introduced from the neuronal environment. It is not inconceivable that this concept might some day even embrace the explanation of acquired idiosyncrasies and selective sensitization and tolerance to drugs.

To what extent the various instances of "revitalization" of the neuron concept which have been outlined in this essay will open and illuminate new avenues to the obscure problems of coordination, regulation, learning, ageing, and so forth, is unpredictable. But it stands to reason that the described additional degrees of freedom of the neuron will at least have to be taken seriously into account in further efforts to reconstruct a reasonably faithful picture of the nervous *system* from what little is known of its elements—that is, provided we want to let our brain exercise the privilege of adaptive change for which its "living" elements so well predispose it. New methods yield new facts. New facts which cannot be accommodated in existing concepts call for adaptive conceptual revisions. The living nervous system is calling.

REFERENCES

1. Weiss, P.: A. Res. Nerv. & Ment. Dis., Proc. (1950) 30:3-23, 1952.
2. Verzár, F., and Weiss, P.: Arch. ges. Physiol. 223:671-684, 1930.
3. Weiss, P.: J. Comp. Neurol. 77:131-169, 1942.
4. Sperry, R. W.: Quart. Rev. Biol. 12:66-73, 1951.
5. Weiss, P.: Biol. Rev. 11:494-531, 1936.
6. Weiss, P.: Yale J. Biol. & Med. 19:235-278, 1947.
7. Weiss, P., and Andres, G.: J. Exper. Zool. 121:449-487, 1952.
8. Moscona, A. A.: Proc. Soc. Exper. Biol. & Med 92:410-416, 1956.
9. Weiss, P.: Internat. Rev. Cytol. 7:319-423, 1958.
10. Weiss, P., and Hiscoe, H. B.: J. Exper. Zool. 107:315-395, 1948.
11. Weiss, P.: A. Res. Nerv. & Ment. Dis., Proc. (1954) 35:8-18, 1956.

V. NERVE REGENERATION AND NERVE REPAIR

Introduction to Part V

A lot has been said about the need for bridging more effectively the gulf between "basic" research and "practical"—in this case, "clinical"—application. Having devoted the book precisely to this objective, it seems fitting to change from precept to demonstration. Therefore, this section is devoted to showing how knowledge of the *mechanisms of nerve growth* could be profitably translated into the design of improved methods of *peripheral nerve repair*. When the exigencies of World War II presented a critical demand for urgent action, the knowledge about the ways of nerve growth and nerve regeneration, summarized in Section IV, however primitive and insufficient, could, at any rate, be promptly exploited for guidelines to pilot experiments that would be adaptable to the *practice of nerve surgery*.

Beyond the undeniable success of the effort—not unmarred, naturally, also by some failures—a major lesson of this phase of our work has been the conviction that the rational exploitation to practical and useful ends of "basic" knowledge is a worthy and noble task, and indeed one destined to supplant, in the long run, the surrogate expedient of purely empirical probings. I take great satisfaction from the fact that some of the major innovations and improvements which have emerged from my laboratory during that period (e.g., the concept and examples of tissue banks; the use of tissues devitalized by freeze-drying for grafting; the splicing of severed nerves by sleeves) have become established practices, obviously with appropriate improvements since.

I cannot hide, however, the sense of disappointment which I experienced when an occasional medical practitioner, appointed or parading as a spokesman for a given specialty, would shrug off efforts like ours as purely "academic"—an attitude that finds its counterpart in the self-righteous disdain by some practitioners of "basic" research for work toward useful goals. One might inform the latter that Benjamin Franklin, in founding the oldest scientific society in America, gave it the name of "American Philosophical Society for the Promotion of Useful Knowledge;" and the former, that Roentgen's first X-ray photograph of the bones in an intact human hand (that of the anatomist Koelliker) was not a purely academic pastime, neither in intent nor future impact. "Basic" and "applied" in science do not refer to subject matter. They merely denote varieties of interest, orientation or emphasis. And whatever an inquisitive mind may find in its search, if it is valid and adds to knowledge and is of benefit to man, potentially or manifestly, is good.

The following Section is added as a humble testimonial to this credo. No commentary to interconnect the selection of papers on peripheral nerve seems necessary, as they all form steps in a continuous series of experiments.

(430)

Reprinted from Jour. Neurosurg., 1, 1944

THE TECHNOLOGY OF NERVE REGENERATION:
A REVIEW. SUTURELESS TUBULATION AND
RELATED METHODS OF NERVE REPAIR*

PAUL WEISS, Ph.D.

INTRODUCTION

IN SEVERAL recent publications,[183,186,188,189,195,200] a method of sutureless reunion of severed nerve stumps by means of cuffs of artery was described and, on the basis of its merits in the laboratory, was recommended for possible adaptation to clinical use. The conclusions were based on experiments with a total of over 700 nerve unions effected in rats, rabbits, chickens, cats and monkeys, followed in the majority of cases by functional and histological studies. These experiments, in conjunction with a broader study of the mechanism of nerve regeneration, have led to important insight into the prerequisites for optimum nerve restoration. Arterial sleeve splicing complies with more of these prerequisites than do other methods, and this has been the basis of its success. But further application of the lessons thus learned gives promise of even more substantial improvements, and sleeve splicing may eventually be superseded by some other, more meritorious procedure incorporating its experiences. The emphasis lies more on the principle than on the current form of its application. An unbiased survey of existing methods of nerve repair, including sutureless sleeve splicing, shows plainly that no one of them is sufficiently superior to the others to deserve a monopoly of attention. In times of urgency such as these, the weighing of one method against another had therefore better give way to a concerted effort to extract the best features from all available methods and combine them to the best practical advantage.

Sleeve splicing bears a certain, though only superficial, resemblance to earlier procedures of joining the stumps of a severed nerve inside a tube ("tubulization") and of wrapping suture lines, procedures which have been practised on and off for more than sixty years (see Table 1). It also shares certain features with the method of plasma suture.[207,163]

None of the reported methods has been generally adopted, and there has been some controversy regarding their merits or demerits; many, in fact, have been thoroughly discredited.[155,130] Nevertheless, trust in their potential usefulness keeps manifesting itself in persistently recurring attempts to reintroduce them into the practice of nerve repair in either the old or some new form.[172,152] The very persistency of these attempts, aside from those simple

* Some of the experimental work referred to in this article was carried out under contract, recommended by the Committee on Medical Research, between the Office of Scientific Research and Development and the University of Chicago; also aided by the Dr. Wallace C. and Clara A. Abbott Memorial Fund of the University of Chicago.

TABLE 1

Main publications on nerve sheathing and tubulation

No.	Author	Year	Material Used
1	Gluck[58]	1880	decalcified bone
2	Vanlair[170]	1882	decalcified bone
3	Kölliker[98]	1890	decalcified bone
4	v. Büngner[23]	1891	artery; vein
5	Huber[85]	1895	Cargile membrane
6	Payr[124]	1900	magnesium
7	Pomerancew[131]	1900	decalcified bone
8	Lotheissen[106]	1901	gelatine
9	Foramitti[51]	1904	artery; live or fixed
10	Craig & Ellis[34]	1905	Cargile membrane
11	Sherren[142]	1906	Cargile membrane
12	Treutlein[169]	1906	artery
13	v. Auffenberg[7]	1907	decalcified bone
14	Hashimoto & Tokuoka[75]	1907	preserved arteries
15	Tilmanns[168]	1907	
16	Wrede[204]	1909	vein
17	Röpke[135]	1910	
18	Perekropoff[125]	1913	artery, vein
19	Denk[37]	1914	fascia
20	Eden & Rehn[44]	1914	fat tissue
21	Hirschel[79]	1915	preserved arteries
22	Auerbach[5]	1915	galalith
23	Fullerton[57]	1915	vein
24	Hans[70]	1915	epineurium
25	Heile & Hezel[76]	1915	unvulcanized rubber
26	Kirk & Lewis[95]	1915	fascia
27	Kredel[100]	1915	fascia and fat
28	Nageotte[117]	1915	vein
29	Bethe[16]	1916	artery
30	Edinger[45]	1916	agar tube
31	Mauclaire[110]	1916	trachea
32	Meisel[111]	1916	fascia
33	Auerbach[6]	1916	casein preparation
34	Stracker[157]	1916	veins; agar tube
35	Blencke[19]	1917	agar tube; artery
36	Burk[24]	1917	agar tube
37	Dustin[41]	1917	artery; vein; fascia
38	Eden[43]	1917	artery *in situ*
39	v. Enderlen & Lobenhoffer[47]	1917	artery; feather quill; agar tube
40	Hohmann & Spielmeyer[84]	1917	agar tube; artery
41	Kirschner[97]	1917	agar tube; fascia and fat
42	Müller & Berblinger[115]	1917	agar tube; artery
43	Perthes[126]	1917	fat tissue
44	Spitzy[151]	1917	agar tube
45	Steinthal[154]	1917	rubber
46	Bielschowsky & Unger[17]	1918	preserved dura
47	Meuriot & Platon[112]	1918	rubber
48	Platt[129]	1919	greased fascia; vein
49	Huber[87]	1920	artery, fascia, Cargile membrane
50	Stopford[156]	1920	fascia; vein
51	Kraus & Reisner[99]	1940	muscle, fat
52	Verne & Iselin[172]	1941	parchment
53	Spurling[152]	1943	tantalum

duplications of effort based on unfamiliarity with facts and literature, signifies that the belief in tubulating or wrapping suture lines stems either from a basic truth or a common delusion. The lack of unanimity in the matter can be ascribed to several reasons. One reason has been the fragmentary state of knowledge about nerve regeneration. Ignorance of the requirements of the different tissue components in nerve regeneration has turned some basically sound procedures into failures merely because some trivial fact, the importance of which had not been known or suspected, was neglected. Another difficulty has been the lack of objective and uniform standards in assessing and describing the experimental and clinical results. Moreover, there were many reports without adequate documentation and many claims unsupported by facts.

This state of affairs has made it desirable to reexamine the whole subject in the light of the increased knowledge and more critical standards of today. The following report undertakes to do this in the spirit of scientific analysis. Neither the biological process of nerve regeneration nor the various techniques to facilitate it for the sake of functional nerve restoration are indivisible wholes. All components of a nerve and of its surroundings—axons, sheath cells, fibroblasts, macrophages, erythrocytes, leucocytes, plasma, collagen, capillaries, etc.—all these contribute in some degree to the outcome of nerve regeneration, and their various peculiarities and requirements want to be taken into account. Every technique of nerve union, in turn, consists of a variety of steps and measures each of which is apt to affect differentially the various tissue components, some beneficially, and some adversely. The net balance decides the outcome for nerve regeneration as a whole, whether beneficial, harmful or irrelevant. There is no justification, therefore, for either accepting or condemning any one method *in toto*, since each one must contain elements worth preserving and exploiting, as well as elements patently detrimental, and elements that do neither good nor harm. By sorting out these elements, scientific analysis prepares the synthesis of improved methods, which will emerge from the combining of the positive features of the different techniques and the elimination of their recognized drawbacks. The results, subject to verification in laboratory experiments, may then be adopted as blueprints for clinical procedures.

THE MECHANISM OF NERVE REGENERATION

Due regard for the realities of nerve regeneration is essential both in judging existing methods of nerve repair and in devising new procedures. Any methodical approach to the problems of nerve repair must be based on strict observance of the growth requirements of regenerating fibers, which in turn presupposes intimate knowledge of nerve growth, and this means not merely descriptive knowledge of the phenomena as recorded in macroscopic and microscopic observation, but analytical understanding of their mechanics. Some valuable progress in this direction has been made during recent years, even though it is still small in the light of what remains to be done. As a directive for future research, it must be stressed that progress in this field is not to be expected simply from continued search for more facts along the classical lines of nerve regeneration studies, but from a basic change of viewpoint. Problems of nerve regeneration will have to be taken out of the province of naturalistic description and transferred into that of physical and chemical reality, where nerves are treated as material systems with verifiable physical and chemical properties. A similar reorientation is noticeable in all current biological thinking, and the field of pathology has greatly benefited from it. Morphological features formerly described as such must be resolved into the dynamics operative in their formation.[182,122] In the case of the nerve fiber, the mere listing of such phenomena as local swellings, terminal bulbs, spiraling, branching, etc., must give way to a dynamic concept of the mechanism of nerve growth so consistent that all those phenomena will appear as logical manifestations of that growth principle under the locally prevailing conditions.

There have been some good efforts to that end in the past, but most of them were either very abstract or based on inconclusive experimentation. The very phenomenon of "growth" of the nerve fiber has only occasionally been stated in sufficiently articulate form to invite analysis.[185,205] If "growth" connotes augmentation by synthesis of the living substance, how much of the elongation of a regenerating axon is due to real growth, and how much to mere draining of preexisting substance from the cell body? And does what actual growth there is occur in the cell body, at the advancing tip, or over the whole length of the axon? And where are the ingredients for this synthesis taken in—centrally, at the tip, in the whole naked part, or at the nodes of the old stump? And does what is valid for the elongation of the fiber hold equally true for its continued growth in width? It is tangible questions like these that will have to guide research, rather than just general talk about "growth" in all its indefiniteness. What sense is there, for instance, in speculating on how essential are blood supply, vitamins, etc., to the young fiber sprouts if one does not even know to what extent the latter depend on local sources for their oxygen and nutrient supply?

Another example of the lack of concern for physical realities which characterizes much of the past work on nerve regeneration is the not uncommon tendency to view nerve fibers, at one time, as if they were growing in a vacuum, and at other times, as if they were not corporeal. One encounters descriptions (occasionally in connection with tubulization experiments) according to which the space into which nerve fibers grow is "empty."[19,43,151,157] Now, physically speaking, there can be no empty space anywhere in an organism; there must be either solids, liquids, gases, or mixtures of them, and the behavior of the nerve fiber will vary significantly, depending on how the space is occupied. The fallacy of identifying lack of histological distinctiveness with physical homogeneity is obvious. On other occasions, the ability or inability of nerve fibers to "grow through" other tissues is discussed with insufficient regard for the physical mass of the fiber. This is very pertinent to such problems as the penetration of scars, invasion of grafts, etc. Obviously, a nerve fiber, like any other physical body, can penetrate another tissue only by displacing a corresponding volume of substance, and since only liquids are freely displaceable, the penetration of nerve fibers, as well as their continued growth and expansion, will be limited by the liquid content of the tissue and possible liquefying potency of the fiber (see below).

These examples may suffice to indicate the need of greater concreteness in dealing with the problems of nerve growth. The following outline of the mechanics of nerve regeneration is a step in this direction. Only those aspects of the larger problem will be taken up that are of immediate bearing on problems of nerve suture. A basic familiarity of the reader with the descriptive facts of nerve regeneration will be taken for granted.* To avoid misunderstandings and for easier reference, the sense in which various terms will be used in this article is defined in the following list.

TERMINOLOGY

Proximal Stump. That part of a severed nerve left connected with the centers.

Distal Stump. That part of a severed nerve disconnected from its centers.

Aneuritic[109] *Nerve.* Nerve after degeneration of all axons.

Gap. The space between the cut faces of two nerve stumps.

Union Tissue. The tissue filling the gap and interweaving the formerly separated stumps.

Matrix. The non-cellular foundation of the union tissue.

Scar. Union tissue with excessive fibrous development.

Junction. The level at which the nerve stumps are reconnected, which after suture is the "suture line," but after sutureless splicing includes the whole extent of the union tissue.

Schwann Cells. The accessory sheath cells of the nerve fibers, both in their normal tubular state and after the hyperplasia attending Wallerian degeneration.

Neurotization.[171] Invasion of a tissue by nerve fibers, e.g., the repopulation of a distal stump by regenerating branches, or the reinnervation of denervated skin and muscle.

Neurilemmal Tubes. The fibrous tubular surface covering of the individual nerve fiber, variously identified as sheath of Henle, Key-Retzius, and Plenk-Laidlaw; regardless of its origin from, and relation to sheath cells, endoneurial cells, or both (see Young[205]); for brevity, called "tubes."

Endoneurium. The connective tissue occupying the spaces between the individual nerve fibers.

Macrophages. Solitary phagocytic cells of hematogenic or histiogenic origin giving the appearance of common macrophages.

Neuroma. An irregular excessive growth containing a dense tangle of nerve fibers.

Glioma.[119,41,109] An irregular excessive growth from an aneuritic nerve, composed largely of Schwann cells.

Edema.[187] Distension of the endoneurial spaces by excess fluid.

NERVE DEGENERATION

A nerve is a composite structure. Its constituent elements—axis cylinders, Schwann cells, tubes, endoneurium, perineurium, epineurium, blood vessels—react differentially to the trauma of transection, their combined responses in the distal stump forming the syndrome known as Wallerian de-

---

* For reviews of the descriptive histology of nerve regeneration, the reader is referred to the works of Ramon y Cajal,[31] Ranson,[133] Huber,[88] Nageotte,[119] Boeke,[21] Rossi and Gastaldi.[137]

generation.[31,119] Degeneration precedes and, in a sense, prepares the ground for regeneration. It involves regressive and progressive changes. Most prominent among the regressive changes of the distal stump is the breakdown of the myelin sheath and the axis cylinder, followed by the dissolution and resorption of the resulting debris (with formation of so-called digestive chambers or "ovoids"). Progressive changes include the appearance of large numbers of macrophages removing nerve debris, and the conversion and proliferation of formerly tubular Schwann cells into solid cell strands (Büngner's cords). In addition, common traumatic and inflammatory reactions may occur at the wound surfaces. In the proximal stump, degenerative changes similar to those of the peripheral stump remain confined to the vicinity of the wound, their extent varying with the nature of the trauma from a few millimeters to several centimeters. They are soon to be superseded by the regenerative processes in which the proximal stump takes the lead.

Save for a few resistant fibers, the regressive changes of the distal stump are nearly completed within a few days after transection. Whether or not degeneration proceeds in proximo-distal direction down the nerve, is still controversial.[23,83,159,123,84,136] The factors controlling Wallerian degeneration are, in spite of some analytical attempts,[119,90] still largely unknown. Its rate varies with the circumstances; it is markedly delayed by nerve compression.[194] Experiments to determine whether nerve fragments which have degenerated at different rates and under different conditions are all equally suitable for neurotization, are under way.

The neurilemmal tubes survive the lytic processes of early degeneration. They become distended by the accumulation of decomposition products and macrophages. This increase of turgor, causing swelling of the nerve as a whole (for actual measurements, see Weiss[187]) and obliteration of the endoneurial spaces, may interfere with blood circulation and stimulate collagen deposition,[109] but no further information on these points is available. Variations of turgor may be the clue to the later differences in fibrosity between different aneuritic stumps and, if so, would be of clinical importance.

Schwann cell reaction promptly follows the fragmentation of the axis cylinder. There are indications that the Schwann cells participate in the digestion and perhaps even phagocytosis of the tube content during the initial phase of degeneration.*,[31,119,41] In fact, direct intake of degeneration products might account for their rapid hypertrophy. However, the main share of the clearing of the tubes is soon taken over by the macrophages, which appear on the scene in large numbers.[118] Their exact origin has never been traced. Many are undoubtedly transformed blood monocytes. Mobilized histiocytes might enter through the wound surface if the latter were left exposed. However, since macrophages are just as numerous in sleeve-spliced nerves[200] (in which immigration from the surroundings is precluded), this source cannot be important. A third conceivable source lies in a possible

---

* In recent tissue culture studies (still unpublished), Schwann cells from peripheral nerve were actually observed in the act of digesting ingested myelin.

conversion of some Schwann cells and endoneurial cells of the nerve itself into macrophages. Although actually observed in tissue culture,[191] the occurrence of such a transformation in nerves *in situ* has not yet been demonstrated. The problem is of considerable practical importance since the ratio between Schwann cells and macrophages in the distal stump has a bearing on the subsequent neurotization process.[191]

The final fate of these macrophages is uncertain. From the standpoint of successful nerve degeneration, it would be desirable to have them move on after ingesting the debris of the tubes so as to make room for the cords of hypertrophied Schwann cells. As a rule, this occurs. However, under certain still undefined conditions, the macrophages remain trapped inside the old tubes, thus preventing the expansion of Schwann cells and barring the entry of regenerating nerve fibers. I have seen aneuritic tubes crammed with immobilized macrophages many months after transection,* and since this condition may well become a permanent obstacle to neurotization, further exploration of the origin, behavior and fate of macrophages as a basis for improved control over their activity in nerve regeneration is urgently needed.

Mitotic activity of the expanded Schwann cells sets in within a week[23] and the enlarging strands (a) fill the tubes,[21, 82, 119] except where "ovoids" and macrophages resist replacement; (b) appear in intertubal positions,[31] partly from former unmyelinated fibers, partly perhaps after escaping through "leaks" in tubes; and (c) spill from the open ends of the tubes into the surroundings, initiating what is often referred to as the "glioma,"[41,119] or "Schwannoma"[109] of the peripheral stump.

All these component processes of Wallerian degeneration are interdependent so that interference with any one of them may alter the course of all, which in turn may seriously affect the subsequent neurotization processes for which they are to prepare the proper setting.

Neurotization, i.e., the supply of new axis cylinders, definitely has been shown to be solely a function of the proximal stump. The concept of "autogenous" nerve regeneration,[14,150] has been conclusively disproved.[31,119] The role of the converted ("degenerated") distal stump is merely that it presents to the outgrowing axons conditions of growth far superior to those offered by any other known environment. This explains why the exploration of the properties of degenerated nerve must be carried on as an integral part of all research on nerve regeneration. First, the degenerated stump does not invariably attain that state of optimum receptiveness for regenerating fibers of which it is intrinsically capable, and knowledge of the reasons for this variability may suggest measures by which that optimal condition may be brought about more consistently; this is particularly evident in the case of nerve grafting in which the often reported inferiority of distal nerve fragments, when used as grafts, contrasts with their effective neurotization when left in place. Unsuspected differences in local conditions can account for such variety of results as that one distal nerve fragment becomes a superb

---

* Compare also figure in Hammond, Nonidez and Hinsey.[69]

bed for regenerating fibers, while another becomes a dense, almost impervious, fibrotic strand, and a third remains clogged up with macrophages. Second, insight into the biophysical and biochemical peculiarities to which degenerated nerve owes its superiority as a growth bed may make it possible to provide growing nerve fibers with their essential prerequisites even in the absence of degenerating nerve, so that perhaps in the future synthetic substitutes for nerve grafts may be devised from this knowledge.

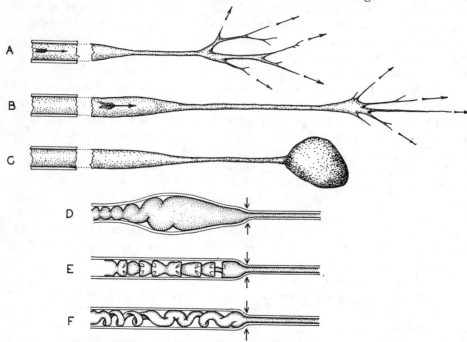

FIG. 1. Diagrams illustrating normal and impeded outgrowth of axons. *A*, *B*, Two successive stages of outgrowth showing progressive elongation by interfacial tensions (simple arrows), which draw out the transitory terminal filopodia to fine points, followed by lateral enlargement resulting from centrifugal convection of axonal substance by intraaxonal pressure (feathered arrow). *C*, Terminal bulb, produced by the damming up of axonal substance in front of an unsurmountable obstacle. *D*, *E*, *F*, Ballooning, telescoping, and coiling of the axonal substance just proximal to a constriction which reduces the diameter of the tubes (level of constriction indicated by arrows). Centrifugal growth pressure in the axon continues to move axonal substance distad, and the damming up of this substance in front of the "bottleneck" leads to the various forms of contortion shown in these schematic reproductions from photomicrographs.

NERVE REGENERATION

The outgrowth of new axons from the proximal stump is the cardinal process in nerve regeneration. As such it has monopolized much of the attention in the past, an attitude accentuated by the preferential use of silver impregnation methods, which visualize the axis cylinder practically to the exclusion of all other structures. It is well, however, to bear in mind that the distal nerve stump, into which the new sprouts grow, makes some substantial, even though less spectacular, contributions to their growth, and that the full restoration of a nerve is a compound process involving the participation not only of the axis cylinders but also of those accessory elements of their surroundings on which they depend for nutriment, guidance, protection, myelinization, maintenance, and perhaps other as yet unrevealed influences. Consequently, nerve regeneration must never be dealt with in terms of the growing axon alone, but always in reference to the environmental conditions under which growth takes place.

The so-called outgrowth of the regenerating axon is primarily protoplasmic movement of the amoeboid type.[71,74,102,177] The tip of the axon becomes mobile and extends into the environment by means of fine filamentous pseudopodia ("filopodia").[114,143,144,145] As it proceeds, it spins out the axoplasm behind it to increasingly greater length (Fig. 1A, B). The motive force

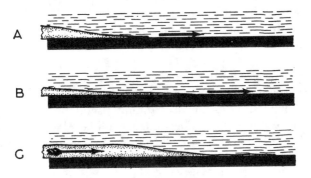

FIG. 2. Pull-push mechanism of nerve fiber advance. Drawn out by interfacial tensions (simple arrow) along solid-liquid interface, fiber receives inflow by intraaxonal pressure (feathered arrow).

actuating this elongation has often been ascribed to pressure inside the neuron (Held's[77] "vis a tergo"; Cajal's[31] "formative turgor"; Young's[205] "outflow"). Evidence of such pressure has been found in the familiar terminal bulbs of arrested nerve fibers (Fig. 1C),[31,41,205] and more recently in the swelling of locally compressed nerve fibers immediately proximal to the level of compression (Fig. 1D, E, F).[192,197] On physical grounds, however, such pressure cannot of itself account for the extension of the filopodia. It is necessary to assume some external pull, which is obviously exerted by interfacial tensions[185] (Fig. 2).

Nerve fibers can extend only along phase boundaries between two media and cannot move into a homogeneous medium in the manner of plant roots.[72, 177] They are drawn out along a solid-liquid interface (Fig. 2A, B) by forces roughly comparable to those causing oil to spread along a water-air interface. Flow of axoplasm into these pseudopodia, presumably sustained by intraaxonal pressure, then fills them up (Fig. 2C). The advance of the axon is thus due to a pull-push mechanism, with interfacial tensions exerting the pull, and internal pressure pushing from behind. Of the several filopodia appearing concurrently, usually only one receives the main inflow, while the others are withdrawn.[144,145] Inflow divided over several filopodia gives rise to terminal branching.[144,185]

This pull-push advance of the fiber tip can proceed for some time *in vitro* in pure inorganic media containing no nutrients or growth implements, such as thiamin or biotin, other than those possibly stored in the nerve cell.[28] This observation suggests that early "outgrowth" is a physical process of elongation, rather than a true "growth" process involving chemical synthesis of new axoplasm. The same conclusion has been reached from the observation that the proximal diameter of nerve fibers decreases during the early stages of regeneration.[67] Only secondarily does the physical elongation then entail increased assimilation and thereby initiate actual growth for the consolidation of the fiber. After the fiber has reached its full length, it continues to grow in width. This growth has been shown to proceed from the central cell body.[202] In reality, the situation is even more complex than here outlined, but this brief sketch will suffice to indicate the intricacy of the mechanism of nerve fiber "growth," and, accordingly, the diversity of provisions required to support it.

The linear character of nerve growth raises the question of what factors orient the outgrowing fibers. Concretely, this problem resolves itself into two questions: what guides the advancing pseudopodia, and what determines which pseudopodia are to become consolidated and which are to be resorbed. Once the tip has been caused to move in a given direction, the rest of the fiber follows automatically. If the tip moves straight, the fiber course will be straight, while an erratic course of the tip will result in contorted fibers, though some bends may later be straightened out by elasticity. Answers to the problem of what guides the fiber tip have been proposed in essentially four different theories: (1) Contact guidance[40,74,80,177,185]; (2) Least resistance[171]; (3) Chemotropism ("neurotropism")[30,31,53,54,107,167]; (4) Galvanotropism.[26,32,93,158] These have been discussed more fully on previous occasions,[38,74,185] and only the most pertinent points will be repeated here.

Contact Guidance. "Contact guidance" implies that the growing tip applies itself blindly to the substratum with which it is in contact. The course of the tip is, therefore, determined solely by the configuration of its contact environment plus such physical and chemical properties of the latter as will make for adhesion or non-adhesion and intimacy of the resulting contact. The original concept, that nerve fibers follow gross mechanical structures,[73,80] is incomplete. It has to be extended to the submicroscopic field.[177] As stated before, fibers can grow only along surfaces; but it takes some additional factor to single out a particular direction along that surface to be followed. This directive factor is presumably provided by the fine structure of the surface. Extensive experimental evidence has been presented,[177,185] to show that nerve fibers follow the direction of oriented fibrillar units of microscopic or submicroscopic dimensions present in their contact substratum. Additional evidence will be cited below.

Both cellular and non-cellular surfaces may serve in the capacity of contact substrata. But in either case, the line of advance is determined by some linear structures ("pathway structures") within that surface. Fibrin fibers are excellent climbing ropes,[177,200] and so are Schwann cells.[96,119,200,205] It is significant that oriented interfaces orient fibroblasts[176] and Schwann cells[177] just as they do nerve fibers. They can, therefore, orient nerve fiber growth either directly or through the intermediary of a correspondingly oriented spindle cell which the nerve fiber then follows. Moreover, nerve fibers already in existence form, under certain conditions, preferential pathways for other advancing nerve tips, which fact accounts for the building up of nerve bundles around pioneering fibers ("fasciculation").[185]

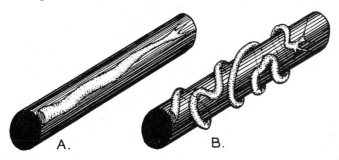

Fig. 3. Straight polarized advance of axons in the direction of the axis of a fiber serving as substratum (A); contrasted with the random winding course (B) to be expected if either simple "stereotropism" or "least resistance" were the determining factors. [A winding course is observed only (a) if the substratum has a spiral surface organization (e.g. in Perroncito's coils), or (b) if the fiber is arrested in its advance, yet keeps increasing in length (e.g., Fig. 1, F), or (c) if a fiber retracts.]

Contact guidance, as here described, implies that the nerve fiber tip reacts solely to cues of its immediate environment. Agents acting from a distance can, therefore, influence the course of a nerve fiber only to the extent to which they affect the physical pathway. Selective affinities between different types of nerve fibers and different kinds of pathways are a possibility worth keeping in mind,[166] although the evidence in favor of selective outgrowth is still incomplete.

Least Resistance. The theory that nerve fibers simply take the course of lowest mechanical resistance—one of the earliest concepts,[171] and one still sporadically encountered in current literature[69]—is partly incorrect and, for the rest, non-committal. Let us recall, for instance, that nerve fibers do not grow into homogeneous fluids, even though the mechanical resistance of liquids is negligible; also that nerve fibers, given an appropriate pathway structure, can grow from a softer into a denser medium,[177] unless the latter is impenetrable (see below). Moreover, "least resistance" cannot explain why fibers which extend along a solid-liquid interface follow definite directions, rather than just move about at random, as the all-round absence of obstacles would enable them to do. Axons on a fibrin thread in serum, for instance, follow a straight longitudinal course (Fig. 3A), and do not wind themselves around the thread (Fig. 3B).* Thus, while it is unquestionably correct to state that nerve fibers are deflected by mechanical obstructions, it takes something more positive than mere lack of obstacles to define their actual course. What serious consequences superficial thinking in these matters may have when applied to practical problems, is well illustrated by the notorious Edinger tubes, introduced during the last war for the bridging of nerve gaps[45] (see below). These were tubes, filled with gelatin or agar-agar, interposed between the nerve stumps. The idea was to present the outgrowing nerve fibers with a "soft" medium. Yet, no fibers grew in—as we now realize, for lack of proper interfaces—and the method proved a sad failure.[81,151,157] Fiber growth needs positive support, not just absence of handicaps.

Chemotropism (neurotropism). The theory that growing nerve tips are attracted toward distant sources of chemical emanations by a mechanism of chemotaxis was first suggested by Cajal[30] and later specifically applied to nerve regeneration.[31,53,54,107,167] It endows the nerve tip with the capacity to perceive and discriminate different chemicals and to orient itself uphill along the concentration gradient leading to their source. Particularly strong attractive potency was ascribed to peripheral nerve in the state of degeneration. It seems that this theory is based wholly on the misinterpretation of experiments undertaken to prove it. Not only are those earlier experiments amenable to other than chemotactic interpretations,[40,91,185] but more recent experiments, carried out under more critically controlled conditions,[201] have conclusively disproved the existence of any chemical attraction or chemotactic orientation of regenerating nerve fibers by tissues in general, and degenerating nerve stumps in particular. Results formerly attributed to "neurotropism" can be ascribed to the orienting effects of tension exerted by the nerve stumps on the intervening union tissue serving as pathway for subsequent nerve growth, plus the accentuating effect produced by fiber aggregation[185] ("fasciculation").

This rejection of the theory of "neurotropism" applies only to the thesis of an attraction of nerve fibers towards distant destinations. That the adhesion of nerve fibers to their like, as well as the effectiveness of synaptic and peripheral connections, might be determined by chemical affinities operating after contact is established, is merely a special aspect of the contact guidance theory discussed above.

Galvanotaxis. The theory that fiber growth is oriented by electric fields,[26,32,93,158] is contradicted by the observation of nerve fibers growing simultaneously in opposite directions.[144,177] Moreover, all experimental tests of the theory have been consistently negative,[60,94,177,203] except for one supposedly positive experiment,[92] in which, to all appearances, mechanical effects were mistaken for electrical ones.[177]

---

* This statement is based on extensive studies on nerve growth along surfaces of different configurations in tissue culture. The results of these studies will be reported more fully on a later occasion.

Nerve Outgrowth. According to the foregoing survey, the tip of the regenerating axon is guided in its advance by structural characteristics of the substratum with which it is in contact. The growing axon traces patterns of its surroundings. Random patterns, such as are presented, for instance, by nerve scars, lead to correspondingly confused nerve growth. Conversely, orderliness of nerve growth presupposes the presence of well aligned parallel pathways. Degenerated nerve offers such pathways in abundance both along the inner and outer surfaces of the tubes and along the strands of Schwann cells. In the gap, however, beyond the limits of degenerated nerve, oriented nerve growth can be enforced only if we provide the nerve fibers with a new system of pathways of the proper constitution and proper orientation. The guiding role of Schwann cells is still controversial. According to some authors,[41,96,119,205] they precede the axons, laying down the tracks, as it were. According to others,[31,69] most axons sprout out independently. Observation under especially favorable conditions[200] has shown that, generally speaking, Schwann cells have a head start over the axons and that the axons, perhaps for this very reason, tend to cling to the Schwann cords. At the same time, examples of freely outgrowing axon tips were observed, even though relatively rarely. Obviously both forms of outgrowth occur, with axon orientation being effected, in one case through the mediation of Schwann cords, previously oriented by the pathway structure, in the other case by the pathway structure directly.

Parallel guide lines in the pathway structure are not only prerequisite for the orderly parallel outgrowth of Schwann cells and axons, but are also instrumental in keeping fibrous connective tissue from intruding into the path of the nerve. Fibroblasts align themselves along linear structures,[73,176] just as do Schwann cells and axons. Consequently, the same oriented structural pattern that guides the nerve fibers also deflects extraneous connective tissue cells and collagen fibers into a longitudinal course along the surface of the nerve, which is a useful course. For here the connective tissue is led to build a new sheath over the gap, instead of penetrating into the path of the nerve where it would scarify and impede regeneration. It may be impossible to prevent scar tissue from forming near a wound, but it is perfectly feasible to render it innocuous by directing it into a course parallel to the nerve where it can do no harm. A parallel pathway structure, therefore, both guides nerve growth and protects it against interference. How then can such favorable pathway structures be established?

Fibrillar structures consist of an oriented array of linear colloidal particles.[56,128] Under random conditions, such particles clump into a spongy framework. If aligned in parallel orientation by some external orienting force they join end-to-end and flank-to-flank, building up larger linear units. The formation of fibrin fibers, for instance, occurs in this manner.[9] The most potent and common force to produce such parallel alignment is mechanical tension.[9,42,176,177] Not only has its orienting effect on colloids long been known, but its molding action on tissues has been amply demonstrated and experimentally tested. Rod-shaped ultramicrons become oriented and aggregate along the lines of prevailing tension. Parallel tensions, therefore, produce fibrils and fibers of corresponding parallel orientation (Fig. 4A).

Tensional stresses arise either from external stretch or from internal shrinkage. An example of stresses arising from shrinkage may be seen in the cracking of drying soil. Local condensation of fibrous tissue, the familiar scar contraction, is a common source of such internal stresses and is very perti-

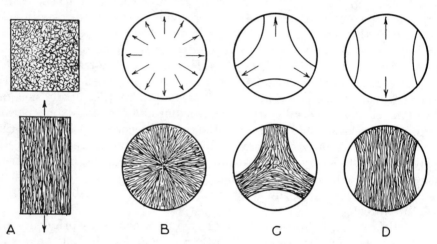

FIG. 4. Effects of tension on fibrous colloids. *A*, Colloid with anisodiametric elements in chaotic arrangement (top), when stretched, assumes orientation in the direction of the prevailing tension (arrows). *B, C, D*, Tension patterns (top row) and resulting fibrillar orientation (bottom row), arising from the shrinkage (e.g., syneresis) of a colloidal matrix firmly attached to its frame along the whole circumference (*B*), detached on three sides (*C*), and detached on two sides (*D*).

nent to problems of nerve suture. The stress pattern is not determined solely, however, by the tensions imposed on the tissue or generated within it, but also by the elastic and plastic properties of the different tissue components. Stress will develop only in those directions in which the tissue does not yield to the deforming force. And since the tissue will yield in all directions in which it is not prevented from yielding by firm attachments, the points of attachment of a tissue under tension are critical parameters of the resulting stress pattern (Fig. 4B, C, D).

In conclusion, a stress pattern lasting sufficiently long to impose its orientation upon the tissue matrix becomes thereby a primary factor in the laying down of pathways for nerve fibers and spindle cells. Conditions thus created affect not only the orientation of growth, but also its rate, as well as the density of the resulting new tissue. To have brought these problems down to earth, from the speculative language of "trophic stimuli" and "attractive influences" to the factual treatment in terms of technology and physico-chemistry, has been an essential step toward rational understanding and control of the mechanics of nerve regeneration and tissue repair.

Advance of healthy nerve fibers and sheath cells can proceed as long as there is an unobstructed pathway; hence, failure to advance in the proper direction will have to be ascribed to either lack of pathways or diversion of existing pathways or inadequacy of the physical and chemical conditions along the pathway. Physical inadequacy results from excessive density of the tissue to be penetrated. In order to appreciate this point, one must visualize the actual physical setting in which nerve regeneration takes place. Axons and Schwann cells invade the tissue of the gap, and axons invade the distal stump. If the tissues to be invaded were solid and compact, invasion would be physically impossible because one physical body (nerve fiber) can move into the space occupied by another physical body (distal stump) only by replacement, that is, to the extent to which it can force out of place an equal volume of the latter. And since only liquids, or solids suspended in liquids, are freely displaceable, the capacity of any tissue for receiving new cells and nerve fibers will be limited by its content in liquids and the ease with which these can be shifted (capillarity, viscosity, etc.). The less liquid space a tissue contains, that is, the denser it is, the fewer fibers will be able to penetrate, and the slower also will be the advance of those which have entered; just as it takes more time to drive a nail into hardwood of dense texture than into softwood of spongy texture.

Under certain conditions, an invading tissue makes room for itself by liquefying (digesting) the invaded tissue as it goes along. Some proteolytic activity has occasionally been observed near nerve fibers growing *in vitro*[177,185] and signs of it can be seen around arrested growth cones.[41] But it is uncertain whether it normally occurs during regeneration and, even if it did, experience has shown that it would be impotent to proteolyze dense collagenous scar tissue. The possibility that the growing axon may absorb some substance directly from adjacent Schwann cells so that it could expand at their expense, cannot be excluded, but no definite information on this point is available.

Without proper room for continued expansion, nerve fibers, even though they may have reached the periphery, cannot swell from the small diameter (1μ or less)[13,31,67,82,133,134] at which they grow out, to the large dimensions of the mature fiber. Therefore, both in the interest of primary outgrowth and of later size increase, due consideration must be given to the space requirements of the new nerve fibers, and this is just as important as is emphasis on proper orientation of the pathway. Tendons have perfect orientation, but are far too dense to serve as conduits for nerve growth. The same is true of heterografts,[86,140,190] and alcohol- or formalin-fixed grafts[67,86,119,139] of nerve or muscle, inasmuch as these are progressively transformed into tough fibrous connective-tissue strands, assuming a texture not unlike that of tendons and equally unfit for adequate nerve growth. While sporadic nerve fibers can be found in the crevices of such grafts,[140] this fact should not be overrated,[67] and the misleading practice of publishing pictures of such finds as evidence of "successful" regeneration[59] should be abandoned. Such trickle of fibers as is present in these cases is apt to be functionally irrelevant, particularly as many of the fibers passing through dense tissue are in danger of being pressure-blocked.

It seems that the ratio between solid and liquid content of tissues has not been properly recognized heretofore as constituting a limiting factor in neurotization. Its recognition makes it imperative to see to it that the union tissue forming between nerve stumps maintains proper liquidity. Provisions to this end will be outlined below.

Nerve Fiber Branching. Fibers have no intrinsic tendency to branch. Branching occurs always in response to local conditions of the environment.[177,185] It may occur terminally, that is, at the growing tip, or collaterally, that is, along the stem of a fiber.[143,144] Terminal branching presupposes, first, forking of the fiber tip, and second, continuation of growth along both branches of the fork. The former is a function of the pathway structure, any branching point of which may call forth the extension of filopodia in both directions. If both branches are successful in drawing supporting inflow of axoplasm, the divided flow may produce permanent twinning; if the competition is unequal, the winning branch will proceed and absorb the weaker one. Collateral sprouts have been seen to arise at points where a fiber has been exposed to mechanical or chemical irritation.[127,144] These sprouts have a better chance of growing if the growth of the main fiber stem is blocked, comparable to the taking over of the growth dominance by side branches in decapitated trees. Statistically, the incidence of branching will be proportional to the abundance of crossings in the pathway structure, which varies inversely with the orderliness of the latter. The more confused the substratum, the more profuse will be the branching of nerve fibers entering upon it. This explains the excess of branches in nerve scars and neuromas. Along well oriented and unobstructed structures fibers advance without branching, the growing tip apparently consisting of a single filopodium. The branching of Schwann cell cords in the glioma seems to follow similar rules.[200] The systematic ramification of regenerating axons in skin and muscle is partly guided by the pattern of the preserved degenerated branches of the original supply,[21] although occlusion of tubes may cause omission of some branches.[206]

Fiber Resorption. During the early phase of the regeneration process self-amputation and withdrawal of young and short fiber branches is common.[21,145] Concerning the later resorption of already established fiber branches, or even whole fibers, however, very little is known.[41] There has been much speculation as to the possible reduction of "functionally inadequate" fiber connections[205] (e.g. those producing "axon reflexes"), but tangible evidence to support that assumption is still lacking. Some slow regression in human amputation neuromas has been reported, but the majority of useless branches survive many years without change.[41] Experimental results with peripherally unconnected fibers confirm the durability of regenerated axons irrespective of their peripheral connections.[201]

Volume of Reinnervation. By this is meant the number of branches actually attaining peripheral connections, expressing the degree of completeness of reinnervation of receptor and effector organs. It depends on the following factors[195]:

(1) Size of the fiber source in the proximal stump.

(2) Amount of branching in the scar. Such branching can amplify the proximal source.[31] A given muscle or skin area might thus be saturated with nerve branches from a nerve smaller than that which had furnished the original supply.[39,103,181,198] However, the clinical exploitation of this fact,[18] recommended by Dogliotti,[39] remains problematical in view of certain complicating features,[4,195] which may offset the advantages of stepped-up branching.

(3) Number of fibers admitted into the peripheral stump. If sufficient time is allowed for regeneration, the number of regenerated fibers in the distal stump approaches more closely the normal fiber quota of that nerve than could be expected by mere chance.[35,63,103] When a distal nerve stump is confronted with an overabundant supply of nerve branches, it admits only a restricted number roughly corresponding to its own original content.[196] Perhaps the capacity of the distal stump diminishes with increasing delay of reinnervation.[82] Just how the distal stump controls the volume of neurotization, remains to be determined. Since fibers regenerate both inside and between old tubes, and often several to a single tube,[21,82,119,196,205] the number of degenerated tubes cannot represent the limiting factor. However, the fact as such is clear and condemns to failure attempts to force into a nerve significantly more nerve fibers than it can hold. It is interesting to note how many basic facts of nerve growth such as the one just outlined have been ignored in the devising of such methods of nerve repair as nerve flap transplantation, nerve implantation, etc., now outmoded.[8,130,155]

(4) Number of fibers persisting. This implies the possibility of secondary resorption of some fiber branches after they have grown through the distal stump.[21,205] To what extent this occurs, and whether as a result of spatial, nutritional, circulatory or functional inadequacies, is still obscure.

(5) Density of terminal connections. The capacity of a tissue to receive functional nerve supply seems to be strictly limited. Spatial conditions permitting, any number of nerve fibers may be crowded into an organ. But from that pool only a limited number of endings will be admitted to form functional connections passing impulses. A muscle fiber, in general, accepts only a single nerve branch and then insulates itself against further innervation.[46,55] For skin, likewise, there seems to be a definite saturation density beyond which innervation cannot be driven. This is indicated by the fact that as soon as a skin district is denervated, collateral supply from the sur-

rounding zone moves in,[147,175] presumably because of the cessation of some restraining action previously exerted by the area's own supply. In view of these facts, surgical attempts at "hyperneurotization"[48] of muscle can serve no useful purpose.

Maturation. In nerve regeneration, as in ontogeny, the outgrowth of the axon is only the first of a series of developments leading to the formation of a mature nerve fiber. Further elaborative developments include the realignment of sheath cells, myelinization, formation of nodes, increase of fiber diameter, and such functional adaptations as may occur after peripheral connection has been established. Common experience indicates that a regenerated nerve never resumes the precise features of a normal nerve. This holds for the nerve fibers as well as for the accessory constituents. Endoneurial cells and Schwann cells remain present in excessive numbers, the endoneurial connective tissue assumes relatively more space, the nodes of Ranvier are more irregularly spaced. Of more significant bearing on the restoration of function is the question of the restitution of the normal fiber size spectrum. Some functional imperfections as a result of incompletely recovered fiber size may be anticipated[205] from the known correlation between fiber diameter on the one hand and conduction velocity and associated physiological properties of the fiber on the other.[49] However, it has never been actually determined how serious such imperfections are, particularly in comparison with the much more profound disturbance of functional relations caused by the intermingling and consequent misconnection of fibers with other than their original end-organs.

The growth in width of the regenerated part of a nerve fiber occurs gradually,[134] and apparently progresses in proximo-distal direction.*[67] The normal size range may be approximated, but grouping into different size classes is less distinct than in normal nerve.[13,67] The caliber which will finally be attained is determined by no single factor. The original size of the fiber, the peripheral channel into which it grows, the number of branches, the nutritive conditions, the mode of peripheral connections, all these may influence the result. The distal parts of fibers which have regenerated through a constricted zone, for instance, remain thin and atrophic.[202] Evidently, continued expansion of distal fiber portions requires continuous supply of some growth prerequisites from the nerve cell body; and when this supply is throttled by a local constriction of the axon, growth of the part lying distal to that point will be impaired.

This fact can explain why large fibers regenerating into small distal tubes tend to remain undersized,[82,121] while small fibers entering large tubes do not expand to the large size of the latter.[121] In either case the dimensions of the tube would be the limiting factor: in the former, the distal tube would

---

* Unpublished oscillographic studies of regenerating rat nerves (carried out jointly with H. Davis and H. Maylander) have demonstrated a gradual decline of impulse velocity, and hence, fiber diameter, along the regenerated distal portion of a fiber.

resist expansion,[82] in the latter, the proximal tube would limit the supply to the distal portion. Moreover, growth pressure may reasonably be assumed to be the lower, the smaller the cell body exerting it. The size of fibers advancing endoneurially between tubes may similarly be determined as the resultant of growth pressure and peripheral limitations of space, nutrients, etc. Secondary atrophy, i.e., shrinkage without disintegration, may occur in fibers which have failed to effect peripheral connections,[201] but the evidence is still meager.

Myelinization has been shown to be a property of the neuron, although myelin cannot be produced except with the collaboration of the Schwann cell.[143,144] Whether the regenerated portion of a fiber does or does not acquire a myelin sheath, depends, therefore, on whether its stump of origin is myelinated or not. Myelinization of fiber parts whose growth has been impaired, remains poor.[61,202]

Specificity of Fibers. The problem of whether fibers can return selectively to their old periphery has remained controversial, in spite of considerable experimental treatment. Functional selectivity in regeneration has sometimes been claimed without clear commitment as to where and how it operated. It might operate (a) by restricting the ingrowth of nerve fibers to tubes of the corresponding type only; (b) by governing the establishment of peripheral connections; (c) by causing inappropriate connections to be dissolved; (d) by modifying the central relations of a misregenerated neuron.

Experimental and clinical evidence contradicts specificity within the major divisions of the peripheral system, inasmuch as any motor fiber is known to regenerate with equal ease into any motor nerve—witness the common crosses between the hypoglossal or spinal accessory and the facial nerve—and the analogous is true of the sensory system. As the functional implications of misregeneration are being made the subject of an extensive review under preparation, the problem need not be discussed here further.

The case is not equally clear with regard to the cross regeneration of motor into sensory channels and *vice versa.* Sensory-motor cross connections can be achieved experimentally,[20,178,179] but whether and to what extent their occurrence in normal regeneration is restricted,[15] either by differential facility of growth (contact specificity) along homologous and non-homologous pathways or by selective resorption of non-homologous terminal connections, is still a matter of conjecture. Penetration of motor fibers into sensory pathways and *vice versa* is undesirable mainly because it wastes part of the limited neurotization space of the distal stump on functionally useless elements.[160] Although antidromic impulses—afferent in motor fibers,[104,105] efferent in sensory fibers[10]—appear as by-products of normal nervous activity, it is doubtful whether they have the proper characteristics to act as sensory or motor excitations in the case of crossed end organs. Consequently, even if the random mixing of motor and sensory pathways in regeneration should prove to be of general occurrence, it would cause no conspicuous functional disturbance.

Trophic Restoration. A discussion of the regression of the denervated tissues and their recovery during reinnervation is beyond the scope of this survey.

Functional Restoration. This implies not simply the reconnection between the central nervous system and the receptors and effectors, i.e., recovery of general sensation and motility, but the recuperation of discriminative functions, i.e., proper discrimination and localization of sensory stimuli, and coordination of muscular activity. The literature on this subject is copious, yet contradictory and inconclusive. Its major deficiencies are lack of standard criteria in the assessing of functional recovery and often failure to take into full account the complexity of functional changes attending denervation and reinnervation. In the motor sphere alone, hypothetical "central reorganization" has often been credited with improvements of motor performance that were obviously due to trick movements, changes in muscle balance, compensatory contraction of unaffected muscles, mechanical transmission of pull, etc. It is difficult to tell from the conflicting evidence how much actual reorganization the centers can accomplish, when confronted with situations in which the majority of neurons have entered into new and unpredictable terminal connections.

A comprehensive discussion of these problems will be presented elsewhere. For the time being, it may be stated that the more critical reports on function after experimental and clinical nerve regeneration indicate a rather limited capacity for "reeducation" of misregenerated fiber connections.* The idea that the regulatory powers of the central nervous system, with or without conscious effort and practice, are great enough to make new and orderly impulse patterns emerge from a system of utterly confused connections, finds no support in known facts. A special kind of reconditioning which new peripheral relations produce in the nerve centers of embryonic or larval animals,[180,184] apparently disappears in the course of development[148,149] and has therefore (contrary to an earlier assumption[180]) no bearing on the clinical situation. In general, the more aberrant the morphological pattern of regeneration (owing to branching, straying, and shunting to the wrong endings), the less orderly will the functional activities be after recovery. And if one considers the mechanics of nerve regeneration, one realizes that full restoration of normal function, as it existed prior to the injury, is wholly beyond attainment. Only statistically can one try to approach this goal by taking measures that will allow the maximum possible number of nerve fibers to restore connections of the old type or, at least, one functionally similar. The recommendation of some neurosurgeons to match the fascicular topography of the stumps in suturing as best as feasible,[173] thus seems to make good sense physiologically. It is partly invalidated by the practical difficulties of identifying the orientation of dislocated stumps, of recognizing their fascicular pattern, and of suturing accurately without distortion; moreover,

---

* Compare, for instance, the articles by Ford and Woodhall[52] and Coleman.[33] An extensive bibliography will accompany the forthcoming review by Sperry.

the greater the gap, the less physiological congruity will there be between the cross sections because of the existence of intraneural plexuses.[155] However, the main factor to offset even the most careful matching of stumps is the profuse straying and branching of the regenerating fibers in the suture scar, and unless this can be avoided, there is no sense in trying to coapt the stumps macroscopically.

The Interdependence of Regeneration Phenomena. The survey of nerve regeneration presented in the preceding pages, even though highly condensed, conveys an idea of the complexity of the processes involved. The functional restoration of a nerve is a composite product of many and diverse interlocking phenomena, and no one of them can be singled out as the master key to the control of the others. While the orderly restitution of the axon remains the central objective, this cannot be attained except in the proper setting, which, in turn, depends on the behavior of the other tissue components. The more our knowledge of this intricate interdependence grows, the more judiciously shall we be able to deal with the practical problems of nerve repair. For example, certain measures that might be devised to stimulate the growth rate of nerve fibers might turn out to promote even more an obstructive fibrosis so that the net effect on nerve restitution would be adverse. Or one might try to amplify an undersized nerve source by causing the fibers to branch profusely during regeneration,[18,39] only to find out eventually perhaps that the number of branches any one neuron can maintain in good functional repair is limited. Numerous similar examples could be cited to illustrate that no single step of nerve regeneration can be viewed as an isolated entity. The intimate interrelationship among the various steps is a reality which one can ill afford to neglect in the practice of nerve repair.

METHODS OF NERVE REPAIR

Measures of nerve repair can accomplish their ends only to the extent to which they conform to the realities of nerve regeneration. In the light of these realities, as we now know them, many successful empirical procedures of the past find a splendid *ex post facto* justification, while, conversely, many past failures can now be traced to the fact that some peculiarities of the tissues involved or some of the subtle interrelationships just mentioned had been disregarded. It has become fairly plain by now that there can be no physical or chemical agent, no manipulation or drug, that would be universally beneficial to all component processes of nerve regeneration alike. What aids one, may hamper another. Any method of nerve repair will, therefore, have to be examined in all its consequences, and rated according to the balance of the good and harm it does. Only by wisely improving this balance sheet, can nerve repair be improved, by small steps, insignificant perhaps individually, but telling in their cumulative effects.

The capacity of a nerve to regenerate is subject to constitutional biological limitations. As in other tissue systems, the growth potential is determined by the properties of the tissue itself,[182] and growth rate cannot be raised above a certain maximum. This need not apply to the purely physical part of the elongation of the regenerating nerve fiber, the rate of which is limited only by elasticity, viscosity, and the like. It does apply, however, to assimilatory growth which supplements and supports the elongation. Therefore, if mammalian nerve fibers have never been seen to exceed a daily rate of free advance of about 4 mm. at best,[65] this presumably defines the maximum output of which they are capable under optimal conditions. Whenever recoveries at much faster rates are reported, there is reason to suspect either that the nerve had not been severed or that nerve sources closer-by had substituted.

Methods of nerve repair must, therefore, aim not at "stimulating" nerve growth, but at providing it with the conditions under which it can best realize its own potentialities. In last analysis, it is the nerve that has to do the repairing. All we can do is facilitate the job by supplying the necessary prerequisites, and by keeping out handicaps. In view of this situation, it is not surprising that attempts at "stimulating" nerve growth directly have had no success in the past. Particularly, the claimed stimulating effect of the Vitamin B group[162] and biotin[68] has not been substantiated in critically controlled experiments, either in vivo[50,101] or in vitro.[27,29] While nerve regeneration under thiamin deficiency may be impaired,[28,108] thiamin excess does not produce excessive nerve growth, although it does seem to facilitate recovery after central lesions,[174] which involves no growth. There seems to be little hope of doing much for nerve regeneration along that general line. At present, it seems that the only way in which nerve regeneration can be effectively promoted is to avoid the natural and clinical hazards that tend to depress it.

Concerning the natural hazards, it must be borne in mind that the general wound healing tendency of the body, by leading to cicatrization, happens to run counter to what would be in the best interest of nerve healing. Part of the surgical effort must, therefore, be devoted to eliminating this conflict. This can be done (a) by holding scar-provoking factors to a minimum, and (b) by directing the unavoidable remainder into a course where nerve restitution will be harmed least, for instance, by forcing scar tissue to grow along, rather than into, the nerve. A nerve scar not only distracts and bars nerve outgrowth, but also is apt to interfere with subsequent maturation and impulse conduction in regenerated fibers. Its avoidance thus becomes a matter of prime concern and has always been recognized as such by the surgeon. Yet, the surgical intervention in itself may intensify rather than alleviate the condition. Trauma, introduction of foreign suture materials, infection, and hemorrhage affect the volume of the scar, while the stress pattern at the junction determines its prevailing orientation. Both must be taken into account.

The perviousness of the distal stump to regenerating fibers may fluctuate within wide limits, with pressure, past history of Wallerian degeneration, vascularization, macrophage activity, and perhaps stretch, being the major variables. Depending on the condition of the distal stump, the rate and volume of nerve fiber regeneration will vary, which in turn will determine how soon and how well the muscle will be reinnervated.

Escape of fiber branches at the suture line will not only produce painful neuromas, but may, if excessive, drain the growth potential of the whole nerve and thus reduce its capacity for functional recovery. The point that such fiber escape should be precluded is therefore well taken.

These examples may suffice to illustrate our contention that the way to improve nerve repair is not by trying to "stimulate" nerve growth, but by eliminating the handicaps which would ordinarily be in its way. These handicaps operate on a microscopic rather than macroscopic plane, and we can avoid them only after we have learned to recognize them.

SUTURELESS TUBULATION

Reunion of severed stumps by means of a fitting cuff of artery or other suitable material without the use of sutures has certain unique advantages for nerve regeneration, which other methods do not provide to an equal degree. This method, referred to for brevity as "tubular splicing" or "sleeve splicing," has thus far been tested in laboratory animals only, but the lessons of the experiments are unquestionably applicable to clinical practice. The experiments, which have been described in detail elsewhere,[186,189,193,200] will be reviewed here only briefly. However, some supplementary information not otherwise published will be added.

The main purpose and effect of sleeve splicing is to prevent the formation of a "suture line." Ordinarily, the suture line represents a zone in which the organization of the nerve is definitely and permanently abnormal. Here the nerve fibers are forced to branch profusely and to stray and commingle at random, with the consequences outlined above, while fibrous tissue penetrating from the sheath and from extraneous sources may make the link so compact as to interfere with growth, maturation, and perhaps conduction, of the regenerated fibers. In contrast, the union tissue of sleeve-spliced nerve stumps assumes the same organization as the rest of the nerve, so much so that in successful cases the transition between the former stumps is perfectly smooth.

Sleeve splicing owes its success to three main facts: (1) absence of sutures; (2) transmission of tension between the stumps and the newly forming union tissue; (3) confinement of fluid within the gap and the union tissue. A thorough histomechanical analysis[200] of the healing process after end-to-end union with and without tubular splicing has demonstrated that if the tissue linking the nerve stumps is to become a well organized nerve segment, rather than a scar, longitudinal stress and high liquid content are indispensable prerequisites.

This may be explained here briefly by the example of an arterial splice, supposing that we are dealing with a case in which the nerve stumps can be closely approximated without stretch. The nerve ends are joined by placing them inside a fitting cuff of artery. The cut surfaces are not brought in contact but are left separated by a gap of a few millimeters, which becomes filled with blood. During the days following the operation, this blood clot undergoes a remarkable transformation, the course of which is of crucial importance for the outcome of the ensuing processes of nerve regeneration. The following events occur in rapid succession[200] (Fig. 5).

(1) The fibrin of the blood clot in the gap fuses firmly with the nerve stumps (Fig. 5, *1*).

(2) The erythrocytes of the clot disintegrate, leaving a spongy fibrin framework with liquid-filled meshes behind (Fig. 5, *2*).

(3) The clot detaches itself from the wall of the sleeve, while firmly stick-

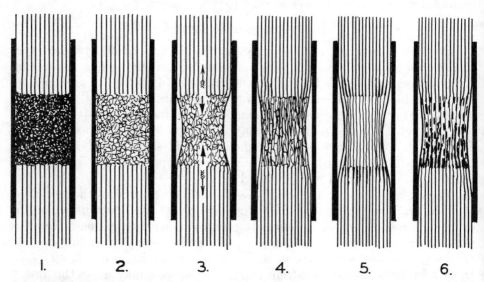

1. **2.** **3.** **4.** **5.** **6.**

Fig. 5. Transformation of the union tissue between sleeve-spliced nerve stumps. The illustrated phases of the process represent operative, rather than chronological, steps. Chronologically the various phases overlap. *1*, Blood clot in gap. *2*, Fibrin formation. *3*, Lateral detachment of union tissue; syneretic shrinkage of clot (plain arrows) and traction from stumps (feathered arrows) lead to longitudinal tension. *4*, Tensional orientation of the fibrin network (corresponding to Fig. 4, *A* and *D*). *5*, Liquefaction of unstretched fibrin. *6*, Outgrowth of sheath cells and axons through the oriented fibrin matrix.

ing to the nerve ends (Fig. 5, *3*). It thus constitutes a mechanical link between the stumps and hence becomes subject to longitudinal traction. Any tension acting on the nerve transmits itself directly to the clot. Similar stresses arise in the clot from the shrinkage attending its syneresis.

(4) These longitudinal stresses act in the manner described above for stress patterns in general. They force the fibrin elements into a predominantly longitudinal orientation, resulting in the formation of straight fibrin threads which span the gap from one nerve end to the other (Fig. 5, *4, 5*).

(5) Fibrinolytic enzymes, liberated presumably from disintegrating leukocytes and possibly also exuded from the nerve stumps, destroy all

finer cross links of the fibrin reticulum, while sparing the heavier, longitudinally oriented threads (Fig. 5, 5).

Through this chain of processes the nerve stumps become reconnected within less than a week by a system of straight parallel fibrin strands. Except for these threads, the space of the former gap is still filled with fluid, partly fibrinolysate, partly perhaps nerve exudate,[187] which the impermeable sleeve prevents from dissipating.

It is in this setting, then, that the outgrowth of sheath cells, axons and capillaries takes place. As these elements are bound to move along the existing solid-liquid interfaces, the fibrin threads serve them readily as climbing ropes (Fig. 5, 6), and since the latter span the original gap in straight lines, the most direct and unconfused transit of the regenerating nerve fibers and accessory tissue components from stump to stump is made possible. As a result, the outgrowing fibers and cells glide over the fibrin rails of the union tissue with great ease, thus retracing the parallel longitudinal lines of the fibrin pattern which, in turn, are a product of the prevailing mechanical stresses. The abundance of interstitial liquid, on the other hand, insures ample space for the advancing tissue mass in the sense indicated previously.

As one can see, the effects of sleeve splicing on subsequent nerve regeneration are subtle and manifold. Specifically the following features stand out.

(1) By insulating the junction, the sleeve prevents the young union tissue which fills the gap from adhering to any structures but the nerve stumps themselves.

(2) By the tensions transmitted directly from one stump to the other through the union tissue, the latter is molded into parallel fiber strands corresponding to, and continuous with, those of the nerve stumps.

(3) This pathway system is free from obstructions, and interlacing of its elements remains at a minimum. Consequently, neither the regenerating axons nor the sheath cell cords are subject to the extensive branching and straying typical of ordinary nerve scars.

(4) The longitudinal organization of the union tissue directs the growth of the intraneural blood vessels straight across the gap and thus effects prompt vascular reconnection between the stumps.

(5) Fibrous connective tissue surrounding the nerve is likewise forced into a longitudinal course, where it develops into a useful sheath around the junction, instead of penetrating into the interior, where it would deflect and block nerve fiber growth.

(6) By suppressing the formation of communications between the inside of the nerve and the surrounding tissues, the sleeve not only precludes the intrusion of extraneous scar tissue into the nerve, but also the escape of regenerating fibers (neuromas) and sheath cells (gliomas) from it.

(7) Acting as a tight container for the liquid in the union tissue, the sleeve insures the necessary space for the passage of nerve fibers in adequate numbers and for their later unimpeded lateral expansion.

(8) Owing to the straightness and parallel arrangement of the guide lines, the regenerating fibers traverse the gap in essentially the same assemblage in which they emerge from the proximal stump. Hence, functional grouping, as far as it is expressed in topographical grouping, is at least partially preserved, in contrast to its complete disruption at ordinary suture scars.

In order to evaluate the method of sleeve splicing, and as a possible guide for further advances in the technique of nerve reunion, it seems advisable to

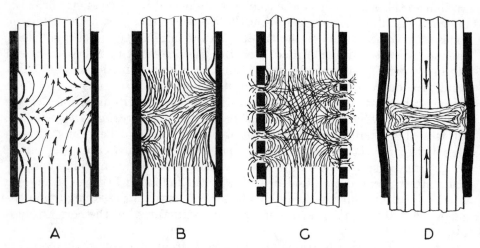

A   B   C   D

FIG. 6. Examples of disorganization of the union tissue. A, B, Stress pattern (A) and resulting structure of the matrix (B) after incomplete lateral detachment of the union tissue from the sleeve wall. C, Distorting effect of pores or holes in the sleeve wall. The tissue is drawn toward the breaks. D, Transverse orientation of the matrix as a result of pressure from the nerve ends (arrows).

assess the various features listed above critically in regard to their significance for final functional restoration. While the contrast between the orderliness of a sleeve-spliced union and the confusion at junctions effected by other means is spectacular, this does not in itself prove the superiority of the former over the latter in practical respects. The following point-for-point discussion aims to facilitate a comparison of sleeve-splicing with other methods. (The various points will be dealt with in the order of the above listing.)

1. Insulation. To insulate a suture line against ingrowth of fibrous tissue, has been the purpose of many wrapping and tubulation attempts of the past (see below). In many cases, these attempts were half measures in that the resorption or perforation of the materials used failed to provide more than perfunctory insulation. The sleeve as used in sleeve splicing does not operate so much as a mechanical shield as by creating conditions which will force scar growth into a longitudinal instead of transversal course. Even though a closely fitting sleeve precludes the intrusion of extraneous tissue, the epineurial sheath inside the sleeve is an ever present source of fibrous tissue, and if it fails to cause trouble in sleeve-spliced nerves, this is because the longitudinal stress pattern diverts the proliferated material into a longitudinal course along the surface of the nerve. Accordingly, any intervention or postoperative occurrence that upsets the longitudinal stress pattern is bound to defeat the purpose of shielding.

Most common failures of this kind arise from adhesions between union tissue and the covering cuff (Fig. 6A, B). Such adhesions produce tension lines directed from the surface into the interior of the gap; hence, they lay down direct inroads for the penetration of epineurial tissue into the nerve (Fig. 6B). The inner lining of the cuff must, therefore, be of such a nature that the blood clot will either not adhere to it from the very first, or, at least, become detached shortly after by fibrinolysis. Arterial tubes satisfy this condition. So do sleeves of tantalum metal,[193] the use of which will be described below. On the other hand, coverings made from materials capable of fusing with the fibrin of the blood clot would fail in this respect.

It is equally futile to expect a longitudinal stress pattern to develop after sheathing the union with cuffs that either are porous or, though initially tight, undergo rapid erosion and resorption (Fig. 6C). Any hole or fissure in a sleeve is apt to become, first, an anchor point for the stress pattern; secondarily, a center upon which fibrin fibers will converge; and ultimately, an entrance point for extraneous connective tissue as well as an escape route for regenerating sheath cells and axons. Materials sufficiently resistant to withstand resorption for several weeks may, however, be acceptable; for during that period the union tissue will have assumed its longitudinal orientation, a continuous fibrous sheath will have covered the junction, and after the sleeve has thus served its purpose, it may be dispensed with.

For similar reasons, a coat of blood plasma such as is used in the so-called "plasma suture"[64 207] of nerve cannot be expected to serve as a real sleeve in the sense here emphasized For the surface coat of plasma and the blood clot in the gap are bound to merge into a single mass, particularly as some suture plasma is apt to seep in between the cut surfaces. The syneresis of such an irregular mass will produce an irregular tension pattern, leading to corresponding irregularities of the subsequent nerve and scar growth. The marked contrast in microscopic appearance between junctions after plasma suture and after sleeve splicing bears out this contention.*

In conclusion, only if there is no adhesion between clot and sleeve, can a strictly longitudinal tension pattern develop.

2. Tension. Mechanical considerations intimate that the most potent factor in the creation of tensions at the junction is the syneretic shrinkage of

---

* A semidiagrammatic illustration of a number of suture lines after plasma suture may be found in the article of Gutmann and Sanders[67]; for illustrations of sleeve-spliced junctions, see the figures in Weiss,[186,189,190,193] and Weiss and Taylor.[199,200] An improved picture of a plasma union was presented by Tarlov[165] at the 1944 meeting of The Harvey Cushing Society.

the clot itself. If the nerve stumps are sufficiently taut to resist the contractile tendency of the clot, the desired longitudinal stresses arise in the latter. No such stresses can be expected between slack nerve stumps. From these facts two postulates can be derived. First, there should be a small blood clot between the nerve stumps not only as a cementing agent but primarily as a foundation for the union tissue, to orient the fibrin bridge between the stumps by its syneresis. Second, the nerve stumps must not be allowed to yield to the contraction of the union tissue. Whether this latter provision requires that the union be placed under active tension, remains to be seen. It may be sufficient to keep the nerve just free from slack. The tendency of freshly transected nerves to retract after the operation will presumably place enough strain on the union tissue to produce satisfactory orientation. Older lesions will show less of this tendency, but even in these it may be unnecessary to apply more than just the gentlest stretch. Later, as the union becomes firmer, traction along the nerve may be allowed to increase as a means of accentuating the longitudinal organization of the union.

The optimal size of the blood gap is an empirical problem. Too short, its syneretic effectiveness will be low; too large, it presents increasing hazards to nerve fiber regeneration. The hundreds of cases thus far studied indicate an optimum length of approximately once or twice the diameter of the nerve. Even though successful regeneration through much larger gaps, filled with specially prepared blood, has been obtained (see below), the longer the gap, the less strict will be the tensional organization of the union tissue.

If the nerve ends are pressed against each other, with or without intermediary blood clot, the result may be serious. It has long been an empirical rule to avoid flanging of the nerve ends in end-to-end sutures.[8] The soundness of the rule becomes evident if one realizes that any axial pressure against the union tissue produces stresses directed at right angles to the nerve axis (Fig. 6D). The union tissue will therefore assume a prevailingly transverse orientation tending to deflect and stop the regenerating nerve fibers instead of guiding them lengthwise to the distal stump. Even if the nerve cross sections are not in immediate contact, but are left separated by a small blood clot, whenever they press toward each other, the result will be the same.[200] Obviously, it is the fate of many end-to-end sutures to create just this kind of pressure.

Sutures at the nerve junction, that is, stitches placed near the rims of the stumps, are objectionable for a variety of reasons, but their most serious defect is that they prevent the formation of a longitudinal stress pattern. Even if foreign body reactions can be wholly avoided by the use of inert suture material; even if the stitches can be strictly confined to the epineurium, and even if we disregard the fact that each thread or wire stitch represents a potential path of penetration for fibrous tissue and of escape for regenerating fibers, interference with the stress pattern is an unavoidable consequence of suturing. For one thing, the drawing together of the stumps gives rise to that undesirable transverse pressure pattern just mentioned. Moreover, since all traction between the stumps is transmitted through the rigid suture threads, it bypasses the union tissue at the suture line and deprives it of the beneficial influence of longitudinal tension. The tensional chaos prevailing at a junction that has been protected by sutures against traction finds its visible expression in the disorganization of the resulting "suture line."

Therefore, from the theoretical as well as the experimental standpoint, omission of sutures near the cut surfaces of nerve stumps seems a prerequisite to optimal regeneration. In practice, forcible approximation of the stumps is often a necessity. However, this can still be effected without suturing at the very level of the junction, simply by placing stay sutures or sling stitches through the nerve stumps at such a distance from the ends that the junction itself remains unaffected. Only the excess tension on the stumps should be taken up in this way, leaving enough available for the free nerve ends to straighten the young union tissue in the gap (see below).

In conclusion, sleeve splicing can have the desired effect only if the nerve stumps are not slack and if the union tissue is enabled to act as the sole mechanical link between the stumps. This implies omission of any sort of rigid sutures between the nerve ends.

3. Growth Orientation. By aligning the fibrin strands lengthwise, the longitudinal stress pattern gives rise to two important effects: it prepares the shortest direct route across the gap for the outgrowing sheath cells and axons, and it removes a most potent incentive to axon branching, namely, intersections in the fibrin matrix. This fact is plainly evident in the microscopic pictures of sleeve-spliced nerves.[200] It is fully borne out by actual fiber counts, which have yielded substantially similar figures for the proximal stump, the region of the junction, and the distal stump.[186]

While sleeve splicing thus definitely reduces branching and straying of fibers to negligible proportions, the question remains as to how much significance one should attach to this fact. The answer will depend on how serious a drawback to nerve regeneration profuse branching and straying of nerve fibers at an ordinary suture line really is. That it may affect functional restoration, will be shown below. What concerns us here is whether it affects morphological repair of the nerve.

The problem can be treated only in statistical terms. If regenerating axons remained unbranched, the proportion of fibers reaching the distal stump would be inversely related to the frequency of diversions in the scar. On the other hand, since intersecting pathways also increase the incidence of axon bifurcation, loss by diversion might be compensated by amplification of the fiber mass by branching. Nerve regeneration as a whole might, therefore, suffer no net numerical loss, provided that all axon branches possess the same power of growth, no matter how many of them there are to a single neuron. However, there is good reason to doubt this premise. While our factual information on this point is still very fragmentary, numerical studies on nerve regeneration,[195] as well as the realization that the axon grows essentially by synthesis from the cell body,[82,202] seem to indicate that the growth energy of a neuron is not unlimited. Consequently, the vigor of growth of a branch which must share the limited resources of the neuron with a number of sister branches is likely to be less than that of an unbranched sprout. When, as occasionally happens, more than one branch of the same neuron reaches the periphery (e.g. in nerves showing so-called "axon reflexes") it is quite conceivable that such multiple branches may never grow to full size. Consequently, if a given neuron can support only a limited amount of axoplasm, the dissipation of a major fraction of it in the form of abortive branches in the scar would evidently stunt the growth of their sister branches that happen to proceed into the periphery. Such branches will presumably grow more slowly, be more easily arrested by obstacles, and retain small caliber.

In conclusion, the oriented pathway system produced by the longitudinal stress pattern is of dual benefit to nerve regeneration: in a positive way, by guiding sheath cells and axons across the gap; in a negative way, by reducing the incidence of branching and straying, which, statistically speaking, affect regeneration adversely.

4. Vascularization. The blood supply of peripheral nerves is furnished by a continuous system of anastomosing longitudinal vessels fed by arteries which enter at a few points along the course of the nerve.[2,12] In view of the continuity of the longitudinal neural vessels, any one of these collateral sources may be eliminated without harm to the nerve.[3] Therefore, the fact that a splicing sleeve over a nerve junction might permanently bar one such source from reentry into the nerve is wholly irrelevant. The union tissue can derive abundant vascularization from intraneural channels and does not require local extraneural contributions. On the contrary, where local ingrowth of blood vessels occurs, as, for instance, in many unshielded junctions, it is frequently attended by fibrosis and strong adhesions. Moreover, it has never been established whether or not in such cases a direct vascular reconnection between the severed nerve stumps is effected, nor can the possibility be ignored that lack of vascular continuity might under certain circumstances impair nerve function.

In contrast, sleeve splicing facilitates vascular reconnection between the stumps. When invading the union tissue, the vascular sprouts join the other regenerating elements in assuming a predominantly longitudinal course.[200,201] Circulation between the two stumps is thus restored promptly, sometimes within a matter of days.

5. Prevention of Scars. Ingrowth of scarifying connective tissue has often been stressed as impeding the advance of regenerating nerve fibers. But while the disorienting effect of the scar during the earlier regeneration phase is a definite handicap, its progressive condensation and contraction during later phases introduces even more serious difficulties by tending to strangle those nerve fibers that have passed through. As was mentioned above, local constriction of a nerve makes it impossible for those parts of the nerve fibers distal to the affected level to regain proper caliber and myelinization.[202] Such underdeveloped fibers are not necessarily unfit for functional use, as regenerated fibers generally resume functional activity long before they have fully matured.[67] However, again in statistical terms, recovery may be assumed to suffer in proportion to the weakness of the fibers. Moreover, excessive scar contraction is apt to produce pressure block of conduction through the strangled region.

In conclusion, by deflecting scar tissue into a longitudinal course, where its contraction cannot encroach upon the nerve, sleeve splicing eliminates a serious hazard.

6. *Suppression of Neuromas and Gliomas.* Nerve fibers and Schwann cells moving into a random scar are not stopped short but may keep on roaming for some time without direction, giving rise to the bulging terminal neuromas of the proximal stump and gliomas ("schwannomas") of the distal stump. The character of these swellings depends largely on the accidental configuration of their environment. If the scar tissue is frayed and radiates into the adhering tissues, nerve fibers and Schwann cells escaping from the nerve ends will infiltrate the surrounding parts. Where the nerve ends have become capped by a fibrous layer, and particularly when edema fluid has accumulated, the trapped nerve fibers are forced to keep circling inside.[187] Either mode of distraction leads to two undesirable effects: hyperaesthesia or pain at the site of the neuroma, and dissipation of nerve fibers which would otherwise be available for regeneration.

Fiber counts of regenerated nerves from which fibers have escaped during the passage from the proximal into the distal stump[195] have shown that such losses are irretrievable and may lead to a corresponding deficit in the peripheral reinnervation. Unprotected suture lines offer opportunities for such fiber escape, not in the crude manner in which it is sometimes stated, by leaving "holes" open for the exit of nerve fibers, but because they favor the formation of fibrous and vascular connections between the interior and exterior of the nerve. As was stressed before, nerve fibers do not grow through openings as such, but only along solid supporting structures. A suture line may, therefore, be macroscopically faultless, with the epineurium tightly closed all around the nerve, and yet, the connective-tissue strands and vessels which will penetrate along the suture threads and between the apposed rims of the epineurium will establish escape routes from the interior. To prevent fiber escape becomes, therefore, a matter of preventing the formation of pathways linking the inside with the outside of a nerve. A splicing sleeve serves this purpose provided it is and remains unperforated and impervious to connective tissue until the union tissue has become organized and the mass of regenerating fibers has passed the critical level. The same considerations apply here as discussed above under point (1). Sleeves from materials undergoing rapid resorption will be no insurance against local fiber escape unless they can force the replacing connective-tissue elements to array themselves longitudinally so as to form a hermetic sheath around the nerve. What counts in this case is the microscopic organization, not the macroscopic appearance of the sheath.

The suppression of Schwann cell overgrowth in sleeve-spliced nerves is remarkable. It seems that Schwann cell cords growing forth from the cut ends of a nerve tend to proceed until they meet other Schwann cells and then stop. Chances of encounter are obviously lower in the tangle of a suture scar than along the straight rails of a sleeve-spliced union. Therefore, Schwann cell proliferation is excessive in the former case, while in the latter it stops after repopulating the straight lines of the union tissue.[200]

In conclusion, sleeve splicing, properly executed, does benefit nerve regeneration by preventing fiber dissipation at the site of the lesion.

7. *Confinement of Liquid.* The necessity of according regenerating nerve fibers sufficient space in which to expand was stressed above. The transformed (degenerated) distal stump provides space approximately equivalent to its own original fiber complement. With an increasing period of denervation, it shrinks[82] and becomes correspondingly less favorable for neurotization. Even with this limitation, spatial conditions in the distal stump are essentially adequate. This is not necessarily true, however, of the union tissue between the stumps. Originally, the liquid content of this tissue is high,[96] fed by syneresis, hemolysis, fibrinolysis,[200] and endoneurial fluid.[187] However, unless this liquid is prevented from oozing out, the solid constituents at the junction will become increasingly denser, occupying more and more of the space that should be kept open for the passage and later expansion of nerve fibers. Thus, even without intrusions from extraneous sources, the tissue at the junction would act like a scar, that is, contract and impede fiber growth.

In conclusion, by providing for the retention of fluid in the young union tissue until the nerve has become reconstituted, impermeable sleeves perform a distinct service to regeneration.

8. *Functional Reorganization.* Functional order, i.e., motor coordination and sensory discrimination, can be restored only to the extent to which either the process of regeneration brings fibers back to their own old terminations or the central nervous system can adjust its functions in accordance with the new pattern of connections. As the former condition is practically unattainable, functional recovery must rely largely on functional readjustments (see above). Critical observers describe the scope within which these can be achieved as rather limited. Much will depend on how much of the original orderliness of the peripheral nerve fiber pattern can be preserved during regeneration. Even though most fibers will end at new terminations, there may be a distinct advantage in leaving them at least assorted in groups, on the premise that it should be easier for a given central cell mass that used to act as a unit to change its functional role as a whole, than for it to reassign to each one of its elements a new role.

While the criss-crossing of fibers at ordinary suture lines dissolves all former functional grouping of the regenerating fibers, sleeve splicing permits them to retain some degree of their original associations. This has been proven both by histological[186,200] and physiological[189] studies of nerves regenerated after sleeve splicing: Individual fascicles of the proximal nerve have become reconnected with circumscribed muscle groups, proving that their fiber complement has remained essentially assembled during the transit into the distal stump.

In conclusion, greater orderliness of connections is rendered possible by sleeve splicing. On theoretical grounds, this should facilitate functional re-education.

_____

The preceding discussion has outlined eight crucial features to which sleeve splicing owes its success. It should be remembered, however, that all conclusions are based on experiments in animals only. So far as these experiments go, the method has proved its value. Not only in small animals,[195] but

TABLE 2*

Specimen	Nerve	Graft	Splicing Artery	Time Months	Muscles	Operated Side (O) g	Control Side (C) g	Difference (O−C) g	Percentage Recovery
						Weight			
cat #3	tibial	+	f.-d.	6	gastrocn.	13.9	14.7	−0.8	95%
	peron.	+	f.-d.	6	peron.	5.7	6.3	−0.6	90%
cat #6	tibial	+	live	12	plantar flexors	36.5	38.5	−2.0	95%
	peron.	+	live	12	dorsi-flexors	16.4	16.7	−0.3	98%
monkey #21	tibial	−	f.-d.	6	plantar flexors	56.0	52.0	+4.0	108%

* The table lists all cases in which terminal muscle weights have been determined. "f.-d." is abbreviation for "frozen-dried."

in cats and monkeys as well,[189,190] have paralyzed muscles after reinnervation through sleeve-spliced nerves recovered nearly their full volume (in terms of the corresponding muscle of the control side), even with the interposition of a frozen-dried nerve graft (Table 2). Failures have occurred, but they could always be traced to faulty technique.[186] When properly executed, sleeve splicing yields sure success in all animal groups thus far tested.

TECHNIQUES OF NERVE REUNION

Artery Cuffs. The clinical success of sleeve splicing will depend on how closely its crucial features can be reproduced in the human subject, as well as on the readiness with which cuffing material of the proper specifications becomes available.

Arteries, while performing excellently in laboratory animals, may not be the final solution for human nerves. Some difficulties have been pointed out previously, one of which is that fresh arteries sometimes tend to tighten around the nerve so as to produce constriction.[186] This can be circumvented by subjecting the arteries before use to quick-freezing and drying. Nerves of rats, cats, rabbits, and monkeys spliced with frozen-dried and rehydrated arteries have, on the whole, shown excellent functional recoveries.[189,190] Frozen-dried arterial sleeves become permanently incorporated. They are just as elastic and handle just as easily as fresh arteries. The fact that they can be kept for many months in the dry state makes it possible to keep a store of assorted sizes on hand. Short rehydration is all that is needed to make a stored sleeve ready for use.

These advantages are partly offset by certain weaknesses. Adhesions between frozen-dried sleeves and their surroundings are more extensive than those of live arteries. Similarly, local adhesions between their inner wall and the union tissue are not uncommon, with the result that the otherwise straight pattern of regeneration suffers sporadic disturbances. Local erosions occur, and through such breaks an appreciable number of fiber branches may penetrate and get lost in the wall of the sleeve. While this need not affect the volume of regeneration, it might leave the junction clinically in a state of potentially painful hyperaesthesia. Moreover, there is still the supply problem to be considered. As the freezing-drying procedure does not abolish the biochemical species differential, only human arteries can be used. Aorta furnishes the most suitable sleeve, but only fetal or early infant aorta qualifies in point of size, and since the sleeve must be free of side branches, the yield from a single specimen is rarely more than three pieces. Other types of arteries are less desirable because of their heavy muscular wall.[186] Veins have proved too flabby, at least in animal experimentation.[186,189]

Tantalum Cuffs. It thus became advisable to look for a substitute for arteries, more easily procurable, without being less effective as a splicing agent. As will be shown below, none of the materials suggested in the past for nerve tubulization could qualify. The favorable results obtained recently with the surgical use of the metal tantalum,[25,132,152] however, pointed to a possible solution. Success came after a method was discovered[193] by which full elasticity could be conferred upon the otherwise soft and pliable tantalum foil. By proper heat treatment, the foil can be fashioned into fully resilient cylindrical rolls with overlapping edges. The overlapping parts stay in intimate contact by their own elastic pressure so that the tubes remain tightly sealed even though their width is adjustable within the limits of elasticity and friction.

Technically, such tubes can be applied for sutureless nerve reunion in much the same manner as arterial sleeves, provided the nerve bed at the junction is straight and can be kept straight during the healing process. Biologically, their performance is equal to that of arterial sleeves.[193] They are inert and provoke little, if any, foreign body reaction. As the union tissue does not adhere to the metal, its longitudinal orientation is assured, while the epineurial and other potentially scar-forming tissue is forced to grow down along the inner wall, where it reconstitutes a smooth cylindrical sheath over the junction. Dissipation of fluid from the interior is prevented. No scar can form at the level of the junction. Vascular connection between the nerve stumps is restored promptly. If adequately executed, such unions show practically no trace of the former break as early as five weeks after the operation in cats and monkeys. There would seem to be no objection to removing the metal sleeves after this period if this should become clinically desirable.

The main shortcomings of tantalum sleeves are their rigidity, which limits use to straight-way unions, and their opacity, which removes the junction from direct visual control. The search for an even superior material, combining the features of tantalum sleeves with greater flexibility and translucency, will therefore have to be continued.

Special Uses of Sleeves. Aside from the fact that it provides an optimal setting for nerve regeneration, sutureless sleeve splicing has certain practical advantages of some consequence. The duration of the operation is considerably shortened as compared to conventional suturing. Furthermore, even nerves of the smallest caliber, too fine for accurate suturing, can easily be mended with sleeves. Where fascicular topography is recognizable, e.g., in freshly severed nerves, separate reunion of individual bundles can be effected with ease. Nerve lesions at branching points can be treated simply by placing the common proximal stump into one end, and the several distal stumps into the other end of a sleeve. Sleeve splicing, thus, not only simplifies the technique of nerve repair, but also makes repair feasible in cases that would defy other less subtle methods.

Sleeve splicing is of particular significance in connection with the use of nerve grafts for the bridging of large defects. Much of the blame for the failure of grafts can unhesitatingly be ascribed to the fact that they were improperly joined to the nerve stumps. If a single scarified suture line after end-to-end suture can impair nerve regeneration, two junctions are bound to be even worse.[11] The suggestion has been made to resect and resuture, in a second operation, the distal suture line.[36] It would seem preferable, however, to avert the formation of suture line partitions and scars in the first instance, a goal which can at least be approximated by sutureless sleeve splicing. As has been shown experimentally, sleeve-spliced nerve stumps become linked in the same orderly fashion whether they contain axons or not. Axon-free ("aneuritic") segments, such as a graft and the distal nerve stump, thus become joined by longitudinal cell strands which afford unimpeded passage for the regenerating axons when they later arrive at this level.[200] The conditions for strict orientation of the union tissue between graft and nerve stumps are not quite so favorable as between directly opposed nerve ends because of the unavoidable slackness of the graft. Even so, the experimental tests in rats,[199] cats and monkeys,[190] using frozen-dried nerves as grafts, have demonstrated the adequacy of the sleeve-splicing technique in grafting. It also simplifies the use of cable grafts, as the multiple strands which are to make up the cable can be introduced one by one into the sleeve without further need of attachment.

The Problem of Gaps. The preceding discussion presupposes conditions under which the nerve ends can be brought and held within close range without force. This is not commonly attainable unless by special measures.[116] The length of the gap between the nerve ends is determined by the original loss of substance, subsequent elastic retraction of the stumps, and in secondary reunion, the length to which the fibrotic ends have to be resected. To gain the lost distance, mobilization and rerouting of the nerve course, extreme flexion of joints, progressive stretching, and even shortening of bones, are being practiced.[8,116,130,139,155] Of these measures those that do not require further stretching of the mended nerves are fully compatible with sutureless sleeve splicing. Where stretching becomes necessary, either at the time of the operation or after healing, the weakness of the link must be taken into account. In such cases, the customary suturing, even if not fully successful in shutting the nerve fibers in and scar tissue out, serves the very real function of holding the stumps in apposition.

Sleeve splicing does not of itself provide a substitute for this latter function, since sleeves must not be fitted too tightly, and hence, have only limited gripping power. Suturing of the nerve ends inside the sleeve, on the other hand, would cancel most of the benefits of the method. A solution has been found in the combination of sutureless sleeve splicing with a "remote" suture for holding purposes.[193] A single loop of thread or wire is stitched through both nerve stumps at points as remote from the ends as is technically feasible, and then drawn just tight enough to bring the cut surfaces within a few millimeters of each other. The free ends are then united by a sleeve as usual, and the syneresis of the blood clot and the slight "give" of the loop in the nerve are relied upon to allow the longitudinal stresses needed for the organization of the union tissue to develop. The tension loop is, of course, not to be enclosed in the sleeve, but to be left on the outside. Another way of securing the approximation of the stumps would be by separate stay sutures, but the former method seems preferable because it leaves the nerve mobile. The practical details of these problems remain to be worked out.

Data on two points, inadequately known at present, are indispensable for judicious action in nerve repair: the amount of stretch which nerve can tolerate without damage, and the maximum acceptable length of the gap between the nerve ends in a sleeve.

As for the former point, the clinical literature is inconclusive (see Sanders[139] for a review), as some authors approve of degrees of stretch certain to rupture nerve fibers and blood vessels, while others caution against even the slightest extension. Animal experiments have revealed the dangers of excessive stretch.[78,113,161] During the embryonic as well as the postnatal growth period of an individual, nerves are definitely under natural stretch, as they are "in tow" by the growing organs.[185] This stretch, however, is exerted very gently and is distributed evenly over the length of the nerve. These conditions, notably the steadiness and evenness of pull, are difficult to reproduce artificially during regeneration. The usual clinical precaution to apply postoperative stretch by small and gentle steps, is well taken. Nevertheless, there is an elasticity and plasticity limit beyond which stretch cannot be carried without serious damage.

In this connection, two points of great practical significance call for attention: the scale on which nerve stretch is to be measured; and the differential effect of stretch on the proximal and distal stumps. As for the former point, it is evident that stretch must be referred to the length of the portion actually undergoing extension. The stress produced by lengthening a five-inch segment by one inch will be twice that of lengthening a ten-inch segment by the same amount. Extensibility of a nerve will, therefore, have to be expressed in percentage of free length, and not in absolute units. If the maximum stretch limit were, say, ten per cent, gradual lengthening by one inch of a stump free to yield over a length of more than ten inches would cause no damage. However, that same one-inch extension would be fatal to another nerve stump that is free for no more than two inches, as this would amount to a fifty per cent extension, which is more than that short nerve piece could stand. In other words, stretch by only a fraction of an inch in one case may impose a much greater strain upon the nerve than stretch of more than one inch in another case.

What length of the nerve is free to yield will often be difficult to ascertain. While liberal mobilization at the time of the operation may free the nerve ends for a sufficient distance up and down, this makes allowance for only such stretch as will be exerted in uniting the ends. All additional stretching, however, to be applied later in the interest of straightening the joints and lengthening the nerve, deals with a wholly unpredictable situation in that adhesions formed in the meantime between the nerve and its bed will have reduced the free portions, which can yield to the stresses, to an unknown fraction of the original length.

The second point to be considered is that a degree of stretch which would rupture the nerve fibers in the proximal stump, might not interfere with nerve regeneration at all when applied to the distal stump. The pathway function of the latter could hardly be assumed to suffer from the rupturing of some neurilemmal tubes and the separation and extension of some Schwann cell columns. The ratio according to which a given amount of stretch will apportion itself between the two stumps will vary with the site of the lesion relative to the moving joint, the fixation of the stumps by adhesions, and the coefficients of extensibility, which will presumably differ for the two stumps. Thus again, each case presents a problem of its own. Moreover, aside from its effects on the nerve fibers, overstretch presents the danger of intraneural hemorrhages from ruptured vessels.

Obviously the technological realities of each case must be duly taken into account. The preceding remarks could no more than briefly expose the situation in its complexity. Continued systematic research would aid materially in removing nerve stretching from the realm of adventure.

The Irreducible Gap. The beneficial effect of a short gap between the nerve ends, discussed earlier, raises the question of the critical length beyond which a gap becomes detrimental to nerve regeneration. This knowledge is indispensable in deciding what to do about gaps that cannot be further reduced by other methods short of grafting. The main factors varying with the length of the gap and the volume of blood which fills it are: degree of syneresis and of the resulting tension; fibrin orientation; intensity of fibrinolysis; rate of vascular penetration; rate and extent of Schwann cell immigration; retention of liquid; collagen deposition; and in further consequence, the rate, orderliness and density of axon passage. With so many variables involved, it is obvious that even the many hundreds of cases of our experience are far from adequate for quantitative evaluation. Any conclusions drawn from them are tentative and subject to future revision.

With this reservation, however, the critical length of the gap can be set at about one to two times the diameter of the nerve. Proportionately longer gaps do not seem to insure optimal conditions for nerve regeneration. This is not to imply that in individual cases much greater distances cannot be successfully spanned, but statistically the prospect of success will decline with the length of the gap. The value just given refers to gaps filled with normal blood. The aspect changes when other fillings are interposed between the nerve stumps. Comparative studies with sleeves filled with Ringer's solution, pure blood plasma, and whole blood of varying composition, have led to the following results.*

Ringer's solution was evidently replaced by a coagulum of nerve exudate and serum. The union tissue forming in this matrix becomes more compact than under standard conditions, and the regenerating nerve fibers have to contend with appreciable fibrosis. This was even more pronounced after the use of pure blood plasma.[200] In this case, syneresis of the clot seems to have been weak, possibly due to the absence of blood platelets, and the orientation of the fibrin pattern, consequently, remained incomplete; above all, the density of the union tissue exceeded by far the range considered favorable for nerve regeneration. Collagen deposition was fairly extensive, and the compactness of the tissue left no adequate liquid spaces for the lateral expansion of regenerated nerve fibers. As a result such unions showed numerous fibrotic foci, with arrested, circling and tortuous nerve fibers, not unlike those seen in ordinary suture scars, though on a smaller scale. There were signs of constriction on many fibers, which implies, as was explained above, impairment of the recovery of fiber caliber. The unfavorable performance of

---

* Most of these experiments have not been previously published.

blood plasma as a gap filling must evidently be ascribed partly to poor syneresis, but mostly to the fact that it lacks the vast liquefied spaces which
develop in whole blood as a result of hemolysis and fibrinolysis.

In an attempt to reduce the consistency of the clot in the gap even below
that of whole blood, experiments were undertaken in which fragments of the
proteolytic buffy coat (leukocytes) of centrifuged blood were added to whole
blood in the splicing sleeve. In these experiments, gaps measuring several
centimeters were left between the nerve ends and filled with the modified
blood. Three cat nerves so treated gave fair functional regeneration; muscle
volume had returned to 71 per cent of normal in one animal which died after
$4\frac{1}{2}$ months, an interval too short for full recovery. Histologically, the picture
was not nearly as good as with short gaps. The nerve fibers had regenerated
in rather tortuous courses, and there was definitely more fibrous tissue between them than is common in ordinary sleeve splicing. This may have been
due in part to the measurable constrictions which these long arterial sleeves
gradually developed, putting the tissue inside under pressure. Or it may be
that blood columns of such length, even with added leukocytes, do not undergo enough liquefaction, hence, become fibrotic. At any rate, these cases
demonstrate that fairly satisfactory regeneration can be obtained with gaps
as long as twenty times the diameter of the nerve. Nevertheless, the potential
dangers of long gaps, particularly in larger nerves, are too great to take the
risk clinically as long as other methods, including grafting, can be applied.

Plasma Union. The use of blood plasma for linking ends of severed
nerves[64,67,141,163,164,165,207] shares one important feature with sleeve splicing,
namely, the omission of sutures near the lesion. In facility of execution, it
rates about intermediate between sleeve splicing and ordinary suturing. Satisfactory results have been reported in animals. Judged by the standards
outlined previously in this article, plasma suture compares with sleeve splicing about as follows.

Insulation against extraneous tissue is presumably insured by the action
of longitudinal traction on the plasma coat. The resulting orientation effect
is fully capable of transforming this coat into a firm sheath around the nerve.
Orientation inside the union tissue is likely to be less orderly, as has been
already indicated earlier in the text. More specifically, the following circumstances would seem to counteract strict longitudinal organization of the
union tissue after plasma suture. In cases in which stretch is required to approximate the stumps, the plasma clot is not firm enough to withstand appreciable tension; its holding power is of the same low order as that of sleeves
and hence must be supplemented, just as in the case of sleeves, by a remote
tension suture. This measure deprives the union tissue of longitudinal traction and leaves syneresis of the clot the sole tension-producing factor. Since
experience has shown that the syneretic shrinkage of pure plasma is very
slight in comparison to that of whole blood, only negligible tensions will be
generated at plasma junctions unless there is a sizable hemorrhage between
the stumps.

Moreover, even those tensions that do develop will not have the required pattern. Since the matrix between the nerve stumps, no matter whether it consists of plasma seeping into the crevices or of a hemorrhagic clot, contains fibrin, it will merge with the surface coat into a single mass. The union tissue will therefore fail to undergo the lateral detachment indispensable for longitudinal orientation. Instead, the tensions, and hence, the pathway structure, will assume a pattern radiating in all possible directions. Though a certain amount of self-straightening may occur in the union tissue after it has become repopulated by cells, it is difficult to imagine that even the best plasma junction could ever approach the orderliness of a sleeve junction.

A second and possibly more serious defect of plasma unions is the practically unavoidable seeping of some of the plasma between the cut surfaces of the nerve. The danger inherent in the progressive condensation of this matrix because of lack of fibrinolytic enzymes, lack of liquid spaces for nerve fiber expansion, and heavy collagen deposition, was outlined earlier in this paper. It cannot be repeated too often that compactness of the union tissue is one of the major impediments of nerve regeneration. The observation that nerve fibers regenerate at significantly slower rates after plasma union than after mere crushing,[64,65,67] may be an expression of some defects at the suture line.

For the reasons outlined, plasma suture does not seem to approximate sleeve splicing in performance. It must be stressed, however, that we do not yet know whether or how much practical significance will have to be attached to the features mentioned. It may turn out that their importance would not show up except statistically.

Nerve Wrapping, Tubulization, etc. From the description of the *modus operandi* of sleeve splicing given above, it should have become plain that the resemblance between this method and past practices of nerve wrapping and tubulation (variously called "tubulization" and "tubularization") is only a superficial one. They all have in common the sheathing in of the lesion, but they differ fundamentally in purpose and execution. Consequently, the satisfactory results of sutureless sleeve splicing do not necessarily conflict with the predominantly unfavorable opinions on those other methods, as practised in the past.[22,130,139,155]

The professed purpose of wrapping nerve sutures with membranes of various descriptions has been to prevent penetration of scar tissue and escape of nerve fibers; that of tubulation, to pipe the regenerating fibers from the proximal into the distal stump through extensive gaps. Both methods have failed in principle because they were based on crude and inadequate conceptions of the mechanics of nerve and scar growth. Both proceeded from essentially macroscopic considerations, ignoring the fact that success or failure are decided not in macroscopic dimensions, but on the microscopic and submicroscopic level, where the cells move and operate. We now know that nerve repair cannot be compared to a plumbing job, that a semblance

of mechanical insulation of the suture site is no insurance against cicatrization, and that an empty pipeline is no suitable link over a nerve gap.

The literature on the subject is controversial and often difficult to assess
because of lack of rigorous standards in executing and describing the operations, and in rating the results obtained. Table 1 on page 401 lists the principal experimental and clinical reports on the sheathing of nerve stumps,
either for insulation or for the bridging of gaps. The list makes no claim to
completeness. Moreover, the various entries are of very unequal value;
some cover carefully controlled work, others constitute rather casual reports. Purely speculative recommendations or warnings have been omitted.
In the following comments the individual articles will be referred to by their
order numbers as listed in Table 1.

To consider wrapping measures first, most of them were by their very
nature unfit to provide the intended safeguards against cicatrization. Some
potentially scar-producing tissue, notably epineurium, remains inside of the
wrapping. When the material is used in sheet form (split arteries, fascia,
etc.), additional connective tissue can enter through the seam or between
the overlapping edges. If the wrapping is loose, it admits further connective
tissue from the ends. As was stated above, the presence of such connective
tissue need not in itself be harmful to the nerve. If it can be forced into alignment along the outside of the nerve, as it is in sutureless sleeve splicing, it
will not interfere with nerve regeneration. However, since in practically all
wrapping techniques the nerve ends are first of all sutured, and since the
very effect of suturing, for the various reasons outlined above, is to favor ingrowth from the surface into the interior of the nerve, loose wrapping over
sutures is of questionable value.

If, on the other hand, one tries to minimize connective-tissue penetration
by wrapping the nerve tightly, subsequent contraction of the coat may produce constrictions as serious as those of primary scars (27). Wrappings subject to early erosion and resorption are not only ineffectual but may be
harmful by prolonging the proliferative period of the surrounding connective
tissue. Unfavorable results must likewise be expected from materials that
evoke strong foreign body reactions because of chemical incompatibility
with the host tissues, or of liberation of irritating substances, or simply by
mechanical irritation (rough surfaces; sharp edges and creases; etc.). However, it cannot be denied that wrapping even over sutures may have some
merit if it is done with an elastic, non-constricting, non-irritative, non-porous
material resistant to resorption and fragmentation (5, 9, 10, 11, 12, 14, 16,
18, 19, 21, 23, 26, 27, 37, 46, 49, 52).

In contrast, tubulation has met rather generally with clinical failure.
Closer inspection of the various procedures that have been tried indicates
that the execution rather than the principle was wrong. The ideal substratum
for nerve regeneration is degenerated peripheral nerve, and no substitute
that would even remotely approach it in adequacy has as yet been discovered. Hence, whatever the medium filling the gap between the nerve stumps

may be, growth in it will be inferior to that in the distal stump or even in a graft. Yet there are different degrees of inferiority, and the better the conditions, the greater will be the length of gap that can be successfully spanned by a sufficient volume of Schwann cells and nerve fibers. For example, good regeneration in arterial sleeves filled with blood with increased fibrinolytic potency was reported above to have occurred over gaps of several centimeters, and there is no reason to question similar reports of earlier authors. But with increasing length of the gap, the hazards to nerve growth increase, and the slightest additional handicap may imperil the whole further progress of regeneration.

The most patent shortcomings were the following:

Open space between the nerve and tube wall. Since it is technically impossible to place cylindrical tubes of wholly or nearly unelastic material over a nerve unless they are wider than the nerve, an open space between sleeve and nerve is almost unavoidable with such materials. Actually, this is the way in which the operation of "tubulization" is usually depicted (Stookey,[155] Fig. 44). Such spaces obviously admit fibrous connective tissue into the gap, preclude the establishment of a longitudinal tension pattern, lead to distortion of the newly forming union tissue and offer an outlet for the indispensable liquid content of the gap.

Perforation and resorption. Tube walls which, even though macroscopically of solid appearance, are full of microscopic pores, are bound to sponge up the regenerating Schwann cells and nerve fibers (28) because of the local suction-like action they exert on the matrix (Fig. 6C). It is immaterial whether these perforations have been present from the beginning or have developed within the first few weeks by erosion. Larger holes act as unfavorably as do the lateral spaces mentioned in the preceding paragraph. Tubes subject to quick resorption (1, 2, 5, 8, 11, 13, 29), or disintegration (6) may, therefore, not only fail to have any beneficial effects, but be actually harmful.

Foreign materials. Tubes from substances foreign and irritative to the body (22, 25, 39, 45, 47, 52) may evoke extensive inflammatory and fibrous reactions, the products of which disrupt the young union tissue and produce heavy scarring in its place.

Collapse. Tubes too flabby to retain their shape collapse and may become completely occluded, thus naturally obstructing nerve regeneration (28, 39, 48).

Inadequate gap fillings. Natural as well as artificial fillings have been used in connection with tubulation, mostly with little knowledge of, and regard for, the requirements of nerve growth. The most spectacular mistake has been the suggestion of Edinger (30) to fill tubes with agar-agar or gelatine, on the supposition that nerves would easily pervade that mass because of its "softness." The method proved a complete failure (34, 35, 36, 39, 40, 41, 42, 44). So did the fantastically unrealistic charging of tubes with dog's fat, fat mixed with lecithin, and brain pulp (39). Of course, no filling that does not afford abundant internal interfaces, such as are formed by the precipitation of fibers, has any chance of becoming invaded by Schwann cells and axons. Any inert mass that does not have the proper chemical and colloidal properties will become blocked off from the living tissue and serve only as obstruction to growth; while any resorbable mass is apt to become replaced by dense connective tissue. Moreover, not only the original composition of the gap filling, but all its subsequent modifications as well as physical transformations must be taken into consideration. For example, a blood clot can serve as a proper gap filling only if the lysate arising from its liquefaction remains collected. The more this fluid is allowed to become dissipated, the denser and more impervious to cell and axon growth will the matrix become. This finds expression in the common experience that hemorrhage between the nerve ends is followed by fibrosis (26, 28, 39, 48). Such fibrosis could presumably be checked by providing for an adequate degree of enzymatic liquefaction of the clot and by safeguards against loss of the resulting fluid.

Some reports on tubulization speak of the space between the nerve ends as having been left "empty" (34, 35, 38, 44). As explained earlier, this is physically absurd. There must have been either air or saline solution or blood or a serous exudate present at first, but since the subsequent fate of these fortuitous fillings, undergoing absorption, transformation, replacement, etc., has remained unknown, it is impossible to determine just what conditions nerve regeneration had to contend with in these instances.

Constriction. Just as is the case with simple wrappings, tubes that are subject to gradual shrinkage may strangle the covered nerve segment, either during regeneration or later (27). Tubes that provoke heavy scar formation along their outer surface without being able to withstand the constrictive force of this scar, likewise cause strangulation.

Most of the well-intentioned measures listed above have suffered not merely from poor execution, but primarily from lack of a clear conception of how they were to attain their objectives. This is excusable in view of the fact that at the time when they were devised analytical understanding (not to be confounded with histological description) of nerve regeneration was still in a very rudimentary state. It would be less excusable, however, to continue to violate or ignore the rules that in the meantime have been revealed to govern nerve regeneration. It has been the prime purpose of this article to show that these rules cannot be formulated in terms of the macroscopic manipulations of the surgeon, but only in terms of the micromechanics of the nerve fibers, their accessory cells, and their environment. The macroscopic aspect of wrappings, scars, "obstructions," "neuromas" and the like, as such, is irrelevant and often misleading. The microscopic and submicroscopic levels are the domain in which the real mechanisms of nerve repair operate, and it is to those levels that one must look for the decision between success and failure. Devices or manipulations that look quite promising from a purely macroscopic viewpoint, often are revealed by micromechanical analysis to be wholly absurd; hence, will lead to equally absurd results in practical application.

The only safe guide in the long run would, therefore, seem to be for the surgeon to become so thoroughly familiar with the biology and microtechnology of the tissues concerned with nerve repair that he will automatically come to view his macroscopic manipulations in terms of their micromechanical consequences; that he will cease to think of tubes as pipes, of sheaths as shields, of connective tissue as necessarily obstructive, or of dense vascularization as invariably desirable, and will instead turn his attention to the microstructural frame in which cells and nerve fibers move. He will then learn to calculate the play of tensions, fiber coagula, syneretic and proteolytic changes, and to recognize their sources; to understand the intricate interrelations of Schwann cells, axons, macrophages, and fibroblasts with one another and with their matrix and to let his actions be guided by this insight.

REFERENCES

1. ABERCROMBIE, M., and JOHNSON, M. L. The outwandering of cells in tissue cultures of nerves undergoing Wallerian degeneration. *J. exp. Biol.*, 1942, *19:* 266–283.
2. ADAMS, W. E. The blood supply of nerves. I. Historical review. *J. Anat., Lond.*, 1942, *76:* 323–341.
3. ADAMS, W. E. The blood supply of nerves. II. The effects of exclusion of its regional sources of supply on the sciatic nerve of the rabbit. *J. Anat., Lond.*, 1943, *77:* 243–250.
4. AIRD, R. B., and NAFFZIGER, H. C. Regeneration of nerves after anastomosis of small proximal to larger peripheral nerves. An experimental study concerned with relief of peripheral neurogenic paresis. *Arch. Surg., Chicago*, 1939, *38:* 906–916.
5. AUERBACH, S. Galalith zur Tubulisation der Nerven nach Neurolysen und Nervennähten. *Münch. med. Wschr.*, 1915, *62:* 1457–1458.
6. AUERBACH, S. Zur Frage der Nerveneinscheidung mittelst Galalith. *Münch. med. Wschr.*, 1916, *63:* 1573–1574.
7. v. AUFFENBERG, F. Ueber Nervennaht und -lösung. *Arch. klin. Chir.*, 1907, *82:* 615–657.
8. BABCOCK, W. W. A standard technique for operations on peripheral nerves. With especial reference to the closure of large gaps. *Surg. Gynec. Obstet.*, 1927, *45:* 364–378.
9. BAITSELL, G. A. A study of the clotting of the plasma of frog's blood and the transformation of the clot into a fibrous tissue. *Amer. J. Physiol.*, 1917, *44:* 109–131.
10. BARRON, D. H. Central course of "recurrent" sensory discharges. *J. Neurophysiol.*, 1940, *3:* 403–406.
11. BENTLEY, F. H., and HILL, M. Nerve grafting. *Brit. J. Surg.*, 1936, *24:* 368–387.
12. BENTLEY, F. H., and SCHLAPP, W. Experiments on the blood supply of nerves. *J. Physiol.*, 1943, *102:* 62–71.
13. BERRY, C. M., GRUNDFEST, H., and HINSEY, J. C. The electrical activity of regenerating nerves in the cat. *J. Neurophysiol.*, 1944, *7:* 103–115.
14. BETHE, A. Neue Versuche über die Regeneration der Nervenfasern. *Pflüg. Arch. ges. Physiol.*, 1907, *116:* 385–478.
15. BETHE, A. Notiz über die Unfähigkeit motorischer Fasern mit rezeptorischen Fasern zu verheilen. *Pflüg. Arch. ges. Physiol.*, 1907, *116:* 479–481.
16. BETHE, A. Zwei neue Methoden der Ueberbrückung grösserer Nervenlücken. *Dtsch. med. Wschr.*, 1916, *2:* 1311–1314.
17. BIELSCHOWSKY, M., and UNGER, E. Die Überbrückung grosser Nervenlücken. Beiträge zur Kenntnis der Degeneration und Regeneration peripherischer Nerven. *J. Psychol. Neurol., Lpz.*, 1918, *22:* 267–318.
18. BILLIG, H. E. and VAN HARREVELD, A. A new aspect of muscle reinnervation. *Nav. med. Bull., Wash.*, 1943, *41:* 410–414.
19. BLENCKE, A. Ein weiterer Beitrag zu den Ueberbrückungsversuchen von Nervendefekten mit Edinger-Röhrchen. *Zbl. Chir.*, 1917, *44:* 236–238.

20. BOEKE, J. Studien zur Nervenregeneration II. Die Regeneration nach Vereinigung ungleichartiger Nervenstücke (heretogene Regeneration), und die Funktion der Augenmuskel- und Zungennerven. Die allgemeinen Gesetze der Nervenregeneration. *Verh. Akad. Wet., Amst.,* 1917, *19:* no. 5, 1–71.

21. BOEKE, J. Nervenregeneration. *Bumke u. Foersters Handb. Neurol.,* 1935, *1:* 995–1122.

22. BRISTOW, R. Discussion on injuries to peripheral nerves. *Proc. R. Soc. Med.,* 1941, *34:* 513–517.

23. v. BÜNGNER, O. Ueber die Degenerations- und Regenerationsvorgänge am Nerven nach Verletzungen. *Beitr. path. Anat.,* 1891, *10:* 321–393.

24. BURK, W. Zu den Ueberbrückungsversuchen von Nervendefekten. (Bemerkungen zu der gleichlautenden Arbeit von Stracker. Zentralblatt für Chirurgie Nr. 50. 1916.) *Zbl. Chir.,* 1917, *44:* 238.

25. BURKE, G. L. The corrosion of metals in tissues; and an introduction to tantalum. *Canad. med. Ass. J.,* 1940, *43:* 125–128.

26. BURR, H. S. An electro-dynamic theory of development suggested by studies of proliferation rates in the brain of Amblystoma. *J. comp. Neurol.,* 1932, *56:* 347–371.

27. BURT, A. S. Chemical factors in nerve growth studied in tissue culture: Vitamin B_1 and the growth of spinal ganglia. *J. cell. comp. Physiol.,* 1943, *21:* 145–159.

28. BURT, A. S. Growth of spinal ganglia in plasma from vitamin B_1-deficient chickens. *J. cell. comp. Physiol.,* 1943, *22:* 205–222.

29. BURT, A. S. Effect of biotin on chick spinal ganglia in tissue culture. *Proc. Soc. exp. Biol., N. Y.,* 1943, *54:* 191–193.

30. CAJAL, S. RAMON y La rétine des vertébrés. *Cellule,* 1893, *9:* 119–255.

31. CAJAL, S. RAMON y Degeneration and regeneration of the nervous system. *London: Oxford Univ. Press,* 1928, 2 vols.

32. CHILD, C. M. The origin and development of the nervous system, from a physiological viewpoint. *Chicago: Univ. of Chicago Press,* 1921, 296 pp.

33. COLEMAN, C. C. Surgical treatment of peripheral nerve injuries. *Surg. Gynec. Obstet.,* 1944, *78:* 113–124.

34. CRAIG, A. B., and ELLIS, A. G. An experimental and histological study of Cargile membrane. With reference to (1) its efficacy in preventing adhesions in the abdominal and cranial cavities and around nerves and tendons, and (2) its ultimate fate in the tissues. *Ann. Surg.,* 1905, *41:* 801–822.

35. DAVENPORT, H. A., CHOR, H., and DOLKART, R. E. The ratio of myelinated to unmyelinated fibers in regenerated sciatic nerves of Macacus rhesus. *J. comp. Neurol.,* 1937, *67:* 483–491.

36. DAVIS, L., and CLEVELAND, D. A. Experimental studies in nerve transplants. *Ann. Surg.,* 1934, *99:* 271–283.

37. DENK, W. Ueber Schussverletzungen der Nerven. *Beitr. klin. Chir.,* 1914, *91:* 217–221.

38. DETWILER, S. R. Neuroembryology. An experimental study. *New York: The Macmillan Co.,* 1936, 218 pp.

39. DOGLIOTTI, A. M. Études expérimentales et première application clinique d'une nouvelle opération destinée à augmenter et à équilibrer la fonction neuro-musculaire dans la paralysie partielle des nerfs. *J. Chir., Paris,* 1935, *45:* 30–48.

40. DUSTIN, A. P. Le rôle des tropismes et de l'odogenèse dans la régénération du système nerveux. *Arch. Biol., Paris,* 1910, *25:* 269–388.

41. DUSTIN, A. P. Les lésions posttraumatiques des nerfs. Contribution à l'histopathologie du système nerveux périphérique chez l'homme. *Ambulance de l'Ocean, Paris,* 1917, *1:* fasc. 2, 71–161.

42. v. EBNER, V. Über die Entwicklung der leimgebenden Fibrillen, besonders im Zahnbein. *S.B. Akad. Wiss. Wien,* 1906, *115:* 281–343.

43. EDEN, R. Sind zur Ueberbrückung von Nervendefekten die Verfahren der Tubulisation und der Nerventransplantation zu empfehlen? *Zbl. Chir.,* 1917, *44:* 138–140.

44. EDEN, R., and REHN, E. Die autoplastische Fetttransplantation zur Neurolysis und Tendolysis. (Klinik und Experiment.) *Arch. klin. Chir.,* 1914, *104:* 65–83.

45. EDINGER, L. Ueber die Vereinigung getrennter Nerven. Grundsätzliches und Mitteilung eines neuen Verfahrens. *Münch. med. Wschr.,* 1916, *63:* 225–228.

46. ELSBERG, C. A. Experiments on motor nerve regeneration and the direct neurotization of paralyzed muscles by their own and by foreign nerves. *Science,* 1917, *45:* 318–320.

47. v. ENDERLEN and LOBENHOFFER. Zur Ueberbrückung von Nervendefekten. *Münch. med. Wschr.,* 1917, *64:* 225.

48. ERLACHER, P. Experimentelle Untersuchungen über Plastik und Transplantation von Nerv und Muskel. *Arch. klin. Chir.,* 1914, *106:* 389–407.

49. ERLANGER, J. and GASSER, H. S. Electrical signs of nervous activity. *Philadelphia: Univ. of Pennsylvania Press,* 1937, 221 pp.

50. FISCHER, E.   Yeast, thiamin and biotin on atrophy and regeneration of denervated skeletal muscle. *Fed. Proc. Amer. Soc. exp. Biol.*, 1943, *2:* 13.

51. FORAMITTI, C.   Zur Technik der Nervennaht. *Arch. klin. Chir.*, 1904, *73:* 643–648.

52. FORD, F. R., and WOODHALL, B.   Phenomena due to misdirection of regenerating fibers of cranial, spinal and autonomic nerves. Clinical observations. *Arch. Surg., Chicago*, 1938, *36:* 480–496.

53. FORSSMAN, J.   Ueber die Ursachen, welche die Wachsthumsrichtung der peripheren Nervenfasern bei der Regeneration bestimmen. *Beitr. path. Anat.*, 1898, *24:* 56–100.

54. FORSSMAN, J.   Zur Kenntniss des Neurotropismus. Weitere Beiträge. *Beitr. path. Anat.*, 1900, *27:* 407–430.

55. FORT, W. B.   An experimental study of the factors involved in the establishment of neuromuscular connections. (Thesis) *Univ. Chicago*, 1940, 88 pp.

56. FREY-WYSSLING, A.   Submikroskopische Morphologie des Protoplasmas und seiner Derivate. *Berlin: Gebrüder Borntraeger*, 1938, xv: 317 pp.

57. FULLERTON, A.   On the use of a sleeve of vein in nerve suture. *Brit. med. J.*, 1915, *2:* 320.

58. GLUCK, T.   Ueber Neuroplastik auf dem Wege der Transplantation. *Arch. klin. Chir.*, 1880, *25:* 606–616.

59. GOSSET, A., and BERTRAND, I.   La moelle épinière, utilisée comme greffon hétéroplastique dans les blessures des nerfs périphériques. Recherches cliniques et expérimentales. *J. Chir., Paris*, 1938, *51:* 481–505.

60. GRAY, P.   Experiments with direct currents on chick embryos. *Arch. EntwMech. Org.*, 1939, *139:* 732–779.

61. GREENFIELD, J. G.   Recent studies of the morphology of the neurone in health and disease. *J. Neurol. Psychiat.*, 1938, n.s. *1:* 306–328.

62. GREENFIELD, J. G.   Discussion on injuries to peripheral nerves. *Proc. R. Soc. Med.*, 1941, *34:* 519.

63. GREENMAN, M. J.   Studies on the regeneration of the peroneal nerve of the albino rat: Number and sectional areas of fibers: Area relation of axis to sheath. *J. comp. Neurol.*, 1913, *23:* 479–513.

64. GUTMANN, E.   Factors affecting recovery of motor function after nerve lesions. *J. Neurol. Psychiat.*, 1942, n.s. *5:* 81–95.

65. GUTMANN, E., GUTTMANN, L., MEDAWAR, P. B., and YOUNG, J. Z.   The rate of regeneration of nerve. *J. exp. Biol.*, 1942, *19:* 14–44.

66. GUTMANN, E., and GUTTMANN, L.   Factors affecting recovery of sensory function after nerve lesions. *J. Neurol. Psychiat.*, 1942, n.s. *5:* 117–129.

67. GUTMANN, E., and SANDERS, F. K.   Recovery of fibre numbers and diameters in the regeneration of peripheral nerves. *J. Physiol.*, 1943, *101:* 489–518.

68. HAMILTON, H. L., and PLOTZ, H.   Use of biotin for stimulating growth of nerve tissue and other cells *in vitro*. *Proc. Soc. exp. Biol., N. Y.*, 1942, *50:* 133–135.

69. HAMMOND, W. S., NONIDEZ, J. F., and HINSEY, J. C.   Effect of various sulfonamide compounds on nerve regeneration. *Arch. Neurol. Psychiat., Chicago*, 1943, *50:* 499–509.

70. HANS, H.   Naht durchtrennter Nerven mittels Einhülsung in Eigengewebe. *Zbl. Chir.*, 1915, *42:* 801–802.

71. HARRISON, R. G.   The outgrowth of the nerve fiber as a mode of protoplasmic movement. *J. exp. Zool.*, 1910, *9:* 787–848.

72. HARRISON, R. G.   The cultivation of tissues in extraneous media as a method of morphogenetic study. *Anat. Rec.*, 1912, *6:* 181–193.

73. HARRISON, R. G.   The reaction of embryonic cells to solid structures. *J. exp. Zool.*, 1914, *17:* 521–544.

74. HARRISON, R. G.   The Croonian lecture. On the origin and development of the nervous system studied by the methods of experimental embryology. *Proc. roy. Soc., Lond.*, 1935, *118B:* 155–196.

75. HASHIMOTO, T., and TOKUOKA, H.   Ueber die Schussverletzungen peripherer Nerven und ihre Behandlung (Tubulisation). *Arch. klin. Chir.*, 1907, *84:* 354–402.

76. HEILE, B., and HEZEL, O.   Unsere bisherigen Erfahrungen bei der Behandlung im Kriege verletzter peripherer Nerven. *Beitr. klin. Chir.*, 1915, *96:* 299–328.

77. HELD, H.   Die Entwickelung des Nervengewebes bei den Wirbeltieren. *Leipzig: J. A. Barth*, 1909, 378 pp.

78. HIGHET, W. B., and SANDERS, F. K.   The effects of stretching nerves after suture. *Brit. J. Surg.*, 1943, *30:* 355–369.

79. HIRSCHEL, G.   Erfahrungen über Schussverletzungen der Nerven und die Verwendung von präparierten Kalbsarterien zu ihrer Umhüllung. *Dtsch. Z. Chir.*, 1915, *132:* 567–573.

80. HIS, W.   Die Entwickelung der ersten Nervenbahnen beim menschlichen Embryo. Uebersichtliche Darstellung. *Arch. Anat. Physiol., Lpz.* 1887, 368–378.

81. HOHMANN, G., and SPIELMEYER, W.   Zur Kritik des Edingerschen und des Betheschen Verfahrens der Ueberbrückung grösserer Nervenlücken. *Münch. med. Wschr.*, 1917, *64:* 97–99.

82. HOLMES, W., and YOUNG, J. Z.   Nerve regeneration after immediate and delayed suture. *J. Anat., Lond.*, 1942, *77:* 63–96.

83. HOLOBUT, W. S., and JALOWY, B.   Die De- und Regeneration des peripheren motorischen Nerven-systems auf einer morphologischfunktionellen Grundlage. *Z. Zellforsch.*, 1936, *25:* 541–564.

84. HOWELL, W. H., and HUBER, G. C.   A physiological, histological and clinical study of the degeneration and regeneration in peripheral nerve fibres after severance of their connections with the nerve centres. *J. Physiol.*, 1892, *13:* 335–406.

85. HUBER, G. C.   A study of the operative treatment for loss of nerve substance in peripheral nerves. *J. Morph.*, 1895, *11:* 629–740.

86. HUBER, G. C.   Transplantation of peripheral nerves. *Arch. Neurol. Psychiat.*, Chicago, 1919, *2:* 466–480.

87. HUBER, G. C.   Repair of peripheral nerve injuries. *Surg. Gynec. Obstet.*, 1920, *30:* 464–471.

88. HUBER, G. C.   Nerve degeneration and regeneration. In: Stookey, B. *Surgical and mechanical treatment of peripheral nerves.* Philadelphia: W. B. Saunders Co., 1922, 41–79.

89. HUBER, G. C.   Experimental observations on peripheral nerve repair. In: *The Medical Department of the United States Army in the World War.* Washington: Govt. Printing Office, 1927, *11:* 1091–1283.

90. INGEBRIGTSEN, R.   Studies of the degeneration and regeneration of axis cylinders in vitro. *J. exp. Med.*, 1913, *17:* 182–191.

91. INGEBRIGTSEN, R.   A contribution to the biology of peripheral nerves in transplantation. II. Life of peripheral nerves of mammals in plasma. *J. exp. Med.*, 1916, *23:* 251–264.

92. INGVAR, S.   Reactions of cells to the galvanic current in tissue cultures. *Proc. Soc. exp. Biol., N. Y.*, 1920, *17:* 198–199.

93. KAPPERS, C. U. A.   Further contributions on neurobiotaxis: IX. An attempt to compare the phenomena of neurobiotaxis with other phenomena of taxis and tropism. The dynamic polarization of the neurone. *J. comp. Neurol.*, 1917, *27:* 261–298.

94. KARSSEN, A., and SAGER, B.   Sur l'influence du courant électrique sur la croissance des neuroblastes in vitro. *Arch. exp. Zellforsch.*, 1934, *16:* 255–259.

95. KIRK, E. G., and LEWIS, D. D.   Fascial tubulization in the repair of nerve defects. *J. Amer. med. Ass.*, 1915, *65:* 486–492.

96. KIRK, E. G., and LEWIS, D. D.   Regeneration in peripheral nerves. An experimental study. *Johns Hopk. Hosp. Bull.*, 1917, *28:* 71–80.

97. KIRSCHNER, M.   Zur Behandlung grosser Nervendefekte. *Dtsch. med. Wschr.*, 1917, *43:* 739–741.

98. KÖLLIKER, T.   Die Verletzungen und chirurgischen Erkrankungen der peripherischen Nerven. *Dtsch. Chir. Lief. 24b.* Stuttgart: F. Enke, 1890, 120 pp.

99. KRAUS, H., and REISNER, H.   Behandlungsergebnisse von Verletzungen peripherer Nerven mit besonderer Berücksichtigung der Schussverletzungen der Jahre 1919, 1927 und 1934. *Arch. klin. Chir.*, 1940, *199:* 318–336.

100. KREDEL, L.   Ueber das Verhalten der auf operierte schussverletzte Nerven überpflanzten Fascien-lappen. *Zbl. Chir.*, 1915, *42:* 201–203.

101. LAZERE, B., THOMSON, J. D., and HINES, H. M.   Studies on muscle and nerve in biotin-deficient rats. *Proc. Soc. exp. Biol., N. Y.*, 1943, *53:* 81–82.

102. LEVI, G.   Explantation, besonders die Struktur und die biologischen Eigenschaften der in vitro gezüchteten Zellen und Gewebe. *Ergebn. Anat. EntwGesch.*, 1934, *31:* 125–707.

103. LITWILLER, R.   Quantitative studies on nerve regeneration in amphibia. I. Factors controlling nerve regeneration in adult limbs. *J. comp. Neurol.*, 1938, *69:* 427–447.

104. LLOYD, D. P. C.   Centripetal discharges in dorsal and ventral roots following stimulation of muscle by ventral root volleys. *Proc. Soc. exp. Biol., N. Y.*, 1941, *47:* 44–47.

105. LLOYD, D. P. C.   Stimulation of peripheral nerve terminations by active muscle. *J. Neurophysiol.*, 1942, *5:* 153–165.

106. LOTHEISSEN, G.   Zur Technik der Nerven- und Sehnennaht. *Arch. klin. Chir.*, 1901, *64:* 310–313.

107. LUGARO, E.   Sul neurotropismo e sui trapianti dei nervi. *Riv. Patol. nerv. ment.*, 1906, *11:* 320–327.

108. McCARRISON, R., and SANKARAN, G.   Effect of plasma from a case of *polyneuritis gallinarum* on growth of tissues *in vitro*. Preliminary note. *Indian J. med. Res.*, 1933, *21:* 187–188.

109. MASSON, P.   Experimental and spontaneous schwannomas (peripheral gliomas). *Amer. J. Path.*, 1932, *8:* 367–416.

110. MAUCLAIRE, P.   Suture nerveuse tubulaire avec des trachées de petits animaux. *Bull. Soc. Chir.*, Paris, 1915, n.s. *41:* 2402–2404.

111. MEISEL, K.   Verletzungen peripherer Nerven. *Beitr. klin. Chir.*, 1916, *98:* 758.

112. MEURIOT, H., and PLATON. Cent observations d'isolement des nerfs par manchonnage au caoutchouc. *Bull. Soc. Chir., Paris*, 1918, *44*: 850–854.

113. MITCHELL, S. W. Injuries of nerves and their consequences. *Philadelphia: J. B. Lippincott &Co.*, 1872, 377 pp.

114. MOSSA, S. La struttura del citoplasma degli elementi viventi coltivati in vitro studiata alla osservazione in campo oscuro. *Arch. exp. Zellforsch.*, 1927, *4*: 447–461.

115. MÜLLER, O., and BERBLINGER, W. Das Endergebnis einer nach der Edinger'schen Methode (Agarröhrchen) vorgenommenen Ueberbrückung des Nervus ulnaris mit anatomischer Untersuchung. *Berl. klin. Wschr.*, 1917, *54*: 1109–1111.

116. NAFFZIGER, H. C. Methods to secure end-to-end suture of peripheral nerves. *Surg. Gynec. Obstet.*, 1921, *32*: 193–204.

117. NAGEOTTE, J. Le processus de la cicatrisation des nerfs. *C. R. Soc. Biol., Paris*, 1915, *78*: 249–254.

118. NAGEOTTE, J. Action à distance exercée par les macrophages sur le développement des travées névrogliques et sur la myélinisation des neurites dans les cicatrices nerveuses. *C. R. Soc. Biol., Paris*, 1915, *78*: 711–714.

119. NAGEOTTE, J. L'organisation de la matière dans ses rapports avec la vie. *Paris: Librairie Félix Alcan*, 1922, vi: 560 pp.

120. NAGEOTTE, J. Sheaths of the peripheral nerves. Nerve degeneration and regeneration. In: *Cytology and cellular pathology of the nervous system.* W. Penfield, Ed. New York: P. B. Hoeber, 1932, i: 189–239.

121. NAGEOTTE, J., and GUYON, L. Différences physiologiques entre la névroglie des fibres motrices et celle des fibres sensitives, dans les nerfs périphériques, mises en évidence par la régénération. *C. R. Soc. Biol., Paris*, 1918, *81*: 571–574.

122. NEEDHAM, J. Biochemistry and Morphogenesis. *Cambridge: Univ. Press*, 1942, 787 pp.

123. PARKER, G. H., and PAINE, V. L. Progressive nerve degeneration and its rate in the lateral-line nerve of the catfish. *Amer. J. Anat.*, 1934, *54*: 1–25.

124. PAYR, E. Beiträge zur Technik der Blutgefäss- und Nervennaht nebst Mittheilungen über die Verwendung eines resorbirbaren Metalles in der Chirurgie. *Arch. klin. Chir.*, 1900, *62*: 67–93.

125. PEREKROPOFF, A. I. Regeneration of defects of nerve trunks by joining the ends with vascular tubules (arteries and veins). Experimental investigation. (Russian) *Kazan*: 1913, 144 pp.

126. PERTHES, G. Die Schussverletzungen der peripheren Nerven. *Z. ges. Neurol. Psychiat.*, 1917, *36*: 400–420.

127. PÉTERFI, T., and KAPEL, O. Die Wirkung des Anstechens auf das Protoplasma der in vitro gezüchteten Gewebezellen. III. Anstichversuche an den Nervenzellen. *Arch. exp. Zellforsch.*, 1928, *5*: 341–348.

128. PICKEN, L. E. R. The fine structure of biological systems. *Biol. Rev.*, 1940, *15*: 133–167.

129. PLATT, H. On the results of bridging gaps in injured nerve trunks by autogenous fascial tubulization and autogenous nerve grafts. *Brit. J. Surg.*, 1919, *7*: 384–389.

130. POLLOCK, L. J., and DAVIS, L. Peripheral nerve injuries. *New York: P. B. Hoeber*, 1933, 678 pp.

131. POMERANCEW. Zur Casuistik der Nervennaht. (Russian) *Wratsch.*, 1900, no. 1, p. 26.

132. PUDENZ, R. H., and ODOM, G. L. Meningocerebral adhesions. An experimental study of the effect of human amniotic membrane, amnioplastin, beef allantoic membrane, Cargile membrane, tantalum foil, and polyvinyl alcohol films. *Surgery*, 1942, *12*: 318–344.

133. RANSON, S. W. Degeneration and regeneration of nerve fibers. *J. comp. Neurol.*, 1912, *22*: 487–545.

134. REXED, B., and SWENSSON, A. Über die Regeneration der Markscheide bei peripheren Nerven nach Kontinuitätstrennungen. *Z. mikr.-anat. Forsch.*, 1940, *49*: 359–387.

135. RÖPKE, W. Chirurgische Behandlung der Verletzungen und Erkrankungen der peripheren Nerven. *Penzoldt u. Stintzings Handb. ges. Therapie, Jena*, 1917, *4*: 513–541.

136. ROSENBLUETH, A., and DEL POZO, E. C. The centrifugal course of Wallerian degeneration. *Amer. J. Physiol.*, 1943, *139*: 247–254.

137. ROSSI, O., and GASTALDI, G. La rigenerazione del tessuto nervoso nei vertebrati superiori. Rivista critica con dati personali. *Riv. Patol nerv. ment.*, 1935, *46*: 1–369.

138. SAITO, M. Zur Frage der Regeneration der peripheren Nerven des erwachsenen Menschen. *Arb. neurol. Inst. (Inst. Anat. Physiol. ZentNerv.) Univ. Wien.*, 1922, *24*: 85–92.

139. SANDERS, F. K. The repair of large gaps in the peripheral nerves. *Brain*, 1942, *65*: 281–337.

140. SANDERS, F. K., and YOUNG, J. Z. The degeneration and re-innervation of grafted nerves. *J. Anat., Lond.*, 1942, *76*: 143–166.

141. SEDDON, H. J., and MEDAWAR, P. B. Fibrin suture of human nerves. *Lancet*, 1942, *2*: 87–88.

142. SHERREN, J. Some points in the surgery of the peripheral nerves. *Edinb. med. J.*, 1906, n.s. *20*: 297–332.

143. Speidel, C. C. Studies of living nerves. I. The movements of individual sheath cells and nerve sprouts correlated with the process of myelin-sheath formation in amphibian larvae. *J. exp. Zool.*, 1932, *61*: 279-331.

144. Speidel, C. C. Studies of living nerves. II. Activities of ameboid growth cones, sheath cells, and myelin segments, as revealed by prolonged observation of individual nerve fibers in frog tadpoles. *Amer. J. Anat.*, 1933, *52*: 1-79.

145. Speidel, C. C. Studies of living nerves. III. Phenomena of nerve irritation and recovery, degeneration and repair. *J. comp. Neurol.*, 1935, *61*: 1-78.

146. Speidel, C. C. Studies of living nerves. IV. Growth, regeneration, and myelination of peripheral nerves in salamanders. *Biol. Bull. Wood's Hole*, 1935, *68*: 140-161.

147. Speidel, C. C. Studies of living nerves. VII. Growth adjustments of cutaneous terminal arborizations. *J. comp. Neurol.*, 1942, *76*: 57-73.

148. Sperry, R. W. The effect of crossing nerves to antagonistic muscles in the hind limb of the rat. *J. comp. Neurol.*, 1941, *75*: 1-19.

149. Sperry, R. W. Functional results of crossing sensory nerves in the rat. *J. comp. Neurol.*, 1943, *78*: 59-90.

150. Spielmeyer, W. Histopathologie des Nervensystems. Berlin: J. Springer, 1922, vi: 493 pp.

151. Spitzy, H. Bemerkung zur Ueberbrückung von Nervendefekten. *Münch. med. Wschr.*, 1917, *64*: 372.

152. Spurling, R. G. The use of tantalum wire and foil in the repair of peripheral nerves. *Surg. Clin. N. Amer.*, 1943, *23*: 1491-1504.

153. Steinthal, C. Die Deckung grösserer Nervendefekte durch Tubularnaht. *Beitr. klin. Chir.*, 1915, *96*: 295-298.

154. Steinthal, C. Die Ueberdeckung von grösseren Nervendefekten mittels Tubularnaht. *Zbl. Chir.*, 1917, *44*: 646-647.

155. Stookey, B. Surgical and mechanical treatment of peripheral nerves. Philadelphia: W. B. Saunders Co., 1922, 475 pp.

156. Stopford, J. S. B. The treatment of large defects in peripheral nerve injuries. *Lancet*, 1920, *2*: 1296-1297.

157. Stracker, O. Zu den Ueberbrückungsversuchen von Nervendefekten. *Zbl. Chir.*, 1916, *43*: 985-990.

158. Strasser, H. Alte und neue Probleme der entwickelungsgeschichtlichen Forschung auf dem Gebiete des Nervensystems. *Ergebn. Anat. EntwGesch.*, 1891, *1*: 721-769.

159. Stroebe, H. Experimentelle Untersuchungen über Degeneration und Regeneration peripherer Nerven nach Verletzungen. *Beitr. path. Anat.*, 1893, *13*: 160-278.

160. Swan, J. Discussion on injuries to the peripheral nerves. *Proc. R. Soc. Med.*, 1941, *34*: 521-529.

161. Takimoto, G. Ueber die Nervendehnung. Experimentelle und klinische Untersuchung. *Mitt. med. Fak. Tokio*, 1916, *16*: 73-136.

162. Tangari, C. Ricerche sperimentali sull'azione dell'aneurina nei processi rigenerativi del tessuto nervoso periferico. *Arch. Sci. med.*, 1940, *69*: 331-345.

163. Tarlov, I. M., and Benjamin, B. Autologous plasma clot suture of nerves. *Science*, 1942, *95*: 258.

164. Tarlov, I. M., Denslow, C., Swarz, S., and Pineles, D. Plasma clot suture of nerves. Experimental technic. *Arch. Surg., Chicago*, 1943, *47*: 44-58.

165. Tarlov, I. M. Plasma clot suture of nerves. *J. Neurosurg.*, 1944, *1*: 359.

166. Taylor, A. C. Selectivity of nerve fibers from the dorsal and ventral roots in the development of the frog limb. *J. exp. Zool.*, 1944, *96*: 159-185.

167. Tello, F. Gegenwärtige Anschauungen über den Neurotropismus. *Vortr. EntwMech. Org.*, 1923, *33*: 1-73.

168. Tillmanns, H. In: *Chirurgie des praktischen Arztes mit Einschluss der Augen-, Ohren- und Zahnkrankheiten*. W. Ebstein and J. Schwalbe, Ed. Stuttgart: F: Enke, 1907, 944 pp.

169. Treutlein, A. Kriegschirurgisches aus Japan. *Münch. med. Wschr.*, 1906, *53*: 1199-1202.

170. Vanlair, C. De la régénération des nerfs périphériques par le procédé de la suture tubulaire. *Arch. Biol., Paris*, 1882, *3*: 379-496.

171. Vanlair, C. Nouvelles recherches expérimentales sur la régénération des nerfs. *Arch. Biol., Paris*, 1885, *6*: 127-235.

172. Verne, J., and Iselin, M. Réflexions sur deux pièces de réparation nerveuse sur l'homme prélevées dix semaines et six mois après l'opération. *Pr. méd.*, 1941, *49*: 789-791.

173. VULPIUS, O., and STOFFEL, A. Orthopädische Operationslehre. *Stuttgart: F. Enke*, 1920, xvi: 744 pp.

174. WARD, A. A., and KENNARD, M. A. Effect of cholinergic drugs on recovery of function following lesions of the central nervous system in monkeys. *Yale J. Biol. Med.*, 1942, *15:* 189–228.

175. WEDDELL, G., and GLEES, P. The early stages in the degeneration of cutaneous nerve fibres. *J. Anat., Lond.*, 1942, *76:* 65–93.

176. WEISS, P. Functional adaptation and the role of ground substances in development. *Amer. Nat.*, 1933, *67:* 322–340.

177. WEISS, P. In vitro experiments on the factors determining the course of the outgrowing nerve fiber. *J. exp. Zool.*, 1934, *68:* 393–448.

178. WEISS, P. Motor effects of sensory nerves experimentally connected with muscles. *Anat. Rec.*, 1934, *60:* 437–448.

179. WEISS, P. Experimental innervation of muscles by the central ends of afferent nerves (establishment of a one-neurone connection between receptor and effector organ), with functional tests. *J. comp. Neurol.*, 1935, *61:* 135–174.

180. WEISS, P. Selectivity controlling the central-peripheral relations in the nervous system. *Biol. Rev.*, 1936, *11:* 494–531.

181. WEISS, P. Further experimental investigations on the phenomenon of homologous response in transplanted amphibian limbs. II. Nerve regeneration and the innervation of transplanted limbs. *J. comp. Neurol.*, 1937, *66:* 481–535.

182. WEISS, P. Principles of development. A text in experimental embryology. *New York: Henry Holt*, 1939, xix, 601 pp.

183. WEISS, P. Reunion of stumps of small nerves by tubulation instead of suture. *Science*, 1941, *93:* 67–68.

184. WEISS, P. Self-differentiation of the basic patterns of coordination. *Comp. Psychol. Monogr.*, 1941, *17:* no. 4, 96 pp.

185. WEISS, P. Nerve patterns: The mechanics of nerve growth. *Growth*, 1941, 5 (suppl.): 163–203.

186. WEISS, P. Nerve regeneration in the rat following tubular splicing of severed nerves. *Arch. Surg., Chicago*, 1943, *46:* 525–547.

187. WEISS, P. Endoneurial edema in constricted nerve. *Anat. Rec.*, 1943, *86:* 491–522.

188. WEISS, P. Experiments on nerve repair. *Trans. Amer. neurol. Ass. 1943*, 42–45.

189. WEISS, P. Nerve reunion with sleeves of frozen-dried artery in rabbits, cats and monkeys. *Proc. Soc. exp. Biol., N. Y.*, 1943, *54:* 274–277.

190. WEISS, P. Functional nerve regeneration through frozen-dried nerve grafts in cats and monkeys. *Proc. Soc. exp. Biol., N. Y.*, 1943, *54:* 277–279.

191. WEISS, P. In vitro transformation of spindle cells of neural origin into macrophages. *Anat. Rec.*, 1944, *88:* 205–221.

192. WEISS, P. Damming of axoplasm in constricted nerve: a sign of perpetual growth in nerve fibers. *Anat. Rec.*, 1944, *88:* 464.

193. WEISS, P. Sutureless reunion of severed nerves with elastic cuffs of tantalum. *J. Neurosurg.*, 1944, *1:* 219–225.

194. WEISS, P., and BURT, A. S. Effect of nerve compression on Wallerian degeneration *in vitro*. *Proc. Soc. exp. Biol., N. Y.*, 1944, *55:* 109–112.

195. WEISS, P., and CAMPBELL, C. J. Nerve fiber counts and muscle tension after nerve regeneration in the rat. *Amer. J. Physiol.*, 1944, *140:* 616–626.

196. WEISS, P., and CUMMINGS, J. B. Regeneration of the lateral line nerve of Amblystoma from different nerve fiber sources. *Anat. Rec.*, 1943, *87:* 119–125.

197. WEISS, P., and DAVIS, H. Pressure block in nerves provided with arterial sleeves. *J. Neurophysiol.*, 1943, *6:* 269–286.

198. WEISS, P., and LITWILLER, R. Quantitative studies on nerve regeneration in amphibia. I. Factors controlling nerve regeneration in adult limbs. *Proc. Soc. exp. Biol., N. Y.*, 1937, *36:* 636–638.

199. WEISS, P., and TAYLOR, A. C. Repair of peripheral nerves by grafts of frozen-dried nerve. *Proc. Soc. exp. Biol., N. Y.*, 1943, *52:* 326–328.

200. WEISS, P., and TAYLOR, A. C. Histomechanical analysis of nerve reunion in the rat after tubular splicing. *Arch. Surg., Chicago*, 1943, *47:* 419–447.

201. WEISS, P., and TAYLOR, A. C. Further experimental evidence against "neurotropism" in nerve regeneration. *J. exp. Zool.*, 1944, *95:* 233–257.

202. WEISS, P., and TAYLOR, A. C. Impairment of growth and myelinization in regenerating nerve fibers subject to constriction. *Proc. Soc. exp. Biol., N. Y.,* 1944, *55:* 77–80.

203. WILLIAMS, S. C. A study of the reactions of growing embryonic nerve fibers to the passage of direct electric current through the surrounding medium. *Anat. Rec.,* 1936, *64* (suppl. 3): 56–57.

204. WREDE, L. Ueberbrückung eines Nervendefektes mittels Seidennaht und lebenden Venenstückes. *Dtsch. med. Wschr.,* 1909, *35:* 1125.

205. YOUNG, J. Z. The functional repair of nervous tissue. *Physiol. Rev.,* 1942, *22:* 318–374.

206. YOUNG, J. Z. The process of regeneration of nerve and muscle following immediate and delayed suture. *Trans. Amer. neurol. Ass.,* 1943, 41–42.

207. YOUNG, J. Z., and MEDAWAR, P. B. Fibrin suture of peripheral nerves. *Lancet,* 1940, *2:* 126–128.

14401

Nerve Reunion with Sleeves of Frozen-Dried Artery in Rabbits, Cats and Monkeys.*

PAUL WEISS.

Sutureless nerve reunion by arterial cuffs in the rat was described in an earlier paper.[1] Instead of live arteries, frozen-dried ones may be used after rehydration. A more recent analysis[2] revealed the reasons for the superiority of this method. Evidence has now accumulated to show that it is equally satisfactory in larger mammals. This conclusion is based on a total of 132 arterial nerve splices in rabbits (21), cats (30) and monkeys (81).

Material and Methods. The nerves used were mostly the peroneal, tibial, or sciatic. No distinction will be made here between simple reunion of severed stumps and reunion with the intercalation of a nerve graft, mostly of frozen-dried nerve (see following article). For arteries, the aorta or carotid was used in most cases; the former is preferable for its lack of musculature. Freezing, drying, storing, and rehydration were done as previously reported,[3] always with strict aseptic precautions. Elasticity, consistency, and histologic character are not noticeably affected by this treatment. For the reunion of severed nerve stumps, arterial segments of matching caliber and measuring from 6 to 10 diameters in

* This work was done under a contract, recommended by the Committee on Medical Research, between the Office of Scientific Research and Development and the University of Chicago; also aided by the Dr. Wallace C. and Clara A. Abbott Memorial Fund of the University of Chicago. The monkey experiments were carried out at the Yerkes Laboratories of Primate Biology, Orange Park, Florida, and I am greatly indebted to Dr. K. S. Lashley for his generous contribution of laboratory facilities. Technical assistance by Dr. R. W. Sperry and Dr. A. C. Taylor is also gratefully acknowledged.

[1] Weiss, P., *Arch. Surgery*, 1943, **46**, 525.

[2] Weiss, P., and Taylor, A. C., *Arch. Surgery*, 1943, **47**, 419.

[3] Weiss, P., and Taylor, A. C., PROC. SOC. EXP. BIOL. AND MED., 1943, **52**, 326.

length were fitted over the nerve ends by the following improved technic (Fig. 1):

First, the sleeve is pulled over one nerve end with the instrument illustrated in Fig. 1A-C. A stainless steel tube (a) contains a movable flexible wire (b), one end of which rests against a coil spring (c), while the other end is fastened to a chuck (d) ending in two half-cylinders (e_1 and e_2) of the same diameter as tube a, which act as a clutch. They are manipulated through lever f: depressing the lever (Fig. 1A) produces retraction of the conical chuck and closure of its jaws; on releasing the lever, spring c forces the end piece out and the clutch (e) opens owing to the elastic spread of the jaws (d). When the lever is depressed and the open end plugged by a fitting cone (g), the instrument forms a continuous pointed rod (Fig. 1A). In this condition, it is threaded through the lumen of the arterial segment, and the latter is slipped over the shaft a. The lever is then released, cone g is removed, and the free nerve end is grasped between the jaws of the clutch by depressing the lever again. The sleeve can now easily be slipped back from the shaft onto the nerve. This corresponds to stages a-e of our earlier practice (Weiss,[1] Fig. 1). In a second step, the other nerve stump is introduced into the open end of the sleeve. To facilitate this, the latter is widened and held open by a "spreader" (Fig. 1D, E), consisting of 2 curved metal strips (h) attached to the ends of a steel spring bow (i). Instruments of several sizes were available to fit different nerves.†

It is advantageous to leave a small blood-filled gap between the nerve ends in the sleeve. When grafts are used, their length can be adjusted so as to avoid either slack or exces-

† The instruments were designed jointly with Dr. A. C. Taylor who also did the actual constructing.

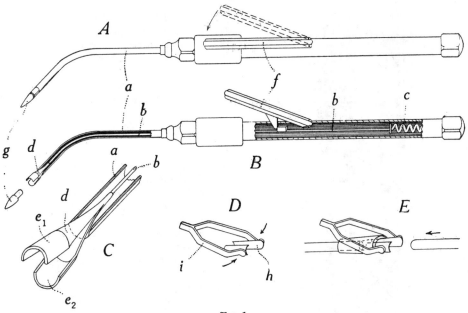

FIG. 1.
Splicing instrument. Explanation in text.

sive stretch, and no further attachment between sleeve and nerve is necessary. The same applies to nerve ends approximated under moderate stretch. Higher degrees of stretch require special provisions (see below). No sutures have been used in any of the cases dealt with in this report: the elastic sleeve, sealed to the nerve by clotting blood, was the only link. No casts or other means of restraining active and passive use of the operated limbs were employed. This placed a severe test upon the arterial unions.

The animals (rabbits, cats, spider monkeys, and rhesus monkeys) have been under observation for up to 10 months. Histological studies thus far completed include 4 rabbit, 8 cat, and 25 monkey splices, in addition to 30 monkey biopsies.

Results. Only in one rabbit and one monkey nerve has the arterial link failed to hold. In all other cases, nerve regeneration has occurred much in the same way as described for the rat under similar conditions. Criteria of success were the rate and completeness of functional recovery and the histological appearance of the union. From the functional standpoint, the results were optimal; histo-logically, there was a greater proportion of cases with some fiber entanglement than was seen in the rat—a difference readily accounted for by the greater variability in the operative handling of larger nerves. An average case is illustrated in Fig. 2 showing a sleeve-spliced rabbit sciatic nerve 2½ months after the operation; it represents the average in that the line of junction is more evident than in optimal cases, yet less than in the worst cases.

Nerves properly operated upon regenerate in the orderly fashion peculiar to arterial sleeve splicing:[1,2] the great mass of the regenerating fibers pass straight, unbranched, unobstructed across the gap into the distal stump, and there is neither fibrosis nor neuroma formation. This orderly regeneration pattern makes it possible for the majority of fibers of a given fascicle to remain together and, therefore, to reinnervate a relatively localized muscle group, instead of becoming dispersed over the whole denervated periphery at random, as commonly happens after ordinary sutures. As an experimental test of this fact, the following example may be cited:

The right tibial nerve of a spider monkey was severed in the proximal half of the thigh,

FIG. 2.

Rabbit sciatic nerve 2½ months after reunion with sleeve of frozen-dried artery. Bodian impregnation. × 12. This illustrates an average case considerably below optimum.

and the ends were spliced with a segment of frozen-dried artery from a spider monkey, which had been stored for 2 months, then rehydrated and kept in Ringer's solution in the refrigerator for 2 days before use. (The right peroneal nerve, likewise severed, had received a graft). When examined 6 months after the operation, motor function was completely recovered. The site of the nerve was then exposed and the tibial trunk proximal to the splice was split into 8 constituent fascicles. By stimulating these individually with induction shocks, 6 different and distinct motor effects were obtained, which demonstrates the preservation of fascicular topography in regeneration through the splice. The combined calf muscles of this animal weighed 56 g on the regenerated side and 52 g on the control side.

Branching and commingling of fibers at the junction result from defective operations, e.g., sagging arteries; slack nerves; overhanging epineurium or perineurium. Aside from greater irregularity of the fiber courses, regeneration seemed, however, unimpaired even in these instances.

The frozen-dried arterial sleeves persist as such for many months, perhaps indefinitely. They become partially repopulated by host cells. In contrast to live sleeves, their walls absorb a certain number of regenerating fiber branches. Homoplastic frozen-dried sleeves provoke no marked inflammatory reaction. However, adhesions are not uncommon, their extent depending more on the condition of the wound bed than of the artery. Heteroplastic frozen-dried arteries (macaque in spider monkey) cause heavier adhesions than do homoplastic ones. Keeping rehydrated arteries for a few days refrigerated in Ringer's solution does not seem to harm them. Fresh arteries stored for several weeks in aqueous solution of Merthiolate 1:1000 and then washed, proved less adequate. Other methods of preservation (boiling, alcohol, formaldehyde) are definitely contraindicated, as they transform the artery into a foreign body and deprive it of many properties essential for nerve splicing. Veins tried in the monkey have proved too flabby for the purpose. No artificial substitute has as yet been found that would come up to the standards of the arterial sleeve; they all fall short of one or more of the principal functions of the sleeve, which are:[2] to align the nerve ends; to permit longitudinal stress to act on the "scar"; to prevent dissipation of fibrinolytic agents from the gap and thus insure proper liquidity of the "scar"; and to keep fibrous tissue and other local growth from penetrating. Continued research may yet produce a synthetic sleeve answering these demands.

For end-to-end reunion of stumps under tensions greater than an arterial cuff can hold, means must be devised to reconcile the need for forcible approximation with the cardinal precept for good regeneration, viz., to keep the zone of union free from artificial intervention, particularly sutures. A solution may lie in approximating the stumps by means of a permanent loop of Tantalum or Columbium wire, stitched either through the nerve stumps or the epineuria at considerable distance (more than one inch) from the cuts, and then splicing the free ends with an arterial sleeve just as in unstretched unions. It may be expected that the gradual "give" at the points of attachment will place enough strain on the young tissue connecting the stumps to produce in it the desired longitudinal organization. Results of this operation will be reported on a later occasion. Experiments are also under way to determine the maximum length of a blood filled gap between stumps compatible with optimal nerve regeneration.

Summary. Results obtained with sutureless nerve reunion by means of cuffs of live or frozen-dried artery in 21 rabbit, 30 cat, and 81 monkey nerve splices have confirmed for the larger mammals the conclusion previously reached in the rat, that optimal nerve regeneration may be secured by this method.

Reprinted from Jour. Neurosurg., 1, 1944

SUTURELESS REUNION OF SEVERED NERVES WITH ELASTIC CUFFS OF TANTALUM*

PAUL WEISS

THE ADVANTAGES of using closely fitting sleeves as links between severed nerve stumps have been described previously.[5,6,7] The sleeves consisted of segments of artery, either fresh or frozen-dried and rehydrated. The experimental material on which the conclusions regarding the merits of the method were based included nearly 700 nerve unions in various animals (rat, over 500; rabbit, 21; fowl, 37; cat, 30; monkey, 81). Analytical studies of the healing and regeneration of nerves following sutureless splicing with arterial sleeves have demonstrated that the salient features to which this method owes its superiority are the following:[7]

(1) *Absence of Sutures.* This permits longitudinal traction to be transmitted directly from stump to stump through the tissue filling the gap, whereby the latter becomes converted into a system of parallel guide rails of strictly longitudinal orientation, over which the regenerating nerve fibers, sheath cells and blood vessels are then conducted into the distal stump without extensive branching, straying or confusion. The same longitudinal stresses turn invading connective tissue into an innocuous longitudinal course along the surface, thus preventing penetration of scar tissue into the space between the nerve stumps. Moreover, foreign body reactions, disorienting tissue whorls, and similar contingencies of sutures are precluded.

(2) *Confinement of Fluid.* A proper degree of liquidity of the tissue uniting the nerve stumps is prerequisite for nerve regeneration of optimal density. Liquid accumulates in the gap as a result of hemolysis, fibrinolysis, exudation from the nerve, and perhaps vascular transudation. The sleeve serves to prevent its dissipation.

(3) *Insulation and Protection.* The sleeve prevents adhesion between the nerve junction and the surrounding tissue, protecting the nerve against invasion by fibrous tissue and precluding the escape of nerve fibers.

Arterial sleeve-splicing shares feature (1) with the method of plasma suture,[4,8] feature (3) with many past and current procedures of nerve wrapping, but is unique in the combination of functions it serves.

It has been evident throughout this work that the clinical application

* The research reported in this paper was done under a contract, recommended by the Committee on Medical Research, between the Office of Scientific Research and Development and the University of Chicago. It was aided by the Dr. Wallace C. and Clara Abbott Memorial Fund of the University of Chicago.

Courtesies of Dr. K. S. Lashley, Director of the Yerkes Laboratories of Primate Biology at Orange Park, Florida, in providing the facilities for the monkey experiments; technical assistance by Dr. R. W. Sperry; and the courtesy of the Tantalum Defense Corporation in furnishing the test material are gratefully acknowledged.

219

of the principle of sutureless sleeve-splicing would be greatly facilitated if sleeves could be made from a material with physical and physiological characteristics similar to arteries, but more readily procurable. The success reported with the shielding of suture lines by tantalum foil[3] suggested that this material might be adaptable for the purpose.* This proved to be the case, as is illustrated in the following account.

METHOD

The problem was primarily a technological one, namely, to fashion tantalum foil into elastic cuffs of the caliber of nerves. Ordinary tantalum foil is highly pliable and unelastic. Unprotected exposure to heat makes it brittle. Yet, after some experimentation a heat treatment was finally discovered by which the foil could be molded into cylindrical rolls of the desired shape and resilience. The best results thus far have been obtained by the following procedure.

Tantalum foil, 0.00025 to 0.0005 inches thick, is wrapped around a cylindrical core which is to serve as heat conductor. The core consists of a central steel rod over which a fitting jacket of glass tubing is pulled. For each size of sleeve a matching size of core is used. The measurements of the foil are so chosen that it will cover two turns when rolled over the glass cylinder. Thin wire is wound around the tightly wrapped foil to keep it in place. The whole unit is then placed into an electric furnace for a specified period, the length of which varies with temperature, thickness of the foil, dimensions of the core and thermal properties of the latter, and must be determined empirically. A few seconds may decide the difference between success or failure. Underexposure leaves the foil unelastic, overexposure renders it brittle and useless. It will be noted that the inside of the foil is in contact with a heat conductor, while the outside is exposed to the radiant heat of the furnace.

When properly treated, the foil emerges from the treatment with changed properties. It has assumed the shape of a cylindrical coil of approximately the diameter of the core, has lost its pliability and instead become highly elastic. Owing to the fact that the outer turn has shielded the inner turn against direct heat radiation, the former turns out harder and more resilient than the latter. This gives the cylinder self-sealing capacity, inasmuch as the outer edge presses downward against the underlying turn, while the inner edge presses outward against the overlying turn. This asymmetry explains the fact that such a roll when forcibly uncoiled and allowed to recoil assumes the shape of an open spiral. To return it to its cylindrical shape, the originally inner edge must be tucked under the more highly curved outer turn. Each sleeve is to be allowed about one-half turn of overlap in its final form. This is achieved by trimming the outer edge.

Such sleeves are not only perfectly elastic, but have considerable structural strength. For instance, a tube, 27 mm. long and 3 mm. wide, made from foil 0.01 mm. thick, is able to withstand compression in the direction of its longitudinal axis up to 2000 g. without collapsing. After lateral compression by 700 g. pressure, it still resumes fully its cylindrical shape.

The sleeves must be chemically clean, for impurities along their surface would provoke tissue reactions.

In using these sleeves for the joining of nerve stumps or for junctions between nerve stumps and grafts, it has proved more convenient to treat them as tubes in the manner previously described for arteries, rather than by uncoiling and recoiling. One may use either a modification of the arterial splicing clutch[6] or adopt the following simplified procedure.

A bevelled thin-walled metal or glass canula, slightly wider than the nerve stump, is at-

---

* I owe my acquaintance with this material to Major W. P. Van Wagenen, M.C., A.U.S.

tached to a saline-filled syringe. The sleeve, slightly distended, is pulled over the canula. The nerve end is placed on the bevel, eased into the orifice, and finally sucked farther in by raising the plunger of the syringe. The sleeve can then be easily slipped from the canula onto the nerve stump, whereupon the nerve end is extruded from the canula by depressing the plunger. An air aspirator may be used in place of the syringe.

In the absence of special equipment, any hollow cone wide enough at its base to hold the nerve stump can be used as an aid in sliding the metal sleeve over. The width of the sleeve should be so chosen that it will fit the nerve closely without tightness. Elasticity and overlap allow for adjustment to local conditions. The length of the sleeve will vary with the requirements of the individual case, particularly the location of the lesion and the extent of nerve adhesions.

The actual linking of nerve stumps which can be approximated to within several millimeters is done as follows. The sleeve which is to serve as link is pulled to full length over the distal stump. In order to facilitate handling of the proximal stump, a shorter tantalum cuff of corresponding diameter is pulled over the proximal end, its rim flush with the cut surface. The longer sleeve is then pulled back from the distal stump and telescoped over the cuffed end of the proximal stump, as in the joining of two stovepipe segments. The grip of the sleeve on the nerve ends may then be tightened by a gentle wrapping movement or by a loop of silk drawn around it and left in place until coagulating blood which has seeped between the overlapping edges has sealed the tube. No further means of attachment are necessary if the sleeve is of sufficient length. Nerve ends in a well-fitting sleeve act like pistons, and the suction which their separation creates tends to hold them in place. The fact that moderate tension can thus be tolerated without risk of rupture of the link, is a major factor in the success of the ensuing regeneration process.

A gap of several millimeters between the nerve ends has been found quite acceptable. The maximum tolerable length compatible with good regeneration remains to be determined. Where force becomes necessary to bring the nerve ends within range, it should not be applied at the ends or within the sleeve, but at more remote levels; for instance, by a sling stitch of tantalum wire looped through both stumps well above and below the sleeve region. This loop should take up only the excess of stress, but must not be shortened to a degree where it would leave the nerve ends in between slack.

Spider monkeys and cats were used for the experiments. Peroneal and tibial nerves severed in midthigh were reunited with tantalum sleeves. The animals received only a thin coat of synthetic resin over the skin suture, but neither casts nor splints. Their movements were in no way restricted. Eight nerve unions were performed in monkeys, and twelve in cats.

RESULTS

Five monkey and six cat unions have thus far been examined, the oldest seven weeks after the operation. In none of them had the nerve stumps pulled loose in spite of the unrestrained exercise of the animals from the very first day after the operation. Only in two of the earliest cases had the sleeves crumbled, evidently owing to inexpert handling. In all other cases, the sleeves had remained unchanged.

There were no or only very slight adhesions between the nerve and the wound bed. A continuous fibrous nerve sheath was present. After its dissection the tantalum sleeve, covered by a very thin, smooth, transparent membrane, came into view. The ends of each sleeve had become walled off by rings of connective tissue continuous with the epineurium, undoubtedly due to the chronic irritation set up by the sharp rims. However, since these scars formed at a safe distance from the nerve gap, did not penetrate into the nerve, and had not given rise, at least not at this stage, to lateral adhesions, they do not seem to present a serious hazard. After slitting the thin cover membrane, the sleeve was grasped by its overlapping edge and stripped off, or rather unwound, from the nerve. It had lost none of its resilience. Its surface was slippery, apparently from serous fluid.

Removal of the sleeve bared the surface of the nerve junction. As early as five days post operative, the nerve ends were found reconnected by a cylindrical sheath which had grown along the inside of the sleeve. The interior was still highly fluid. At five and seven weeks post operative, the connection was firm. Except for its greater transparency, the level of the former gap could not be distinguished. The nerve in this re-

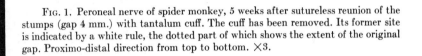

FIG. 1. Peroneal nerve of spider monkey, 5 weeks after sutureless reunion of the stumps (gap 4 mm.) with tantalum cuff. The cuff has been removed. Its former site is indicated by a white rule, the dotted part of which shows the extent of the original gap. Proximo-distal direction from top to bottom. ×3.

gion offered the aspect of a continuous cylinder (Fig. 1) with a perfectly smooth glossy surface without a trace of scar tissue or other unfavorable reaction against the metal.* The fact that the nerve can thus slide freely in the sleeve, constitutes one feature in which the tantalum cuff is superior to frozen-dried arteries, in which local adhesions of the nerve to the inner wall of the sleeve are not uncommon.

The microscopic picture bears out the macroscopic appearance of perfect reunion. Figure 2 illustrates the junction of a peroneal nerve as it appeared after the removal of the cuff without further trimming of the surface. One notes that no foreign body reaction or perineurial scar formation has occurred anywhere within the sleeve. For the rest, the picture speaks for itself. Specifically, the following points describe the character of the union.

(1) The gap has become bridged by a tissue which proceeded to form an integral link between the stumps, rather than merely a cementing scar.

(2) Sheath cell cords and nerve fibers have passed in straight parallel alignment through the gap into the distal stump and straight on down the latter.

(3) There is no profuse branching, straying and commingling of fibers at the level of the union.

---

* Concerning the indifference of tissues to tantalum, see Burke,[1] and Pudenz and Odom.[2]

(4) There has been no ingrowth into the junction of cicatricial connective tissue. All endoneurial and perineurial connective tissue has likewise been turned into a strictly longitudinal course, where it cannot impede nerve fiber growth.

(5) High liquid content of the tissue forming the junction has been preserved. This can be told directly from the loose texture of the tissue and also from its greater shrinkage during fixation, which gives it a

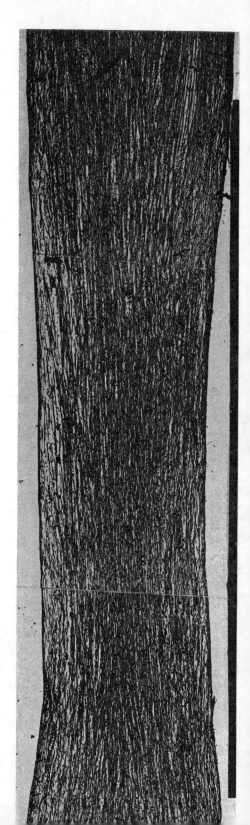

Fig. 2. Photomicrograph of a longitudinal section of the same nerve as in Figure 1. Silver impregnation after Bodian. The extent of the original gap between the stumps is indicated by the black rule on the margin. Note that the old perineurium of the stumps ends at the levels of the original cut surfaces, thus marking the limits of the former gap. Proximo-distal direction from top to bottom. ×43.

"waistline" appearance. In spite of the abundance of liquid channels, the mechanical firmness of the link is assured by the tensile strength of the longitudinal strands of endoneurial fibers serving as ties.[7]

(6) No local edemas, neuromas or gliomas have formed.

(7) Since the nerve fibers, in passing from the proximal to the distal stump, maintain a steady straight course, they will restore a more orderly pattern of connections between the centers and the periphery than would otherwise be possible. This may have an important bearing on functional recovery.[6]

(8) Vascularization of the junction has been ample. The main vessels have grown straight through, following the general longitudinal di-

rection, and have supplied the whole region with a network of capillaries. In fact, this vascular supply from the intraneural sources is so abundant that it makes the recurrent warnings against the wrapping of suture lines, on the grounds that such procedures prevent extraneural vessels from penetrating, appear wholly unwarranted.

Rate of axon downgrowth has not yet been established. After 5 weeks, the peripheral stump was densely populated with regenerated axons at a level 20 mm. beyond the original cut surface. There is no record of just how much farther they had advanced, except that they had not yet reached the next distal sample level, 55 mm. from the cut. The whole picture, however, is such that the later outcome can be predicted on the basis of past experience with many hundreds of nerve unions studied both histologically and functionally. Unions such as the ones described here will lead to prompt and full reinnervation of the periphery, free from the impeding and delaying effects of intraneural fibrosis. In view of the predictability of the outcome, presentation of the results in this early phase has seemed justified. The functional results will be reported at a later date.

The two cases mentioned above, in which the sleeves had become buckled up, were total failures. Holes had formed at the dents and scar tissue had penetrated freely through these openings. The interior was filled with a bloody soft mass, evidently a residue of repeated hemorrhages. Except for a few strands along undamaged parts of the sleeve wall, there was no firm connection between the stumps. The proximal stump ended in a neuroma. The failure of effective reunion was so patent that no histological study was made. Creased and dented sleeves are obviously a potential source of injury and irritation to the nerve. However, no further mishaps of this kind have occurred since those early accidents. Yet, it is well to keep in mind that the danger of such an occurrence would increase in the vicinity of a joint, calling for protective measures such as temporary fixation.

The contrast between the successful and unsuccessful cases makes it clear that the question of the merit of using tantalum—or any other material, for that matter—in the repair of nerves, cannot be answered in a general way. Much depends on how the material is being used. If used properly, tantalum sleeves seem to perform very adequately as links between unsutured nerve stumps.

The obvious limitation, that they are applicable to straightway unions only and would be unsuitable where nerves are subject to bending, e.g., at a joint, might in some cases be overcome by leaving the sleeve in place only just long enough to permit firm reunion of the stumps and the formation of a new nerve sheath, while the joint is in fixation, and then reoperating for removal of the cuff, which can be easily pulled out in one piece, with a single move, without danger to the nerve or its circulation. But there will undoubtedly remain certain classes of lesions in which the use of rigid sleeves will be impracticable.

Aside from the excellent frame they provide for nerve regeneration, tantalum sleeves simplify the technique of nerve union considerably, and thus save time. Moreover, they can be easily applied to nerves of even the smallest caliber which would defy neat end-to-end suture.

SUMMARY

A method is described by which tantalum foil can be fashioned into resilient self-sealing tubes, which may be used as cuffs for the sutureless linking of severed nerve stumps in the manner previously described for arterial sleeves.

Preliminary observations on monkey and cat nerves joined by this method have demonstrated that excellent reunion between the stumps with the properties required for optimal nerve regeneration may be achieved if the sleeves have been suitably shaped and properly handled.

REFERENCES

1. BURKE, G. L. The corrosion of metals in tissues; and an introduction to tantalum. *Canad. med. Ass. J.*, 1940, *43:* 125–128.
2. PUDENZ, R. H., and ODOM, G. L. Meningocerebral adhesions. *Surgery*, 1942, *12:* 318–344.
3. SPURLING, R. G. The use of tantalum wire and foil in the repair of peripheral nerves. *Surg. Clin. N. Amer.*, 1943, *23:* 1491–1504.
4. TARLOV, I. M., and BENJAMIN, B. Autologous plasma clot suture of nerves. *Science*, 1942, *95:* 258.
5. WEISS, P. Nerve regeneration in the rat following tubular splicing of severed nerves. *Arch. Surg., Chicago*, 1943, *46:* 525–547.
6. WEISS, P. Nerve reunion with sleeves of frozen-dried artery in rabbits, cats and monkeys. *Proc. Soc. exp. Biol., N. Y.*, 1943, *54:* 274–277.
7. WEISS, P., and TAYLOR, A. C. Histomechanical analysis of nerve reunion in the rat after tubular splicing. *Arch. Surg., Chicago*, 1943, *47:* 419–447.
8. YOUNG, J. Z., and MEDAWAR, P. B. Fibrin suture of peripheral nerves. *Lancet*, 1940, *2:* 126–128.

Reprinted from Jour. Neurophysiol., 6, 1943

PRESSURE BLOCK IN NERVES PROVIDED WITH ARTERIAL SLEEVES*

PAUL WEISS AND HALLOWELL DAVIS

THE SEARCH for an improved method of re-uniting severed nerve stumps has yielded what appears to be a superior method in the use of arterial segments as splicing agents (15, 16). The cut ends of the nerve are joined without suture inside of a snugly fitting sleeve of artery, which serves the multiple purpose of holding the nerve ends together, preventing fiber escape, branching and neuroma formation, and precluding the ingrowth of fibrous connective tissue detrimental to nerve regeneration. The success of the operation and of the subsequent regeneration depends largely upon the correct fit of the artery. If the artery is chosen too wide for the given size of nerve, it fails to seal the nerve ends, and the space left between tube and nerve invites fibrosis and nerve fiber escape. In order to avoid these hazards, one would feel tempted to use arteries with a lumen narrow enough to clamp down tightly on the nerve ends. Fresh arteries are sufficiently distensible to be fitted over a nerve of considerably larger diameter, so that a firm seal between nerve and artery could be insured. However, it was soon found out that such a tight fit was harmful in that it produced permanent compression of the underlying nerve. Moreover, some arterial sleeves which at the time of operation did not seem to compress the nerve, were at a later time found to have narrowed down appreciably, causing a bottleneck-shaped constriction (see 16, fig. 7). This was never observed when aorta had been used, but was quite common with carotid or femoral arteries; *i.e.*, vessels with a muscular wall. The tightening of the sleeve resulted from a gradual contracture of its wall, which may be ascribed to a direct response of the musculature to pressor substances in the blood. This is the more plausible as vascular muscles after denervation acquire increased sensitivity toward adrenalin (2).

In view of the potential clinical value of the sleeve splicing method, the syndrome of the constricted sleeve deserved more than passing attention. The histological analysis, which revealed a number of interesting facts of more general significance, will be presented in greater detail elsewhere (17). It was the purpose of the experiments reported in the present paper to ascertain the minimum size of artery compatible with undisturbed functioning of the nerve in its interior, as well as the functional disturbances, particu-

* The work described in this paper was done under a contract, recommended by the Committee on Medical Research, between the Office of Scientific Research and Development and the University of Chicago. It was also aided by the Dr. Wallace C. and Clara A. Abbott Memorial Fund of the University of Chicago. We are indebted to Dr. A. Cecil Taylor for assistance in the operations and to Miss Harriet Mylander for technical help in the electrical tests.

larly pressure block, caused by arteries below that tolerable minimum. For this purpose, long nerves, cut at a distal level, were threaded through the lumen of a small segment of artery, and then the blocking of conduction of impulses through that region was studied. Hermann (9) ascribes the earliest observations on pressure block of nerve conduction to Fontana (1797). The first work to overcome the technical inadequacies inherent in most of the earlier studies was that of Meek and Leaper (11; contains review of earlier literature), describing reversible block in frog nerves after application of uniform pressures of up to 90 pounds for less than five minutes.

Our own experiments consisted of two groups. In both a limb nerve of a rat was cut and a piece of artery was then pulled for some distance over the proximal stump. In one group, the effects of the sleeve on conduction along the nerve were studied immediately after the operation, while in the other, the examination was not made until the second week after the operation. Nerves prepared in this way were stimulated at the proximal end with "maximal" stimuli, and the resulting action potentials were recorded oscillographically from farther distal levels on either side of the arterial sleeve. Pressure block could thus be identified by the decline and eventual disappearance of the potentials beyond the sleeve. Sleeves which were not naturally constricted could be made to compress the nerve by the local application of adrenalin, and the gradual development of a pressure block could then be followed directly.

MATERIALS AND METHODS

A total of 10 white rats was used in the experiments. The sciatic nerve was exposed and either the peroneal or the tibial division was transected at the knee. The transected nerve was freed from its partner as far proximally as could be done without injury. Arteries from small donor animals had been dissected previously and kept in Ringer's solution on ice. Either the carotid or the proximal femoral artery was used. By means of a splicing clutch described previously (16), a segment approximately 5 mm. in length was slipped over the proximal nerve stump from its free end. Save for two cases examined immediately, all wounds were closed, and healed without complication. After a lapse of from 8 to 13 days, the operated nerves were again exposed, excised, and placed in a specially constructed stimulation chamber for electrical recording. All operations were done under nembutal anesthesia.

The stimulation cell consisted of a trough of lucite, cca. 1 cm. wide, 1 cm. deep and 14 cm. long. At intervals of 5 mm. silver wires crossed the trough. In the middle each wire was fashioned into a U-shaped receptacle for the nerve. Save for these bends, the wires were insulated over their full length with "Amphenol 901" cement. From the outside the wires were connected with the binding posts of a multiple selector switch box, the contacts of which were so arranged that by the turning of two dials any combinations of wires could be made to serve as stimulating electrodes and as leads. After its introduction into the chamber, the nerve rested freely on the U-shaped supports of the silver wires in air saturated with moisture.

Action potentials were amplified by means of a condenser-coupled amplifier (time constant 0.01 sec.) and were viewed and photographed on the screen of a cathode-ray oscillograph. With this apparatus it was not difficult to recognize repetitive impulses as a standing wave if their voltage was a microvolt or more. Measurements of latency from the stimulus artifact and of peak voltage were made on enlarged projections of the photographic records.

Stimuli were provided by a square-wave stimulating circuit that was triggered by the sweep circuit of the oscillograph. Pulses of less than 0.1 msec. duration were employed and were passed through a capacity-shielded transformer to reduce artifacts and render the stimuli diphasic. The stimuli were always adjusted to a strength slightly but definitely supramaximal for the A fibers. Their adequacy was verified frequently during each experiment.

Five of the tested nerves were prepared for histological sections. They were fixed in Bouin's fluid, impregnated with silver according to Bodian, with or without Mallory's Triple Azan Stain.

EXPERIMENTAL

A. *Pressure block by adrenalin constriction of fresh arteries.* In these tests oscillographic records were taken immediately after the arterial fragment was slipped over the nerve. Two cases were studied. The nerve was transferred to the stimulation chamber from Ringer's solution and excess fluid was blotted off. The nerve was crushed just proximal to the most distal supporting wire, which also served as one of the recording leads. The positions of stimulating electrodes, arterial sleeve, and recording electrodes are indicated in the diagrams accompanying fig. 1 and 2. After constancy of the response had been ascertained, a drop of adrenalin (1:1000) was placed on the arterial sleeve, and as soon as a diminution of the action potential spike beyond the sleeve became noticeable, a series of photographs was started. The elevation of the peaks of the response over the base line was used as an index of the volume of nerve fibers conducting through the sleeve. For easier comparison, percentage values instead of absolute values were used in making the graphs, with the amplitude of the "maximal" response at the beginning of an experiment set at 100 per cent.

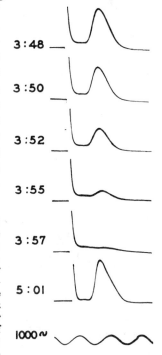

Fig. 1. Decline and recovery of oscillographic response recorded from nerve distal to constriction sleeve after adrenalin application and washing. Adrenalin was applied at 3:48. The times at which records were taken are indicated on the margin. Further details in text.

Case RA (Fig. 1 and 2) Segment of carotid artery (3 mm.) slipped over tibial nerve. Temperature 23.5°C. Records were taken alternately from a point distal to the sleeve (solid line) and a point near the proximal end of the sleeve (broken line). At both points, the action potentials dropped rapidly after adrenalin was applied (A). The reduction expresses the progressive interruption of conduction in the nerve fibers at the level of the sleeve. It is not due to a possible shunting effect of the drop of adrenalin placed upon the nerve, for neither does the application of the drop itself produce a decrease of the amplitude, nor does the blotting off of the drop (at B) arrest further decline. Eleven minutes after adrenalin administration conduction of impulses through the area of the sleeve has practically ceased. Even at the highest amplifications, there was no evidence of impulses passing through the compressed area. The pressure block has become complete. Records from the area proximal to the sleeve have, in the meantime, dropped to about one-fourth of their original size.

In order to test the reversibility of the block, the sleeve was rinsed with Ringer's solution while remaining on the electrodes (W). At first, the response returned to only about 10 per cent. Either the sleeve had failed to relax its grip on the nerve, or the nerve fibers had been permanently damaged, or finally, the constricted nerve segment being shut off from the medium by the sleeve, had become asphyxiated. The last explanation may be discounted in view of the shortness of the exposure. Moreover, the response recorded from a point proximal to the sleeve and fully exposed to the surrounding air likewise failed to recover. The sleeve was removed after 30 minutes (R) with the nerve left in its original position. Records taken 20 minutes later showed no significant recovery of conductivity. The nerve was then removed from the stimulation chamber and placed in Ringer's solution for the next

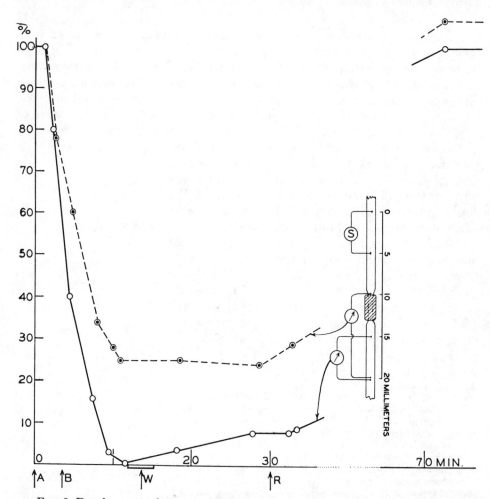

Fig. 2. Development of pressure block during adrenalin constriction of sleeve, as revealed by the decline of the amplitude of the action potentials recorded from the points indicated in the diagram, after maximal stimulation at S. Further explanation in text. Ordinates give percentage of the original size of the response at the beginning of the experiment. A, Adrenalin application. B, Blotting. W, Washing. R, Removal to Ringer bath.

twenty minutes. When returned to its original position in the stimulation chamber, it proved to have recovered full conductivity through the formerly compressed region
    The sluggishness with which the pressure block disappeared is attributable to two factors: firstly, even after washing the artery relaxes only gradually, and secondly, the nerve, being relatively plastic and unelastic in its transverse direction, returns to its original diameter but slowly.
    Case RB (Fig. 3) Segment of carotid artery (3 mm.) pulled over tibial nerve. Temperature

25°C. Adrenalin was put on the sleeve (A₁) and the excess fluid was sponged off three minutes later. Eleven minutes after the application of adrenalin, the response has dropped to 10 per cent of its initial size. The nerve was then washed by filling the whole stimulation chamber with Ringer's solution for three minutes (W). Records taken after the fluid had again been pumped out showed that conduction through the sleeve had not improved and that the response proximal to the sleeve, which had dropped to slightly over 40 per cent, had likewise held its level. The bath in Ringer's solution was then repeated for another three minutes but there was no perceptible change in the response. The artery was still

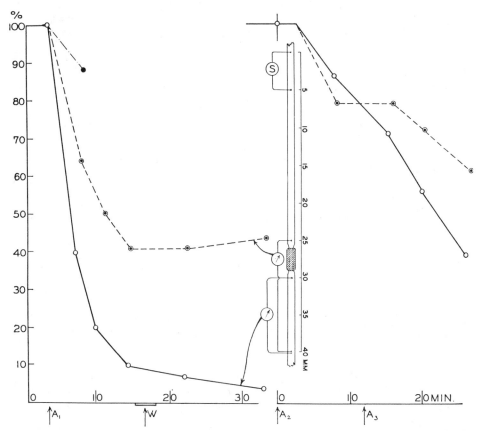

Fig. 3. Decline of the oscillographic response after adrenalin application (A) and constriction of the sleeve and recovery after prolonged washing. Symbols as in Fig. 2. Further explanation in text.

tightly clamped around the nerve with the total diameter of artery plus enclosed nerve still slightly smaller than that of the free nerve alone. Thirty-five minutes after the beginning of the experiment, the artery was stripped off. The resistance encountered in this manipulation proved that the sleeve was still actively contracted, and its mark on the nerve could be seen in the form of a conspicuous constriction. This region was then washed again thoroughly, but only an exceedingly small response had returned at 40 and 42 minutes.

The nerve was then transferred to Ringer's solution and placed in the ice box. The next morning, it was remounted in the stimulation chamber. Stimulation thresholds were found to be approximately the same as on the previous day and good responses were obtained at all points through the area of the former constriction. The temperature was 23.5°C. The arterial sleeve was then again slipped on to its position of the previous day.

Damage to some of the nerve fibers along the surface diminished the distal response as compared with the earlier determinations. In the graph, Figure 3, second half, the size of this response was set as 100 per cent. Adrenalin was then applied. As can be seen from the graph, the pressure block developed much more slowly than it did either in the same preparation on the previous day, or in case RA. Even 26 minutes after the first (A_2), and 15 minutes after the second adrenalin administration (A_3), the response distal to the sleeve had lost only 61 per cent of its amplitude. This slowness can be explained by the fact that a considerable number of fibers had been ripped off, so that the nerve was thinner than on the preceding day, rendering the arterial grip less effective.

Otherwise, case RB corroborates case RA in showing that a nerve which was exposed to a local compression block with complete interruption of conduction may gradually regain its conductivity after being released from the compressing agent. That the conduction block is due to the compression by the sleeve rather than to a direct effect of adrenalin, can be considered as certain. Not only has adrenalin never been shown to have any such blocking effect on nerves, but it has failed in our own experiments to affect conduction when placed upon the nerve directly.

The reason for the reduction of the response in the proximal nerve portion immediately adjoining the sleeve is not entirely clear. Above all, we do not know whether it indicates an actual drop in the number of conducting fibers or an increase in the shunting within the nerve, which reduces the fraction of the total action potential recordable from the surface, or possibly a distance effect of the kind observed by Gerard (6) after lcoal nerve asphyxiation. Tangl (14) and Stroebe (13) both have observed that strong compression of a nerve forces axonal substance back into the uncompressed portions of the fibers. This might cause an ascending disturbance of conductivity. However, it is doubtful whether the volume of fibers blocked proximal to the actual constriction would be large enough to account for a decline of such magnitude as was registered at this level (e.g., in case RB, within 5 minutes a 12 per cent decline 6 mm. proximal to the sleeve; Fig. 3, black dot). This leaves as main explanation of the proximal decline the fact of increased shunting.

One must bear in mind that all the interstitial liquid has been squeezed from the sleeve and thereby added to the liquid content of the nerve on either side. Since, owing to the shunting effect of extraneuronal fluid, the volume of action potential recordable from the surface varies with the ratio of axonal to non-axonal nerve content, any such increase of interstitial liquid for a given fiber volume means a reduction of the recordable fraction of generated potential. The increase in fluid content of the nerve near the constriction can actually be recognized as a slight bulbous swelling, and histological studies of chronic cases show the presence of voluminous edemas (Fig. 4, 5). It, therefore, seems reasonable to ascribe most of the observed reduction of the amplitude of the records at some distance from the compression to a registration artifact rather than to real interference with conduction.

B. *Cases with chronic constriction.* Table 1 lists the 8 cases in which an arterial sleeve has been present over the nerve for from eight to thirteen days prior to the oscillographic tests. In six of them (R45, R47A, R47B, R48, R50, R51) impulses were found to be conducted no farther than the proximal end of the sleeve. No trace of conduction into and through the sleeve was ever noticed, even at highest levels of amplification. In all these cases the artery, when first placed over the nerve, fitted tightly. In the days following the operation, it had undergone further contraction, a fact which became clear from the histological preparations.

Lack of conduction through the sleeve raises the question of whether there was merely a physiological pressure block or whether the nerve had undergone degeneration. Thus, five of the six specimens were sectioned and studied histologically. The impregnation of one (R51) was unsatisfactory; the remaining four showed various degrees of degeneration, which may be briefly described.

In general, the histological appearance of these nerves duplicates some of the features described in spliced and regenerated nerves with constricted sleeves kept for much longer periods (16). These are: (i) edema of the nerve proximal to the constriction; (ii) swelling of the axons proximal to the constriction; (iii) tight packing and loss of diameter of the nerve fibers within the compression zone. As these features are discussed in greater detail elsewhere, they may be illustrated here merely by a sample case. Figure 4 shows cross sections through the nerve of specimen R50, 10 days after putting on the sleeve. The levels from which these sections were selected are indicated in the diagram, Fig. 5. All sections being photographed at an identical magnifica-

Table I

Speci-men	Host weight	Nerve	Artery				Exam-ined after days	Edema	Conduction Block			Histology	
			Name	Weight of donor gr.	Fit				Permanent	After adrenalin		Sec-tions	Degener-ation
45	210	Per.	Fem.	30	Tight	12	+	+		Long.	Complete
46	210	Per.	Fem.	220	Loose	13	−	−	+	—	—
47A	180	Per.	Fem.	65	Tight	10	+ +	+		Long.	Complete
47B	180	Tib.	Car.	65	Tight	10	+ +	+		—	—
48	180	Per.	Fem.	60	Tight	10	+	+		Long.	Partial
49	180	Per.	Car.	80	Close	8	−	−		—	—
50	180	Tib.	Car.	80	Tight	10	+ +	+		Cross	?
51	180	Tib.	Car.	80	Tight	10	+ +	+		Nega-tive	—

tion, the variations in the diameter of the nerve become at once evident. Moreover, the graph, Fig. 5, gives the actual values of cross sectional area, as determined by planigraphy of camera lucida drawings, plotted over the length of the nerve.

Figure. 4A illustrates the almost unaffected proximal portion of the sciatic nerve; one recognizes the internal division of the nerve into a peroneal and a tibial branch, the latter being the experimental nerve to be followed in the subsequent figures. In the region of the edema, which begins about 3 mm. proximal to the sleeve, the nerve is swollen to nearly twice its proximal diameter (Fig. 4B), owing to the accumulation of large amounts of fluid in the endoneural spaces. This edema indicates, as is discussed more fully elsewhere (17), that there occurs in the endoneural spaces a persistent centrifugal seepage of fluid. The constriction of the sleeve, by obliterating the endoneural channels, causes a damming up of this fluid in front of the bottleneck, thus swelling the nerve—in the present case, to about three times its original cross sectional area. The appearance of the nerve inside of the sleeve (Fig. 4C) is in marked contrast to that of the edematous region. The fibers are tightly packed and there are few endoneural spaces left. All fibers are of small diam-

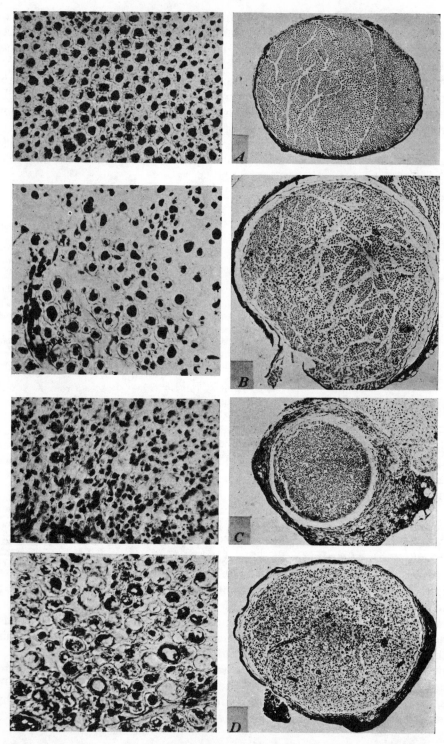

Fig 4. For legend see opposite page.

eter. Degenerating fibers, scarce at the entrance into the sleeve, appear in increasing numbers as one proceeds distally. At the exit from the sleeve, the nerve suddenly widens again and reaches a cross sectional area of about 50 per cent above normal (Fig. 4D). This peripheral swelling is definitely not due to an edematous condition, as the nerve fibers are contiguous and there is no excess interstitial fluid. Its main cause is the extensive degeneration going on in this area, the individual degenerating axons being transformed into swollen tubes of Schwann. The slight flanging of this portion, shown in Fig. 5, may be an elasticity effect. In our cases, true edematous swelling invariably appeared at the proximal, but never at the peripheral side of the constriction.

Many axons are widened at the level just proximal to the bottleneck, narrowing suddenly to the smaller caliber observed inside the sleeve. As will be shown in a subsequent paper, this phenomenon indicates that the column of axonal substance is subjected to a steady centrifugal pressure or flow.

The histology of the other 4 cases presents essentially the same picture. The only variation lies in the different proportions of intact fibers in the region beyond the sleeve. This can be better estimated in longitudinal than in cross sections. Three of the nerves, R45, R47A, and R48, have been sectioned longitudinally. All three have in common that many fibers within the compressed area are intact, with the axons continuous, of smooth contour, and well impregnated with silver; that as one proceeds peripherally, more and more fibers in various stages of typical Wallerian degeneration come into view; and that the transition

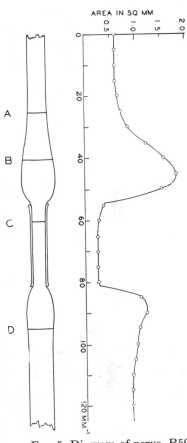

FIG. 5. Diagram of nerve, R50, constructed from measurements of the diameters at consecutive levels. In the right half of the figure, total cross sectional area is plotted over the length of the nerve from planimetric determinations made at 0.5 mm. intervals.

FIG. 4. Cross sections taken at four different levels of a tibial nerve constricted by a sleeve of artery (R50). The dimensions of the nerve and the positions from which the cross sections were chosen are indicated in correct proportions in the diagram, Fig. 5.

A, intact part of sciatic nerve; tibial division (experimental nerve) at left.
B, edematous portion of tibial nerve.
C, compressed region.
D, degenerating peripheral part.
Representative portions of each section are reproduced under higher magnification at the left.

from undegenerated to predominantly degenerated portions is fairly abrupt.
At levels peripheral to the sleeve, the proportion of intact fibers is rather

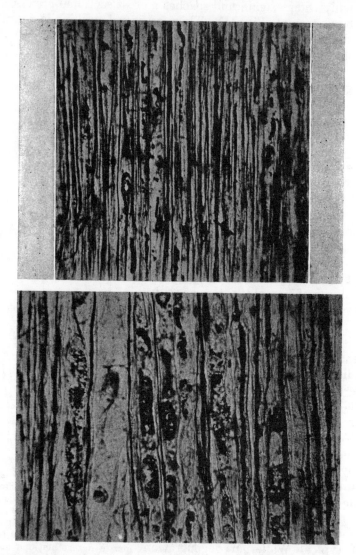

Fig. 6. Photomicrographs of longitudinal sections through the compressed (top) and
the farther distal portion (bottom) of the nerve, R47A. Note the number of intact fibers,
mostly of small caliber, in the sleeve region (top), and the presence of numerous intact
fibers of small and medium caliber, as well as of some regenerated fibers, amidst remnants
of degenerating fibers in the peripheral portion (bottom).

small. Moreover, in animals R45 and R48 all fibers present are extremely fine,
and there is every reason to assume that they represent regenerated rather
than the original branches. This they reveal by occasional branching, certain

irregularities of their course and their position relative to the degenerated Schwann tubes. On the basis of a most conservative estimate of regeneration speed of 2 mm. per day (8) the 10 to 12 days available to these fibers after the operation would have been ample for regeneration through the 5 to 6 mm. stretch beyond the end of the sleeve, which is all there was in our preparations.

In these two cases, the apparent extinction of the impulses in the sleeve region is, therefore, readily explained by the absence of sufficiently large and numerous nerve fibers to give a recordable response. The fine newly regenerated fiber branches were imbedded in such a mass of non-axonic shunting tissue that their potentials may well have been lost before reaching the recording electrodes.

In contrast, the third case, specimen R47A, contained a much larger proportion of intact fibers in its peripheral part, and most of these could be recognized as old rather than regenerated fibers. This is indicated by their position and, above all, size, some being of medium caliber with distinct sheath (Fig. 6). Since the volume of these intact fibers passing through the sleeve into the peripheral region was large enough to have yielded a fair action potential, the fact that no trace of such activity was discernible proves that these fibers were physiologically blocked in the compressed region.

Prolonged pressure block may, therefore, exist without destroying the integrity and continuity of the nerve fiber. The fact that only one in three cases has given this result in our series, clearly indicates that the margin of pressure between one which merely blocks the nerve physiologically and one which leads to morphological degeneration is not very wide.

C. *Adrenalin constriction in transplanted sleeves.* Two cases, R46 and R49, failed to show pressure block, and conduction through the sleeve region was wholly unimpaired. The sleeves in these cases were marked at the time of the operation as fitting "loosely" or "closely" rather than "tightly." Lack of constriction was demonstrated by biopsy. Table 1 shows that these two arteries were, relatively speaking, the largest of the set. In R46, the sleeve came from a donor of the same size as the host, and in R49, it was transplanted from an 80-gram donor to the peroneal nerve of a 180-gram host. As is shown by cases R50 and R41, the same size of artery over a tibial nerve would produce pressure block, but the tibial at this level is about twice the size of the peroneal.

Conduction through the sleeve of nerve R46 being perfect, this specimen was used to test the effectiveness of adrenalin in sleeves transplanted for nearly two weeks. The experiment was done in the same manner as described for cases RA and RB. Figure 7 shows the results (temperature 23° C).

Seven minutes after adrenalin application (A_1), the response has dropped to 25 per cent of the initial size. After rinsing with Ringer's solution (W_1), the response recovered to 88 per cent. After that, records were taken not only from points distal to the sleeve but also from within the sleeve and proximal to it, as indicated in the diagram. For the purpose of easier comparison of subsequent relative changes, the second readings from the proximal points were adjusted in the graph to the same relative strength as the simultaneous value of the distal record, *i.e.*, 88 per cent. After renewed adrenalin application (A₂), it took less than ten minutes for the distal response (at the 25 mm. mark) to decline again to about 20 per cent. Simultaneously, a less extensive decline was recorded from points 20 and 15 mm. After renewed washing (W₂), the response from beyond the sleeve failed to recover appreciably and the experiment was discontinued.

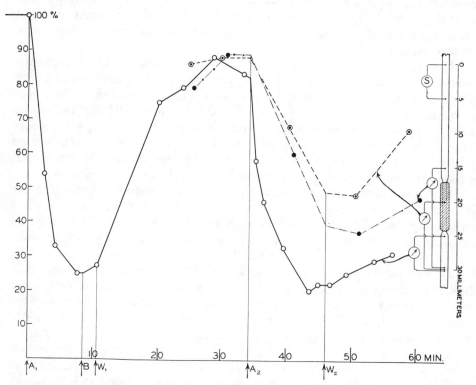

Fig. 7. Decline and recovery of action potential during adrenalin constriction and relaxation of an arterial sleeve transplanted 13 days previously. Electrode position indicated in diagram. Symbols and units as in Fig. 2 and 3. Further explanation in text.

The following conclusions can be drawn from this experiment. The transplanted segment of artery was still responsive to adrenalin after 13 days in the body. The time course according to which pressure block developed was of the same order in the fresh and in the transplanted artery. In contrast to experiments RA and RB, the first Ringer's bath produced a fairly rapid recovery of conductivity through the sleeve region. This may be ascribed either to the fact that the adrenalin was washed off before the constriction had reached its full extent, or to a slight weakening of the arterial wall after transplantation, permitting the nerve to redistend the relaxing artery and recover its former diameter sooner. At any rate, the experiment proves that a pressure block of short duration is promptly reversible, although after a second adrenalin constriction (A_2), washing failed to have the same restorative effect as before. The response recorded from within the sleeve region (Fig. 7, broken line) declined markedly less than that recorded from beyond the sleeve (to 49 per cent as compared with 18 per cent), which reveals that at least half of the fibers, even at the height of the compression, were not blocked until in the distal portion of the sleeve. The decline of the response at the 15 mm. mark (2 mm. proximal to the sleeve) can again be ascribed to the shunting effect of nerve fluid squeezed from the compressed area.

DISCUSSION

According to these experiments, an arterial segment pulled over a nerve may behave in three different ways, depending on its caliber. If wide enough, it may leave the nerve permanently undisturbed. If of medium width, it will not interfere with the nerve under ordinary circumstances but will clamp down and produce pressure block of varying intensity when exposed to adrenalin. If of smaller diameter than the nerve itself, it will produce permanent compression, resulting in loss of conductivity and, in more serious cases, degeneration of the nerve distal to the constriction.

In studying the development of the physiological pressue block oscillographically, we have tacitly ascribed any decline in electric response registered from the nerve beyond the constriction to the extinction of impulses in some of the fibers at the level of the block. This assumption, however, needs qualification. As illustrated in Fig. 5, compression by an arterial sleeve may reduce the nerve in its lumen to less than half its former size. Under this lateral compression, the interstitial fluid of the endoneural spaces is displaced longitudinally and squeezed into the parts of the nerve bordering on the compressed area. As this augments the non-axonal shunting material in the nerve, a certain reduction of the recordable action potential in this region should be expected. The size of any decline referable to this source can be estimated from the records taken proximal to the sleeve (dotted lines in Fig. 2 and 3). Comparing these values with the drop recorded distally, one realizes immediately that no more than a minor fraction of the latter can be ascribed to shunting.

Within 10 minutes after the initiation of the constriction of the sleeve by adrenalin, the passage of impulses through the constricted area may have become completely abolished. That the block of transmission is due to the compression, and to no other influence, is clear. Neither adrenalin applied to the nerve directly without a sleeve, nor the presence of a sleeve without adrenalin has any similar effect on the nerve. The sleeve may be left on the nerve for a considerable length of time without interfering with conductivity, yet upon applying adrenalin, the pressure block appears within several minutes.

Our graphs (Fig. 2, 3, 7) reveal a systematic trend in the development of the pressure block. They resemble logarithmic functions, which would indicate that the response declines in proportionate steps within successive intervals. The initial steepness of the decline can be attributed to the fact that the large caliber fibers are the ones to succumb to pressure block first (5).

Since the pressure within the sleeves must, for physical reasons, distribute itself evenly throughout the compressed area, the localization of the actual block must be explained in terms of differences in sensitivity of the nerve fiber to the acting pressure. In case R46, for instance, many fibers conducted more than half way through the compressed zone. Other fibers are blocked farther proximally. Denny-Brown (personal communication) finds that the first morphological changes under continued pressure occur at the nodes of Ranvier. In view of the fact, however, that nerve fibers with definite signs of Wallerian degeneration may still be capable of conducting impulses (10), a precise localization of the point of pressure block from purely morphological criteria may not be possible.

A question of considerable importance is whether or not nerve compression produces an actual change in the size of the axon. In the chronic experiments of our series, the nerve was compressed to less than half its original size (see Fig. 5 and 6). If such a diminution were to be achieved merely by the obliteration of the endoneural spaces without reduction of the size of the axons, at least half of the nerve cross section would have to consist of endoneural spaces. In the rat this is definitely not the case, and part of the observed shrinkage in our cases must, therefore, be ascribed to actual decrease in the diameter of the fibers. Our histological studies seem to bear out this contention. Nerves which have been under compression for from one to two weeks show total absence of larger fibers even in the most proximal parts of the sleeve where little degeneration has occurred (see Fig. 4C and 6). If the large fibers had been destroyed, their remnants would be plainly visible. Thus the only valid conclusion seems to be that the continued compression has reduced the fiber diameters to such an extent as to bring them all into the small or medium caliber class. Similar observations have been reported by Cajal (1, p. 302) after moderate ligation of nerves.

The fact that the arterial constriction has produced physiological pressure block on the one hand, and morphological degeneration of the fibers on the other, might suggest that a common alteration of the nerve underlies both phenomena. This view is contradicted, however, by the fact that a fair proportion of nerve fibers have been able to survive a pressure block of ten days duration (case R47A). At the end of this period, the fibers were intact morphologically, yet incapable of conducting impulses across the compressed area. This, then, proves that the local change which blocks transmission in the fiber does not necessarily entail degeneration of a physiologically isolated peripheral portion. A prediction to this effect was made by Cook and Gerard (4), and the same conclusion must be reached from numerous clinical observations of nerves which have become paralyzed by the pressure of scar tissue or other constrictions. In some instances, the mere operative removal of the scar tissue brought almost instantaneous relief of the paralytic condition and resumption of conduction in the nerve, a condition which could not possibly have been obtained if the blocked fibers had been in a state of degeneration. Likewise, some reports in the literature about crushed nerves quote time values for the recovery far too brief to have allowed for regenerative outgrowth of new fibers from the crushed area to the end organs. One would suspect, therefore, that in these cases, while the paralysis after crushing was complete, not all fibers may have been actually interrupted, the intact ones merely suffering from temporary pressure block.

The occurrence of degeneration of the peripheral parts of fibers within constricted sleeves indicates that the constriction has produced a trauma as severe as if the fiber had been transected or crushed. That Wallerian regeneration may occur even without the opening of the neurilemmal sheath has, of course been known from previous studies on ligated nerves (1, 13) and from the observations on beri-beri (3), and our present cases are merely another illustration. On the positive side, however, they give us little information about the actual cause of the degeneration. We cannot entirely exclude the possibility that ischemia may have been involved inasmuch as the strangling action of the sleeve shuts the peripheral nerve end off from circulation for as much time as is needed for collateral vascularization to become established. This, however, takes only a few days, and it is questionable whether this could cause degeneration. It is much more likely that the compression has arrested the centrifugal flow inside the axon of substances or factors vital for the maintenance of axonal integrity, much along the lines of Gerard's (7) and Parker's concept of degeneration (12). This flow can apparently still proceed in a state in which impulse conduction along the fiber is locally blocked. This we must conclude from the cases of partial degeneration with complete pressure block.

It is interesting to note that the symptoms of degeneration were much more evident in the nerve distal to the sleeve than within the sleeve itself, where the actual compression was taking place. This corroborates more extensive observations by Denny-Brown (personal communication). Cajal (1, p. 292) likewise notes that in ligated nerves the parts of the fibers directly under the ligature fail to break down. The fact is not easy to explain unless it were by the assumption that the pressure has not only paralyzed the conductive mechanism but also those properties of the nerve fiber and of the accompanying sheath cells which are responsible for the thorough transformations after trauma which we commonly call degeneration. We know that degeneration is an active process involving cell activities, and not a merely passive breakdown. It is possible that these progressive changes were inhibited either by lack of space or by interference of pressure with a more subtle mechanism.

In practical respects, these experiments underscore the importance of the correct choice of artery for nerve splicing. The choice must consider both the size of the lumen in proportion to the nerve caliber and the amount and contractility of the musculature of the walls. It can be seen from table 1 that only arteries above a certain size qualify for a nerve of given caliber. What appears as a comfortable fit at the time of the operation may yet later develop into a tight grip owing to the contracture of the wall of the arterial sleeve, possibly sensitized to adrenalin by denervation. Moreover, a splice which might leave the nerve undisturbed for most of the time might yet, at times of great emotion or otherwise raised adrenalin level in the blood, contract and produce a partial pressure block in the nerve with undesirable consequences to the patient.

In consideration of these facts, it would seem indicated to use splicing arteries with as little musculature as possible. This can be achieved in three ways: either so-called conducting arteries may be used, such as the aorta, proximal carotid, pulmonary, subclavian; being the largest arteries, these will, of course, be useful only in very special cases, when largest nerves are concerned and arteries can be obtained from infants or fetal donors. The second possibility is to strip much of the muscular layer from the elastic intima, which can be done with a certain amount of success. The third and by far preferable possibility is to destroy the contractility of the muscular coat by methods which will not interfere with the elasticity and consistency and those other properties of the arterial wall which make it uniquely suited as a splicing agent. A method recently developed for this purpose and consisting of freezing the artery at the temperature of liquid nitrogen, drying for a week or longer in a high vacuum over P_2O_5, and then rehydrating, has given excellent results in animal experimentation* and will be reported in detail on a later occasion.

Our results impose a certain caution in the interpretation of histological pictures of regenerated nerves, in that they show that a fiber of morphologically sound appearance may yet be inoperative physiologically. Consequently, histological continuity of nerve fibers between the proximal and distal stumps of a nerve does not necessarily imply passage of impulses. Specifically, in all instances in which the regenerated fibers pass through a relatively dense fibrous or sclerotic tissue, their conductive capacity may be questioned. One must assume that under these conditions many of the fibers are strangled by the progressive condensation of the surrounding matrix and subjected to chronic pressure block. The same force will prevent them from recovering the caliber of normal nerve fibers. It is presumably by this strangling action, even more than by the less favorable conditions it creates for nerve outgrowth in general, that fibrosis forms one of the chief obstructions to functional nerve restoration. One of the main advantages of a good arterial splice lies in preventing such fibrosis from occurring.

---

* The generous assistance of Professor Robert R. Bensley and Dr. Sylvia H. Bensley in freezing-drying the tissues is gratefully acknowledged.

SUMMARY

The strangling effect of sleeves of artery pulled over peripheral nerve on the underlying nerve fibers was investigated in limb nerves of the rat. Adrenalin applied to an arterial sleeve over a nerve produces rapid constriction and, as a result, progressive pressure block of conduction. The development of this block was studied oscillographically by stimulating the nerve proximal to the sleeve with "maximal" stimuli and recording the decline of the action potential led off from distal levels during various phases of the constriction. Most or all of the fibers are blocked within 10 minutes after the application of the adrenalin. The block is reversible after washing but conductivity returns only very slowly.

Sleeves pulled over nerves of much larger caliber and left for from one to two weeks produce pressure block with total or partial degeneration of the nerve fibers distal to the level of compression. The nerve proximal to the constriction is characterized by edema, resulting from the damming up of endoneural fluid, and by swelling of the axis cylinders. Degeneration within the compressed area itself is restrained, but becomes extensive at levels distal to the sleeve. Numerous fibers may persist throughout the compressed area in histological integrity in spite of chronic pressure block. Likewise, fiber regeneration occurs throughout the compressed area.

Sleeves of wide caliber, which have not affected the enclosed nerve during the period of transplantation, produce reversible pressure block upon application of adrenalin much as do freshly transplanted sleeves.

The bearing of these findings on the method of splicing severed nerves by arterial sleeves is discussed.

REFERENCES

1. CAJAL, S. RAMON y. *Degeneration and regeneration of the nervous system*. Oxford University Press, 1928.
2. CANNON, W. B. A law of denervation. *Amer. J. med. Sci.*, 1929, *198*: 737–750.
3. CLARK, E. Regeneration of medullated nerves in the absence of embryonic nerve fibers, following experimental non-traumatic degeneration. *J. comp. Neurol.*, 1914, *24*: 61–111.
4. COOK, D. D., and GERARD, R. W. The effect of stimulation on the degeneration of a severed peripheral nerve. *Amer. J. Physiol.*, 1931, *97*: 412–425.
5. GASSER, H. S., and ERLANGER, J. The role of fiber size in the establishment of a nerve block by pressure or cocaine. *Amer. J. Physiol.*, 1929, *88*: 581–591.
6. GERARD, R. W. The response of nerve to oxygen lack. *Amer. J. Phsyiol.*, 1930, *92*: 498–541.
7. GERARD, R. W. Nerve metabolism. *Physiol. Rev.*, 1932, *12*: 469–592.
8. GUTMANN, E., GUTMANN, L., MEDAWAR, P. B., and YOUNG, J. Z. The rate of regeneration of nerve. *J. exp. Biol.*, 1942, *19*: 14–44.
9. HERMANN, L. *Handbuch der Physiologie*, 1879. (See vol. 11, p. 95.)
10. HOLOBUT, W. S., and JALOWY, B. Die De- und Regeneration des peripheren motorischen Nervensystems auf einer morphologisch-funktionellen Grundlage. *Z. f. Zellforsch*, 1937, *25*: 541–564.
11. MEEK, W. J., and LEAPER, W. E. Effects of pressure on conductivity in nerve and muscle. *Amer. J. Physiol.*, 1911, *27*: 308–322.
12. PARKER, G. H., and PAINE, V. L. Progressive nerve degeneration and its rate in the lateral-line nerve of the catfish. *Amer. J. Anat.*, 1934, *54*: 1–25.

13. STROEBE, H.   Experimentelle Untersuchungen über Degeneration und Regeneration peripherer Nerven nach Verletzungen. *Beitr. path. Anat.*, 1893, *13:* 160–278.
14. TANGL, F.   Zur Histologie des gequetschten peripheren Nerven. *Arch. mikr. Anat.*, 1887, *29:* 464–470.
15. WEISS, P.   Re-union of stumps of small nerves by tubulation instead of suture. *Science*, 1941, *93:* 67.
16. WEISS, P.   Nerve regeneration following tubular splicing of severed nerves in the rat. *Arch. exp. Surg.*, 1943, *46:* 525–547.
17. WEISS, P.   Endoneural edema in constricted nerves. *Anat. Rec.*, 1943, *86* (in press).

REPAIR OF PERIPHERAL NERVES BY GRAFTS OF FROZEN-DRIED NERVE.*

PAUL WEISS AND A. CECIL TAYLOR.

Orientation, growth rate and grouping of growing nerve fibers are determined by the biophysical and biochemical constitution of the interfaces along which they advance.[1] Their most favorable growth medium is degenerated peripheral nerve.[2] Accordingly, peripheral nerve fragments are the best means of bridging traumatic nerve gaps.[3] In mammals, autografts can be fully, homografts adequately successful;[4] heterografts are largely discredited.[4,5] Nerve grafting in man has met

with the difficulties of (1) growth-obstructing fibrosis of the distal suture line, and (2) unavailability of grafts. The former may be obviated by resection of the barrier,[6] or possibly completely avoided if sutureless nerve splicing by arterial sleeves[7] should prove as successful in man as it has been in animals. The supply difficulty is more serious, since commonly no source other than the patient's own intact nerves is available. In order to avoid having to sacrifice a "minor" nerve for the repair of a more vital one, several authors have tried preserved or fixed nerves. Storage in petrolatum[8] leaves the grafts viable, but presumably not indefinitely. Alcohol-fixed grafts[8,9] lead to poor regeneration,[5] formalin-fixed grafts to complete failure.[9]

Basically, these past failures are attributable to the denaturation of the grafts. Therefore, one of us (P. W.) thought of trying a preserva-

* Work done under a contract, recommended by the Committee on Medical Research, between the Office of Scientific Research and Development and the University of Chicago; also aided by the Dr. Wallace C. and Clara A. Abbott Memorial Fund of the University of Chicago. The generous cooperation of Professor Robert R. Bensley and Dr. Sylvia S. Bensley in the technical phases of the experiments is gratefully acknowledged.

1 Weiss, P., *Growth*, 1941, **5**, 163.

2 Young, J. Z., *Physiol. Rev.*, 1942, **22**, 318.

3 Stookey, B. P., *Surgical and Mechanical Treatment of Peripheral Nerves*, Phila. and London, 1922; Pollock, L. J., and Davis, Loyal, *Peripheral Nerve Injuries*, New York, 1933.

4 Sanders, F. K., and Young, J. Z., *J. Anat.*, 1942, **76**, 143.

5 Sanders, F. K., *Brain*, 1942, **65**, 281.

6 Davis, L., and Cleveland, D. A., *Ann. Surg.*, 1934, **99**, 271.

7 Weiss, P., *Science*, 1941, **93**, 67; *Arch. Surgery*, 1943, **46**.

8 Huber, G. C., *Surg. Gynec. Obstet.*, 1920, **30**, 464.

9 Nageotte, J., *L'organisation de la matière*, Paris, 1922.

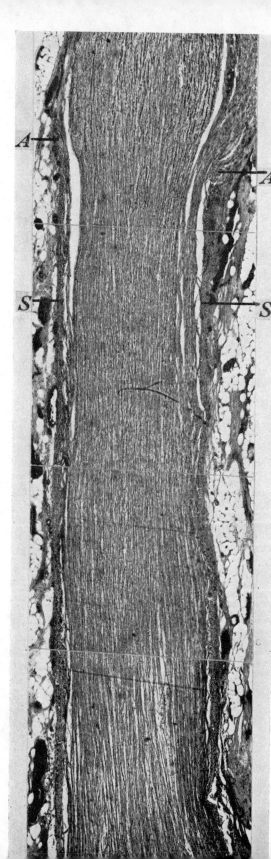

FIG. 1.
Regeneration through frozen-dried-rehydrated nerve graft sleeve-spliced to proximal stump of tibial nerve in rat, 127 days after operation. A, proximal end of arterial splicing sleeve. S-S, original level of fusion of proximal stump and graft.

tive, but non-denaturing treatment: the Altmann-Gersh freezing-drying method[10] used with great success in histology and histochemistry.[11] This method preserves microstructure and major biochemical (e.g., enzyme) constitution without essential alteration. This very feature determines its suitability for the preparation of nerve grafts.

Our procedure is as follows: Nerves dissected aseptically are dropped into Isopentane[12] immersed in liquid nitrogen (–195°C), where they freeze instantaneously, and transferred to high vacuum and mercury pumps for about one week of dehydration over P_2O_5 at –40°C. The dry specimens are stored in sealed sterile containers. Before use, they are rehydrated in vapor at –40°C or in Ringer's solution in vacuo at room temperature. They resume their normal appearance and major histological characteristics,[13] including specific staining reaction (silver impregnation and Mallory Triple Azan).

Segments of these "devitalized" nerves of about 1-2 cm length were grafted into gaps of hind limb nerves of 38 rats, 4 cats, and 18 monkeys. These grafts were spliced to the nerve stumps by 2 short arterial sleeves,[7] or a single long sleeve containing the graft. Twenty-nine rat nerves (21 homoplastic, 8 cat-to-rat) have thus far been studied microscopically, and a few oscillographically, from 6 days to 18 weeks after the operation.

Homoplastic grafts heal and promote regeneration much as does live nerve. The regenerating sheath cells and nerve fibers invade them promptly, traveling in straight parallel courses, without appreciable branching or confusion. Fig. 1 shows a typical case, 4 months after grafting: regeneration is so perfect that there is no evidence of the old proximal "suture line" (level marked S-S). The regenerated fibers regain caliber (Fig. 2), impulse conduction is restored, and motility and sensitivity return. Nerves predegenerated

[10] Gersh, I., Anat. Rec., 1932, 53, 309.
[11] Bensley, R. R., and Gersh, I., Anat. Rec., 1933, 57, 205.
[12] Hoerr, N. L., Anat. Rec., 1936, 65, 293.
[13] Hoerr, N. L., Anat. Rec., 1936, 66, 81, 91.

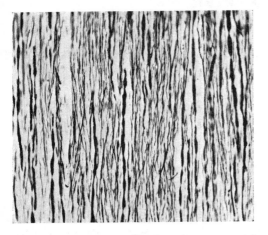

Detail from Fig. 1, showing the regenerated nerve in the zone of the graft. × 230.

FIG. 2.

before treatment do not seem superior to undegenerated ones. Details will be reported later. Sclerotic islands present in a few grafts may tentatively be ascribed to imperfections in the freezing or rehydration process.

Most devitalized heteroplastic grafts behave like foreign bodies. However, masses of nerve fibers use their oriented surface as pathway.

The results indicate that the biophysical and biochemical benefits to regenerative nerve growth inherent in peripheral nerve are essentially preserved in the freezing-drying process. The fitness of devitalized nerve as graft brings the supply problem in nerve grafting nearer its solution. Banks of assorted nerve sizes stored in the dry condition could readily fill a steady demand.

Reprinted from TRANSPLANTATION BULLETIN, Vol. 1, 98–99, 1954

Storage of Transplants

PAUL WEISS

The growing interest in the use of preserved grafts and the consistent absence in the pertinent literature of reference to the war-time work of our laboratory, which, to the best of my knowledge, inaugurated the grafting of quick-frozen and dehydrated tissues, prompts me to present in the following a brief annotated bibliography of these experiments.

WEISS, P., and A. C. TAYLOR. Repair of peripheral nerves by grafts of frozen-dried nerve. Proc. Soc. Exp. Biol. & Med., 52:326–328, 1943. (Description of technique of freezing-drying, preserving and rehydrating nerve fragments for grafts; with a recommendation for "nerve banks").

WEISS, P. Experiments on nerve repair. Trans. Am. Neurol. Assoc., 42–45, 1943. (Preliminary testing of "nerve banks" in experiments on monkeys).

WEISS, P. Nerve reunion with sleeves of frozen-dried artery in rabbits, cats and monkeys. Proc. Soc. Exp. Biol. & Med., 54:274–277, 1943. (Report on the use of frozen-dried, preserved and rehydrated artery in 21 rabbits, 30 cats and 81 monkeys, including reference to the fate of frozen-dried preserved arterial grafts after heteroplastic transplantation, storage and various types of preservation).

WEISS, P. Functional nerve regeneration through frozen-dried nerve grafts in cats and monkeys. Proc. Soc. Exp. Biol. & Med., 54:277–279, 1943. (Report on the results with frozen-dried, stored and rehydrated nerve grafts in cats and monkeys).

TAYLOR, A. C. Apparatus for the freezing-drying of tissues for storage. J. Lab. & Clin. Med., 29:657–663, 1944. (Description of a simplified freeze-drying apparatus for tissue fragments for graft banks).

WEISS, P. The morphogenetic properties of frozen-dried tissues. Anat. Rec., 88 (supplement): 48, 1944. (Properties of frozen-dried grafts of liver, cartilage, bone, muscle in amphibians).

WEISS, P., and A. C. TAYLOR. Transplantation of frozen-dried cornea in the rat. Anat. Rec., 88 (supplement): 49, 1944. (Results obtained with the grafting of frozen-dried and preserved cornea of the rat).

TAYLOR, A. C. The rates of freezing, drying and rehydration of nerves. J. Cell. & Comp. Physiol., *25*:161–173, 1945. (Investigation of the time course of freezing, dehydration and rehydration of grafts in relation to different techniques of treatment).

BOELL, E. J. Cholinesterase activity of peripheral nerves. J. Cell. & Comp. Physiol., *25:* 75–84, 1945. (Data on the rate of rehydration and residual cholinesterase activity in frozen-dried and stored nerve as functions of freezing rate).

WEISS, P., and A. C. TAYLOR. The viability of isolated nerve fragments and its modification by methylene blue. J. Cell. & Comp. Physiol., *27*:87–104, 1946. (Extension of the viability of stored tissue fragments by methylene blue treatment).

LEOPOLD, I. H., and F. H. ADLER. Use of frozen-dried cornea as transplant material. Arch. Opthalmol., *37*:268–276, 1947. (Results with the use of frozen-dried, stored and rehydrated cornea as transplant in rabbits).

The purpose of this listing is simply to help investigators in this field to locate scattered references to data that might be useful to them in their work.

Reprinted from *Journal of Neurosurgery*
1946, Vol. III, No. 5, pages 375-389

GUIDES FOR NERVE REGENERATION ACROSS GAPS*

PAUL WEISS, Ph.D., and A. CECIL TAYLOR, Ph.D.

THE PROBLEM of how to bridge nerve gaps that cannot be further reduced by manipulative procedures (mobilization, rerouting, stretching, etc.) has not yet been adequately solved. The results of nerve grafts in man have been disappointing,[3,4,5] and though improvements in technique or the use of devitalized undenatured grafts [10,15] might yet bring better success, the prospects are so uncertain that it is indicated to explore other alternatives. Several attempts in that direction have been made in the past. Various tissues, living or fixed, as well as artificial structures, organic or inorganic, have been tried as guides for regenerating nerve fibers, mostly without significant success. As has been pointed out in a recent review of this subject by Weiss,[12] most of the former failures can be explained by errors of technique, often based on misconceptions about the mechanism of nerve regeneration. We have, therefore, continued the search for improved methods on an experimental scale, and the results are summarized in this article.

On a previous occasion,[12] brief mention was made of experiments on the bridging of nerve gaps by arterial tubes filled with blood. While resembling superficially some older methods of "tubulation," these experiments observed more closely the known requisites of nerve regeneration, and hence, yielded markedly better success. A more detailed account of these experiments is presented in the following.

TUBULATED BLOOD BRIDGES IN THE RAT

Pieces were cut out from various nerves of rats (sciatic, peroneal, vagus) leaving gaps of about 10 mm. in length. The nerve ends were then fitted into a tube of artery of proper length and width by the technique described previously.[8] The empty part of the tube was then filled with blood or some other medium to be tested, guarding against the introduction of air bubbles. Experience has shown that fillings of Ringer's solution or blood plasma lead to fibrosis with obstruction of nerve regeneration. Therefore, only gaps filled with whole blood will be considered here.

Seven rats thus operated upon were biopsied after from 4 to 17 weeks. The experimental nerves were studied histologically (Bodian's silver impregnation). In the older cases, recovery of function had occurred but was decidedly inferior to that observed after end-to-end union or even after the use of frozen-dried grafts.[15] Aside from technical accidents (slipping of one of the nerve ends from the tube in one case), the method had inherent defects, which were revealed by the microscopic study.

* This work was done under the direction of Dr. Paul Weiss under contracts between the Offices of Scientific Research and Development (Committee on Medical Research) and of the Surgeon General, United States Army, and the University of Chicago. It was also aided by the Dr. Wallace C. and Clara A. Abbott Memorial Fund of the University of Chicago.

In a number of cases, the blood-filled part of the artery had collapsed, presumably because of leakage; the wall was creased longitudinally, with practically no lumen left. A narrow strand of dense connective tissue, sometimes containing a large longitudinal blood vessel, occupied the limited central space, and regenerating nerve fibers had not been able to penetrate it.

In cases in which the lumen had remained wide open, nerve regeneration across the gap had proceeded satisfactorily for varying distances, but then been impeded by islands of heavily fibrosed or areolar tissue. As already noted in previous similar experiments,[17] the orientation of the cellular strands and nerve fiber bundles was remarkably straight.

On the basis of earlier experiments,[16] we thought that the formation of fibrous blocks could perhaps be prevented by increasing the fibrinolytic potency of the initial clot through the admixture of large masses of leukocytes, taken from the buffy coat (stratum between red cells and plasma) of centrifuged homologous blood.

TUBULATED BLOOD BRIDGES IN THE CAT

In five cats (F7–11), pieces were cut out from the tibial or peroneal nerves in midthigh, leaving the stumps after retraction separated by gaps of 20, 18, 10, 28 and 25 mm., i.e., fifteen to thirty times as long as the width of the nerves. The ends were introduced into a matching segment of carotid artery, which was then filled with the modified blood. Except for cat F11, in which one nerve end was found at autopsy to have slipped out, the operations and subsequent recovery histories were satisfactory. Brief case descriptions follow.

Cat F7. Gap in tibial nerve, 20 mm. long, bridged with carotid artery (kept refrigerated in Ringer's solution for 3 days), filled with blood plasma and erythrocytes from centrifuged heparinized blood in a volume ratio of 2:1 and an added amount of buffy coat.

At 58 days p.op., the gastrocnemius was well palpable, but active function was doubtful. Active plantar flexion was definitely present at 105 days p.op.; it was still subnormal in strength at 202 days, but well recovered after one year; even then, the animal, digitigrade for most of the time, would occasionally relapse into a few plantigrade steps.

At biopsy (393 days p.op.), the artery was found to have narrowed so as to cause a "bottleneck" with consequent bulbous enlargement of the proximal stump;[9] there was no distal swelling. The muscle weights were 27.8 gm. for the tibial group, and 8.3 gm. for the peroneal group. Since the opposite leg had been subjected to another operation, it could not be used as control for muscle weights. But the weight ratio of 3.35 between tibial (reinnervated) and peroneal (undisturbed) muscles in the experimental leg is approximately the same as that of normal legs, hence indicates full weight recovery of the reinnervated muscles.

Microscopic examination: The nerve in the area of the former gap has a characteristic pattern, differing from that observed after regeneration over short gaps,[8] but even more strikingly from that noted in gaps filled with scar tissue. It differs from the former in that it is less well oriented and contains more connective tissue, but its constitution is much nearer that of normal nerve than would ever be obtained in ordinary scar tissue. The regenerated nerve fibers are grouped into large bundles which are separated by partitions of connective tissue thicker than regular perineuria. The general direction of these bundles is longitudinal, but not straight; they interweave and give the nerve a braided appearance. Fig. 1 shows a longitudinal section through this region. The most significant difference between this type of regeneration and that in ordinary scars is that the nerve fibers are assembled into well organized strands with plenty of rather liquid (light colored in Fig. 1) spaces for the expansion and addition of new fibers, and that the connective tissue runs parallel to, and in between, the channels, instead of forming solid blocks across. The transition between this new bridge tissue and the old nerve stumps is continuous and smooth. Only at the transition to the distal stump, the tissue assumes a denser consistency, with collagen deposits inside the nerve bundles. The distal stump itself was well filled with regenerated fibers, and sample cross sections (osmic acid) at various levels down to the ankle reveal abundant reinnervation and good myelinization. Fiber sizes in these distal nerve samples, however, were subnormal, with the majority of fibers measuring less than 3μ, a fair number up to 5μ, and only a few between 5 and 7μ. This deficit is evidently a result of the compression to which the fibers are subjected

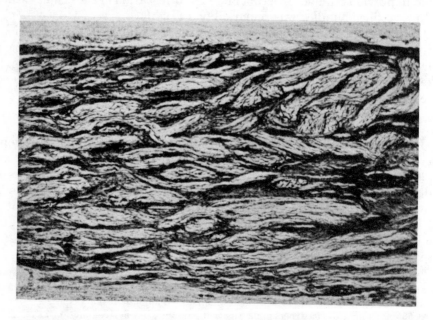

Fig. 1. Longitudinal section through the whole width of the regenerated nerve portion in the region of the former gap (F7), showing braiding of nerve bundles. Bodian and Mallory stain, ×98.

in the more compact fibrotic zone just mentioned, since lack of space for expansion anywhere along the course of a nerve fiber prevents the whole farther distal portion from growing in width.[18]

Cat F8. Gap in tibial nerve, 18 mm. long, bridged with kitten aorta filled with local blood. It was attempted to add some buffy layer to the clotting blood through a side branch of the aorta, but upon withdrawing of the pipette most of it spilled back, so that the gap filling in this case consisted essentially of unmodified blood. At 8 weeks p.op., signs of recovery appeared as feeble plantar extensions and palpable gastrocnemius contractions. Five weeks later, the animal died.

Autopsy: The nerve lay in a very smooth bed with no major adhesions. Upon slitting the sleeve longitudinally, a smooth cylindrical nerve segment was found to have formed over the former gap. No demarkation could be seen between this new segment and the former stumps. The weight of the calf muscles was still only 40 per cent of that of the control side, three months being too short a time for complete recovery.

Histological examination: Nerve fiber regeneration of normal density, oriented essentially longitudinally, in bundles braided as described in the preceding case. Some endoneurial fibrosis, which had affected the diameter, but not the number, of the regenerated fibers. The distal stump was well neurotized.

Cat F9. Gap in peroneal nerve, 10 mm. long, bridged with coeliac artery of kitten, filled with whole blood and buffy coat from heparinized kitten blood; sleeve sealed to epineurium of stumps by diathermic electrocoagulation. Eight weeks p.op., toe spreading and withdrawal dorsiflexion had reappeared and kept steadily improving in strength. Biopsy after one year showed moderate adhesions and slight bulbous enlargement of the nerve indicative of a too tight sleeve. Muscle weight was fully recovered (weights of the combined peroneus and tibialis anticus muscles: 11.4 gm. on the experimental, 11.3 on the control side).

Histological examination: Full volume of fiber regeneration with little weaving and fairly straight longitudinal orientation (Fig. 2). Only a trace of fibrosis near entrance to distal stump; the latter fully neurotized. The superiority of this case over the two previous ones in

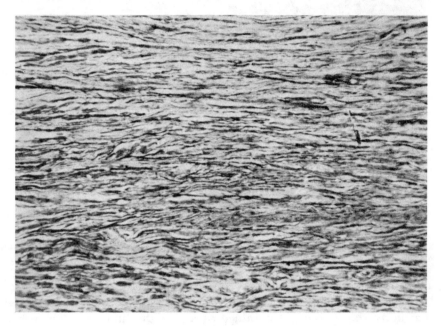

Fig. 2. Portion of longitudinal section of regenerated nerve segment in the former gap region (F9); showing straight fiber course. Silver impregnation after Bodian, ×185.

regard to straightness of the fiber course can be correlated with the shortness of the original gap (10 mm.).

Cat F10. Gap in peroneal nerve, 28 mm. long, bridged with kitten carotid filled with a mixture of plasma and erythrocytes from heparinized centrifuged kitten blood in a ratio of 1:4, with additions of buffy layer. A tantalum wire loop, threaded through the nerve stumps for holding purposes, was removed 8 days p.op. At that time, the artery appeared somewhat flattened. At 10 weeks p.op., dorsiflexion was definite, toe spreading indicated. At 19 weeks p.op., when the animal was sacrificed, function was recovered, though still somewhat weaker than on the control side.

Autopsy: Distal two thirds of the sleeve appear partly collapsed. Weight of dorsiflexor muscles (peroneus and tibialis anticus: 5.65 on experimental side, 7.95 on control side, i.e., only 71 per cent weight recovery.

Histological examination: Longitudinal folds of sleeve are evidence of the partial collapse mentioned above; however, unlike the more severe cases of collapsed sleeves described in earlier reports,[8,14] the lumen had remained sufficiently wide to accommodate copious nerve regeneration. The fibers are again grouped into small fascicles separated by fibrous partitions and slightly braided. But, on the whole, the fiber course is remarkably straight and unconfused (Fig. 3). No fibrotic foci have developed in this case. Cross sections through the regenerated nerve at the ankle (osmic acid) show most fibers still of relatively small diameter, few above 3μ. (Regeneration distance from cut to ankle was 160 mm., total regeneration time 131 days.)

FIG. 3. Portion of longitudinal section of regenerated nerve in former gap (F10), showing straight fiber course without much braiding. The wall of the arterial sleeve can be seen. Bodian, ×190.

These results prove that gaps of several centimeters can be successfully bridged if the nerve fibers are offered an oriented bed of blood with augmented liquefying potency, contained in a straight tube. The regenerated nerve contains large streams of fibers, not merely those insignificant trickles occasionally found in the scars between separated, but unbridged, stumps. Since there has been no appreciable decline in the volume of regenerated fibers over gaps of nearly 3 cm., there is no reason to doubt that regeneration would have continued over even greater distances. However, the technical difficulties, particularly the danger of collapse, would mount rapidly with increasing length of the free portion of the sleeve. It was mainly to meet these difficulties that we began to modify the method in the following manner.

TUBULATED BLOOD BRIDGES WITH FIBER CORES

Experiments carried out with peripheral nerve fragments in tissue culture have shown that Schwann cells tend to adhere to the surfaces of artificial fibers of glass or synthetic resins even when the latter are embedded in a clot of blood plasma.[13] The cells move out rapidly in tandem strands strictly aligned with the fiber axis. Since regenerating axons, in turn, tend to advance along Schwann cell strands, extension of these tissue culture experiments to problems of actual nerve repair suggested itself. We therefore supplemented the simple tubulation technique described above by including in the blood bridge large numbers of thin, parallel, longitudinally oriented artificial fibers of various kinds, for the double purpose of giving the link greater consistency and of giving the Schwann cells and axons oriented pathways leading straight from stump to stump.

EXPERIMENTS IN RATS

Most of the fibers used measured less than 0.03 mm. in diameter. They were of the same types as those used in the earlier tissue culture tests,[13] namely, glass wool (8μ or 26μ), Nylon, textile rayon, cellulose acetate, and "Cordura" (tire rayon).* These fibers were combed into parallel strands, cut to proper length, and inserted into the lumen of a somewhat longer sleeve of artery mounted on a special stand and filled with Ringer's solution. The fibers were dispersed by gentle manipulation, and the Ringer's solution was then gradually replaced by whole blood. After this had firmly clotted, the whole preparation was used much as if it were a nerve graft. A segment was excised from the peroneal nerve so as to leave a gap of ca. 10 mm., and the two stumps were inserted in the usual manner into the open ends of the arterial sleeve until they met the fiber-blood core. No further means of attachment were used.

The 24 animals included in this series were sacrificed between 7 and 77 days p.op. Our main purpose was to study the microscopic picture; all bridges except those containing glass fibers could be sectioned, as the fibers either dissolved or softened during the histological treatment. No motor recovery had occurred, and stimulation of the distal stumps at autopsy gave no evidence of sensory fiber regeneration. Functionally, these cases were complete failures. Microscopic examination revealed the reason, which was a purely technical one.

The artificial fiber core had failed to form an intimate union with at least one, and often both, stumps. It was separated from them by a small, but distinct, cavity filled with liquid. As neither spindle cells nor nerve fibers cross liquid gaps, no organic junction had been effected. The explanation of this non-union lies in the relative rigidity of the fiber core. As the blood menstruum in the sleeve became dissolved, the fibers were forced closer together into a rather stiff bundle, which then acted as a mechanical unit. While the arterial sleeve was elastic, the fiber core was not. The movements of the animal, therefore, caused continual slight displacements between the fiber bundle and the nerve stumps, and any incipient tissue links were thus constantly ruptured before they had a chance to become consolidated. The inset could thus become firmly attached to one stump or the other, but not to both.

In those cases in which the graft had become firmly fused with the proxi-

---

* The fiber samples were obtained through the courtesy of Dr. M. M. Brubaker of the Experimental Station of E. I. duPont de Nemours and Company.

mal stump, it was invaded by regenerating nerve fibers in various ways and degrees. When the filaments of the core were too tightly packed, no tissue penetrated between them. When spaced more loosely, the interstices became invaded by a tissue composed of blood cells, mesenchyme, Schwann cells, nerve fibers and serous spaces, in varying ratios. Textile rayon evoked in all cases a strong foreign body reaction with small-cell infiltration, liquid exudates, and poor growth of organized tissue. Nylon, cellulose acetate and "Cordura," on the other hand, were much better tolerated. There was little or no liquefaction, and the regenerating tissue adhered firmly to the fiber surfaces. The cells and axons followed strictly longitudinal courses, not only where they were in direct contact with the guide fibers, but also in the intervening meshes. In some cases, the interior of the fiber bundle had remained devoid of cells, while there was ample growth in the more superficial layers, and these, in turn, were surrounded by a layer of pure regenerated nerve tissue, which filled the space between the fiber core and the wall of the sleeve. Similar observations were made in the cat experiments and will be reported below.

Even apart from the technical defects, nerve regeneration in this series cannot be rated as superior to that observed in rats with tubulated blood gaps without fiber cores.

EXPERIMENTS IN CATS

A. *Unattached fiber cores*

This series followed the same general plan as the previous one in rats, except that only glass fibers were used as cores, and collagen tubes, instead of arteries, for sleeves. These tubes, spun from fibers of dissolved and reprecipitated bovine collagen by a process developed at the Massachusetts Institute of Technology under the direction of Dr. F. O. Schmitt, were prepared for our nerve repair work according to our specifications. Both tanned and untanned tubes were available. The former are relatively unelastic, produce some slight tissue reaction, but persist for long periods without change, while the latter are highly elastic, but rather rapidly resorbed. We have made comparative studies on the relative merits of the various collagen sleeves in ordinary nerve splicing experiments, but have been unable to reach final conclusions because of the great number of variables involved (variability of the preparations, animals, operative incidents, etc.). For the present experiments, we used plain untanned collagen because of its greater elasticity.

In six of the seven animals of this series, the sleeve was filled with whole blood, in the seventh with gelatin. Gaps in the peroneal or tibial nerves of from 10 to 20 mm. were bridged in this manner; the animals were biopsied between 11 and 31 weeks p.op.

Five of these cases were complete failures, again for technical reasons. As in the corresponding rat series, the rigid compacted glass fiber bundle had become attached to one of the stumps only. Moreover, the collagen tubes underwent resorption at a time when their content would still have needed protection against loss of liquid and ingrowth of fibrous tissue.

In two other cases, a tenuous union had been established between the insert and both stumps, and this tissue bridge then acted as a foundation for the gradual building up by further regeneration along its sides of a good-sized nerve. In one of these cases (gap of 12 mm. in tibial nerve), plantar extension had returned after 15 weeks, and at biopsy (16 weeks p.op.), electric stimulation of the proximal tibial nerve produced vigorous contraction of the plantar flexors; the weight of the latter was only 15 per cent below that of the controls from the opposite side. The proximal two thirds of the glass core were intimately interwoven with the substance of the nerve, but the distal third came to the surface and protruded at an acute angle. In the other case, in which a gap of 17 mm. in the peroneal nerve had been bridged, toe spreading and dorsiflexion had reappeared 12 weeks p.op. Biopsy revealed a well organized cylindrical nerve segment that had formed across the gap and from which the glass core bulged laterally. Electric stimulation of the proximal peroneal produced toe spreading and dorsiflexion of medium strength, and sensory responses could be evoked by stimulation of the nerve 125 mm. distal to the original lesion. Histological examination of the distal stump in the lower leg showed abundant neurotization.

These two cases prove that the method as such may lead to good results, provided the bridge has effected a firm primary union with both stumps. Once this has happened and the outgrowing tissue has formed a straight oriented connection between the stumps, the glass bridge can gradually be dispensed with. Its protrusion from the repaired nerve is apparently due to secondary elimination. It remains undecided, however, whether the addition of a fiber core in these cases was of any real advantage; a direct comparison with the coreless tubulated blood bridge described above is not possible, because in the present series unmodified whole blood was used, which is not an optimal medium.

B. *Attached fiber cores*

The simplest way to avoid the hazards encountered in the preceding series and to secure a firm union between stumps and bridge is to sew the fiber strands directly through the stumps. This has the double advantage of bringing the regenerating tissue into intimate contact with the guide fibers and of linking stumps and fiber bridge into a continuous chain, but has the disadvantage of disrupting the architecture of the nerve stumps at the suture points. It developed that the advantages overbalance the disadvantages. Of several procedures tried, the following proved most satisfactory (Fig. 4).

Synthetic resin fibers are combed out and a few hundred of them are threaded as a single strand through a wide-eyed straight needle. The needle is thrust through the side of the proximal stump (P), several mm. above the gap, and then guided along the axis of the nerve until it emerges in the center of the proximal cut, as shown in Fig. 4*A*. A collagen sleeve (S) of proper dimensions is slipped over the distal stump (D) and gathered so as to leave the nerve end free. After connecting the two nerve stumps by a single suture thread (E; Fig. 4*B*), fastened to the edges of the respective epineuria under some tension, the needle with the fiber cable is threaded through the center of the distal stump for about 1 cm. and finally brought out laterally, as shown in Fig. 4*B*; the fiber cable is then cut at both ends flush with the wall of the nerve. The holding suture (E) is then removed, allowing the nerve ends to retract slightly. This makes the ends of the cable slip into the center of the nerve and also tends to straighten the fascicles of the distal stump which have been pushed back by the friction of the cable when it was first drawn through. Next, a semicylindrical trough (G), fashioned from annealed tantalum foil[11] to fit the dimensions of the nerve, is placed under the gap, as shown in Fig. 4*C*. The trough is filled with Ringer's solution, in which the fibers, which had been clinging together, separate again. The Ringer's solution is then gradually replaced with blood

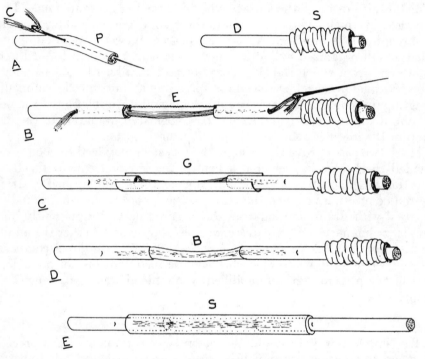

Fig. 4. Diagram of operation. Explanation in text.

taken from one of the local veins and dripped into the trough from a pipette. Excess blood flows off, but a clot soon begins to form along the fibers. After the whole content of the trough has firmly clotted, the trough is removed, leaving a blood segment (B; Fig. 4*D*) intercalated between the stumps. The collagen sleeve (S) is then pulled over the region (Fig. 4*E*). A description of three cases follows.

Cat F41. Peroneal gap of 21 mm. bridged with "Cordura" fibers (12μ diameter) in tubulated blood clot. Sacrificed after 20 weeks. Toe spreading and dorsiflexion were very well restored. Biopsy revealed a smooth cylindrical nerve (Fig. 5) with two slight bulbous swellings in the proximal stump, one (A) at the level where the cable had been drawn across the fascicles, and the other (B) just proximal to the entrance of the collagen tube, which evidently had been fitted too tightly. Electrical stimulation proved that no nerve fibers had escaped,

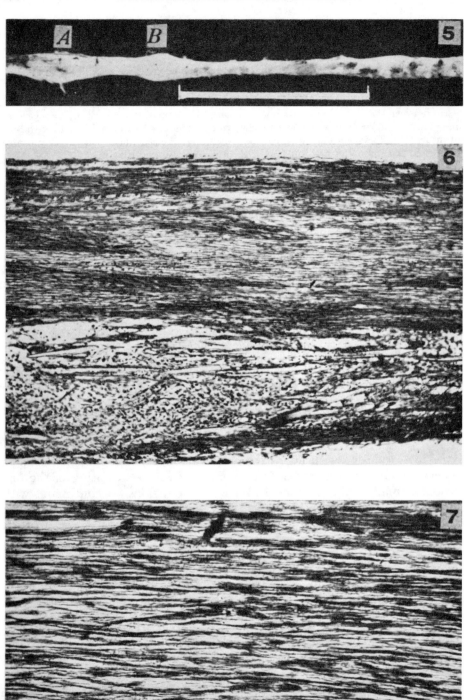

Figs. 5, 6 and 7. See opposite page for description.

and there were only minor adhesions. Sensory responses could be elicited from the distal stump at a distance of 180 mm. from the level of the lesion, which is as far as the nerve could be dissected free. The dorsiflexors had recovered to 84 per cent of the weight of their opposite controls.

Histological examination (Fig. 6): The "Cordura" fibers lay excentrically in the newly formed nerve segment. A moderate foreign body reaction with small-cell infiltration is noticeable. Some regenerated tissue, consisting of fibrocytes, Schwann cells and some axons was present between the fibers, but it was relatively small in amount. In contrast, nerve regeneration around this fiber bundle, and particularly to one side, was as abundant as after end-to-end suture. It differs from that in coreless blood clots by the straightness of the fiber course (Fig. 7) and the absence of braiding and of fibrotic partitions and islands.

Cat F42. Peroneal gap of 28 mm. bridged with "Cordura" cable in tubulated blood clot. Sacrificed 20 weeks p.op. Toe spreading and dorsiflexion had recovered to nearly full strength; the dorsiflexors had returned to 87 per cent of the weight of the controls. Biopsy revealed moderate adhesions between the sheath of the new nerve segment and its surroundings, but upon dissection of the sheath a perfectly smooth cylindrical regenerated nerve appeared in the interior.

Histological examination: The filaments had remained more widely spaced than in the preceding case. Here and there strands of dense fibrous tissue with strictly longitudinal orientation separated the large and equally well oriented fascicles of nerve fibers. There was no trace of transverse fibrosis.

Cat F43. Peroneal gap of 19 mm. bridged with cable of Nylon fibers in blood clot in sleeve of frozen and thawed artery. Sacrificed 30 weeks p.op., when no functional recovery was noticed. Biopsy revealed that the distal nerve stump had slipped from the sleeve, the free end of which had then collapsed. The whole length of the sleeve up to that point, however, was filled with regenerated nerve.

Histological examination: Excellent straight nerve fiber regeneration in full volume has occurred along and between the Nylon filaments. Most of the latter are coated by thin endothelioid cell sheaths, but otherwise there has been no cellular reaction. There is no evidence of fibrosis. The histological picture leaves no doubt that if the distal stump had not pulled out by accident functional recovery would have been as good as after gapless nerve reunion.

In all three cases with fiber cables, the architecture of the nerve stumps was considerably disorganized at the points of suture, resulting in the formation of small local neuromas. But since these regions are continuous with the much less disturbed end segments of the stumps, where the cable runs parallel to the nerve axis, the effect on regeneration is no more serious than in an ordinary lesion "in continuity."

COMMENT

The reported experiments demonstrate the feasibility of bridging nerve gaps twenty to thirty times as long as the diameter of the nerve by methods other than nerve grafts. All techniques here described as more or less successful have two features in common: (1) the use of a connecting bridge be-

FIG. 5. Regenerated nerve of F41 at biopsy after removal of sleeve. The length of the former gap is marked by a bracket. For further explanation, see text. ($\times 2.5$)

FIG. 6. Part of longitudinal section of regenerated nerve in zone of former gap (F 41). "Cordura" cable with small-cell infiltration below; bulk of regenerated nerve above; weak nerve bundle also at lower margin of "Cordura" cable. ($\times 100$)

FIG. 7. Detail from regenerated part of nerve of Figs. 5 and 6, showing parallel orientation of regenerated fibers. (Bodian, $\times 455$)

tween the stumps to serve indirectly as a trellis for the regenerating nerve tissue, and (2) the enclosure of this bridge, for reasons of orientation, consistency and protection, in an elastic tube. Let us consider these two provisions separately.

(1) The medium between the stumps must be so chosen as (a) to facilitate physically the permeation and resettlement of the gap with true nerve elements (Schwann cells, axons, etc.) of the distribution and orientation of typical nerve, and (b) not to impede chemically the regeneration process, either through toxic substances or by destroying physical guide structures indispensable for regeneration. The physical prerequisites referred to in (a) include (α) the presence of oriented interfaces (guide structures) along which cells and axons can advance, and (β) provisions for an adequate amount of liquid in the spaces between the guide structures. This liquid fulfills several functions: it enhances the association of nerve fibers into bundles ("fasciculation");[7] it provides space needed for the expansion of the regenerating tissue, particularly the growth in width of the nerve fibers;[12] and there are indications that it may also have an antifibrotic effect, since in our experience, there is a direct relation between compactness of the early union tissue and later fibrosis.

The bridges of coagulated blood described above satisfy both conditions (α) and (β). The fibrin framework furnishes the guide structures, and enzymatic liquefaction of the clot provides for the liquid spaces.[16] However, the longitudinal orientation of the fibrin was evidently less strict, and the liquid less abundant, than was the case in our earlier experiments with shorter gaps. Hence, the "braiding" of the nerve fibers, and with the use of whole blood, the greater incidence of fibrotic islands. It was in order to remedy the latter condition that we attempted to increase the liquid content of the union tissue by adding more leukocytes as proteolytic agents to the original clot. The results indicate that this had the desired effect, but the number of cases is too small to be fully conclusive.

The introduction of fiber cables into the blood bridges was intended to insure a straighter course of regeneration across the gap and to give the bridge enough consistency to prevent the collapse of the sleeve. Both effects were attained. The numerous parallel filaments caused the regenerating tissue to assume a corresponding longitudinal orientation, with the result that nerve regeneration became straight instead of wavy. The detailed mechanism by which the parallel organization of the bridge tissue is effected remains to be determined. But the effect as such is clear. Quite unexpectedly, the fiber cables served another useful purpose by increasing the liquidity of the union tissue in the sense outlined before. Some types of these synthetic fibers gave rise to a mild foreign body reaction, and the proteolytic activity of the accumulating leukocytes then produced automatically the effect achieved in the earlier series by the addition of buffy coat.

(2) Enclosure of the blood bridges in elastic tubes is necessary for a variety of reasons, most of which have been analytically discussed on pre-

vious occasions[8,12,16] and need not be repeated here in detail. Briefly, the sleeve makes it possible for the enclosed segment to form an oriented integral link between the nerve stumps and yet to retain morphological independence from the surroundings. The effects of the sleeve can best be appreciated by considering what would happen if the sleeve were omitted. Lacking insulation from the surroundings, the bridge would adhere to its bed all along the exposed surface, and the resulting disorganization of the stress pattern[12] would establish pathways both for the intrusion of fibrous tissue and for the dissipation of Schwann cells (glioma) and axons (neuroma). Moreover, the liquid referred to in point (1) would seep off, leaving the tissue in a state of progressive condensation. It should be pointed out that while adhesions between the outside of the sleeve and the wound bed are a common occurrence, the new nerve segment itself retains a smooth surface and slides freely within the sleeve—a fact noted particularly in the earlier observations with tantalum sleeves[11,20] and confirmed again in the present experiments.

The fact that sleeves also cut the regenerating segment off from outside sources of vascularization, has proved to be immaterial for the regeneration process under the given conditions. Blood supply is furnished entirely by vessels and capillaries sprouting from the stumps *pari passu* with the rest of the tissue. This supply is adequate. In this regard, blood gaps offer an advantage over live nerve grafts, which cannot maintain themselves unless promptly revascularized. As Tarlov and Epstein[6] have demonstrated, and as we have confirmed by *in vitro* experiments,[19] vascularization from the ends has to be supplemented by vascularization from the surface in order to permit a graft above a certain length to survive; sheathing of such grafts, therefore, impairs their viability. It should be noted, however, that such surface vascularization is needed for the preservation of the old tissue of the graft, and not for the newly regenerating tissue of the nerve. Necrosis due to inadequate blood supply renders a graft useless and even harmful. However, neither frozen-dried grafts, nor the blood bridges of the present series need oxygen for their maintenance; they may, therefore, be left devoid of blood supply for prolonged periods without becoming "necrotic" blocks to regeneration. This explains why sheathing, though definitely contraindicated around live grafts, is wholly innocuous with the present technique.

The sleeve affects the regeneration process by a combination of interrelated factors, and to describe it as if it were a pipe line in a gross mechanical sense, is not just a simplified expression, but an outright misrepresentation. Consequently, the practice of lumping all techniques of nerve repair in which sleeves of one form or another are used into a common class "tubulation" is wholly arbitrary, and if used as a basis for judgement, scientifically unsound. Many methods described as "tubulation" or under similar names have nothing in common but the name. Therefore, the success of the "tubulation" method—if anyone should care to designate it as such—described in this article is in no way at variance with the patent failures of other "tubulation" methods. The idea of bridging nerve gaps by tubes, following the naive pipe-line concept, is old. Except for the experiments of Kirk and Lewis,[2] which came close to the ones reported above, the results were bad, largely because either the material or the filling or the application of the tube was wrong. (For a detailed evaluation of these earlier attempts, see Weiss.[12]) The idea of guide structures over a gap is likewise not new. Assaky[1] spanned gaps of several cm. in sciatic nerves (four dogs and three rabbits) by a few catgut threads, which he left lying exposed in the wound bed. He observed heavy scarring, but nerve fibers had regenerated across the gap into the distal stump; how far, is not evident from his histological description. Although he reports functional recovery and response to electrical stimuli applied above the lesion, the fact that in two of the dogs, almost full "recovery" was present as early as 35 and 39 days after the operation, a time much too brief to allow for adequate sciatic regeneration even after end-to-end suture, makes the validity of his report somewhat questionable.

The clinical value of our present method remains to be explored. The animal experiments have revealed no features that would discourage a clinical test. Local veins could perhaps serve as source of sleeves.

SUMMARY

Experiments were carried out in a total of 31 rats and 15 cats to test the practicability of bridging nerve gaps by cylindrical blood clots sheathed by sleeves of artery or collagen tubing. The gaps measured up to 3 cm. in length, i.e., thirty times the diameter of the nerve. In one series, the liquefying potency of the blood core was increased by the addition of large amounts of leukocytes (buffy coat). In other series, various types of fine artificial fibers (glass, Nylon, rayon, "Cordura") were embedded lengthwise in the blood core for purposes of consistency and orientation.

Aside from certain technical failures, excellent nerve regeneration was obtained in blood bridges without or with fiber cores; in the latter case only, if the fiber cables were firmly secured to both stumps. Functional recovery and histological appearance proved that in many cases the results were not appreciably inferior to those after end-to-end union.

REFERENCES

1. ASSAKY, G. De la suture des nerfs à distance. *Arch. gén. Méd.*, 1886, *2:* 529–553.
2. KIRK, E. G., and LEWIS, D. D. Regeneration in peripheral nerves. An experimental study. *Johns Hopk. Hosp. Bull.*, 1917, *28:* 71–80.
3. SANDERS, F. K. The repair of large gaps in the peripheral nerves. *Brain*, 1942, *65:* 281–337.
4. SEDDON, H. J., and HOLMES, W. The late condition of nerve homografts in man. *Surg. Gynec. Obstet.*, 1944, *79:* 342–351.
5. SPURLING, R. G., LYONS, W. R., WHITCOMB, B. B., and WOODHALL, B. The failure of whole fresh homogenous nerve grafts in man. *J. Neurosurg.*, 1945, *2:* 79–101.
6. TARLOV, I. M., and EPSTEIN, J. A. Nerve grafts: The importance of an adequate blood supply. *J. Neurosurg.*, 1945, *2:* 49–71.
7. WEISS, P. Nerve patterns: The mechanics of nerve growth. *Growth*, 1941, *5* (suppl.): 163–203.
8. WEISS, P. Nerve regeneration in the rat following tubular splicing of severed nerves. *Arch. Surg., Chicago*, 1943, *46:* 525–547.
9. WEISS, P. Endoneurial edema in constricted nerve. *Anat. Rec.*, 1943, *86:* 491–522.

10. WEISS, P.   Functional nerve regeneration through frozen-dried nerve grafts in cats and monkeys. *Proc. Soc. exp. Biol., N. Y.*, 1943, *54:* 277–279.
11. WEISS, P.   Sutureless reunion of severed nerves with elastic cuffs of tantalum. *J. Neurosurg.*, 1944, *1:* 219–225.
12. WEISS, P.   The technology of nerve regeneration: A review. Sutureless tubulation and related methods of nerve repair. *J. Neurosurg.*, 1944, *1:* 400–450.
13. WEISS, P.   Experiments on cell and axon orientation in vitro: The role of colloidal exudates in tissue organization. *J. exp. Zool.*, 1945, *100:* 353–386.
14. WEISS, P., and CAMPBELL, C. J.   Nerve fiber counts and muscle tension after nerve regeneration in the rat. *Amer. J. Physiol.*, 1944, *140:* 616–626.
15. WEISS, P., and TAYLOR, A. C.   Repair of peripheral nerves by grafts of frozen-dried nerve. *Proc. Soc. exp. Biol., N. Y.*, 1943, *52:* 326–328.
16. WEISS, P., and TAYLOR, A. C.   Histomechanical analysis of nerve reunion in the rat after tubular splicing. *Arch. Surg., Chicago*, 1943, *47:* 419–447.
17. WEISS, P., and TAYLOR, A. C.   Further experimental evidence against "neurotropism" in nerve regeneration. *J. exp. Zool.*, 1944, *95:* 233–257.
18. WEISS, P., and TAYLOR, A. C.   Impairment of growth and myelinization in regenerating nerve fibers subject to constriction. *Proc. Soc. exp. Biol., N. Y.*, 1944, *55:* 77–80.
19. WEISS, P., and TAYLOR, A. C.   The viability of isolated nerve fragments and its modification by Methylene Blue. *J. cell. comp. Physiol.*, 1946, *27:* 87–103.
20. WHITE, J. C., and HAMLIN, H.   New uses of tantalum in nerve suture, control of neuroma formation, and prevention of regeneration after thoracic sympathectomy. Illustration of technical procedures. *J. Neurosurg.*, 1945, *2:* 402–413.

Reprinted from Proc. Soc. Exp. Biol. and Med., 48, 1941

EXPERIMENTS ON THE BRIDGING OF GAPS IN SEVERED PERIPHERAL NERVES OF MONKEYS*

DONALD D. MATSON, M.D., EBEN ALEXANDER, JR., M.D.,
AND PAUL WEISS, PH.D.†

B RIDGING gaps that cannot be reduced by methods other than grafting continues to be one of the most significant as well as one of the most difficult problems in the technical management of peripheral nerve injuries in human patients. These gaps result from actual loss of substance at the time of injury, from subsequent retraction of the severed nerve ends, or from the necessary wide resection of proximal neuromas and densely scarred distal nerve ends (Schwannomas) at the time of delayed exploration. Many types of surgical manipulations have been employed in the attempt to accomplish primary anastomosis across such large gaps. These include: (1) Complete mobilization of the proximal and distal segments for long distances; (2) transposition of nerves; (3) extreme positioning of joints to shorten the course of the nerve, followed by slow progressive stretching of the nerve in single or multiple stage procedures as the joint is extended; and (4) shortening of extremities by sacrifice of a segment of long bone.

In view of the often asserted and experimentally demonstrated hazards of any but the most moderate degrees of tension,[4] it has seemed important to pursue the search for new methods of bridging gaps that are irreducible by means other than extreme nerve stretching.

The use of nerve grafts has proved disappointing in human patients, in spite of numerous improvements in technique in the use of both fresh and preserved homografts.[6,7,8,9,13,16] Autogenous grafts have been successful only in very small nerves, such as the facial[3] or digital nerves,[1] and in isolated reports of fresh cable grafts.[10] According to Weiss,[14] the critical distance which can be spanned in any significant number of cases by simple spontaneous regeneration of nerve fibers is no more than one to two times the diameter of the nerve for small nerves. As this distance is increased, the regenerating nerve fibers pursue such tortuous courses, and are obstructed by such an extensive degree of fibrous tissue invasion, that chances of successful regeneration across the gap decline materially.

If a gap between severed nerve ends can be bridged by a means that does not depend for its function upon the viability of an autogenous or homog-

* This work has been aided by the Dr. Wallace C. and Clara A. Abbott Memorial Fund of the University of Chicago, and partly by contract with the Research and Development Board Office of the Surgeon General, U.S. Army.

† Planning and histological studies were under the supervision of the senior author (P.W.), while operations and follow-up were carried out by the other two authors.

enous nerve graft, some form of tubulation of the gap becomes possible, since under these circumstances, the regenerating nerve fibers and sheaths carry their own blood supply with them. Tubulation of simple blood bridges by various substances, such as arterial, collagen, or annealed tantalum tubes, has indeed been used experimentally with some success.[12,14] However, technical difficulties resulted in numerous failures with this type of anastomosis.

Tissue culture investigations showed that Schwann cells tend to adhere to the surface of glass or synthetic resin fibers in clotted blood.[15] This suggested the use of such fibers as guides to effect preliminary longitudinal orientation of regenerating axis cylinders across a blood bridge. Weiss and Taylor[19] reported a technique for such a procedure, which they carried out in a series of cats and rats, using fine artificial fibers embedded lengthwise in a blood bridge between the cut surfaces of the proximal and distal segments of the divided sciatic nerve. In their original description of this method they stated that it had the advantages of bringing the regenerating tissue into intimate contact with the guide fibers, and also of linking the stumps and fiber-blood bridge into a continuous chain, but had the disadvantage of disrupting the architecture of the nerve stumps at the actual suture point. They felt that the advantages overbalanced the disadvantages sufficiently to warrant further experimentation with the method. For further details on the rationale of the method, the original article may be consulted.

Because of the well-known limitations of clinical interpretation of nerve regeneration on the basis of experiments in lower mammals, it was felt desirable to attempt the bridging of irreducible gaps in peripheral nerves in higher forms by this technique. Therefore, a series of experiments was carried out in monkeys, bridging gaps in the posterior tibial division of the sciatic nerve in the mid-thigh. The diameter of the nerve at this point was approximately 2.0 to 2.5 mm. Gaps measuring from 6 to 14 mm. between proximal and distal segments were bridged, that is, gaps which were three to seven times the diameter of the nerve, a distance not usually bridged satisfactorily by spontaneous regeneration.

These experiments are subject to the same criticism which is justly levelled at all laboratory investigations dealing with peripheral nerve surgery, namely, that it is impossible to reproduce in the laboratory the type of complicated lacerated wounds with obliteration of tissue planes and formation of dense adherent scar tissue that is seen in a large proportion of human extremity wounds, especially those incurred in warfare. It is not justifiable to transpose unreservedly information obtained from clean operative wounds followed by immediate repair in laboratory animals to the complex, delayed wounds of human patients. However, the feasibility of operative techniques can be estimated and the functional results evaluated with sufficient accuracy at least to point the way to methods that deserve trial in human patients.

EXPERIMENTAL MATERIAL

The method reported by Weiss and Taylor[19] was modified in certain minor respects in the present investigations. Instead of an arterial sleeve or one made of collagen, the suggestion of these authors, to use a fresh autogenous vein graft as sleeve, was followed. In practice, arteries would be unobtainable in human patients, while veins are readily available. The earlier objection to the use of veins because of insufficient rigidity is met in the present technique by the supporting turgor of the blood-filled lumen. This vein graft was a segment of the internal jugular vein, removed at the same operation.

A series of 15 adult *Macacus rhesus* monkeys was used in this study. They averaged 5 to 6 pounds in weight at the time of operation. All operations were carried out under intravenous nembutal anesthesia with complete aseptic precautions. An incision was first made in the mid-

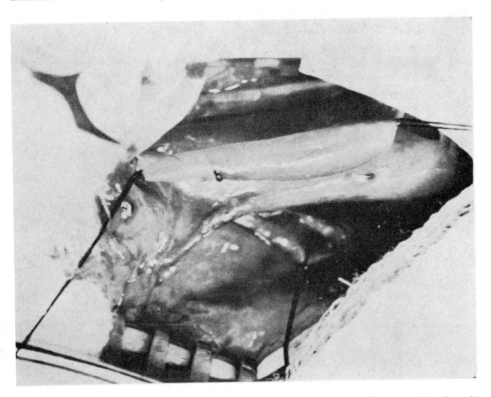

Fig. 1. Method of preparing sheath for the anastomosis from a vein graft. The internal jugular vein has been doubly ligated and the intervening segment distended with saline solution to minimize the extreme shrinkage which otherwise occurs after removal of the vein.

line of the neck. The internal jugular vein on one side was identified and a segment approximately 5 cm. in length was dissected free. This was doubly ligated, proximally and distally. Before removal, this isolated segment of vein was distended with normal saline solution, as shown in Fig. 1. Distention of the vein in this manner had the effect of paralyzing elastic tissues in the vein wall. If this was not done, the vein shrank so remarkably in size after removal (usually up to 50 per cent) that it was difficult to use as a nerve sheath.

Incision was next made on the posterolateral aspect of the left thigh and the sciatic nerve identified. A segment of the nerve approximately 8 cm. in length was exposed. The peroneal and posterior tibial divisions were separated, and the tibial division was cut. The severed ends were allowed to retract or a small segment was removed. The previously prepared vein sheath was threaded over the proximal segment of the divided nerve (Fig. 2). At first, this proved a rather tedious procedure, but was accomplished with comparative ease after some practice by triangulating the lumen of the vein with three fine silk sutures and thus guiding the vein sleeve on to the nerve. It was retracted well back of the cut end of the nerve, and allowed to remain in this position until the end of the procedure.

A 0.003 inch tantalum wire suture on a small straight milliner's needle was then passed directly through the proximal and distal segments at right angles to the long axis of the nerve about 4 to 5 mm. from the cut end. This suture was tied snugly so as to fix the severed ends at a distance equal to the length of the desired gap to be bridged (Fig. 2). It should be empha-

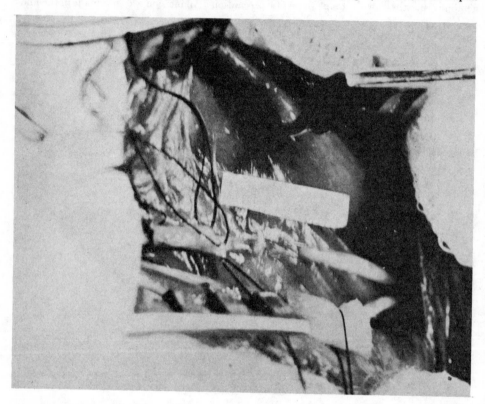

Fig. 2. The peroneal division of the sciatic nerve has been separated from the tibial and reflected upward. A 13 mm. segment has been removed from the tibial nerve. The previously prepared vein sheath has been drawn back over the proximal segment. The proximal and distal segments have been fixed in position with a 0.003 inch tantalum wire suture.

sized that this tantalum suture served simply as a sling stitch to hold the nerve ends at the desired distance and not as a tension suture.

Bundles of very fine fibers, of either nylon (.0006 inch) or tantalum (.002 inch)* were then selected and threaded on a one-half-round taper-point needle with a small eye. Between 200 and 300 fibers were included in each bundle of nylon and slightly less than this number in each bundle of tantalum. This needle was passed from a point about 7 or 8 mm. from the cut surface of the proximal segment into the lateral aspect of the nerve, down its core, and out the middle of the cut surface. It was then passed into the middle of the cut surface of the distal

---

* The tantalum wire for this purpose was obtained through the courtesy of the Ethicon Suture Laboratories of New Brunswick, New Jersey.

segment and out the lateral aspect of the nerve about 7 mm. from this cut end (Fig. 3). Care was taken as the suture was passed into the distal segment to disrupt the architecture at this point as little as possible. The nylon or tantalum fibers were pulled taut, so that they bridged the gap without slack.

A trough was next fashioned out of plastic tubing (polyethylene)[5] by cutting a longitudinal segment out of the circumference. This trough was fitted around the proximal and distal nerve ends in the manner illustrated in Fig. 4. Using a syringe and hypodermic needle, normal

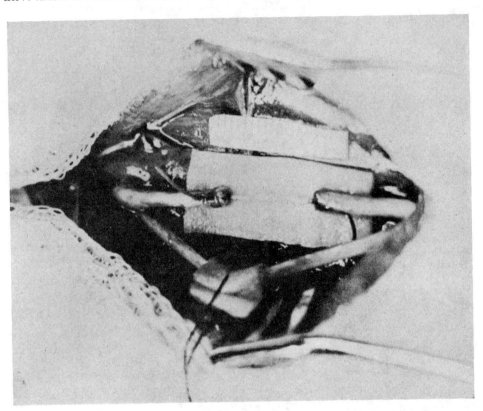

Fig. 3. Here the gap in the posterior tibial nerve has been spanned by a bundle of fine nylon fibers in the manner described in the text. The excess fibers will later be removed at the surface of the peri- neurium on the lateral aspect of the proximal and distal segments. Pulling the nerve ends slightly apart will draw the nylon cable inside the nerve at each end.

saline solution was irrigated through the trough, thus floating apart the nylon or tantalum fibers. The saline was replaced gradually with whole blood, taken from the same animal. The blood was allowed to clot firmly. It was then possible to free the plastic tubing trough from the clot and the nerve ends and slip it off, leaving the solid blood clot connecting the proximal and distal ends and containing in its core the multiple fibers of nylon or tantalum (Fig. 5).

The excess fibers protruding from the lateral side of the proximal and distal segments were cut off flush with the epineurium and the vein graft was pulled down into position over the blood bridge. If the nerve ends were pulled slightly apart after the fibers had been cut, the cable ends would slip into the inside of the nerve. This is illustrated in Fig. 6. Careful hemo- stasis was carried out, and all wounds were closed in layers with silk sutures. The monkeys recovered from anesthesia usually within 2 to 6 hours after completion of the operation. Al-

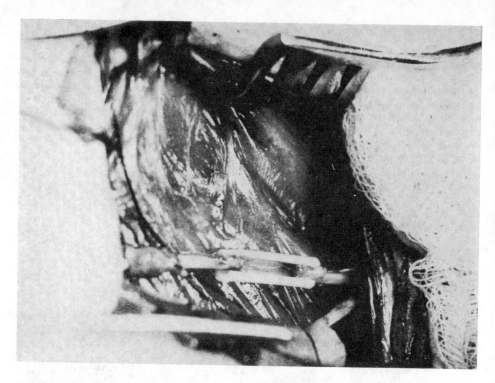

FIG. 4. A closely fitting trough, made by removing a longitudinal segment from the wall of a plastic (polyethylene) tube, has been fitted into position across the gap between proximal and distal segments. Note the vein sheath retracted on the proximal segment of the nerve.

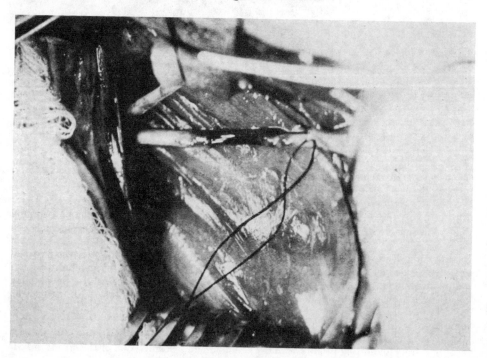

FIG. 5. The trough has been removed, showing the gap bridged by clotted whole blood which contains in its core the nylon fibers. The vein graft is still seen retracted on the proximal segment of the nerve.

most immediately they became very active, climbing, jumping, and running about large cages. No plaster casts or other splinting of the extremity were employed.

Fifteen animals were operated on by this technique in the present series. One animal died 11 days after operation, following induction of nembutal anesthesia for another operative procedure, not connected with the nerve suture. One animal died of tuberculosis 81 days after operation, and 3 others died from progressive emaciation of unknown cause within 125 days of operation. This left 10 animals who survived and whose functional recovery was evaluated between 222 and 288 days after operation. One of these was a control animal in which the nerve was severed and no form of anastomosis done. At this time when final study was carried

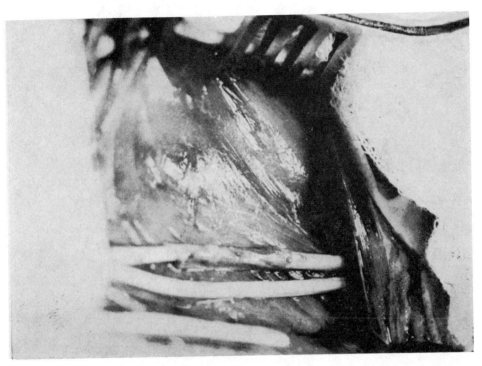

Fig. 6. The vein graft has been drawn down over the blood clot bridging the gap; no sutures are used to hold this in position. The peroneal division of the nerve lies in its normal position. The operation is now complete and the wound is closed in layers with silk sutures.

out, a section of tibial nerve including the anastomotic site was removed for histological study, sections of the posterior tibial nerve in the midcalf were removed for nerve fiber counts, and the gastrocnemius muscles on both the operated and the unoperated sides were removed for comparison of muscle weights.

RESULTS

In this group there were no technical failures. The wounds all healed per primam. In spite of unlimited activity immediately on recovery from anesthesia, there was no evidence that the nerve ends had pulled apart, or that the blood bridge had collapsed, in any animal. The vein graft was found to have stayed in place across the gap in every instance. Most of the animals were re-explored at periods earlier than the date of final removal of the specimens for histological study. At the time of these explorations, and at the final exploration when the experiment was terminated, direct stimulation of the posterior tibial nerve was carried out with faradic current, using a bipolar electrode. The nerve was carefully stimulated both above and below the site of the anastomosis, and the extremity observed for contractions of the various muscle groups. The results obtained have been summarized in the accompanying table. In all of the animals examined after 220 days, faradic

Fig. 7. Gastrocnemius muscles removed 288 days after bridging a gap of 14 mm. in the left posterior tibial nerve in the midthigh with tantalum fibers. The gastrocnemius on the operated side (left) weighed 16 gm., and on the control side (right) 27 gm. In spite of only 59.3% recovery in weight, there were strong contractions of this muscle, as well as of other muscles supplied by the posterior tibial nerve, including the intrinsic muscles of the foot.

stimulation produced good contractions of the gastrocnemius group of muscles of the posterior tibial, and the long flexors of the toes. By cutting the tendons of the gastrocnemius group and then stimulating the posterior tibial nerve, it was possible to make observations on the intrinsic musculature of the foot. In 3 of the 9 specimens, good contractions of these muscles were observed, principally adduction of the large toe and spreading of the other digits; in 3 more slight contractions of these muscles were observed; and in another 3 instances, no contractions of the intrinsic musculature of the foot could be obtained, even with greatly increased faradic stimulation.

As will be seen from Table 1 the gastrocnemius muscle on the operated

TABLE 1

Number of monkey	Date anastomosis	Date specimen removed. Days after anastomosis	Length of gap bridged. Type of fiber core	Circumference of calf at time of sacrifice Left (operated) Right (control)	Anastomosis when specimen removed	Contractions on direct faradic stimulation (1) Gastrocnemius (2) Posterior tibial (3) Long flexors (4) Intrinsic foot muscles	Weight of gastrocnemius muscles (gm.) Left (operated) Right (control)	Per cent of weight recovery	Remarks
50	5-8-46	104 days	8 mm. nylon		Free of adhesions. Slight induration, no swelling.				Died of progressive emaciation.
51	5-8-46	2-4-47 272 days	5 mm. nylon	L. 3¾" R. 4⅜"	Moderate number of adhesions. Anastomotic site 2× diameter proximal segment	(1) ++ (2) ++ (3) + (4) 0	L. 14.1 gm. R. 28.0 gm.	50.4	In good health at time of removal of specimens
52	5-9-46	2-12-47 279 days	8 mm. nylon	L. 4¾" R. 5⅝"	Moderate number of adhesions. Anastomotic site 2× diameter proximal segment	(1) ++ (2) +++ (3) +++ (4) +++	L. 18.9 R. 26.9	70.3	In good health at time of removal of specimens
53	5-9-46	12-17-46 222 days	8 mm. nylon	¼" less than control	Few filmy adhesions. Anastomotic site 1½× diameter proximal segment	(1) ++ (2) +++ (3) ++ (4) 0	L. 34.0 R. 53.0	64.1	In good health at time of removal of specimens
54	5-10-46	12-27-46 231 days	10 mm. nylon		Filmy adhesions. Anastomotic site slightly wider than proximal segment	(1) ++ (2) ++++ (3) +++ (4) +++	L. 24.7 R. 41.2	60.0	In good health at time of removal of specimens
55	5-10-46	2-21-47 287 days	10 mm. nylon	L. 4⅞" R. 5⅛"	Anastomotic site bound down by many dense adhesions. Anastomotic site 2½× diameter of proximal segment	(1) +++ (2) +++ (3) +++ (4) 0	L. 15.2 R. 28.4	53.3	In good health at time of removal of specimens
56	5-10-46	9-12-46 125 days	6 mm. nylon		Few filmy adhesions. Anastomotic site 1½× diameter of proximal segment	(1) ++			Died of progressive emaciation
57	5-15-46	7-1-46 47 days	6 mm. tantalum		Free of adhesions. No swelling of anastomotic site				Died of progressive emaciation

Number of monkey	Date anastomosis	Date specimen removed. Days after anastomosis	Length of gap bridged. Type of fiber core	Circumference of calf at time of sacrifice — Left (operated) Right (control)	Anastomosis when specimen removed	Contractions on direct faradic stimulation (1) Gastrocnemius (2) Posterior tibial (3) Long flexors (4) Intrinsic foot muscles	Weight of gastrocnemius muscles (gm.) Left (operated) Right (control)	Per cent of weight recovery	Remarks
58	5-15-46	1-8-47 238 days	6 mm. tantalum	L. 5" R. 5"	Moderate number of adhesions. Anastomotic site 1½× diameter of proximal segment	(1) ++ (2) ++++ (3) ++++ (4)	L. 20.1 R. 21.5	93.5	In good health at time of removal of specimens
59	5-15-46	1-13-47 238 days	8 mm. tantalum	L. 4½" R. 5"	Few filmy adhesions about anastomotic site. Anastomotic site 1½× diameter of proximal segment	(1) ++ (2) +++ (3) +++ (4)	L. 16.0 R. 27.5	58.0	In good health at time of removal of specimens
60	5-15-46	1-23-47 243 days	6 mm. tantalum	L. 4¼" R. 4¾"	Few adhesions. Anastomotic site 1¼× diameter of proximal segment	(1) +++ (2) +++ (3) +++ (4)	L. 15.4 R. 26.0	59.2	In good health at time of removal of specimens
61	5-16-46	8-5-46 81 days	11 mm. tantalum		Almost no adhesions. No swelling of anastomotic site				Died of tuberculosis
62	5-16-46	2-28-47 288 days	14 mm. tantalum	L. 4½" R. 5½"	Dense adhesions about anastomotic site. Anastomotic site 2½× diameter of proximal segment	(1) ++ (2) ++++ (3) ++++ (4)	L. 16.0 R. 27.0	59.3	In good health at time of removal of specimens o
63	5-17-46	5-28-46 11 days	11 mm. nylon		No adhesions. No swelling of anastomotic site				Died anesthetic death not related to this experiment
64	5-17-46	3-3-47 290 days	No anastomosis. Spontaneous regeneration	L. 4¾" R. 5¾"	Dense adhesions. Proximal neuroma and distal glioma 8 mm. apart. Bridge between narrower than proximal segment	(1) ++ (2) +++ (3)			In good health at time of removal of specimens

side weighed from 50 to 93 per cent of the control muscle on the opposite side, the average of the group being 63 per cent (Fig. 7). By comparison, a gastrocnemius which remained uninnervated after the excision of a segment of tibial nerve without reparative measures, weighed after 80 days only 30 per cent of the normal gastrocnemius muscle. It was interesting to note that

Fig. 8. Appearance 129 days following bridging of an 8 mm. gap by a blood clot including nylon fibers. There were very few adhesions to the outside of the vein graft, which is still in position. Small swellings are noted at the proximal and distal ends of the gap. Stimulation at this time proximal to the anastomosis showed good contractions of the gastrocnemius group, the posterior tibial muscle, and the long flexors of the toes. At the time this animal was sacrificed, 279 days after anastomosis, there was also function of the intrinsic musculature of the foot.

strong contractions were observed with muscles 50 to 60 per cent the size of the control muscles, as well as in those 70 to 90 per cent. However, no quantitative measurements of isometric tensions developed by these various specimens were made.

At the time of initial re-operation, a minimal number of filmy adhesions was found about the vein graft covering the blood bridge across the gap. Animals which were explored two or three times for direct stimulation of the nerve showed an increasing number of adhesions at each successive exploration. The nerve distal to the point of anastomosis was usually slightly larger than the proximal nerve. The anastomosis itself was from $1\frac{1}{2}$ to $2\frac{1}{2}$ times the size of the proximal nerve; there were usually small swellings at the sites of the proximal and distal cut ends of the nerve, as shown in the accompanying illustrations (Figs. 8 and 9). Although the vein graft was frequently adherent to the peroneal division of the nerve, and to the surrounding tissues, there was no gross evidence of invasion of fibrous tissue within the vein cuff, and the adhesions to the outer surface of the vein could be separated readily. There was no gross difference in the amount of fibrous reaction or in the degree of return of function in those gaps bridged with tantalum fibers as compared with those bridged with nylon.

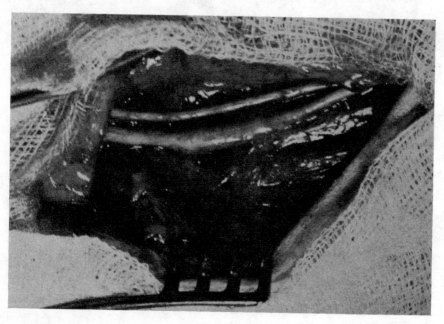

Fig. 9. Appearance of the site of anastomosis in the posterior tibial nerve 209 days after bridging a 10 mm. gap with clotted whole blood containing a core of nylon fibers. The vein graft has remained in position and singularly free from adhesions to the peroneal nerve and surrounding tissues. Note the increase in size of the nerve at the site of the bridge across the gap. Also note the slightly increased width of the distal segment (left) as compared with the proximal segment (right). This animal showed excellent return of function of all muscles supplied by the posterior tibial nerve.

In every instance, at the conclusion of the experiment, a segment of the nerve including the anastomotic site was removed, and placed immediately on a nerve stretcher in Bouin's solution for fixation. Segments of the posterior tibial nerve in the midcalf were removed and placed immediately in 10 per cent formalin.

The one control animal (Monkey 64) used in this series was not a satisfactory control. The tibial nerve was severed and the ends allowed to retract. Nylon fibers were passed through the nerve exactly as in the other animals and a photograph taken (Fig. 3), after which the nylon cable was removed. The nerve ends apparently later came to lie in relatively close approximation and spontaneous regeneration occurred across the gap. The functional result in this animal was as satisfactory as in those in which the bridging technique was used. Although the result with this single control animal was disturbing, it appears to have been merely a fortuitous circumstance. Such isolated instances of spontaneous nerve regeneration are known to occur,[14] but not with any consistency. The constancy with which satisfactory functional regeneration did occur across gaps three to seven times the diameter of the nerve when the bridging technique was used is of statistical significance. The second series of animals, making nerve gaps 20 to 30 mm. in length, both in the specimens used for the bridging operation and the controls, serves to establish this point. A subsequent report will be made of that series.

HISTOLOGICAL OBSERVATIONS

Of the fixed specimens, 3 (Nos. 52, 54, 56) were sectioned longitudinally, and 1 (No. 50) transversally, through the region of the former gap, including the old nerve ends. Longitudinal sections were also made from samples immediately distal to the nerve union in 5 cases (Nos. 50, 53, 54, 56, 61). All these sections were treated by Bodian's silver technique for the impregnation of nerve fibers. To determine the degree of reinnervation at farther peripheral levels, cross sections were prepared from the tibial nerves in midcalf of both the experimental and control sides in 6 cases (Nos. 52, 54, 59, 60, 62, 64). These were stained with osmic acid. The observations on all these cases proved so consistent that they can be dealt with jointly.

The nylon fibers have retained their position and together with the longitudinal fibrin trellis of the blood bridge, have served the intended purpose of guiding cables of regenerating nerve fibers straight from the proximal into the distal stump. In line with previous experience,[14,17] the menstruum of whole blood has insured the requisite looseness and liquidity of the endoneurial spaces in the former gap region. The sleeve has successfully insulated the nerve bridge across the gap from extraneural invasion. Orderliness and volume of regeneration reflect the degree of functional recovery reported above. The following particulars deserve mention.

The proximal end of the nylon cable shows the bent course given to it when it was threaded into the nerve. The nerve fiber bundles in the vicinity are arranged in a corresponding arcuate pattern. Islands of fibrous connective tissue are frequent at this level. Another fibrotic zone is seen at the level where the bridge cable is anchored in the distal stump. In this respect the ends of the old nerve stumps contrast markedly with the relatively loose and scar-free consistency of the newly regenerated intermediate segment. There is some commingling of nerve fibers near the entry of the nylon cable, but from there on distally the nerve is notably free from any neuromatous aspects.

The new nerve segment which has developed in the former gap consists of an inner portion, containing the nylon filaments with their accompanying nerve bundles, and a slightly denser mantle, composed of nerve fiber cables and sporadic strands of connective tissue. These fibrous strands, also observed in the earlier experiments of Weiss and Taylor, run longitudinally in the direction of the nerve, hence constitute no obstacles to regeneration. The central portion is practically devoid of condensed connective tissue. A very mild degree of small cell infiltration in most regions with nylon filaments is evidence of a minor foreign body reaction. The nylon filaments are well dispersed and the space between them is filled with parallel bundles of nerve

Fig. 10. Longitudinal, slightly oblique section through region of former gap in Monkey 54 (same as Fig. 9). Note large bundles of regenerated nerve fibers coursing along and between the heavily stained nylon filaments. (×270)

fibers embedded in a loose endoneurial network with wide serous spaces and abundant vascularization. The most striking feature of this part is the close dependence of the nerve fibers upon the nylon filaments. Each nylon fiber is surrounded by several dozen parallel nerve fibers. These are straight, unbranched and assembled into fascicles. Fig. 10 shows a longitudinal section through the fiber bridge in Monkey 54 (231 days postoperative). Due to a slight slant between the plane of sectioning and the nerve axis, only segments of the obliquely cut nylon fibers (dark dashes) appear in the picture. Each of these can be seen to form the center of a bundle of satellite nerve fibers.

Closer microscopic study reveals that the nerve fibers are not applied to the naked nylon surfaces but to a very thin film of organic matter coating each filament. This film seems to consist, at least in part, of extremely flattened endothelioid cells, but the silver impregnation employed is unsuitable for a more detailed analysis of this relation. An intermediary coat of this sort, however, was to be expected from the analogous results obtained with cell growth and nerve fiber regeneration along nylon fibers *in vitro*,[15] which had demonstrated the role of exudates adsorbed to the surfaces of filaments. Physical factors, which cannot be discussed here in detail, force

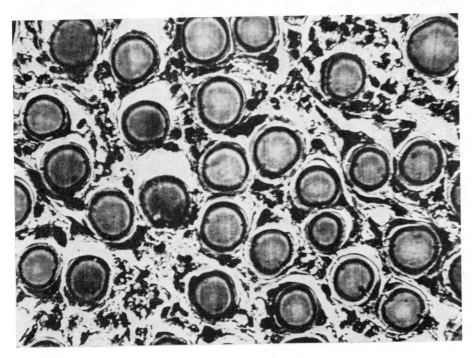

Fig. 11. Cross section through region of fiber bridge in Monkey 50. Nylon filaments appear as dark-rimmed circles, nerve fibers as black dots, mostly assembled in clusters. Blank spaces at upper side of some nylon fibers are artifacts produced by the sectioning process. (×700)

the elements of such surface coats to assume a prevailing orientation in the direction of the axes of the filaments, and the first regenerating nerve fibers are then guided by these oriented films. Additional nerve fibers tend to stack up along the earlier ones by selective adhesion to their kind ("fasciculation"),[11] and thus build up larger bundles. Fig. 11 shows a cross section through an earlier phase of this process (Monkey 50; 104 days postoperative). Clusters of regenerated nerve fibers (black specks) can be seen in the spaces between the nylon fibers (which, in this case, are more closely packed than in other specimens). In both Figs. 10 and 11, one notices looseness of the endoneurial tissue and absence of fibrosis.

The core of the nerve containing the nylon bridge is surrounded by an outer zone of varying thickness, corresponding to the more marginal layers of the original blood clot, in which additional strands of nerve fibers have grown down. These are likewise oriented longitudinally and often outnumber the fibers in the core portion. Sections through the zone immediately distal to the bridge show that after passing the area of local disturbance at the distal end of the nylon cable, the regenerated fibers have filled the distal

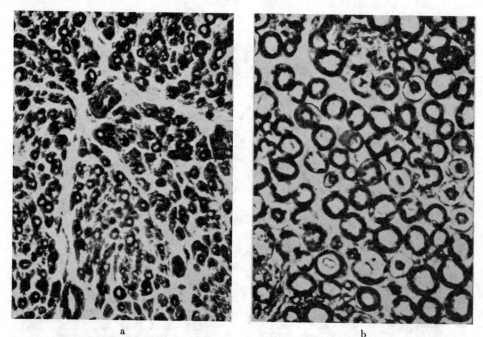

a   b

Fig. 12. Cross sections through the distal tibial nerves of the experimental (a) and control (b) leg of Monkey 54 (same as Figs. 9 and 10). Note the normal density, but subnormal size of the regenerated fibers. (×630)

stump in normal density. No difference could be detected at this level between nylon- and tantalum-bridged nerves, which latter could obviously not be sectioned through the bridge zone itself.

In all cases, however, the regenerated fibers, while abundant in numbers, were conspicuously undersized. This is readily shown by a comparison between cross sections of the regenerated tibial nerve in midcalf and sections from the same level of the normal nerve of the opposite leg. Representative samples are reproduced at identical magnifications in Fig. 12 a and b (Monkey 54; 231 days postoperative).

For an accurate determination of the degree of reinnervation of the distal stump, a complete count of the myelinated nerve fibers was made for the regenerated and control tibial nerves in midcalf of Monkey 52 (279 days postoperative). The nerve fibers were traced by means of a projection apparatus at 850 times magnification and then checked off individually and computed on a mechanical counter. In past practice, this method has been found to operate with a combined error of no more than 3 per cent. The counts in the present case were 10072 fibers in the regenerated nerve and 10031 fibers in the control. These figures prove that, numerically, regeneration has been complete. To judge from their histological appearance, this seems to be essentially true also of the other cases, in which no actual counts were made.

The completeness in the number of regenerated fibers is in striking contrast to their deficiency as to size. This latter deficiency deserves some comment. The time elapsed would have been sufficient for recovery of near-normal calibers, if the nerves had merely been severed and sutured end-to-end without gap.[2] The fibers in our cases can, therefore, be assumed to have already attained their final sizes, and their size deficiency may be regarded as permanent. Previous studies[18] have shown that whenever the cross section of a nerve fiber tube has been forcibly narrowed at a more proximal level, the whole part of the fiber lying distal to that point henceforth remains correspondingly small. This effect can be produced not only by extraneous constriction or compression but as well by intraneural fibrosis encroaching upon the enclosed nerve fibers. The fibrosis at the end of the proximal stump, observed in our specimens, thus furnishes a plausible explanation of the arrested caliber growth of the regenerated fibers distal to that zone.

It is significant to note, however, that in spite of the greatly subnormal size of these motor fibers, the function of the muscles innervated by them was not grossly impaired. While more elaborate studies would undoubtedly have revealed certain functional defects, it is yet evident that the consequences of incomplete size recovery of fibers are not so serious as has at times been suggested. On the other hand, there is a conceivable relation between the reduced size of these fibers and the observed failure of the reinnervated muscles to regain their full weight. The number of regenerated nerve fibers has been sufficient to insure full reinnervation of all muscle fibers. Weight deficit would, therefore, have to be ascribed to incomplete recovery from atrophy of the individual muscle fibers rather than to numerically incomplete reinnervation. It will be interesting to examine whether this might not be the result of a direct trophic dependence of the size of a muscle fiber upon the size of the motor neuron innervating it, rather than an expression of insufficient functional use. Since our muscle specimens have been discarded without histological study, the matter will have to be left for future investigation.

In conclusion, the microscopic study of our cases has revealed essentially the same picture as that obtained by Weiss and Taylor in lower mammals. The technique employed has succeeded in securing to the newly formed nerve link an organization optimal for nerve regeneration, with the neurons taking unconfused and unbranched courses straight from stump to stump, with adequate vascularization and plenty of space, without encroachment of fibrous tissue. These advantages are partly offset by the definite local scarring reaction and disorientation caused in the nerve stumps at the suture levels. Although this has not prevented a full normal quota of regenerated branches from reaching the periphery, it has prevented the new fibers from recovering their normal calibers.

DISCUSSION

The gaps bridged in the present series of experiments were all comparatively short, although they were actually much longer with relation to the diameter of the nerve than the distance considered traversable by spontaneous regeneration without some form of guide. The early results in these animals, based on direct faradic stimulation and gross observation of the anastomotic site at preliminary explorations, seemed sufficiently promising so that a smaller series, bridging gaps up to 3 cm., or fifteen times the diameter of the nerve, was also undertaken. These studies will be reported at a later date.

Although the results presented in this report are not striking with respect to the return of muscle weight, they are quite encouraging with respect to return of function, both in observation of the animals' use of the extremity and of the contractions of individual muscles obtained on direct faradic stimulation. The results do not compare as a group with those that can be achieved by careful end-to-end anastomosis without tension, either with the use of fine sutures or by a non-suture technique. There is, however, very little practical point in such a comparison. It is more pertinent to observe that the results are extremely favorable when compared with those of nerve grafting.

In human patients, where the degree of muscle atrophy can be lessened during the period from injury to nerve regeneration by appropriate physiotherapy and galvanic stimulation, a more complete recovery of muscle weight and function should be anticipated.

SUMMARY

1. The sutureless technique for bridging irreducible gaps in severed peripheral nerves described by Weiss and Taylor for lower mammals has been extended, with slight modifications, to monkeys. This technique involves the use of a tubulated blood bridge, in the core of which run multiple fine fibers of nylon or tantalum. These fibers serve as guides to facilitate longitudinal orientation of the regenerating axons and sheath cells.

2. This technique suggests a means other than grafting for bridging gaps that cannot be reduced except by extreme stretching of the proximal and distal nerve segments.

3. Gaps three to seven times the diameter of the nerve were bridged in the posterior tibial nerve of 15 monkeys by this technique. There were no technical failures. A moderate number of adhesions usually developed between the outer surface of the vein sheath and the surrounding tissues. However, this did not produce gross distortion of the anastomotic site or

dislodge the vein sheath from its position covering the nerve ends and the blood bridge between them.

4. Nine animals were observed for periods of $7\frac{1}{2}$ to $9\frac{1}{2}$ months. All of these showed good contractions of the gastrocnemius group, the posterior tibial muscle, and the long flexors of the toes. Six also showed action of the intrinsic musculature of the foot. Weight recovery in the gastrocnemius muscle varied from 50 to 93 per cent as compared with 30 per cent in a divided unrepaired control specimen.

5. The histological examination showed straight unbranched nerve fiber regeneration with no appreciable fibrosis in the bridge zone. The regenerated distal nerves contained the full normal number of nerve fibers, although the caliber of these fibers has remained subnormal.

REFERENCES

1. BUNNELL, S., and BOYES, J. H.   Nerve grafts. *Amer. J. Surg.*, 1939, n.s. *44:* 64–75.
2. DAVENPORT, H. A., CHOR, H., and DOLKART, R. E.   The ratio of myelinated to unmyelinated fibers in regenerated sciatic nerves of Macacus rhesus. *J. comp. Neurol.*, 1937, *67:* 483–491.
3. DUEL, A. B.   The surgical repair of facial nerve paralyses: a clinical presentation. *Ann. Otol., etc., St. Louis*, 1936, *45:* 3–6.
4. HIGHET, W. B., and SANDERS, F. K.   The effects of stretching nerves after suture. *Brit. J. Surg.*, 1943, *30:* 355–369.
5. INGRAHAM, F. D., ALEXANDER, E., JR., and MATSON, D. D.   Polyethylene, a new synthetic plastic for use in surgery. Experimental applications in neurosurgery. *J. Amer. med. Ass.*, 1947, *135:* 82–87.
6. SANDERS, F. K.   The repair of large gaps in the peripheral nerves. *Brain*, 1942, *65:* 281–337.
7 SEDDON, H. J., and HOLMES, W.   The late condition of nerve homografts in man. *Surg. Gynec. Obstet.*, 1944, *79:* 342–351.
8. SPURLING, R. G., LYONS, W. R., WHITCOMB, B. B., and WOODHALL, B.   The failure of whole fresh homogenous nerve grafts in man. *J. Neurosurg.*, 1945, *2:* 79–101.
9. TARLOV, I. M., and EPSTEIN, J. A.   Nerve grafts: the importance of an adequate blood supply. *J Neurosurg.*, 1945, *2:* 49–71.
10. TITRUD, L. A.   A successful autogenous graft for radial nerve paralysis. Case report. *J. Neurosurg.*, 1947, *4:* 92–95.
11. WEISS, P.   Nerve patterns: the mechanics of nerve growth. *Growth*, 1941, 5 (suppl.): 163–203.
12. WEISS, P.   Nerve reunion with sleeves of frozen-dried artery in rabbits, cats and monkeys. *Proc. Soc. exp. Biol., N.Y.*, 1943, *54:* 274–277.
13. WEISS, P.   Functional nerve regeneration through frozen-dried nerve grafts in cats and monkeys. *Proc. Soc. exp. Biol., N.Y.*, 1943, *54:* 277–279.
14. WEISS, P.   The technology of nerve regeneration: a review. Sutureless tubulation and related methods of nerve repair. *J. Neurosurg.*, 1944, *1:* 400–450.
15. WEISS, P.   Experiments on cell and axon orientation in vitro: the role of colloidal exudates in tissue organization. *J. exp. Zool.*, 1945, *100:* 353–386.
16. WEISS, P., and TAYLOR, A. C.   Repair of peripheral nerves by grafts of frozen-dried nerve. *Proc. Soc. exp. Biol., N.Y.*, 1943, *52:* 326–328.
17. WEISS, P., and TAYLOR, A. C.   Histomechanical analysis of nerve reunion in the rat after tubular splicing. *Arch. Surg., Chicago*, 1943, *47:* 419–447.
18. WEISS, P., and TAYLOR, A. C.   Impairment of growth and myelinization in regenerating nerve fibers subject to constriction. *Proc. Soc. exp. Biol., N.Y.*, 1944, *55:* 77–80.
19. WEISS, P., and TAYLOR, A. C.   Guides for nerve regeneration across gaps. *J. Neurosurg.*, 1946, *3:* 375–389.

Copyright, 1948, by the Society for Experimental Biology and Medicine.
Reprinted from PROCEEDINGS OF THE SOCIETY FOR EXPERIMENTAL BIOLOGY AND MEDICINE,
1948, **68**, 380-382

FURTHER EXPERIMENTS ON BRIDGING OF LONG NERVE GAPS IN MONKEYS.*

EBEN ALEXANDER, JR., ROBERT P. WOODS, PAUL WEISS.

The method of bridging gaps in peripheral nerves by a fiber cable embedded in a tubulated blood bridge, as described by Weiss and Taylor[1] for lower mammals has been successfully extended to monkeys by Matson, Alexander and Weiss.[2] The nerve gaps in these experiments measured up to 14 mm in length. The present experiments were undertaken to determine the feasibility of bridging longer gaps (from 22 to 32 mm), by the same technic.

Experiments. Five adult *Macaca rhesus* monkeys were used. The technic was essentially the same as in the earlier experiments. A section of the tibial nerve was cut out and the stumps allowed to retract; a segment of internal jugular vein was threaded over the proximal stump; the desired length of the gap was fixed by a tantalum sling stitch without tension; the nerve stumps were connected axially by a cable of finest nylon fibers (.006 inch); a trough made from polyethylene tubing of nerve caliber was placed under the

* This work has been aided by the Dr. Wallace C. and Clara A. Abbott Memorial Fund of the University of Chicago.

[1] Weiss, Paul, and Taylor, A. C., *J. Neurosurg.*, 1946, **3**, 375.

[2] Matson, D. D., Alexander, Eben, Jr., and Weiss, Paul, *J. Neurosurg.*, 1948, in press.

cable-spanned gap and filled with blood from the jugular vein; after firm clotting had occurred, the trough was removed; finally, the sleeve of the vein was pulled over the bridged gap and secured to each nerve stump by a silk stitch. After wound closure with silk, no further provisions were made for the protection of the site of operation. The animals were set free in large cages. All remained in good health.

No detailed records were kept of the course of nerve recovery, and all tests were left to the terminal exploration, which was made under intravenous nembutal anesthesia, 289 to 333 days after the operation. After measuring both calves and exposing the nerve, the responses of leg and foot muscles to faradic stimulation of the nerve were determined. Segments of the regenerated nerve and of the control nerve from the opposite side were removed for histological study. In 4 of the 5 cases, the weights of the gastrocnemius muscles of both sides were also recorded.

Results. There were no technical failures in this series. Wounds healed without infection. In no case had the activities of the animals during the early postoperative period disrupted the nerve bridge. On re-exploration, the nerve bridge, after being freed from moderate adhesions, presented itself as an elon-

TABLE I.
Recovery of Muscles After Nerve Regeneration Over Long Nerve Gaps with Bridges.

No. of monkey	Length of gap, mm	Days post-op.	Atrophy* of calf, %	Response to faradic stimulation of nerve				% of wt recovery in Gastrocnemius
				Gastrocnemius	Posterior tibial	Long flexors	Intrinsic foot muscles	
66	32	333		+	+	+	0	(Control muscle unavailable)
72	23	321	6	++	++	++	0	82
73	25	302	13	++	++	+	±	86
74	26	289	5	++	++	++	+	77
75	22	307	5	+	+	+	±	95

* Percentage difference of circumference between calves on reinnervated and opposite control sides.

gated swelling of the nerve 1½ to 2 times the diameter of the normal nerve.

The degrees of recovery in the various cases are summarized in Table I. To gross observation, the functional use of the limbs appeared recuperated, but no detailed study of coordination has been attempted. The electrical stimulation of the exposed tibial nerve above, as well as below, the anastomotic site, yielded good contractions in the gastrocnemius muscles, the posterior tibial muscles and the long flexor muscles of the toes in all animals. The intrinsic muscles of the foot, studied after severance of the Achilles tendon, showed no perceptible response in two cases, fibrillary twitching in two others, and a marked response, with clear-cut opposing motion of the great toe, in the fifth.

Weight recovery in the reinnervated muscles was likewise very satisfactory. While denervated muscles are reduced to 30% of control weight (88 days after transection of the tibial),[2] the calf muscles innervated by the bridged nerves have recovered 77-95% of their controls, with an average of 85% (Table I). The degree of recovery expressed in these figures is actually higher than that observed in the previous series with shorter gaps (50-93%, with an average of 63%), but this difference may be attributable to the longer recovery period in the present series (289-333 days, as compared to 222-288 days). It is evident that the increase in the length of the gap has not reduced the effectiveness of the bridge in facilitating nerve regeneration in this series of experiments.

Histological observations. Sections through corresponding levels in midcalf of the regenerated and control tibial nerves, treated with osmic acid, fully confirm the results of the earlier series with shorter gaps. The regenerated distal nerve stumps contain approximately their normal quota of fibers. An actual count (monkey 74) showed 10,460 fibers in the regenerated nerve, and 11,565 fibers in the opposite control nerve. Numerically speaking, the volume of innervation has thus been practically fully restored. This point deserves emphasis since one encounters reports of successful nerve regeneration containing histological pictures of regenerated fibers in the distal stump, but without substantiation of their number.

As in the former series, the diameters of the regenerated branches were subnormal, with only a few reaching the 8-9 micra class. This caliber deficit indicates that the fibers have been encroached upon at some proximal level by endoneural fibrosis, possibly at the points where the nylon cable was sewn through the stumps. It has been shown that the narrowing of the lumen of a fiber at any one level limits the caliber growth of the distal portion of the fiber.[3,4] While one must suspect that permanently subnormal calibers entail some deficiencies in function,[5] these have not been severe enough to become grossly discernible.[2]

[3] Weiss, Paul, and Taylor, A. C., PROC. SOC. EXP. BIOL. AND MED., 1944, 55, 77.

[4] Weiss, Paul, and Hiscoe, Helen B., J. Exp. Zool., 1948, 107, 315.

Conclusions. Comparing these results with those of the earlier series involving gaps of about half the length, no evidence of a decline of the power of regeneration with the increase in the length of the gap can be detected. It may be reasonable to assume that the gap could be lengthened even more without becoming unbridgeable.

Summary. Gaps of from 22-32 mm in length in tibial nerves of monkeys were closed by nylon cables embedded in tubulated blood bridges.[1,2] The reinnervated muscles regained an average of 85% of their normal weight. The distal regenerated nerve fibers were approximately normal in number, though subnormal in size. There has been no reduction of regenerative power with increased length of the gap in this series as compared to a previous series with shorter gaps.

[5] Young, John Z., *Physiol. Rev.*, 1942, 22, 318.

Reprinted from The American Journal of Physiology
Vol. 145, No. 4, February, 1946

SPONTANEOUS RECOVERY OF MUSCLE FOLLOWING PARTIAL DENERVATION[1]

PAUL WEISS and MAC V. EDDS, Jr.

In previous experiments (Weiss and Edds, 1945), we found indications that when the major portion of the motor nerve supply of a muscle is removed, stimulation of the remaining motor fibers eventually yields disproportionately strong contractions.[2] The explanation had to be sought either in a marked hypertrophy of the still innervated muscle fibers or in the taking over of part of the denervated fibers by sprouts from the residual intramuscular nerve branches. The present experiments were undertaken to decide this alternative and to obtain quantitative data on the spontaneous improvement of partially denervated muscle in the absence of regeneration of the severed nerve fibers.

The plurisegmental origin of most limb nerves makes section of one or more of the contributory segmental roots the most effective method for partial denervation. The method had been used previously (Hines, 1942; Weiss and Campbell, 1944), but met with complications from some unchecked nerve regeneration. With the added precautions described below, it proved fully satisfactory. The muscles innervated by the sciatic plexus of the rat receive their nerve fibers through the ventral roots of L4, L5, and L6 in varying proportions. Since, as a rule, muscle fibers possess only a single motor nerve ending (literature in Fort, 1940), each root is connected with a different group of muscle fibers. Section of all three roots produces complete denervation. Assuming a relatively constant ratio of root contributions to any given muscle, the effects of cutting one root in one animal, and the other two roots in a second animal, should add up to the effect of total denervation done in a single animal. If a muscle after partial denervation changes less than it ought to according to the rule, this would prove that the effects of partial and total denervation are not directly comparable. Our experiments followed this general plan. In pairs of animals, one was subjected to unilateral section of the spinal root L5, and the other of L4 and L6 (henceforth designated as L4, 6). The leg muscles were examined at various intervals after the operation and compared both with normal controls and muscles that had been completely denervated for the same period of time. The examinations included a, muscle weight; b, isometric tension after direct and

[1] This work was done under a contract, recommended by the Committee on Medical Research, between the Office of Scientific Research and Development and the University of Chicago. It was also aided by the Dr. Wallace C. and Clara A. Abbott Memorial Fund of the University of Chicago.

[2] In a personal communication, Dr. H. M. Hines mentioned similar observations after partial denervation of muscle. His remark partly motivated the present study. He has in the meantime published a preliminary report (Wehrmacher and Hines, Fed. Proc., **4**: 75, 1945).

587

indirect stimulation; c, histological study. While all major leg muscles were studied in some detail, the m. soleus was selected for more comprehensive analysis.

MATERIALS AND METHODS. All experiments were done with the sciatic plexus of white rats (150–300 grams). Of the spinal nerves contributing to the sciatic nerve, L5 is usually the strongest and rather constant in size. L4 and L6 are shared between the sciatic and the lumbar and pudendal plexuses, respectively, and their contributions are more variable. The animals were operated and biopsied in pairs. To offset the size variations in the lumbar nerves, pairs of animals were selected in which the relative contributions of the three roots to the sciatic plexus were similar. The plexus was approached through a paramedian incision from the third lumbar to the third sacral vertebrae, severing the attachments of the abdominal muscles to the lumbo-dorsal fascia and the ilium. By separating fibers of the iliacus and psoas major muscles and retracting the ilium dorsally, the entire left sacral plexus was exposed without removing any bone or muscle tissue. The chosen nerves were then identified, transected and capped with a solution of methylmethacrylate in acetone to prevent regeneration (Edds, 1945). In a few animals, the partially denervated plantar extensors were deprived of the antagonistic action of the dorsi-flexors by cutting the peroneal nerve at the knee.

The animals were biopsied from 8 to 120 days after the operation. Under nembutal anesthesia, the maximum isometric tensions of the gastrocnemius and soleus muscles (tibial innervation) and of the tibialis anticus and extensor digitorum longus muscles (peroneal innervation) of both the operated and contralateral control leg were determined kymographically. In order to preserve circulation, only the tendons and the origins of the muscles were exposed. Indirect stimulation was applied from the tibial and peroneal nerves above the knee. For direct stimulation, the muscle was pierced with two needle electrodes at its origin and insertion. After the recordings, the following muscles, experimental and controls, were dissected and weighed: Mm. gastrocnemius lateralis, gastrocnemius medialis, plantaris, soleus, tibialis anticus and extensor digitorum longus. The soleus muscles were then fixed under even tension in chrome-sublimate solution, sectioned transversally and stained in Mallory's phosphotungstic acid hematoxylin or azan connective tissue stain. The motor nerves to the soleus muscles were fixed in osmic acid vapor for cross sections to show the ratio of degenerated to intact nerve fibers. Finally, the operated sacral plexus was re-exposed as a check of both the completeness of the original operation and any possible abnormalities in the distribution of the plexus components.

Sizes of muscle fibers were compared microscopically in sections of experimental and control soleus muscles. A normal soleus muscle of a 200 gram rat contains cca. 2000 fibers. Since this muscle is of the fusiform type, with all fibers extending over its full length, a cross section through the middle shows all fibers at their maximum width. In most of the specimens, muscle fiber diameters were measured directly with an ocular micrometer. For greater accuracy, some of the muscle sections were projected on drawing paper, and the fiber outlines were traced and measured with a planimeter. Up to one month postoperative, the size range of denervated atrophying fibers is still close to the lower range of normal fibers. In older cases, however, the denervated fibers can be clearly distinguished by their small sizes (figs. 3 and 4). Complete counts of intact and denervated fibers could thus be made.

The nerve fibers in the soleus nerves were counted directly under oil immersion.

EXPERIMENTAL. The animals recovered quickly from the operation and began to use the legs on the operated side within a few days. Co-ordination was not noticeably impaired, except for loss of strength. The biopsies proved that the operation had been successful in all cases; the lumbar nerves had been correctly identified and the methacrylate caps prevented any regeneration of the severed nerve fibers into the distal stumps (Edds, 1945).

Weight loss following complete denervation. In seven animals, the sciatic nerve of one side was cut and the six major leg muscles of both sides were weighed after periods of from 14 to 74 days. The graph, figure 1, gives the weights of these six muscles, expressed in per cent of their normal controls, plotted over the period of denervation. The graph shows that atrophy is nearly complete about 80 days after denervation, when the weight of the muscles has become stationary at cca. 22 per cent of the initial weight, which value represents the residual content of non-contractile tissue (blood vessels, fascia, connective tissue). According to Knowlton and Hines (1936), a denervated gastrocnemius muscle in the rat loses weight faster than is indicated by the above curve. The difference can be partly accounted for by the fact that the gastrocnemius contains a higher proportion of contractile tissue than the average of all six leg muscles on which our graph is based. It would be better for comparative purposes, to introduce a "half-time" value of degeneration, that is, the time at which a denervated muscle has lost just 50 per cent of its contractile tissue. In our cases, with a contractile fraction of $100 - 22 = 78$ per cent, half of this fraction (39 per cent) has disappeared when the muscle weight totals $39 + 22 = 61$ per cent, which occurs about the sixteenth day. This compares with a "half-time" of 13 days for the gastrocnemius as calculated from Knowlton and Hines' data.

Comparisons between totally and partially denervated muscles should be based on the weight losses of the contractile muscle fractions alone, after deducting the weight of the non-contractile portion. We have estimated the constant deduction for the soleus muscle as of the order of 25 per cent. The heavy aponeurosis along the posterior surface of the muscle accounts for this relatively high value. A sample soleus muscle after 74 days of complete denervation weighed 32 per cent of its normal control, and since atrophy after this period is nearly complete, the 25 per cent estimate for residual non-atrophying tissue is conservatively low.

The graph, figure 2, expressing weight loss of the contractile portion only of the soleus muscle, was computed on that basis. From the weight of each denervated muscle (W_d), an amount equalling 25 per cent of the weight of its control (W_c) was deducted, and the difference ($W_d - \frac{25}{100} W_c$), which is the actual weight of residual contractile tissue in the experimental muscle, was expressed in per cent of the control.   The smoothed curve gives the percentage reduction which the average contractile unit has undergone after a given period of complete denervation.

Weight loss after partial denervation.　Sixteen animals with unilateral section of either L5 or L4, 6 were grouped in complementary pairs and sacrificed after periods of from 8 to 120 days.   For a preliminary survey, the total weights of the six main leg muscles of the operated side were computed in per cent of the corresponding muscles of the control side of the same animals.   They are listed in table 1.   Also included are two pairs with additional transection of the peroneal nerve.   The table reveals the following facts.

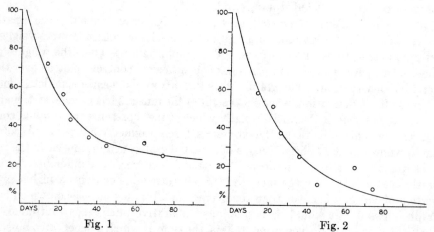

Fig. 1.　Progress of atrophy of six major leg muscles (gastrocn. lat., gastrocn. med., plantaris, soleus, tibialis ant., ext. digit. long.) after transection of the sciatic nerve.

Fig. 2.　Weight loss of the contractile fraction only of denervated soleus muscles, calculated on the basis of 25 per cent non-contractile tissue content.

Elimination of L5 generally affects the plantar extensors (with the possible exception of the m. plantaris) more severely than it does the dorsi-flexors, while the reverse is true for L4, 6.   However, the relative contributions of the various roots to any one muscle vary considerably, as pointed out for the leg muscles of the dog by Huddleston and White (1943).

If the denervated parts of these muscles had undergone the same progressive atrophy as after total denervation, their weights should have steadily declined with time.   Instead, the figures of the table show not only no continued decline after the first week, but often a marked increase, returning the muscle to fully or nearly its original weight (= weight of the controls).   Evidently, the presence of some residual innervation in the muscle has somehow arrested the atrophy of the denervated portion.   We shall refer to this effect as the "compensatory reaction."   A more detailed analysis of it follows.

We have found that the contributions of L5 and L4, 6 to the combined mass of the leg muscles are of about equal size, with only a slight preponderance of L5. Transection of either L5 or L4, 6, therefore, denervates about one half of the contractile tissue, leaving the other half intact. If we designate the mass of the intact muscles as M_i, the mass of muscles completely denervated as M_d, and the mass of half denervated muscles as M_p, we can argue as follows. Let us

TABLE 1

Percentage weights of partially denervated muscles

CASE	DAYS P. OP.	RESID. INNERV.	MUSCLE WEIGHTS EXPRESSED AS PER CENT OF CONTROL					
			Gastroc-nemius lateralis	Gastroc-nemius medialis	Plantaris	Soleus	Tibialis anticus	Extensor digitorum longus
R748	8	4, 6	79	52	88	65	98	95
R744	8	5	68	79	67	70	76	104
R745	14	4, 6	73	58	93	82	92	100
R749	14	5	74	94	73	86	54	71
R765	22	4, 6	68	59	104	94	103	93
R764	21	5	75	89	72	90	49	73
R649	30	4, 6	47	103	62	97	88	55
R647	29	5	93	97	97	85	28	90
R654	44	4, 6	79	51	95	100‡	94	98
R651	44	5	86	110	103	92	39	103
R673	62	4, 6	95	44	96	77	87	88
R672	61	5	93	100	68	102	37	72
R669	103	4, 6	78	54	108	79	96	90
R666	102	5	98	104	100	111	65	105
R652	118	4, 6	95	53	113	89	98	91
R653	120	5	100	114	96	110	42	92
R772*	32	4, 6	76	24	93	100	(36)†	(46)
R771*	31	5	85	87	88	86	(32)	(44)
R741*	66	4, 6	92	62	97	66	(19)	(24)
R743*	65	5	75	83	75	71	(25)	(31)

* Cases with peroneal nerve transected.
† Figures in brackets refer to completely denervated muscles.
‡ Excessive value because of undersized control muscle; see table 4, column *a*.

first assume that the intact and denervated halves of these muscles behave independently, that is, each half as if it were one half of a fully intact or of a completely denervated muscle. Then, $M_p = \dfrac{M_i}{2} + \dfrac{M_d}{2}$. However, if contrary to our assumption, either the intact half $(\dfrac{M_i}{2})$ grows by hypertrophy, or the denervated half $\left(\dfrac{M_d}{2}\right)$ atrophies less than expected, or both, then $M_p > \dfrac{M_i + M_d}{2}$, with the magnitude of the inequality indicating the extent of the compensatory reaction. A comparison between observed M_p values and the calculated values of $\dfrac{M_i + M_d}{2}$ for various periods of denervation is given in table 2. Column a gives the total weight of the control muscles, M_i; column b, the calculated weight of these muscles after total denervation, M_d, as determined from the

TABLE 2

Comparison of expected and observed weights of six leg muscles following partial denervation

CASE	DAYS	RESID. INNERV.	a M_i	b M_d	c $\dfrac{M_i + M_d}{2}$	d M_p	e $100\dfrac{d-c}{c}$
			grams	*grams*	*grams*	*grams*	*per cent*
R748	8	4, 6	2.077	1.660	1.869	1.588	−15
R744	8	5	1.509	1.206	1.358	1.196	−12
R745	14	4, 6	1.518	0.971	1.245	1.324	7
R749	14	5	1.805	1.155	1.480	1.363	−8
R765	22	4, 6	1.542	0.787	1.165	1.239	7
R764	21	5	1.676	0.888	1.282	1.230	−4
R649	30	4, 6	2.063	0.865	1.464	1.553	6
R647	29	5	1.461	0.629	1.045	1.144	10
R654	44	4, 6	1.577	0.489	1.033	1.245	20
R651	44	5	1.812	0.562	1.187	1.545	30
R673	62	4, 6	1.936	0.503	1.220	1.543	27
R672	61	5	2.308	0.624	1.466	1.811	24
R669	103	4, 6	2.204	0.484	1.344	1.769	32
R666	102	5	2.115	0.464	1.290	1.960	52
R652	118	4, 6	1.971	0.394	1.183	1.700	44
R653	120	5	1.921	0.384	1.153	1.742	51

graph, figure 1; column c, the values $\dfrac{M_i + M_d}{2}$; column d, the observed values of M_p; and column e, the percentage excess of M_p over $\dfrac{M_i + M_d}{2}$.

It is evident from column e that after an initial slight deficit, there appears a marked excess, the magnitude of which tends to increase with time. These results prove that intact and denervated portions of a partially denervated muscle do not behave independently and cannot be treated in additive fashion. Either the intact portion actually increases in weight, or the denervated portion decreases less than after total denervation.

For closer study, the soleus muscle was singled out.

Nerve supply. The relative share of L5 and L4, 6 in the innervation of the soleus was determined from cross sections of the soleus nerve at its entrance into the muscle. The number of myelinated fibers present in the nerve at various intervals after elimination of either L5 or L4, 6 was compared with the number of myelinated fibers on the intact control side. The normal nerve contains approximately 100 myelinated fibers. The average of ten animals studied from 1 to 6 weeks after operation shows that about 80 per cent of these fibers are derived from L5 and 20 per cent from L4, 6. The computations presented farther below are based on these figures.

During later stages of denervation an interesting variety of nerve regeneration intruded into the picture. Already on a previous occasion (Weiss and Campbell, 1944), it was noticed that the section of part of the sciatic roots did not entail a permanent deficit in the fiber content of the nerve. After some time, masses of regenerating fibers were seen in the nerve. It was taken for granted that these had come from the proximal roots, even though such an origin appeared highly dubious in view of the practice of evulsing the root stumps. In our present experiments, regeneration of the severed nerves was effectively suppressed by capping, and the absence of such regeneration was confirmed at autopsy and

TABLE 3

Numbers of myelinated fibers in the soleus nerve after section of L5

CASE	DAYS	NUMBER OF FIBERS*		
		Large (above 2μ)	Small (below 2μ)	Total
R748	8	19 (20)	2 (2)	21 (22)
R745	14	29 (28)	7 (7)	36 (35)
R765	22	9 (10)	3 (3)	12 (13)
R649	30	12 (12)	9 (9)	21 (21)
R654	44	6 (6)	13 (13)	19 (19)
R673	62	6 (5)	55 (45)	61 (50)
R669	103	6 (5)	57 (40)	63 (45)
R652	118	8 (7)	51 (46)	59 (53)

* Values in brackets give the ratio of fibers in per cent of the intact control nerve of the same animal.

histologically. Nevertheless, fibers, which can only be interpreted as regenerating ones, again appeared in the partially denervated nerve. They could be recognized by their smaller size and by the fact that several—up to four—were often contained in a single neurilemmal tube. The following table (table 3) lists the number of small ($<2\mu$) and large ($>2\mu$) fibers found in soleus nerves after elimination of L5.

As one can see from the table, there are only few small fibers present in these nerves at the beginning. Then, towards the end of the first month, their number starts to increase markedly, while the number of large fibers shows an equally significant drop. During the second month, the smaller fibers keep increasing in number up to between fifty and sixty, while the large fiber class remains stationary.

The trend of these figures is so consistent that the following interpretation seems inescapable. Evidently, some of the larger ones among the residual unsevered fibers of the sciatic nerve had suffered some belated damage, had broken down within 20 to 30 days, and then regenerated again, undergoing some branching on the way. Therefore, it is a case of nerve regeneration, but from the surviving, not from the severed fibers. Pressure from the greatly swelling and degenerating fiber stumps, among which the intact fibers lie interspersed, may reasonably be assumed to be the cause of the damage. The soleus nerve of course, presents only a small sample of what has been occurring on a much larger scale in the whole sciatic. In the soleus nerve, about ten to fifteen large fibers succumbed, and in their stead some forty to fifty new small fibers appeared, indicating branching at an average of three times. The gradual increase in the count of small fibers between 22 and 62 days ($3 < 9 < 13 < 55$), in contrast to the more abrupt reduction of the larger fibers, indicates that the old fibers were not injured all at the same level, but at different sites, so that the regeneration distances varied and the regenerating branches arrived at the far distal counting level at different times. Since they do not reach the muscle in force until 2 months after the operation, they can be discounted as a source of the earlier compensatory changes.

Muscle weight. We know for each period of denervation a, the weight of the contractile fraction of the intact soleus muscles; b, the weight of the residual contractile tissue in completely denervated muscles; c, the ratio of intact to denervated tissue after the section of either L5 or L4, 6; d, the weight of the contractile fraction of the partially denervated muscles. These values were obtained as follows.

a is the weight of the control muscle of the animal in question, minus a deduction of 25 per cent for noncontractile tissue, according to the statements on page 589.

b is computed by reading the per cent of residual contractile tissue for the given period of denervation from the graph, figure 2, and multiplying by the weight of the control a.

c, according to the nerve fiber counts reported above, is 1:4 after section of L5, and 4:1 after section of L4, 6.

d is calculated by deducting from the gross weight of the partially denervated muscles, 25 per cent of the gross weight of their control muscles, as in a, for unchanged noncontractile substance.

Tables 4 and 5 list the results for the groups with severed L5 and L4, 6, respectively. Column c was computed on the basis of the 1:4 contribution ratio between L4, 6 and L5. Thus after section of L5 (table 4), there is left one-fifth innervated tissue, i.e., one-fifth of the weight indicated in column a, and four-fifths denervated tissue, which in totally denervated muscle, would amount to four-fifths of the figure in column b. The sums of these values, $\dfrac{a + 4b}{5}$, therefore, give the weights to be expected if denervated and innervated fractions behaved independently. These values are listed in column c. After section of L4, 6 (table 5), the corresponding c values are $\dfrac{4a + b}{5}$. Column e gives the excess in per cent of the actually observed weights d over those calculated in c.

It is clear from column e of table 4 that except for an initial deficit during the first week, the observed weights exceed the expected weights by progressively larger amounts.   To judge from the rather stationary absolute weights (col-

TABLE 4

Soleus muscles after section of L5

CASE	DAYS	a Intact muscle (contract. fraction)	b Compl. denerv. muscle	c $\dfrac{a + 4b}{5}$	d Part. denerv. muscle	e Compens. effect $100\,\dfrac{d-c}{c}$
		grams	grams	grams	grams	per cent
R748	8	0.0840	0.0630	0.067	0.050	−25
R745	14	0.0795	0.0469	0.053	0.061	15
R765	22	0.0593	0.0255	0.032	0.054	69
R649	30	0.0660	0.0211	0.030	0.063	110
R654	44	0.0413†	0.0074	0.014†	0.041	193†
R673	62	0.0645	0.0052	0.017	0.045	165
R669	103	0.0653	0.0	0.013	0.042	223
R652	118	0.0720	0.0	0.014	0.061	336
R772*	32	0.0715	0.0207	0.0309	0.0715	132
R741*	66	0.1043	0.0063	0.026	0.057	119

* Cases with peroneal nerve transected.
† Control muscle of subnormal weight.

TABLE 5

Soleus muscles after section of L4, 6

CASE	DAYS	a Intact muscle (contract. fraction)	b Compl. denerv. muscle	c $\dfrac{4a + b}{5}$	d Part. denerv. muscle	e Compens. effect $100\,\dfrac{d-c}{c}$
		grams	grams	grams	grams	per cent
R744	8	0.0652	0.0489	0.062	0.039	−37
R749	14	0.0788	0.0465	0.072	0.064	−11
R764	21	0.0645	0.0290	0.057	0.056	−2
R647	29	0.0488	0.0161	0.042	0.039	−7
R651	44	0.0938	0.0169	0.078	0.084	8
R672	61	0.0930	0.0074	0.076	0.096	26
R666	102	0.0712	0.0	0.057	0.081	42
R653	120	0.0683	0.0	0.055	0.077	40
R771*	31	0.0795	0.0238	0.068	0.065	−4
R743*	65	0.1125	0.0067	0.091	0.070	−23

* Cases with peroneal nerve transected.

umn d) of the partially denervated muscles, either atrophy of the denervated fraction has been arrested at an early date, or hypertrophy of the intact fractions had compensated for the loss.

Table 5 shows the same trend, but less strikingly. The difference must be ascribed to the fact that in these muscles four fifths of the original mass had remained intact, as against only one fifth in the previous series; since the tables express both degeneration and compensation in relation to the total mass of the muscle, the relative effect is obviously the less, the more muscle tissue had been left innervated.

The negative values at 8 days p. op. are paradoxical, since they imply that these muscles have lost more weight than after complete denervation (compare column d and b). The case remains unexplained. The slightly negative values at later stages in table 5 are presumably due to the fact that the value of 80 per cent allocated to the contribution of L5 is slightly too high, and that a downward correction would have reduced the mass of residual intact tissue, hence the values in column c, accordingly. Considering the many estimates that had to enter our calculations, the results are, on the whole, of satisfactory consistency.

Since stretch has been shown to have a marked effect on the trophic state of muscle (Weiss, 1934; Eccles, 1944; Thomsen and Luco, 1944), it seemed desirable to examine to what extent the arrest of atrophy after partial denervation depends on functional activity. In four animals, elimination of L5 or L4, 6 was combined with transection of the peroneal nerve, paralyzing the dorsi-flexors. The plantar extensors were thus deprived of the periodical stretching normally produced by their antagonists. The results are summarized in the bottom lines of tables 4 and 5. The compensatory reaction was still pronounced in the animals lacking L5, while case R743 (L4, 6 removed) is definitely aberrant. The positive cases R772 and R741 prove that stretch is not an essential factor in the compensatory reaction.

Muscle strength after partial denervation. The maximum isometric tensions developed by control and experimental plantar and dorsi-flexor muscle groups, following stimulation of the muscles directly or through their nerves, were recorded in six pairs of animals with either L5 or L4, 6 cut, at intervals of from 8 to 120 days. The results of direct muscle stimulation, contracting both the innervated and denervated fibers, were in good agreement with the weight determinations. The tension of fifteen partially denervated muscles (gastrocnemius and soleus) averaged 78 per cent of that of their controls, which compares with an average weight ratio for the same muscles, after correction for the non-contractile fraction, of 79 per cent.

Since the compensatory reaction consists of an increase of the innervated muscle portion, by hypertrophy or reinnervation, indirect stimulation should produce increasingly stronger contractions as time goes on. This was verified as follows.

Having paired animals with matching plexus patterns, we can assume that the fractions of muscle left innervated after transection of L5 and L4, 6, respectively, are complementary, that is, add up to one total muscle set. Isometric tensions obtained by stimulating the remaining roots L5 in one, and L4, 6 in the other, should then add up approximately to the average of the tensions obtained from stimulating the whole intact sciatic nerves of the two control sides. A technical point to be considered is that even in normal muscles the sum of tensions after separate stimulation of two roots is slightly larger than after simultaneous stimulation (for a review of the literature, see Fort, 1940), partly because of a small percentage of muscle fibers with two endings, and partly for mechanical reasons (Löwenbach and Markee, 1945). However, since the error from this source is evidently smaller than that introduced by matching different individuals, we may ignore it for the present purpose. The results of the measurements are listed in table 6. Column a gives the total isometric tensions of fully innervated leg muscles for control. The values represent the mean for each pair of animals. Column b gives the combined isometric tensions of the innervated fractions of the partially denervated muscles. These values were obtained by simple addition of the values recorded separately for each member of a given pair. Column c gives the excess of b over a in per cent.

The figures prove that except for the earliest period, the combined strength of the innervated fractions of pairs of complementary muscle sets greatly exceeds the strength of an intact single set. The effect is striking in the plantar extensors, but erratic in the dorsi-flexors. The reasons for this discrepancy are obscure. It is noteworthy that the tensions of complementary pairs have never added up to fully twice the control tension. This indicates that the experimental muscles have not recovered full strength within the period of observation. As will be described below, however, histological study showed even the oldest cases still in the process of improvement.

Histological observations. As outlined above, there are two possible explanations for the observed compensatory reactions. Either the muscle fibers with residual intact innervation have undergone compensatory hypertrophy, or some of the denervated fibers have received new nerve connections and thus regained their normal size and strength. The following histological observations have decided unequivocally in favor of the latter alternative.

Conclusions as to the response of muscle fibers to experimental changes are of questionable value, unless they are based on an adequate sampling of the whole fiber population. A statistical study of the variability of fiber size, the results of which will be reported on a later occasion, has demonstrated, for instance, that maximum fiber size alone is no reliable criterion of the trophic state of a muscle, since maximum size varies much more between individual fascicles than does mean fiber size; it is the latter that correlates with weight and strength. In order to illustrate how partial denervation affects the fiber population, we have selected some typical examples from our records. The graph, figure 3, shows representative sample fascicles from three different soleus muscles, with the fibers of each fascicle arranged in the order of size (diameter). The two fascicles in the left box are from a muscle 45 days after complete denervation; the four fascicles in the box at the right are from a muscle (R654), 44 days after partial denervation by section of L5; the three middle ones from the normal control muscle of this latter animal.

Comparing first the normal with the completely denervated muscle, it can be seen that their fibers fall into two sharply distinct classes, the former above, the latter below, cca. 15 micra (dotted line). The ratio of the mean cross sections of the former over the latter (square of mean diameter ratios) is more the 5:1, which means that the denervated fibers have shrunk to an average of less than 20 per cent of their original weight, a value well in agreement with that extrapolated from the curve of weight loss of contractile tissue at 45 days (fig. 2). The fiber population of the partially denervated muscle is clearly intermediate

TABLE 6

Isometric tensions of complementary pairs of partially denervated muscle groups and their controls

CASE	DAYS	RESID. INNERV.	a ISOMETRIC TENSIONS OF CONTROL MUSCLES AFTER INDIRECT STIMULATION: AVERAGES OF COMPLEMENTARY PAIRS		b ISOMETRIC TENSIONS OF PARTIALLY DENERVATED MUSCLES AFTER INDIRECT STIMULATION: SUMS OF COMPLEMENTARY PAIRS		c EXCESS OF EXPERIMENTAL OVER CONTROL TENSIONS	
			Plantar extensors	Dorsi-flexors	Plantar extensors	Dorsi-flexors	Plantar extensors	Dorsi-flexors
			grams	*grams*	*grams*	*grams*	*per cent*	*per cent*
R748	8	L4, 6	1168		1000		−14	
R744	8	L5						
R745	14	L4, 6	918	425	935	550	2	29
R749	14	L5						
R765	22	L4, 6	1520	688	2200	710	45	3
R764	21	L5						
R673	62	L4, 6	2150	515	2605	630	21	22
R672	61	L5						
R669	103	L4, 6	1878	850	2893	855	54	0.6
R666	102	L5						
R652	118	L4, 6	1540	888	2400	1030	56	16
R653	120	L5						
R772*	32	L4, 6	1883		2470		31	
R771*	31	L5						
R741*	66	L4, 6	2125		4000		88	
R743*	65	L5						

* Cases with peroneal nerve transected.

between normal and fully denervated muscle. While some of its fascicles contain fibers of either kind only, the majority of fascicles are of the mixed composition exemplified in the graph. They contain variable proportions of *a*, fibers of normal size; *b*, fully atrophied fibers, and *c*, fibers of intermediate size. Their frequency distribution (humps of the enveloping contour curve) often shows them as belonging to three distinct classes, as can be seen in all but the second to the last fascicle of the graph. The interpretation is obvious. Group *a* contains the fibers that had remained unaffected by the operation; group *b* consists of fibers that had lost their innervation and not regained it; while fibers of group *c* had lost their original innervation and begun to atrophy, but then had intercepted new innervation and thus cut short further atrophy. The earlier this occurred, the less atrophy and the more time there has been for recovery. Therefore, some of the fibers now in class *a* are presumably former *c* members. Of the eighty-seven fibers of the four sample fascicles, sixty-three (i.e., 72 per cent) lie within the normal size range. For the whole muscle, the figure is slightly lower, namely, 65 per cent. Actually, the proportion of innervated muscle fibers is even higher, since as one can readily see from the graph, some of the fibers below 15 micra range definitely with the group of recovering, rather than of denervated, fibers.[3]

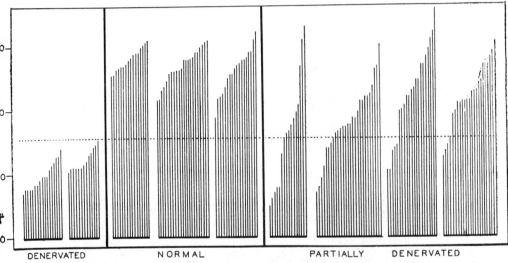

Fig. 3. Muscle fiber sizes (diameter) in sample fascicles from normal soleus muscle and from soleus muscles totally and partially denervated for 44 days (R654).

Now, the nerve of this muscle, by actual count (table 3, R654), contained only six large and thirteen small medullated fibers, which is less than 20 per cent of the normal quota. Thus, while at least 80 per cent of the muscle fibers were initially denervated, less than 35 per cent are still in this class after 44 days. This shows the rapid rate at which the denervated fibers pick up innervation. As a result, each residual motoneuron has become connected with an average of three to four times as many muscle fibers as it had originally supplied. The actual nerve fiber to muscle fiber ratios in this case were approximately 1:15 for

[3] The figures reported here for histological recovery seem to conflict with the apparent full weight recovery of this muscle (R654) indicated in table 1. However, since the control muscle in this case was of abnormally low weight (table 4, column *a*), the experimental muscle, which had reached the same weight as its control (100 per cent, table 1), actually is still considerably short of its full normal weight.

the control and 1:60 for the experimental muscle. However, because the nerve count includes a few proprioceptive fibers, the actual size of the motor units is somewhat larger than is indicated by these figures.

These data make it plain that the compensatory reaction is due to prompt reinnervation of some of the denervated muscle fibers. Since the number of nerve fibers just proximal to the muscle has not materially increased at the time when the compensatory reaction is already well advanced, the source of this compensatory innervation must be sought in intramuscular nerve sprouts. Later, extramuscular sprouts of the origin described above (p. 593) add to the effect, as is illustrated by the following case, of which sample fascicles are shown in figure 4.

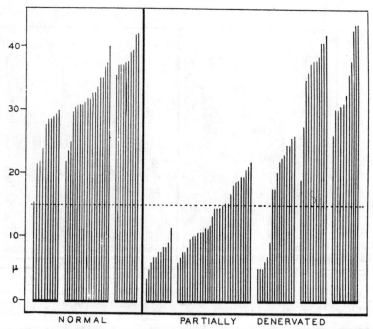

Fig. 4. Muscle fiber sizes in sample fascicles from a normal and partially denervated (R669) soleus muscle, 102 days p. op.

In animal R669, sacrificed 103 days after elimination of L5, the soleus nerve contained 45 per cent of its normal quota (40 per cent of them regenerated branches of small caliber; table 3). These have innervated 80 per cent of the muscle fibers, that is, about double their normal load. In contrast to the previous case, R654, many fascicles contain only fibers of the b and c types, but none of class a. These are, therefore, fascicles that had first undergone complete atrophy, but eventually regained some nerve connections. As the size of their fibers indicates (see graph), they are still in relatively early stages of recovery. This corroborates the assumption that they have received their innervation from nerve fiber branches that had arisen at levels higher up in the nerve and had not reached the muscle until the end of the second month.

By comparing these two cases (R654 and R669), the relative contributions of intramuscular and extramuscular branching to the compensatory reaction can be roughly estimated. In R654, after about 6 weeks, as many as 57 per cent of the originally denervated fibers were already reconnected with intramuscular sprouts. In R669, after an additional 8 weeks, 75 per cent of the denervated fibers had received reinnervation, which is an increase of only about another 18 per cent. Therefore, even if this whole later recovery were to be credited to the forty-odd extramuscular branches of late arrival (table 3), it still would have had only about one-third the effectiveness of the earlier intramuscular expansion. It thus appears that the rate of reinnervation is merely a matter of opportunity. Since the chances for nerve sprouts to encounter uninnervated muscle fibers decline as reinnervation progresses, it is to be expected that the rate of recovery will show a corresponding decline with time. Eventually, a great majority of the muscle fibers may receive reinnervation and recuperate. Thus, in our oldest case, R652, 118 days p. op., only about 5 per cent of the total fibers gave the histological appearance of being completely atrophied, i.e., still denervated. Of the reinnervated fibers, many were still of reduced sizes (i.e., on the way to recovery), which explains the fact that muscle strength at this stage was still deficient (table 6).

The results here reported for soleus muscles deprived of L5 are confirmed by the reciprocal cases lacking L4, 6. Only because of the smaller size of the latter contribution, the original deficiency was less marked and the compensatory recovery quicker. Muscles examined 6 weeks after the operation or later rarely contained any atrophying fibers. This histological finding is in full agreement with the observation that these muscles had completely recovered their normal weights, and even slightly overshot their controls (table 1).

In contrast to the clear proof of compensatory innervation, we have found no evidence of appreciable hypertrophy of fibers. Such hypertrophy could manifest itself either in a uniform enlargement of all residual innervated fibers, raising the size maximum, or in an increase of the smaller fibers only, without exceeding the normal upper size limit. Our preparations have revealed no certain signs of either. The largest fibers of the various control soleus muscles measured 45 micra, and none of the fibers of the experimental muscles exceeded this limit. The largest fibers of figures 3 and 4 happen to be slightly larger in the partially denervated than in the control muscles, but this difference does not apply generally. Moreover, the partially denervated fascicles contain decidedly fewer, not more, fibers of sizes close to the upper limit.

In this connection, we call attention to a technical source of deception in deducing fiber hypertrophy from cross sections. Some of our preparations contained fibers with greatly oversized cross sections, suggestive of hypertrophy. They appeared in both control and partially denervated muscles in variable numbers, measured up to 100 micra across, and were circular in outline. Closer study revealed an artifact, resulting from excessive retraction in the fixing fluid of occasional loose fibers in an otherwise stretched muscle. Wohlfart (1937) has described fibers of this type as "Kontraktionsknoten," and emphasized their deceptiveness. For a crucial test, we made a small cut across the posterior border of a soleus muscle a few millimeters proximal to the tendon of insertion, and then stretched and fixed the muscle in the usual way. Cross sections through the middle showed that the muscle fibers which had not been held under tension during fixation all had excessively large diameters.

DISCUSSION. The reported experiments have 1, established the fact of "spontaneous" recovery of partially denervated muscle, referred to above as "compensatory reaction"; and 2, produced evidence concerning its mechanism. By the combined use of several criteria and methods of examination—muscle weights; isometric tensions; nerve counts; muscle histology—, a fully consistent concept of the events following partial denervation has been obtained.

Partial denervation was achieved by severing some of the roots of nerves of plurisegmental origin. The standard reduction of nerve supply thereby produced was determined and its permanency insured by effective occlusion of the severed roots. Nerve regeneration in the ordinary sense, namely, from the cut ends of the proximal nerve stumps, was thus excluded. After the operation, the nerves consisted of intact and interrupted fibers in various known proportions. The interrupted fibers underwent Wallerian degeneration, and the muscle became composed of two kinds of fibers, innervated and denervated ones, in proportions reflecting the composition of its nerve. If the intact muscle units behaved as they would in normal muscle, and the denervated ones as they would after total denervation, there should follow a period of progressive atrophy, reducing the muscles to sizes and strengths in proportion to the initial innervation deficit. This did not happen.

We have no data on the events during the first week; nor do we consider the deficits in our only two 8-day cases (tables 2, 4, 5, 6) as typical. From the second week on, however, the trend is clear. All muscles after that period exhibit greater weight and strength than could be accounted for by adding up intact and denervated parts in their original proportions. The partially denervated muscle, taken as a whole, not only loses less weight, and more slowly, than would be commensurate to its loss of innervation, but the losing trend is gradually reversed and the muscle regains part or all of its previously lost weight and strength (tables 1, 2, 5, 6).

In explanation of this "compensatory reaction", we first looked for hypertrophy of the unharmed muscle fibers, but our histological studies have failed to substantiate it. In human pathology, on the other hand, hypertrophy of individual fibers has been noted in cases of progressive muscular dystrophies (e.g., amyotrophic lateral sclerosis; Pilcz, 1898, and others), but according to the careful studies of the Wohlfarts (1935), the occurrence is sporadic and the degree rather slight (see also Karlström and Wohlfart, 1939). However, these cases and our own experiments are not strictly comparable, because of the great difference between human and rat muscles in regard to load and functional stress, which predisposes the former to a wider range of "functional" hypertrophy.

All our observations concur in proving that the "compensatory reaction" is due chiefly to reinnervation of the denervated muscle fibers. Since the nerve fibers severed in the operation have been blocked from growing back into the muscle, a spontaneous peripheral amplification by branching of the residual intact fibers seems to have taken place; "spontaneous" insofar as the production of new branches did not start from the site of the operative lesion. A similar "spontaneous" extension of collateral nerve branches into a denervated area has been observed in the skin (Speidel, 1940; Weddell, Guttmann and Gutmann, 1941), but the precise mechanism of this phenomenon has remained obscure (see Weiss, 1941). Our present experiments contain at least certain positive clues. The problem poses three main questions: 1. Where are the new nerve branches formed, and as a result of what stimulus? 2. Do the mother fibers, from which they sprout, retain their peripheral connections intact (collateral regeneration), or do they first undergo some degeneration, followed by regeneration with terminal branching? 3. Are the new sprouts actively drawn towards the denervated muscle fibers, or do they simply roam and make connections by accident?

1. *Source of branches.* It seems an established fact that a single muscle fiber rarely accepts more than one nerve ending (Elsberg, 1917; Fort, 1940). Though immune to supernumerary innervation during its innervated state, the muscle fiber becomes receptive again within several days after the loss of its innervation (Fort, 1940). In view of this situation, it is conceivable that muscle normally contains a surplus of terminal nerve fiber branches which have failed to connect and are functionally idle. Wholly unconnected nerve fibers certainly persist without resorption (Weiss and Taylor, 1944; Weiss and Edds, 1945; Weiss, Edds and Cavanaugh, 1945), and so do unattached terminal branches (Gutmann and Young, 1944). If such terminal fiber reservoirs exist, they could be claimed as source of the "compensatory reaction." There is at present no definite proof either for or against such an assumption, but if the reservoirs were so abundant as to account for our results, it is doubtful that they could have escaped notice. It is more likely that the excess branches in our experiments were newly formed after the operation in response to a stimulus vaguely identifiable with some "traumatic" or "irritant" action of the degenerating nerve branches and their denervated end-organs.

The nature of this action remains to be investigated. It could either be a mass effect of chemical products diffusing from an injured region and "irritating" healthy axon branches, even at some distance, or it could be simply a local effect exerted by a degenerating nerve fiber or denervated muscle fiber upon any healthy axon in immediate contact with it. Our experiments favor the latter view for the following reasons. Innervated and denervated units in our experimental muscles are not cleanly segregated but lie interspersed with each other. Contrary to a common notion, the individual fascicle does not correspond to a single motor unit, that is, the muscle fibers of any given fascicle may receive innervation from more than one motoneuron, and branches of any given motoneuron may terminate in more than one fascicle (Wohlfart, 1935). This is confirmed by the fact that many fascicles of our partially denervated muscles contain both innervated and denervated fibers (fig. 3). There is thus ample opportunity for direct contact between surviving nerve branches and denervated elements.

In order to test experimentally whether such intimacy of contact between defective and intact units was essential for the "compensatory reaction", we chose a muscle preparation in which denervated and innervated portions could be obtained in strict segregation, namely, the diaphragm. The two halves are partly separated by a tendinous inscription, but there is a triangular area ventrally where there is no mechanical barrier to oppose the passage of nerve fibers from one half to the other. Normally there is no overlap of innervation between the two halves. We cut the phrenic nerve on one side in three animals. Histological examination 3 weeks afterwards revealed that no nerve branches had crossed over the midline from the intact side to take over the denervated portion. Clearly, therefore, denervated muscle fibers, when lying in a solid and sharply delimited block free of intact axons, do not evoke the compensatory axon branching which they evoke when interspersed with innervated fibers.

The same seems to apply to "spontaneous" branching within the nerve itself. As reported above, the surviving axons of the partially denervated nerve trunks proliferate branches. Counts of old and regenerated fibers present in the soleus nerve at various periods after partial denervation (table 3) revealed that for some time after the operation, individual old fibers tend to break down at some peripheral point and then regenerate with one or two dichotomies. This delayed axon disruption may be a result of the local pressure exerted by the enormous swelling of surrounding fibers undergoing Wallerian degeneration. Such a compression of intraneural origin would have the same disruptive effect on axons as does external constriction (Cajal, 1928; Weiss and Davis, 1943; Denny-Brown and Brenner, 1944).

(2). *Collateral or terminal regeneration?* The fact that the appearance of regenerating branches is preceded by the disappearance of old fibers (table 3) is proof that the former do not arise as collaterals from intact fiber stems, but by the standard process of terminal regeneration following breakdown of the distal portion of the original fiber. Presumably the same happens in intramuscular branching; that is, prior to its compensatory proliferation, a nerve fiber branch would first have to lose temporarily its old peripheral connections. The collateral sprouting of cutaneous fibers observed by Speidel (1942) to occur near wounds in frog larvae, may no longer be possible in mature fibers possessing firm neurilemmal and myelin sheaths.

As in the case of intramuscular proliferation, so the compensatory branching inside the nerve seems to occur only if intact and degenerating units lie intermingled. This is the case after section of segmental roots. If, on the other hand, a partial lesion is made in a peripheral nerve trunk distal to the plexus, so that intact and degenerating portions remain in separate groups, the intact fibers retain their integrity and no compensatory regeneration occurs (Lugaro, 1906). As Lugaro has correctly inferred, there is no "neurotropic" stimulus of the degenerated half that would invite the fibers of the intact half to send forth collateral sprouts; only actual physical disruption can initiate regeneration in the mature axon. The concept of "neurotropism" thus becomes just as untenable as a factor of fiber proliferation as it is invalid in fiber orientation (Weiss and Taylor, 1944).

3. *Neuro-muscular connections.* In view of the persistent failure to detect any sign of positive "neurotropic attraction" of nerve branches toward distant destinations, the extension of the new nerve fiber branches over the denervated muscle fibers must be viewed as a matter of chance. Since muscle fibers can be reinnervated either through the old end-plate or at a new site (Fort, 1940; Gutmann and Young, 1944), the new branches need not even follow the old pathways, but may simply attach themselves to any uninnervated muscle fibers that lie across their path. With the progress of reinnervation, the chances of roaming branches to encounter still uninnervated muscle units decline. This explains why the compensatory reaction is much more spectacular during the earlier than during the later stages (see p. 601). It is even likely that some of the late coming branches, which have regenerated from high up in the nerve, fail to find unoccupied muscle fibers; this is indicated by the unusually high quota of small fibers in the nerve even after 4 months (R652, table 3), for unconnected fibers always remain small (Weiss, Edds and Cavanaugh, 1945; Sanders and Young, 1945).

The reported facts suggest that clinically, a similar "spontaneous" improvement in the muscular condition could be expected after any partial nerve lesion in which the involved axons are scattered among healthy axons. This is true of partial poliomyelitic lesions, and it would seem indicated to examine whether a major share of the gradual gain in muscle strength after partial paralysis might not be attributable to this source. Actually, the body produces here automatically what Dogliotti (1935) and Billig and van Harreveld (1943) have proposed to enforce surgically, namely, a compensatory peripheral amplification of the reduced nerve source. In view of this fact, the surgical procedure of nerve crushing advocated by Billig (1944) would seem to be not only risky, but superfluous. On the other hand, partial severance of a peripheral nerve trunk, leaving degenerated and healthy portions segregated, cannot be expected to result in a marked compensatory reaction except in the rather narrow zone of overlap along the boundary between the denervated and intact areas.

SUMMARY

Incomplete denervation of muscles in the rat was found to be followed by "spontaneous" recovery not attributable to regeneration of the severed nerve fibers. This recovery was studied quantitatively by following the weight, strength and histological changes in the muscles and comparing them with the residual nerve supply.

Partial denervation was effected by cutting the spinal nerves L4 and 6 or L5. The proximal stumps were prevented from regenerating by capping. Weight changes were recorded for six major leg muscles (tables 1, 2). For a more detailed study the soleus muscle was selected (table 4, 5).

From the knowledge of the size of the denervated fraction and of the amount of atrophy following total denervation, the expected weights of muscles partially denervated for various periods could be computed. Except for the first week, the weights actually observed were much higher than calculated, that is, the denervated portion of a partially intact muscle atrophies less than it would if the muscle were completely denervated. Within a few weeks, atrophy is checked and the muscle gradually returns to nearly its original size.

Isometric tensions after stimulation of the nerve show a trend roughly parallel to the weight changes (table 6).

Histological study showed a progressively increasing number of muscle fibers recovering normal size after some initial atrophy. Four months after the denervation of 80 per cent of the muscle fibers, only 5 per cent were still in an atrophic (i.e., denervated) state. At no time was there evidence of hypertrophied fibers.

All observed facts lead to the conclusion that the intramuscular branches of the intact motor nerve fibers undergo additional branching and take over the supply of the denervated muscle fibers. This occurs only when intact and denervated elements lie intermingled; the stimulus for branching lies presumably in some traumatic contact action, and no "neurotropic" stimulation of branching or "attraction" of branches toward a solid denervated area has been noted.

A similar phenomenon was discovered in the nerve trunk, where some of the fibers which had not been severed in the operation, later broke down "spontaneously" and then regenerated with some branching. This occurrence, too, is conditional on the diffuse dispersal of intact among degenerating nerve fibers, and the pressure of the latter may be assumed to furnish the traumatic stimulus.

The results suggest that similar compensatory branching with consequent improvement of muscle weight and strength might occur after diffuse poliomyelitic lesions, but not after partial traumatic injury.

REFERENCES

BILLIG, H. E.   J. Int. Coll. Surg. **7**: 457, 1944.

BILLIG, H. E. AND A. VAN HARREVELD.   U. S. Naval Med. Bull. **41**: 1, 1943.

CAJAL, S. RAMON Y.   Degeneration and regeneration of the nervous system.   Oxford University Press, London, 2 vols., 1928.

DENNY-BROWN, D. AND C. BRENNER.   Arch. Neurol. and Psychiat. **52**: 1, 1944.

DOGLIOTTI, A. M.   J. Chir. **45**: 30, 1935.

ECCLES, J. C.   J. Physiol. **103**: 253, 1944.

EDDS, M. V., JR.   J. Neurosurg. **2**: 507, 1945.

ELSBERG, C. A.   Science **45**: 318, 1917.

FORT, W. B.   An experimental study of the factors involved in the establishment of neuromuscular connections.   Dissertation, Chicago, 88 pp., 1940.

GUTMANN, E. AND J. Z. YOUNG.   J. Anat. **78**: 16, 1944.

HINES, H. M.   J. A. M. A. **120**: 515, 1942.

HUDDLESTON, O. L. AND C. S. WHITE.   This Journal **138**: 772, 1943.

KARLSTRÖM, F. AND G. WOHLFART.   Acta Psychiat. et Neurol. **14**: 453, 1939.

KNOWLTON, G. C. AND H. M. HINES.   Proc. Soc. Exper. Biol. and Med. **35**: 394, 1936.

LÖWENBACH, H. AND J. E. MARKEE.   Fed. Proc. **4**: 47, 1945.

LUGARO, E.   Riv. di patol. nerv. e. ment. **11**: 320, 1906.

SANDERS, F. K. AND J. Z. YOUNG.   Nature **155**: 237, 1945.

SPEIDEL, C. C.   The Harvey Lectures **36**: 126, 1940; Proc. Am. Phil. Soc. **85**: 168, 1942.

THOMSEN, P. AND J. V. LUCO.   J. Neurophysiol. **7**: 245, 1944.

WEDDELL, G., L. GUTTMANN AND E. GUTMAN.   J. Neurol. and Psychiat. **4**: 206, 1941.

WEISS, P.   This Journal **106**: 156, 1933; Growth **5**: 163, 1941.

WEISS, P. AND C. J. CAMPBELL. This Journal 140: 616, 1944.

WEISS, P. AND H. DAVIS. J. Neurophysiol. 6: 269, 1943.

WEISS, P. AND M. V. EDDS, JR. J. Neurophysiol. 8: 173, 1945.

WEISS, P., M. V. EDDS, JR. AND M. CAVANAUGH. Anat. Rec. 92: 215, 1945.

WEISS, P. AND A. C. TAYLOR. J. Exper. Zool. 95: 233, 1944.

WOHLFART, G. Ztschr. mikr.-anat. Forschg. 37: 621, 1935; Acta Psychiat. et Neur., Suppl. XII, 119 pp., 1937.

WOHLFART, S. AND G. WOHLFART. Acta Med. Scand. Suppl. 63: 1, 1935.

Addendum to proofs: After the completion of the work described in this article, a paper reporting similar results was published by A. van Harreveld (This Journal 144: 477, 1945), too late for inclusion in the discussion.

All papers in this series have dealt exclusively with aspects of the anatomical restoration of pathways between nerve centers and periphery, indispensable for mutual functional communication. The question of recovery of true coordinated use of the regenerated network has been deliberately bypassed. That problem would have occupied the space of another book. However, for some general orientation on that problem, the reader may be referred to a comprehensive review, compiled under my direction by Roger W. Sperry (The problem of central nervous reorganization after nerve regeneration and muscle transposition. Quart. Rev. Biol., 20, 311–369, 1945) and to a basic monograph on motor coordination (P. Weiss, Self-differentiation of the basic patterns of coordination. Comp. Psychol. Monogr., 17, 1–96, 1941, reprinted in: Dynamics of Development: Experiments and Inferences. *Academic Press, New York, 1968). In general, the prospects for reasonably satisfactory* functional recovery of a denervated peripheral area *will be the dimmer, the higher up toward the centers the level of nerve severance, i.e., the point of issue of the regenerating nerve fibers, lies. Even though muscle coordination remains faulty, at least the trophic nerve effects on tissue maintenance return. When recuperation of even a semblance of useful function is ruled out, clinical practice resorts to* substitutive measures. *The next and final article illustrates one such procedure, in which we could follow the course of central adjustments after the transposition of the tendinous insertions of healthy muscles so as to vicariate for paralyzed muscles.*

Reprinted from PROCEEDINGS OF THE SOCIETY FOR EXPERIMENTAL BIOLOGY AND MEDICINE, 1941, **48**, 284-287

13298 P

Electromyographic Studies on Recoördination of Leg Movements in Poliomyelitis Patients With Transposed Tendons.*

PAUL WEISS AND PAUL F. BROWN.†

Man, in contrast to lower mammals,[1] can retime the action phase of a transposed muscle in accordance with its new function. Just how this occurs, is largely unknown. A systematic investigation of "recoördination," therefore, offers points of great theoretical and practical interest. A first report of our results is herewith presented.

Technic. The muscular action potentials were amplified in an ordinary vacuum tube amplifier set and recorded by an electromagnetically driven stylus writing on "Teledeltos" paper. Before entering the recorder, the amplified action currents passed through rectifying and integrating sets, partially summating and integrating individual spikes so as to give an estimate of the intensity of the contraction. Three identical channels were in operation, admitting independent simultaneous recording from three muscles. Provisions were made for the synchronization of these records with motion pictures. The electrodes consisted of copper mesh embedded in moist agar pads and strapped to the skin, cca 1 inch apart. Needle electrodes inserted through the skin did not prove significantly superior to surface leads. Elaborate precautions and checks were devised to guard against leakage of current from other than immediately subjacent muscles.

---

* These investigations were aided by a grant from the National Foundation for Infantile Paralysis, Inc.

† With the invaluable and most gratifying coöperation of Dr. C. Howard Hatcher, Department of Surgery, and Mrs. Margaret C. Winters, Physiotherapy.

[1] Rat—R. W. Sperry, *J. Comp. Neur.*, 1940, **73**, 379. For full review of the problem, see P. Weiss, *Comp. Psychol. Monogr.*, 1941, **17**, No. 4.

Tests. For the sake of standardization, the tests were restricted to a single type of operation, namely, transposition of the tendon of the M. biceps femoris to the extensor side of the knee joint to substitute for the weakened or lost action of a paralyzed M. quadriceps. The action of the transplant was to be compared with its preoperative flexor and extensor relations. The muscles chosen to represent the knee extensor and flexor group were the residual M. rectus femoris and the inner hamstrings, respectively. The action phases of these muscles during a number of standardized test performances (simple voluntary movements on command, resisted and unresisted; from prone, supine, seated, standing position; stretch reflexes; walking; bicycling; stooping, etc) were determined in both normal and poliomyelitic (unoperated) individuals. With these data as background, the behavior of the transplanted M. biceps could be systematically followed.

Results. Twenty cases of biceps transplantation (18 poliomyelitis, 2 spastics) have thus far been explored. Six of them were available for study both before and after the operation, while the others were old cases operated on from 2-10 years previously. The following observations are condensed from cca. 2500 feet of records.

Pre-operative. The electromyogram has revealed appreciable residual activity in many paralyzed muscles rated as negative by palpation. Steady activity of the weak M. quadriceps during flexor as well as extensor phases seems to be characteristic of coördination in poliomyelitics (except in side-lying position), in contrast to normal and spastic individuals. The M. biceps operates in flexor phase only.

Postoperative. Records taken when the operated leg was removed from the cast for the first time, showed no activity of the transplant during the early efforts of the patient to move. Soon, however, either during the first or one of the succeeding sessions, the transplant began to come in, at first in flexor phase. After that, only surprisingly few trials were required to make the transplant suddenly contract in extensor phase, too. Visualization of the task to extend the leg seems to be the prime aid to the patient; actual visual control and proprioceptive cues seem to be less important during the early phase of recovery. The transplant continues for some time to act in both flexor and extensor prases, and there is no evidence of automatic resumption of reciprocal innervation. Association of the biceps with the extensors does not by itself produce dissociation from the flexors. Only after a further practice period of individually

FIGS. 1 AND 2.

Electromyograms of thigh muscles during voluntary extension (E) and flexion (F) of knee. In all records the tracings, read from top to bottom, represent (1) M. biceps femoris, (2) Inner hamstring muscles, (3) M. rectus femoris, (4) Time signal in seconds.

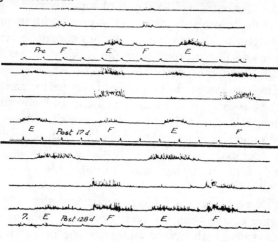

Fig. 1.

Three records taken from the same patient at different times. *Top:* Prior to the operation (side-lying position). Note Biceps action in flexor phase only. *Middle:* 17 days after tendon transposition. Note Biceps action in both flexor and extensor phases (F, E). *Bottom:* 128 days after the operation. Note absence of Biceps action during flexor phase.

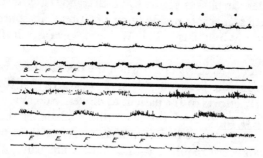

Fig. 2.

Relapse of transplanted Biceps into original flexor phase. *Top:* During fatigue towards end of prolonged test. Dots indicate occurrence of relapse. *Bottom:* Disorientation at beginning of performance. After two initial errors (marked by dots) transplant drops again its flexor association.

varying duration, does the transplant begin to be omitted during flexor actions.

Even then, however, temporary relapses into the old flexor association occur repeatedly, even years after the operation. These relapses seem to be favored by fatigue, lack of concentration, automaticity of movement, etc. Their occurrence supports the view that the adjusted use of the transplant is not based on the substitution of a permanent extensor association for its former flexor association in the elementary motor mechanisms, but rather on the development in higher centers of a new type of action which can effectively override the innate coördinative associations without abolishing them. This corroborates the distinction between lower, rigid, and higher, plastic systems in the control of coördination suggested by earlier observations.[2]

These and numerous other facts still under examination (the fate of stretch reflexes; action of motor units; differential fatigue) exemplify the advancement of theoretical insight and practical knowledge concerning coördination which physiologists and orthopedic surgeons alike may expect to result from the electromyographic study of transplanted muscles in man.

---

2 Weiss, P., and Ruch, T. C., PROC. SOC. EXP. BIOL. AND MED., 1936, **34**, 569.